D1025323

INTRODUCTION TO MATHEMATICAL SOCIOLOGY

JAMES S. COLEMAN
Johns Hopkins University

The Free Press of Glencoe
Collier-Macmillan Limited, *London*

TO

Paul F. Lazarsfeld

PREFACE

In the development of any science, two things are crucial: systematic empirical study and systematic conceptual elaboration. Each of these requires its special tools. Experimental techniques, systematic observation in natural settings, and the whole apparatus of research methodology is necessary if empirical study is to carry the science beyond the distillation of personal experience. Similarly, if conceptual elaboration is to progress beyond the proverbs of the ancients, special tools are necessary. The most remarkable of these is mathematics. Mathematics provides a battery of languages which, when carefully fitted to a set of ideas, can lend those ideas great power. The mind falters when faced with a complex system or a long chain of deductions. The crutch that mathematics provides to everyday reasoning becomes essential as sociology moves toward the analysis of complex systems and predictions based on extended chains of deductions.

This book aims to provide mathematical tools for conceptual elaboration in sociology. Such tools are not easily come by in an area of behavior as complex as that which sociology covers, and consequently this book only makes a beginning in this direction. But its principal aim is exactly that—to begin the development of a mathematical language which is equally at home with the empirical results of social research and the ideas of social theory.

Chapter 1 provides a survey of uses of mathematics in sociology. This chapter attempts to indicate both the variety of styles of mathematics presently used in sociology and the variety of purposes to which the mathematics is put.

This chapter is not encyclopedic, but gives examples representative of the different styles and purposes employed.

Chapter 2 examines in some detail the problems of measurement that confront systematic sociology. Are the criteria for fundamental measurement as developed in physical science essential to the development of mathematical sociology, and if so, how can they be met? Strategies for surmounting or bypassing the problem of measurement are discussed. This provides the context for the development in Chapters 3–13 of one such strategy which I believe will be particularly productive.

In Chapters 3–13, a mathematical language for the study of social and psychological processes is introduced. When sociology is more fully developed perhaps a book on social theory can be written in two sections, labelled "Dynamics" and "Statics," or "Processes" and "Structure." In such a book, Chapters 3–13 of this book would fall squarely in the center of the "Processes" section. The work presented in Chapters 3–5 was first developed in 1955–56, as a mathematical framework within which both the results of cross-sectional surveys and panels of successive waves of observations could be stated. Such a framework seemed to me then, and seems to me now, essential if survey research and other qualitative observations are to be relevant to social theory.

Every science requires a language in which both its empirical results and its theoretical propositions can be stated. In the early stages of the science— the stages through which sociology has been passing—ordinary statements in natural language, abounding in terms like "more" and "less," can suffice. However, when these stages are passed, when more discriminatory power is required of the theory and more precision of the data, then such looseness can no longer suffice. It is this stage at which sociology presently finds itself, and it is for traversing this stage that the mathematical models of Chapters 3–5 are introduced. Formally, the processes may be described as continuous-time stochastic processes. The mathematics used in this section is rather simple, being confined in most cases to algebra and elementary calculus.

Chapters 6–9 are elaborations of this language and application of it to varying forms of problems or data. For example, Chapter 6 shows its application to problems of multivariate analysis with qualitative data, while Chapter 7 deals with the problem of shifting between individual and group levels of aggregation.

Chapters 10 and 11 are elaborations of the basic mathematics of these processes to systems involving a simple repetitive action, and thus many states. The processes into which these models lead are all related to a Poisson process; and models of medical epidemics bear a close resemblance to some of these processes.

Chapters 12 and 13 continue the elaboration of these processes by allowing the relation between an individual's *state* and the *response* he makes to be a probabilistic one. Such an elaboration becomes especially valuable for handling data from multi-wave panels, which almost never conform to the simple processes described in Chapters 3–5.

The next three chapters, 14, 15, and 16, are a minor excursion into problems of structure in sociology. Chapter 14 treats the problems of structural measurement by the use of processes imposed upon the structure. Such processes by their outcomes provide measures of the structure which derive directly from its functioning under these processes. Chapter 15 examines a particular structural problem, that of relations between spatially separate groups of varying size, and gives an approach to its solution. Chapter 16 uses a very simple situation involving the interaction between members of different subgroups in a community to show the logical implications of certain variations in group structure.

Chapter 17 is a kind of amalgam of the structure and process models. It takes a problem—non-homogeneous structure—which is poorly handled by all diffusion models and presents two partial solutions.

Finally, Chapter 18 suggests tactics and strategies which I believe will be profitable in the use of mathematics in sociology. Most of these strategies are exemplified in the earlier chapters, and Chapter 18 makes explicit the tactics and strategies which led to the development of these chapters.

Two other chapters were to have been included in this book, one entitled "Reaction to Events: Individual and Social," and the other "Decay of Attention." However, the data for the first of these were too insubstantial, and the methods of analysis of the data for the second could not be developed in time for this publication. In addition, the developments of Chapter 13 have led in extremely profitable directions, resulting in a monograph which elaborates and applies this model (Coleman, 1964).

I hope that this book will help stimulate such work in mathematical sociology as to make it quickly outmoded. It is truly an *introduction* to mathematical sociology, and I trust that this introduction will be quickly followed by systematic growth, particularly in the area of mathematics for social processes.

The mathematics used in different chapters of this book is at quite different levels. Chapters 1 and 2, for example, require only a good grounding in algebra, while Chapters 10–13 and 17 make substantial use of calculus.

Throughout the volume I have avoided the use of difficult mathematics and mathematics likely to be unfamiliar to the general reader. This is in part because of my own greater facility with simpler mathematics, and in part because I think it is important that we keep to as simple a mathematics as possible. If we allow the complexity of the mathematics to reach an insoluble stage (as can easily happen) before the social phenomena it represents becomes complicated enough to be substantively useful, then our mathematics is obviously of little value.

It will become evident to the reader that further developments in mathematical sociology will soon require techniques that go beyond those used here.

Thus the knowledge of advanced probability theory, advanced calculus, and other areas of mathematics will soon become necessary skills for those who will innovate in certain branches of mathematical sociology.

My endeavors in these areas have been greatly aided by many people. My greatest debt is to Paul Lazarsfeld, who first engaged my interest in mathematical sociology and who posed many of the problems to which the chapters of this book are directed. Indeed, his stimulation has been so important to my work in this area that I have dedicated this book to him.

For the very conception of this book I am indebted to Jeremiah Kaplan, who proposed nearly ten years ago that I begin such an undertaking, before either he or I had any idea of the ultimate shape it would finally assume.

I owe particular thanks to several other persons: William McPhee and Lee Wiggins have long been engaged in related enterprises, and my work owes much to their stimulation. To Richard Savage I am grateful for guiding me toward continuous-time stochastic processes as the clothing for data on social and psychological processes. I regard this as perhaps the greatest innovation in this book, and Savage was in part responsible for it.

To many persons, especially Duncan Luce, Herbert Menzel, and Arthur Stinchcombe, I am grateful for reading and commenting on drafts of various chapters. Several graduate students, in particular Louis Goldberg and Seymour Spilerman, checked equations and solutions of examples. Virginia Bailey carried out the arduous task of typing numerous drafts of the manuscript. My wife, Lucille Coleman, survived the more arduous task of living with the discontent which an unfinished book creates.

Work on this book was carried out at the University of Chicago and Johns Hopkins University, to which I am grateful for the free time that allowed such activity. Grants from the Ford Foundation and the National Science Foundation helped make this free time productive. A special warmth, however, I reserve for the Center for Advanced Study in the Behavioral Sciences, where this book was begun. Had I not had the extended periods of contemplation that the Center provided, the ideas which form the central core of the book might not have emerged.

James S. Coleman

Baltimore, Maryland
March 1964

CONTENTS

Contents

Contents xiii

Contents

INTRODUCTION TO
MATHEMATICAL SOCIOLOGY

CHAPTER 1

USES OF MATHEMATICS
IN SOCIOLOGY

The ordinary languages we converse and write in are very rich in meaning.
Vocabularies in natural languages run to hundreds of thousands of words,
and even this is not enough: each word has its numerous shades of meaning
and connotations. The richness of our language reflects the richness of our
experience, and it is much of this same richness of experience which social
science attempts to capture and codify. This may be one reason why sociology
is perhaps the last of the empirical sciences in which the main stream of effort
is as yet almost wholly discursive and nonmathematical.

Yet it is the essence of empirical science that, whatever the richness and
complexity of the behavior it aims to describe, it must proceed first by analysis
into simple regularities, and only then by synthesis into more complex structures. As most sociologists realize, intuitively or explicitly, the problems with
which they must deal if they are to go beyond mere description and into
analysis of social phenomena are those which abstract from the richness of
behavior only a few elements and treat those alone. To examine behavior in
all its complexity in any fashion but a purely descriptive one is far beyond our
intellectual capacities. We must slowly analyze small parts at a time before we
can hope to put the parts together again.

1

Thus although the complexity of social behavior is overwhelming, the problems which we set ourselves in research and theory are narrow and relatively simple. It is in such a situation that the less rich but more precise language of mathematics becomes a useful—and sometimes very powerful—tool. It may be, then, that despite the ultimate complexity of the behavior which sociologists attempt to explain, a language as bare and unadorned as that of mathematics can prove useful. It is, in fact, the paradoxical combination of simplicity and a potential for expansion into complexity which constitutes much of the value of mathematics as a language for science. The real number system, for example, is extremely simple in the kinds of elements it contains and the kinds of operations which can be carried out upon them. At the same time, quite complex algebraic structures may be fashioned from these basic building blocks.

Mathematics consists of numerous different languages, of which ordinary algebra is but one. The different geometries—Euclidean, Riemannian, Lobachevskian—illustrate this varietal nature of mathematics well. Each of them constitutes a language for representing the spatial characteristics of a particular kind of world. It happens to be the case that terrestrial space is well represented by Euclidean geometry, while certain aspects of celestial space are well represented by Riemannian geometry.

Only a few of the languages which mathematics provides, however, can act as representations of aspects of the real world (or as representations of our theories about the real world) as does algebra, say, for the field of mechanics. When the behavior of physical objects is conceptualized into such elements as mass, length, time, force, velocity, density, and a number of other derived elements,[1] then the structure of relations between these elements is similar to—or *isomorphic* with—the structure of relations defined by the operations of vector algebra. It is this isomorphism which allows the operations of algebra, carried out with real numbers, to substitute for the actual manipulation of physical objects and thus to constitute a useful language for the science of mechanics. The power of algebra and calculus in the theory of mechanics lies in the fact that once the isomorphism is established, then many paper-and-pencil operations with symbols can be carried out which could never be carried out in practice with the objects themselves. Thus serving as a proxy for the actual mechanical objects, mathematical symbols allow a multitude of results which could never be obtained if either the common language of English, in all its richness, were used to symbolize the theory of mechanics, or the physical objects themselves were manipulated in order to gain further knowledge about them.

As with mechanics, so it has been with many other areas of natural science.

---

[1] No attempt will be made here to distinguish between the fundamental concepts and the derived concepts of mechanics, as physicists and philosophers of science find necessary to do when discussing problems of measurement. Such subjects are mentioned in the discussion of measurement in Chapter 2.

A part of mathematics (usually the same algebra and calculus used in mechanics) is found to be largely isomorphic with a given substantive area of science as conceptualized. This mathematics, with its symbols, then can serve as a proxy for experimental manipulations of the objects themselves, so that behavior of an actual object may easily be predicted by the behavior of these symbols alone, if one knows the initial conditions for the system.

For various reasons, there has never been such a simple correspondence between mathematical structures and the structures of relations between elements in social science. One of the reasons has been that no generally useful and easily measurable set of elements (or "concepts") has been posited in most of social science. In those few areas where such concepts have been specified, particularly in economics, the use of mathematics has flowered. Formal economic theories, with their sets of concepts precisely related to one another, have found mathematics extremely useful. They too have a partial isomorphism with algebra and calculus. The extent to which such theories adequately represent economic behavior is sometimes questioned, but this is another matter, a question of the correspondence of the predictions of economic theory to actual economic behavior, and not a question of the correspondence between economic theory and mathematical representation.[2]

In sociology, it is this last correspondence which has created much difficulty; the kinds of verbal theories and research results which have been set forth are so vaguely stated or so weak that it is difficult to translate them to mathematical language, and once translated they often fail to show an isomorphism with powerful parts of mathematics.

Such matters as the relation of a formal theory to actual behavior on the one hand and to mathematical structures on the other will be dealt with more fully in Chapter 2. The above discussion suffices to give some idea of the way in which mathematics has been found useful as a language for theory in natural sciences, and even in certain of the social sciences. In contrast, in sociology a set of concepts has never been developed which has some such correspondence to a simple yet powerful mathematical language, and at the same time, to actual social behavior. In general, theory construction in sociology has kept to the richness—and the ambiguity—of ordinary language, without change except for the addition of neologisms to represent certain special concepts. This is true of both theory which arises from speculation and that which arises from research. Both speculation and research have led to the elaboration of verbal theory, seldom to the development of mathematically stated theory.

It may prove useful if examples from present and past research in sociology are examined in order to gain some idea why mathematics has been so little

[2] On the other hand, the use of mathematics in psychology has often met with the opposite difficulty. The isomorphism of the theoretical structures and the mathematics used to represent them has often been questioned. See, for example, Andre Wietzenhofer (1951) and Sigmund Koch (1951), p. 148.

used. This will provide a better background for discussing some of the ways in which mathematics *has* been used in sociology, and some of the beginnings which are presently being made in this direction. Too often mathematical sociology is discussed as an end in and of itself, rather than in the context of the kinds of problems with which sociology has been characteristically concerned. Mathematics is a tool, and if it is to be a useful tool for sociology, it must be used in full recognition of the state in which sociology presently finds itself.

THE RESULTS OF SOCIAL RESEARCH

One of the forerunners of modern social research was Émile Durkheim, the French sociologist who studied, among other things, the social causes of suicide. In his study of suicide, Durkheim collected much data on suicide rates in various countries, among various age groups, religious groups, marital groups, and under different economic conditions. Durkheim's problem was to locate the causes of suicide, and he used these data to generate and test numerous hypotheses about the factors which various groups who had high suicide rates (Protestants, old people, widows and widowers, unmarried men and married women without children, and numerous others) held in common. Using the method described above, he arrived at several factors which gave evidence of being important causes of suicide. One of these was the lack of a purpose in life which one could share with his associates. Durkheim presented powerful evidence, which has been reinforced since his time, that this lack of a purpose in common with one's fellows (which he labelled *égoïsme*) was an important cause of suicide.

This example is characteristic of much social research, in this respect: it isolated one important determinant of a certain behavioral phenomenon, suicide. Before the investigation, Durkheim was faced with this kind of problem: what are $x_1, x_2, \ldots, x_n$ in the relation $p_s = f(x_1, x_2, \ldots, x_n)$, where p_s is the probability that a person will commit suicide? His partial solution to the problem lay in characterizing x_1 as the lack of a shared purpose, and in indicating the direction in which p_s varies as x_1 varies.[3] Note that although Durkheim used many tables of suicide rates, which could give numerical values for p_s, his inferred result was completely nonnumerical, indicating only the direction of variation of p_s with variation in x_1. Durkheim's work, therefore, lay primarily in *locating* the important variables affecting the probability of suicide, and not in further specifying the form of the relation.

This is one of the most common kinds of result which occurs in social research today. The problem is to find what are "the determinants" of some behavior or of some feeling state or of some social configuration. The analysis

---

[3] This result implies certain things about the kind of variable which x_1 is, namely that at least a weak-order relation exists between all values of x_1 (i.e., for every two values x_{1i} and x_{1j}, either $x_{1i} > x_{1j}$, or $x_{1i} \leqslant x_{1j}$).

proceeds by locating one or more factors which, on the basis of the evidence presented, are inferred to be determinants of the phenomenon in question. The empirical research in current sociological journals very largely follows this pattern. Take, for example, a piece from an issue of the *American Sociological Review*. John M. Foskett (1955) examines a number of factors (age, education, occupation, income) in relation to individuals' participation in community organizations. He presents several tables similar to the one shown, which show that participation increases as education, income, and social status increases.

From several such tables, Foskett infers that a major determinant of social participation is "role behavior." That is, persons participate to the degree that is consistent with the demands or constraints created by their occupational role, socioeconomic status, and other attributes of their position in society. It is easy to see that the kind of analysis which Foskett is carrying out

Table 1.1

MEAN GENERAL COMMUNITY PARTICIPATION SCORES BY
EDUCATIONAL LEVELS

	VALLEY CITY I		VALLEY CITY II	
		Mean		*Mean*
EDUCATION	*No.*	*score*	*No.*	*score*
Grades 1–6	12	.75	42	1.45
Grades 7–9	101	1.63	240	2.01
Grades 10–12	105	2.74	370	3.11
College (nongraduates)	28	5.25	63	4.79
College (graduates)	13	5.77	34	5.62
Total	260	2.63	749	2.92

is precisely the same as that of Durkheim in his study of suicide. Both attempt to locate the important social and psychological determinants of a given behavior. It is more than a little disconcerting to see that, for the most part, our research has not progressed in the past thirty years or more, either in the kinds of goals it seeks or in the means it uses to gain them.[4]

Now since this problem exemplified by Durkheim's and Foskett's work is such a prevalent kind of problem in social research today, it is reasonable to ask how, if at all, mathematics could help in its solution. It is true, of course, that the data themselves are numerical even though the inferences from the data are qualitative ones; to this extent a tiny bit of mathematics is already

---

[4] As a matter of fact, Foskett's methodology is considerably less sophisticated than that of Durkheim. He fails even to mention any alternative hypotheses, his explanation is of the sort that almost any results could be explained by it, and his data are little more than a verification, for two particular communities, of results that had been known for some time. But at that, his paper compares favorably with others which frequent our journals.

used in such research.[5] But the question is, could mathematics have been useful at all in formulating the results of the research?

If one excludes the use of statistical tests in determining whether or not the data might have arisen by chance, then it is hard to see how this general class of problems could be substantially aided by the use of mathematics. The inference is a qualitative one, of the general form, "As X increases, Y will increase." In neither of these cases was the determinant ("degree of shared purpose," "degree to which social role facilitated and motivated participation") directly measurable, even in terms of a simple order without a metric, although the dependent behavior was quantitatively measured in both cases. The evidence was of the sort which took subgroups differing rather sharply in some attribute (e.g., religion, education), and compared them with respect to the dependent behavior (suicide, social participation). Because of an assumed relation between this attribute and the possible determinant, it is assumed that the average value of the possible determinant must be greater in one subgroup than in the other. The major task of such research, and its primary value for ensuing work, is in finding a unifying explanation (e.g., "shared purpose," "facilitation and motivation of participation by one's social role") which accounts for many of the observed relationships which are presented in contingency tables. Under such conditions, it is hard to see that a greater use of mathematics could have been fruitful for either of these two problems, and thus for much of the social research which is carried on today, that is, the research which has as its general purpose the task of locating a variable X which explains much of the variation of some phenomenon Y.

This is not to say that more mathematics could not have been used in these investigations. It is to say only that a greater use of mathematics might not have been fruitful. Durkheim could have taken the determining variables as given (e.g., religion, marital status, age, etc.), and attempted to characterize p_s, the probability of suicide, as a function of these phenomenal variables. He might have seen his task as specifying the coefficients in the equation, $p_s = bx_1 + b_2x_2 + b_3x_3 + \ldots$, where x_1, x_2, x_3, $\ldots$ were taken as given, the variables which entered explicitly into his tables of suicide rates. Efficient methods which were unknown in Durkheim's time exist today for identifying these coefficients (see, for example, Kendall, 1952, and Cooley and Lohnes, 1962), and there are some present-day researchers, trained in these methods, who would quickly have applied them if they had been faced with Durkheim's problem and given somewhat better data than he had.

The question is, then, Would this be an advance over Durkheim's work? On the surface it may seem so, for it would result in a completely specified functional relation between p_s and x_1, $x_2 \ldots$, yet it is far from certain that

[5] The quantitative tables may seem to some to be a considerable use of mathematics, and to others, no mathematics at all. Such a difference of definition is unimportant; for convenience I shall use the term mathematics very broadly, to include any use of numbers, as well as any use of symbols with specific rules of combination.

this would be an improvement. It represents a quite different philosophy of scientific endeavor than that of Durkheim. It takes as *given* what Durkheim set out to *find*: the variables which should go into the relation as determinants of p_s. It takes as its task the *identification of parameters* b_1, b_2, b_3, ... Durkheim took his task to be one of *respecification* of the phenomenal variables until he found a single variable which would account for their relationship to suicide rates.

Which procedure would have been the more useful, the highly quantitative one or the qualitative one which Durkheim followed? It is difficult to say, since no one can yet assess the ultimate value for sociopsychological theory of Durkheim's having shown the importance of a "shared purpose," and since the alternative procedure was not in fact carried out. Yet in this case and in others like it, it is reasonable to believe that Durkheim's approach contains more long-range benefits for social science than does the more quantitative one, for it attacks the logically prior problem of finding appropriate variables before finding the size of the parameters. It is easy to be intrigued by the rigor of formal techniques and led down the primrose path of too early formalization. It is important to guard against this tendency as one learns quantitative techniques.

Does this mean, then, that mathematics would have been of no use to Durkheim, Foskett, and other investigators? And by extension, does it mean that mathematics is generally of little use in social research? The answer is clearly no to both questions. Analyses such as those of Durkheim and Foskett *leave* the problem precisely at the point when mathematics becomes necessary. They "locate the important variables" in an area of behavior, and then move on. This is an extremely important part of investigation in any science, and many men prefer to concentrate their energies here. If so, they may leave their mark upon the history of the science without any use of mathematics whatsoever.

But if fruitful theory is to be developed, far more than this is necessary. A logically consistent framework of variables incorporating or explaining the empirically established relations is necessary. The latter may play their role directly as qualitative phenomena to be explained, or, after further work in quantification, as quantitative "laws." But whichever direction the further work takes, the point is that there *is* further work; that the "location of important variables" is only the beginning.

But even this extension of work like that of Durkheim and Foskett constitutes too narrow a focus in social research. In some areas of investigation, mathematics is necessary almost from the start. For example, anyone who works with sociometric data finds himself looking for mathematical tools to aid in analysis. Several such tools have been developed. Matrix multiplication may be used to discover the indirect connections between people, and to characterize the clique structure of the group (Luce, 1950). Various methods in graph theory may be used in similar ways to determine the maximum number of pairs into which a group can be divided (Berge, 1962), for relating the communication structure of a group to the structure of the task in which it is engaged (Flament, 1963), and for other purposes. These methods are valuable wherever the empirical data consist of elements and all-or-none relations between them. Sociometric data, as well as organizational charts in formal organizations, find great need for such mathematics even to answer simple research questions.

Thus not all social research is of the sort illustrated earlier by the examples of Durkheim and Foskett. When it is not, it often has need for mathematics at a relatively early point in the research. Some such uses of mathematics will be discussed later in this chapter.

Quite apart from research results, in the realm of theory-construction, mathematics plays at least an equally important role. The very character of much mathematics, as logically consistent systems of elements and transformations, parallels closely our general conception of what a "theory" consists of. It appears to be a language peculiarly fitted for the representation of theory in whatever area of science the theory may subsist.

USES OF MATHEMATICS IN RESEARCH AND THEORY

The various uses which have been made of mathematics[6] in sociology may be conveniently classified under several headings, moving from the simpler to the more complex.

(1) First, there has been quantitative description of the various units of social science, whether they be individuals, social groups, organizations, or other units. Such quantification has occurred when the operation by which the units are classified results in assignment of numbers which are then added, multiplied, etc.[7] Though I do not mean to suggest that such quantitative description of individuals and groups as has been carried out in social research constitutes measurement of some fundamental and theoretically relevant property, it remains true that quantitative descriptions are often made in social research. Since quantitative description is a prerequisite for the use of some kinds of mathematics, this will constitute the first type of work to be examined.

[6] As mentioned before, no strict distinction between what is mathematical and what is not will be made here. Though the use of numbers (e.g., as a result of measurement) without clearly defined rules of operation which can be applied to them is not strictly mathematics, such use will be considered as mathematics here, simply for convenience.

[7] I do not mean to say that these operations which result in a metric constitute "measurement" in the sense that the term is used by most philosophers of science and by physical scientists. However, I will not consider those classifications in which numerals without the properties of real numbers are used, unless mathematical techniques are used to arrive at them, as discussed under (2) in the text. A general discussion of these matters of measurement is reserved for Chapter 2. In the present chapter, only examples will be presented.

(2) A second use of mathematics in sociology is in the combination of a number of observations to provide a measure for some hypothetical construct, some inferred property of an individual or a group, such as an "attitude" or a "norm." Techniques for attitude measurement which employ mathematical operations, such as scale analysis, latent structure analysis, and Coombs' unfolding technique are examples of this use of mathematics. More generally, much of what is usually termed "index construction" in social research, on the level of groups as well as individuals, falls in this area. Mathematical operations are employed to obtain from a number of observations the value which some inferred disposition variable should take on. It is not always true that such index formation results in a quantitative measure of the underlying construct; in attitude measurement, it often results only in a weak order,[8] in which individuals are put in ordered classes.

(3) The third point to be examined is the development of quantitative empirical generalizations about behavior which relate two or more quantitative measures such as those discussed under (1) and (2). It is such empirical relations which constitute "laws" when confirmed over a wide class of situations. Such generalizations are of course infrequent in social science, and those which do exist have been confirmed only over a small class of situations, so that they can hardly have the status of laws. Some nevertheless do exist.

(4) A fourth use of mathematics is as a language for theory. In any empirical science, theories are first stated in the ordinary language of everyday discourse. It is only when the logical structure of relations between concepts becomes clear and precise that the shift to a formal structure of mathematics is possible. With this comes the power of the mathematical structure whose rules of combination allow paper-and-pencil calculation with symbols to mirror the behavior of the objects of the science. It is as such a language that mathematics finds its natural role in an empirical science, and this will be its ultimate usefulness in sociology.

Theories in sociology take quite different forms, and it will be useful to distinguish two general types in the presentation, keeping in mind that this is no sharp and definitive distinction, but only one which may prove heuristically useful. The first are "explanatory" theories, which take empirical generalizations like those mentioned in (3) above, and set forth hypothetical constructs (i.e., sets of postulates), to explain the generalizations. These hypothetical constructs are related to the observed generalizations by a formal system of relations which constitute the theory. Just as there are few cases of quantitative generalizations in sociology, there are few cases of this nascent quantitative theorizing. Nevertheless, some do exist, and they provide examples of what might someday be rather widespread in sociology.

The second type of theories may be termed "synthetic" theories. They proceed in quite the opposite direction from the observed data than do

---

[8] See footnote, p. 4, for definition of a weak order.

explanatory theories. Sets of postulates are put down, using observed generalizations (either quantitative generalizations as in (2) above, or qualitative
ones). From these postulates, which are known to be true, deductions are then
generated. Some theories of diffusion, of population growth, and others fall
into this category. These theories are comparable to the theory of mechanics,
which begins with certain postulates relating the basic properties and then
generates deductions from them, in contrast to explanatory theories like the
atomic theory of matter, which begins with a generalization from which one
"works back" to the hypothesized underlying constructs.

Some theories in sociology are partly of the explanatory sort and partly
synthetic; others can hardly be called either, because of their lack of any
empirical reference. These theories will be mentioned in this section along
with the others.

(5) Finally, the use of mathematics in the development of predictive
models is discussed. These models, such as factor analysis, certain models
using Markov chains, and others, differ from theories in the same way that
simple extrapolation of a curve differs from extension of the curve on the
basis of the known (or assumed) functional relationship. Though they are of
little aid in the development of social theory and broadly applicable generalizations, their use in applied research problems may allow very efficient utiliza-
tion of the observed data for the problem at hand.

It should be noted that one general use of mathematics has not been
mentioned above and will not be discussed in what is to come. This is the use
of statistics in sampling, in design of experiments, and in confirmation of
hypotheses or theories. These are large and important problems in research,
but problems which are dealt with in a number of books on the use of statistics
in social science.

1. DESCRIPTIVE STATEMENTS OF OBSERVED BEHAVIOR

The simplest use of numbers in social research is nothing more than their
use in recording observed behavior. Whether in experiment or field research,
observed behavior is often recorded in terms of numbers, which may then be
related to some other measure of some sort. Two cases, those in which the
number characterizes individuals, and those in which it characterizes some
social unit made up of individuals (a group, organization, etc.), should be
examined separately.

1.1 Characterization of individuals

Perhaps the most frequent use of numbers in social research is classification by two variables followed by cross-tabulation or correlation of the two
variables. The two examples cited earlier are of this sort, as is Table 1.2,
taken from a study of child rearing practices (Havighurst and Davis, 1955).

In this simple example, the two sets of mothers, classified as lower class and middle class, are tabulated according to their response to a question about control of their children. In such cases as this, the use of numbers is as follows: One classification (middle class or lower class) is used to divide persons into classes about which some statement can then be made; the second classification provides a *count* of the persons in each class who behave a given way. Though each person's behavior is measured only dichotomously, this allows a numerical ratio to be posited as the measure associated with each class (.82 to middle-class women, .42 to lower-class). Further, since the inference drawn from such a tabulation is an inference about individuals who are members of the classes ("middle-class mothers report more permissiveness about fighting among their children"), this proportion is usually considered as a measure of the probability that the "average" person in the first classification (e.g., the "average" middle-class mother) will behave in the specified way. In this fashion, numerical measures are attached to classes of individuals, and by the above considerations, to the "average" individual in each class. Thus a form of quantification occurs, even though the measure made on each

Table 1.2

AGGRESSION CONTROL

	Middle-class mothers	Lower-class mothers
Per cent of families where mothers let children "fight each other so long as they do not hurt each other badly"	82	42

individual is only qualitative. However, it is generally true, as pointed out earlier, that after such a quantitative measure is applied, the inference made is only a qualitative one, so that the possibilities for added information gained from quantification are lost. There is good reason for this, primarily the fact that the classifications (e.g., "social class," and "permissiveness toward aggression") are rather arbitrary, being only rough indicators of the desired attributes. Thus there might be little value in going to the added effort of developing a quantitative generalization.

This, then, is an example of one way in which numbers are used to characterize individuals in social research. Such numbers are proportions attached to classes of people, or probabilities attached to the "average" member of the class, formed through the procedure of multiple classification with qualitative attributes.

A second means by which individual behavior is quantified is through direct quantitative measure on the individual level. For example, in a study of the process of the adoption of new drugs by doctors, the date at which the doctor first prescribed the drug in question was measured (Coleman, Katz, and Menzel, 1957). In this case, *time* serves as the measure for behavior. Similarly, *length* (e.g., the distance one lives from his closest neighbor), *area* (e.g., in measuring population density), and other physical measurements can serve as the dimension in which an individual's behavior or other attribute is measured. And in some cases, counting numbers of events serves as a measure of this sort as well. For example, many investigators of small groups make their measurements by counting the number of acts of verbal participation a given individual initiates in a group discussion, and the number directed toward him. These serve as measures which may be attributed to the individual, or to the position that the individual occupies in a group. These measures have been used to make qualitative generalizations about behavior of individuals in group discussion. Though the present uses to which such measures are put is usually only qualitative, the measures themselves are quantitative in nature, and may potentially serve as part of a quantitatively specified relation. (See, for example, a discussion of Keller's use of these measures later in this chapter.)

Upon reading through these examples of quantitative measures of behavior, the reader is likely to protest that they are not "really" quantification in social science. What is emphatically true is that they are not quantitative measures of some theoretically relevant "property" of an individual or of a sociopsychological "concept" which is independent of the particular situation. The fact that these examples, quantitative to be sure, are not at all measures of some such "property" makes evident the distinction between quantification and theoretical relevance. Similarly, the number of leaves on a tree, quantitative though it may be, is hardly a theoretically useful concept in physics.

The existence of quantitative measures of theoretically relevant individual properties is quite a different matter than the existence of quantitative measures of behavior in a given situation. Few such quantitative sociopsychological measures exist, because of considerable measurement difficulties. Since most of them would not be directly observable, but inferred disposition properties, they would be dealt with under Section 2 below anyway. The possibilities of developing such quantitative measures of individual properties are discussed in Chapter 2.

Nevertheless, quantitative measures of behavior such as those described above are not unimportant. The empirical confirmation of a theory depends upon the measurement of behavior itself, not only of constructs within the individual. In order to do this, such measures of behavior as described above are necessary.

1.2 Characterization of groups or other social units

When groups rather than individuals are considered, considerably more quantification with potential theoretical relevance is evident in research, if not in theoretical statements. Whenever aggregates of people are involved, then

Table 1.3

ACTUAL MOBILITY, SONS OF NATIVE-BORN FATHERS, 1940

SON'S OCCUPATIONAL CLASS

FATHER'S OCCUPATIONAL CLASS	Professional	Semiprofessional	Proprietors, managers, officials	Clerical and sales	Skilled	Semiskilled	Unskilled	Protective service	Personal service	Farming	All classes
Professional	126	23	33	127	69	42	12	4	6	1	443
Semi-professional	13	17	3	18	25	12	3	2	4	–	97
Proprietors, managers, officials	81	38	175	320	160	221	27	14	22	5	1063
Clerical and sales	77	56	73	436	159	171	24	13	20	2	1031
Skilled	73	69	108	471	808	673	144	57	76	14	2493
Semiskilled	35	28	61	248	254	619	76	33	60	7	1421
Unskilled	14	11	15	90	102	206	189	16	25	2	670
Protective service	5	2	15	49	33	72	20	19	3	–	218
Personal service	6	6	7	27	34	46	6	3	15	–	150
Farming	58	26	89	234	356	464	142	54	80	67	1570
All classes	488	276	579	2020	2000	2526	643	215	311	98	9156

mere counting gives measures which are numbers of people. The *size* of a group is the simplest such measure; the *proportion* or *rate* of members doing one thing or another is nearly as simple. Though the suicide rates for various countries or the tolerance for aggression by middle- and lower-class mothers can be construed as a probability measure for individuals in these countries or social classes (as indicated in Section 1.1 above), they can be considered attributes of the nation or social class as well, just as a body of gas may be characterized by the mean velocity of its molecules. The choice between the two interpretations depends of course upon the kind of proposition or hypothesis in which the measure is located.[9] When one realizes that census volumes are packed full of quantitative measures of a nation, state, city, or

[9] For example, at equilibrium, the temperature of a gas is a simple transformation of the mean velocity of its molecules. In the theory of thermodynamics, temperature is the concept used; in the theory of statistical mechanics, mean velocity is used; in the theory of mechanics at the molecular level, the molecule's velocity itself is used. These matters are discussed more fully in Chapter 2.

county of precisely this sort, it becomes immediately evident how often this kind of measurement is made. To be sure, most of these measures are tied to the time and place of the particular situation, and have little theoretical relevance, just as the individual measures discussed above.

Many times, measures of social units (groups, societies, etc.) are not scalar quantities (i.e., not single numbers) but are vectors (i.e., composed of several numbers). For example, one investigator of small discussion groups finds his groups with six members to be characterized by the following relative rates of participation:[10] .428, .238, .154, .100, .059, .020. This, then, is a quantitative measure of the group which this investigator relates to other attributes such as group size.

Similarly, for society as a whole, such multidimensional measurements are often made. By counting the persons in each occupational category whose father was in a particular occupational category, investigators have arrived at matrices like Table 1.3 (Rogoff, 1953). Such matrices of social mobility are proving of considerable use in understanding the working of the occupational structure of a society (Rogoff, 1953; Blumen, Kogan, and McCarthy, 1955; White, 1963; Goodman, 1963b). They provide an abundant source of quantitative information from which generalizations can be drawn and about which theories may be constructed.

1.3 Structural measures for groups and individuals

Besides the kind of numerical data discussed above, sociologists often obtain another kind of data for which mathematical treatment is especially useful, and often even necessary. This is structural data consisting of a set of elements, with all-or-none relations existing between them. Often the elements are individuals, as in a sociometric test where each individual is asked to name those persons to whom he stands in a certain relationship. Organization charts, kinship structures, communication nets, and "pecking orders" (the latter established by a tournament or pairwise comparison of some other sort) are other such examples. Obviously, the elements may be larger units than individuals: teams in a tournament, departments in an organization chart, local chapters of a national organization in a communication net, and so on.

Such elements-in-relation have been studied extensively for two purposes: to characterize the *elements* in terms of their position in the structure, and to show certain properties of the *structure* itself. The mathematics used has been of two kinds: matrix algebra and graph theory. In matrix algebra, the existence of a relation from element i to element j is signified by an entry "1" in the ijth cell, and the absence of a relation by a "0" in the cell. (In a few cases, "-1" has been used to signify a negative relation; but in general, the opera-

---

[10] Participation rates were measured by counting the number of times each individual spoke in the discussion, and were averaged over different groups. See Stephan and Mischler (1952) and pages 28–30 in this chapter for further details.

tions then carried out on such matrices produce few substantively useful measures.) In graph theory, the representation is by means of points and lines. For example, sociometric choices among four persons would be represented as follows in the two approaches:

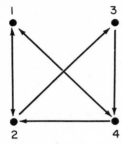

$$\text{From:} \begin{array}{c} \text{To:} \\ \begin{bmatrix} 0 & 1 & 0 & 1 \\ 1 & 0 & 1 & 0 \\ 0 & 0 & 0 & 1 \\ 1 & 1 & 0 & 0 \end{bmatrix} \end{array}$$

The use of matrix algebra has ordinarily been to locate "cliques" of elements which are highly interconnected, and thus form a kind of subgroup in the larger network. Festinger (1949), Luce and Perry (1949), and Luce (1950), began this work, which has been continued by Harary and Ross (1957), Weiss (1956), and others. The general approach has been to carry out matrix multiplication, and then to infer, from entries in the product matrices, what persons are involved in cliques, and with whom. This can be carried out only for relatively small groups because of the ambiguity existing concerning which clique a person is in. More generally, however, matrix multiplication may be used to find the connections at any remove between pairs of persons: an entry of n in the ijth cell of the rth power matrix means that there are n paths of exactly length r from i to j.[11] Thus such manipulation can be useful for finding the indirect linkages in any structure of this sort.

The use of graph theory has been in part merely definitional, matching up a term of substantive interest (e.g., "liaison person") with a graph theoretic term signifying a special position in the structure (e.g., "cut point"). The result of this is simply to make precise the position that certain elements have, showing what happens to the graph when they are removed. The use of graph theory has gone beyond this, however, e.g., toward a correspondence with the "theory of balance" developed by several social psychologists (Harary, 1959), in which graph theoretic methods are used to show the properties of a balanced structure, and to measure the degree of balance in a structure. In another direction, Flament (1958) has examined structures in which there is no transitive relation between the elements, but which may be viewed as "multi-dimensionally transitive." In a two-dimensionally transitive structure, the observed relation between two elements is the result of either of two independent relations between them, each of which is transitive in itself. (See also Berge, 1962, for a number of applications of graph theory in related areas.)

[11] These paths may not be totally distinct, and may also include paths which have already gone through himself.

In general, the problem of characterizing structures and individuals' positions in a structure provides many opportunities for the use of mathematics—without the necessity for quantitative measurement. However, most mathematical treatment of such structures has to date been concerned with definition, static measurement, and theorems relating one property of the structure to another. There has yet to be much application of this mathematics to the kinetics of social or psychological processes.

The kinds of quantitative measures of social units are not at all limited to these aggregative and structural measures based on counting individuals or relations between individuals. Other measures made directly on the group as a whole sometimes occur. For example, experimenters have measured the length of *time* it takes an experimental group to complete a task, relating this to some property of the group, such as the type of communication network which was prescribed for the group (see Bavelas, 1948). Altogether, there are numerous forms which quantitative measures of groups may take, and there are numerous kinds of operations by which such measures are obtained. The prospects for quantification on the group level appear considerably brighter than those on the individual level, where quantitative measurement is considerably less frequent and harder to come by.

2. MATHEMATICAL TECHNIQUES FOR ARRIVING AT "DISPOSITION" PROPERTIES

One of the difficulties which arises with many of the measures discussed above, particularly those on the individual level, is that they are trivial in the development of useful generalizations or theories in social science. Since these quantities are directly observed, they are often less "fundamental," more tied to a particular situation than one would wish if he is to use them to establish general laws or aid in the development of theory. A metallurgist often finds that measures made upon a heterogeneous mixture of ores tell him little, while a chemical analysis which separates out the elements tells him a great deal. Similarly, the survey analyst can often tell little from a single contingency table relating specific opinions, but must go deeper into the composition of attitudes if he is to learn much about his subjects. In most analyses of contingency tables such as the ones presented on pages 5 and 11, the particular classifications which are cross-tabulated are considered as no more than "indicators" of the underlying variables under consideration.

The underlying variables, the hypothetical constructs like attitudes, values, motives, and on the group level, norms, expectations, obligations, are ordinarily hypothesized on the basis of a somewhat vague theory about what makes people or groups behave as they do. But since they are not directly measurable, some means of constructing a measure for them is necessary if they are to play an explicit role in a theory or in prediction of behavior.

If one knew precisely the theory which related these unobservables to observable quantities, then it would be simple to construct a measure for them simply by transforming the observable measurements in the fashion dictated by the theory. This unfortunately is seldom the case, since we are engaged in a kind of bootstrap operation in the construction of laws and theories.

Sometimes science is fortunate, as was physics in the measurement of temperature: it just so happened that the change in volume of a quantity of mercury, by which the first temperature measurements were made, occurred according to simple laws of physics, and was independent of changes in many other conditions (air pressure, amount of mercury, rate of heat transfer, etc.), varying only with changes in an important property of a substance, its temperature. Whether social science can be so fortunate remains to be seen.

But in the meantime, we take our vague and fragmentary theories, about attitudes being the determinants of behavior, about norms being social prescriptions for behavior, and on the basis of these vague and often implicit theories we construct measurements of these hypothesized underlying properties, using manifest observations of one sort or another. Sometimes such construction is highly rationalized, with mathematical operations made upon the data in order to construct the underlying property.

2.1 Disposition properties of individuals

As mentioned before, it is the mathematical operations in moving from data to the hypothetical property which constitute the quantitative mathematics in this area; it is not the resulting measure, for that is usually non-quantitative. For example, three of the most widely known methods of constructing attitude scales—scale analysis, latent structure analysis, and Coombs' unfolding scale—do not give a quantitative attitude measurement at all. They all result in a weak order, by locating the respondents in ordered classes.[12] A discussion of one of these procedures will give some idea of the rationale behind them, as well as an indication of the kinds of mathematical operations they use.

In accordance with the theory that attitudes determine behavior, it is assumed in scale analysis that they determine verbal behavior as well, that is, the response to questions which "elicit" the attitude being examined. Suppose four such questions are asked, to which the respondent can answer yes or no. It is hypothesized that respondents' attitudes which determine their answers to these questions lie along a continuum. Each question is assumed to have a "cutting point" on the continuum, such that everyone to the left of the cutting point answers the question positively, while everyone to the right answers it negatively. The situation may be visualized as follows:

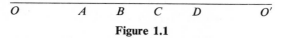

Figure 1.1

[12] In addition, Coombs' technique can give some information about distances on the scale, depending upon the number of stimulus objects presented. See Coombs (1950).

The points A, B, C, and D are the cutting points of the four items. Everyone to the left of A answers question A positively; everyone to the right answers it negatively, and similarly with the other questions. Thus everyone in the segment OA will answer questions A, B, C, and D positively; everyone in the segment AB will answer A negatively and B, C, D positively; everyone in the segment BC will answer A and B negatively, C and D positively; and so on. These responses should show the following patterns:

	Question			Segment
A	B	C	D	
yes	yes	yes	yes	OA
no	yes	yes	yes	AB
no	no	yes	yes	BC
no	no	no	yes	CD
no	no	no	no	DO'

In contrast, no one should answer as follows:

	Question		
A	B	C	D
Yes	No	No	Yes
No	Yes	No	Yes

or give answers forming any of the nine other possible response patterns. Thus five particular response patterns out of a total possible of sixteen should occur if there is a "scalable attitude" elicited by this combination of four questions. If these five do not occur with high frequency (and methods exist for judging how high beyond chance the frequency of these patterns is; see Chapter 12 and Menzel, 1953), then it is assumed that no single attitude continuum is elicited by these questions.

These are the bare details of scale analysis. Further information and elaboration can be found in Stouffer (1950) (Chapters 3–9), or Torgerson (1958).

Latent structure analysis uses a more general conceptual model about the way in which attitudes are elicited by questions. It assumes, in effect, that each individual has only a particular *probability* of responding positively to the given question on the basis of his position on an attitude continuum, and it is this probability which determines his response.[13] Surprising as it may be, this innocent-looking and very reasonable generalization adds great complications to the mathematics necessary to locate people in response classes. Latent structure analysis is as complex mathematically as scale analysis is simple.

---

[13] A very clear exposition of the conceptual basis of latent structure analysis can be found in Lazarsfeld (1954); see Chapter 2. Techniques for computing latent structures can be found in Stouffer, Chaps. 10, 11 (1950), and Lazarsfeld (1959).

Coombs' (1950) unfolding technique for scaling attitudes has a conceptual model somewhat similar to that of Guttman's scale analysis, except that it is stimulus objects which are located on the continuum rather than cutting points of questions, and the individual ranks these stimulus objects on the basis of their distance from his own position, or his "preference." As with scale analysis, only certain patterns are permissible if the model is to fit the data. If a fit is found, then individuals can be placed in ordered classes according to their position on the continuum, inferred from their response.

It is easy to see that the ranking responses of Coombs' unfolding technique give more information than do the yes-no responses of scale analysis. In Figure 1.2, an individual located at X would respond No, No, Yes, Yes, to questions A, B, C, D, respectively, if the questions formed a scale. Intuitively the notion is that he has "passed" items C and D, but "failed" A and B. But when the items form a Coombs' scale, the individual ranks them according to

O	a		A	B	X	C		D	O'
Scale analysis:			No	No		Yes		Yes	
Unfolding technique:			3	2		1		4	

Figure 1.2

their closeness to him, and thus ranks in the order C, B, A, D. In the yes-no responses of scale analysis, we have no information from his responses about the relative distance he stands from A, B, C, and D; but from his rankings, we know the order of the absolute distances: $\overline{CX} < \overline{BX} < \overline{AX} < \overline{DX}$ (where $\overline{BX}, \ldots$ are the absolute distances between the two points). As a consequence, it is possible, upon looking at the response patterns actually obtained, to infer something about the relative distances between the items A, B, C, and D. For example, the ranking $C\ B\ A\ D$ in Figure 1.2 would be impossible if item A were located at a. In that case, even though it is still the leftmost item, it would be impossible to obtain the ranking $C\ B\ A\ D$, *no matter where* the individual were located on the continuum.[14] It is the middle ranking which differs in these two cases. If only the left set of ranks in footnote 14 occurs, then the data are consistent with a continuum with items as located at A, B, C, D;

[14] More completely, the possible rankings are as follows with item A located at A and a, respectively:

	A					a		
A	B	C	D		A	B	C	D
B	A	C	D		B	A	C	D
B	C	A	D		B	C	A	D
C	B	A	D		B	C	D	A
C	B	D	A		C	B	D	A
C	D	B	A		C	D	B	A
D	C	B	A		D	C	B	A

if only the right set of ranks occurs, then the data are consistent with a continuum having items located at a, B, C, D.

There have been extensions of scale analysis, Coombs' unfolding technique, and latent structure analysis considerably beyond the presentation here. The furthest developments, however, have been in the extension of cumulative scales to multidimensional scales. In a two-dimensional scale, for example, the individual's response on an item is determined by his position on two underlying dimensions and by the mixture of these two dimensions in the item. A one-dimensional scale can be tested with two items (only responses yes-yes, no-yes, and no-no are allowable; yes-no responses are inconsistent with the scale). Similarly, by direct extension, a two-dimensional scale can be tested with three items, only seven of the eight possible responses being allowable (see Coleman, 1957b). However, multidimensional scales of several kinds have been developed (see Shepard, 1962; Torgerson, 1958), and different restrictions are implied by each.

Another technique for locating "underlying" attributes of the individual, and one more widely used than any of these, is Thurstone's (1947) factor analysis (the ordinary R technique). This method, which has come to have quite solid statistical foundations, provides a means of accounting for scores on many items by means of a smaller number of "factors." It is a data-reduction technique, and one which has become extremely useful since the advent of large-scale electronic computers.

However, factor analysis seems unfitted for the task under discussion here, though it is sometimes used for this purpose. The other methods discussed above, whatever their imperfections, are all concerned with measuring a hypothesized underlying attribute of the individual; the models derive from a conception of how these underlying attributes relate to observable behavior. As a consequence, the model may be disconfirmed by behavior; factor analysis cannot. Also, when these other models are designed for measuring two or more variables at once, these are *meaningfully independent* variables, which combine in various ways. Multiple-factor analysis, in contrast, locates *statistically independent* factors which combine additively. Then, after having isolated these factors, many investigators attempt to give the factors meaningful independence by giving them names. It is evident that two variables like arithmetic ability and verbal ability, or economic liberalism and foreign-policy liberalism, may be not at all statistically independent and therefore not separated by factor analysis, even though they are meaningfully quite independent.[15]

[15] The rather unreasonable assumption of factor analysis may be seen by investigating the basis postulate of factor analysis: If S is the score matrix (m tests by n persons), then it is factorable into FP, where F is a factor loading matrix for the tests (m tests by r factors), and P is a population factor matrix (r factors by n persons). Then $SS' = FPP'F'$, and the crucial assumption of factor analysis (R technique) is that $PP' = I$, where I is the identity matrix. This is equivalent to the assumption that the factors are uncorrelated in the population.

This general approach of factor analysis is certainly appropriate for some situations,[16] but because of its logical defects it is hard to see how it can be fruitfully used in the development of social and psychological theory.[17]

A modification of factor analysis, the Q technique, appears to be a quite useful tool in inferring individual attributes. This is an inversion of the usual factor analysis, in which correlations between pairs of individuals over a number of tests replace the usual correlations between pairs of tests over a number of individuals. Because the investigator has control over the nature of the tests, though not over the nature of the individuals, he can vary the tests so that statistical independence and meaningful independence do reasonably well coincide.[18]

2.2 Disposition properties of groups

There are few general formal methods on the group level for inferring underlying attributes comparable to the methods discussed above. This is not to say that there has not been a great deal of "index construction" by which attributes like "cohesiveness" of a group, "moral integration" of cities, and "group norms" have been inferred. But this index construction has been rather *ad hoc*, and while it has utilized quantitative data and algebraic operations, the theory by which the observable data are assumed to be related to the underlying construct is usually implicit, and often completely missing.

Yet some procedures have been developed. In one sense, all statistical estimation procedures are of this sort, for the task is to estimate some "underlying" property such as the mean of a population variable, on the basis of observables which according to hypothesis bear a particular relation (e.g., through a normal distribution) to this unobservable. However, many of the parameters inferred through statistical inference are not properties which one desires to use in a sociological proposition or a generalization. Only in a few cases, some of which are mentioned below, have statistical models been used to infer "meaningful" properties of a group which are substantively useful.

One such case is that of segregation measures. The problem which one faces in constructing a measure of residential "segregation" in a city (e.g., segregation of nonwhites) is the problem of combining a great many numbers in some meaningful fashion into a single summary "index" or measure. If the city is marked off into segments (say census tracts), then it is possible, and very reasonable, to think of segregation as a function of the distribution of

[16] For example, it has proved quite useful in prediction of individuals' responses on tests similar to those on which the factor analysis was carried out.

[17] A criticism which indicates this difficulty with the use of factor analysis is Block (1955).

[18] That is, the correlation matrix would be $S'S$, and equal to $P'F'FP$ (using the notation used in the earlier footnote). By controlling the kind of tests he uses, the investigator can control the factor loading matrix F, so that $F'F$ is nearly equal to I. This control would hardly exist with the P matrix, so that the investigator cannot remedy things if $PP' \neq I$.

whites and nonwhites throughout these census tracts. But this gives a great many numbers, one white-nonwhite ratio for each census tract, whereas usually only a single measure is wanted, in order to compare the segregation in one city to that in another. Many such measures have been proposed, most of which vary slightly from one another in concept and in the resulting measures they give.

Suppose, for example, that in city A one-fourth of the population is Negro and these Negroes are distributed throughout half of the census tracts fairly evenly, but are completely *absent* in the other half of the tracts. Is this city more or less segregated than city B, also with one-fourth its population Negro, which has 90% of its Negroes clustered in one-third of its census tracts, but the other 10% is spread throughout the other two-thirds of the tracts? Some segregation measures would show city A more segregated than B; others would show it less segregated.

All these measures, however, have this in common: each of them is associated with an underlying notion of what is "really meant" by segregation; and each of them provides a mathematical procedure for collapsing the great mass of data to give a single number. O. D. and Beverly Duncan (1955) have examined a number of these measures, showing some of the conditions under which they would give different ordering of the cities, and conditions under which they would give the same. In carrying out their comparison these authors use a "segregation curve," which does *not* summarize this census tract information, but preserves it fully. This curve could itself serve as a measure of segregation, but it is a multidimensional one, which will allow no ranking or scaling of cities along a single continuum.

Another case in which a meaningful group property has been inferred through application of a statistical model is one which I developed a few years ago and have used in numerous instances since that time (1953, 1960, 1961). It is a measure of the "interdependence" of actions in a subgroup, and is based on the following observation: If a large group shows a certain distribution of actions (say a certain proportion, p, of persons voting for candidate A in an election), and the group is subdivided into subgroups (e.g., precincts, counties, etc.), then the p_i's of these subgroups usually show much wider variation than one would expect by chance alone (assuming independence of actions with all persons having the same probability, For example, one precinct may vote 90% for A and another votes 5% for A, while the chance variation about p (based on the sizes of the precincts) is such that even a variation as small as $\pm 5\%$ about p should occur only once in a hundred times. Now such wide variations in p_i could occur if there were *interdependence*[19] of actions within each subgroup relative to the larger group. The amount of such interdependence is a function of the amount of variation between the p_i's and the size of the subgroups, and can easily be calculated.

---

[19] Or alternatively, dependence on a common element. Statistical interdependence must not be identified as behavioral interdependence.

Thus one arrives at a measure of the amount of dependence of each person's action on those of his fellow-subgroup members which would have given data similar to those which were actually found.[20] It is still necessary to be careful in interpretation of such a measure as this, depending on the conditions under which it is used, for the apparent interdependence may result from any of a number of sources, only one of which is interpersonal influence. But with careful interpretation, the use of this measure constitutes a good example of inferring an underlying group attribute with the use of a model which conforms to the way we feel behavior occurs.

Other examples of such measurement models for inferring structural characteristics of a group are presented in Chapter 14. I believe that the further development of such explicit and generally applicable procedures for inferring structural group attributes can be an important immediate contribution of mathematics to social research and theory.

An example of the development of a more complex mathematical model in order to infer an unobservable from existing data occurred in a paper on the incidence of mental disease by Marshall and Goldhamer (1955). The existing data were the following:

(1) For various age categories, the proportion of persons within a category admitted to a mental hospital within one year after onset of mental disease, the proportion of admissions one to three years after onset, five to seven years, and so on.

(2) Age-specific death rates of the population as a whole.

(3) Age-specific death rates of mental patients (estimated from other sources of approximate information).

Their goal was to determine the probability of onset of mental illness at each age level, given these admission data and death rate data. To make this inference, Marshall and Goldhamer set up a stochastic model, a Markov process which hypothesized several *states* (alive and sane; alive and mildly insane but unhospitalized; alive and severely insane but unhospitalized; insane and hospitalized; and dead outside of mental hospital), and hypothesized further that at each age level there were particular *transition probabilities* from each state to other states.[21] This constituted the underlying process which they hypothesized to be at work. On the basis of their data,

---

[20] The form of this measure is a function of χ^2 and is similar to others found in statistics, such as Kendall's coefficient of concordance. It is the particular conceptualization of this measure, however, in terms of a meaningful attribute of the group, which makes it especially useful when applied to social behavior. This usefulness can be seen by the remarkably wide range of applications that variants of the measure, based on the same conceptual foundation, have. These are mentioned in Chapter 14, when the measure is discussed.

[21] A transition probability from state i to state j in a stochastic process is the probability of moving to state j in the next time period, given that one is in state i. A Markov process is a stochastic process in which the transition probabilities can be specified by knowing only the present state, and not the past history, of the individual.

which provided values for some of the parameters of the model (i.e., for some of the probabilities of being in a given state, and for some of the transition probabilities), they could calculate other parameters, the rates of onset of mild and severe mental disease for each age group. Thus by use of a stochastic process in the formal structure of mathematics which mirrored (in a simplified fashion) the sociopsychological process which they believed to be occurring, Marshall and Goldhamer were able to obtain estimated values for an unobservable, the age-specific rates of onset of mental disease.[22]

Another example illustrates the ingenious use of a mathematical model to infer underlying parameters in consumer behavior. Lester Telser (1963) has taken the following approach: Suppose we consider a set of consumers of a certain product, say cigarettes. Then suppose we had information about each person's purchase at time t, and his purchase at time $t+1$, to give a matrix for the r brands, such as that below, in which n_{ij} is the number of consumers

Time $t+1$

	n_{1i}	.	.	.	.	.	n_{1r}	$n_1.$
	.							
	.							
	.		n_{ij}					
Time t	.							
	.							
	n_{ri}	.	.	.	.	.	n_{rr}	$n_r.$
	$n._1$						$n._r$	n

who purchased brand i at time t and brand j at time $t+1$. Now if the cell entries, n_{ij}, are divided by the row sums n_i, the resulting proportions p_{ij} are the proportions in state i at time t who have moved to state j at time $t+1$ (i.e., purchasers of brand i at time t, who purchased brand j at time $t+1$). Then the total number of purchasers of brand i at time $t+1$ can be expressed as follows:

$$n._i = \sum_{j=1}^{r} n_j.p_{ij} \qquad (2.1)$$

Suppose now we did not have the internal entries n_{ij} (or p_{ij}) in the matrix, but had only the n_i's (the brand shares) at a number of times $t, t+1, t+2, \ldots,$ $t+m$. Would it be possible to estimate the p_{ij}'s? Telser uses the following assumptions to do so:

(a) Assume that eq. (2.1) governs the relation between the n_i's at time t and

[22] This "unobservable," and many others on the group level, are not unobservable in any ultimate sense nor are they as purely hypothetical as are the unobservables of psychology and physics. Marshall and Goldhamer could have used survey research to measure directly the age-specific rates of onset of mental disease. Not having these data in hand, however, they inferred them from other data which they did have. The general status of unobservable properties on the level of groups is discussed in Chapter 2.

the n_i's at time $t+1$ for all n_i, except for a random shock (uncorrelated over time) with mean zero:

$$n_{.i} = \sum_{j=1}^{r} n_j . p_{ij} + \varepsilon \qquad (2.2)$$

where ε is a normally distributed random variable with mean zero.

(b) Assume that the p_{ij}'s are constant over the times $t, t+1, \ldots, t+m$ under consideration.[23]

(c) Assume that no one enters or leaves the market.[24]

Then by regression analysis, the p_{ij}'s in eq. (2.1) can be estimated. This regression analysis will not give good estimates unless the random disturbance, ε, has a large enough variance to give variation in brand share ($n_i.$) over time. But for Telser's data, the variation was wide enough to make possible estimates of p_{ij} for brands within a number of product classes.[25]

In this case, then, using a procedure different from, but comparable to, Marshall and Goldhamer's, Telser used observable data (brand shares) in conjunction with a mathematical model, to estimate an unobservable, the brand-specific probability of repurchase and of shifting to another brand.

It is of course true that the validity of this and other procedures for inferring unobservables depends completely on the correctness (or perhaps it is better to speak of "theoretical usefulness") of one's assumptions about the relation between the observables and the unobservables. Many of these models, however, have built into them a test of some of these assumptions, so that by testing the fit of the model, one is partially testing the validity of his assumptions which led to development of the mathematical structure.

These examples should provide some idea of just how mathematics has been—and can be in the future—used to infer underlying attributes of individuals and of groups from observable data. As I mentioned earlier, this general use of mathematics, particularly on the group level, seems to me to constitute a valuable immediate contribution which mathematics can make to social research.

3. QUANTITATIVE EMPIRICAL GENERALIZATIONS

The first two general uses of mathematics in social science which have been examined were exclusively in the area of measurement, the first being direct measurement of observable phenomena, and the second indirect

---

[23] This assumption implicitly includes two others, which must hold if it is to hold: p_{ij}'s for a given person do not depend upon earlier purchases, and the p_{ij}'s for all persons are alike.

[24] Telser shows that a weaker assumption will suffice: the number entering or leaving the market for brand i relative to the total number entering or leaving the market is equal to the brand share, n_i/n.

[25] Telser in fact did more than this: he introduced price differential into the regression analysis and estimated its effect on p_{ii} and p_{ij}. However, to simplify matters, he assumed that $p_{ij} = p_{ik}$ for all j, k ($\neq i$) for a given i.

measurement of latent "dispositional" states. Such measurements are the components out of which quantitative laws and theories are built. It is the first of these—quantitative laws—to which we turn now. As mentioned earlier in this chapter, these will be referred to as empirical generalizations rather than laws because the term "law" suggests a wider range of verification than exists for the few quantitative regularities which have been found in sociology.

In contrast to measurement techniques, very few quantitative generalizations exist in present-day social science. Anyone can propose a measurement, and go ahead and measure some phenomenon; but it is not so easy to uncover quantitative regularities between such phenomena after they have been measured. These regularities are not ours for the asking, but depend upon the conjunction of a peculiarly fortunate set of circumstances. Such conjunctions have unfortunately been rare in social science, and there are only a very few quantitative generalizations about behavior that one can point to. Yet it is such generalizations out of which theories are built, by acting either as data to be explained or as postulates which can combine with others to explain or predict other phenomena.[26]

The few generalizations I am going to mention may not be a good sample of those which exist in social science; they are simply ones of which I am aware. Some of them may seem trivial, and I am certain that some of them are. But even so, they can serve as examples of generalizations which can be constructed in social science.

It is interesting to note that none of the quantitative generalizations presented below is on the level of individuals. The first generalization discussed below concerns the relative prestige of occupations in societies with industrial economic structures, while the others concern distributional phenomena. After discussing these, however, a case will be examined which gives some insight into just how quantitative generalizations on the level of the individual might be developed.

The first example concerns the prestige rankings given occupations in various industrial societies. In our own society, for example, North and Hatt found (see National Opinion Research Center, 1953) that occupations have something approximating the prestige scores given in Table 1.4, based upon rankings made by a random sample of the population.[27,28] Such a set of data is

---

[26] These quantitative generalizations are not, of course, the *only* source of theories in social science; the proliferation of theories in the face of a dearth of quantitative laws attests to this. Qualitative generalizations (e.g., "If *X* increases, *Y* will increase") based upon ordinary experience or upon research, together with disparate bits of information, are the usual empirical bases for theory in social science.

[27] It is perhaps true that the scores are not really quantitative, for they are merely scores aggregated from responses to occupations; there is no notion that operations of ordinary algebra are wholly legitimate, as is necessary in most theories. But let us merely note the objection and set down the generalization anyway.

[28] It might be argued that empirical data which exist in the form of voting

hardly a generalization or regularity; what does make it into a generalization, however, is the fact that such scores are remarkably constant, not only from time to time in our own country (a repeat of the 1947 study in 1963 in the U.S. showed very little change), but over a number of *other* countries as well: England, New Zealand, Japan, Germany, and the U.S.S.R. (Inkeles and Rossi, 1956). Table 1.5 shows the correlations of the above scores with scores

Table 1.4

PRESTIGE SCORES OF VARIOUS OCCUPATIONS IN THE UNITED STATES

United States	Score	United States	Score
Physician	93	Bookkeeper	68
State governor	93	Insurance agent	68
College professor	89	Travelling salesman for wholesale	
Scientist	89	concern	68
County judge	87	Policeman	67
Head of dept. in state government	87	Mail carrier	66
Minister	87	Carpenter	65
Architect	86	Corporal in regular army	60
Lawyer	86	Machine operator in factory	60
Member of Board of Directors of		Barber	59
large corporation	86	Clerk in a store	58
Civil engineer	84	Fisherman who owns own boat	58
Owner of factory employing about		Streetcar motorman	58
100 people	82	Restaurant cook	54
Accountant for a large business	81	Truck driver	54
Captain in regular army	80	Farm hand	50
Building contractor	79	Coal miner	49
Instructor in public schools (teacher)	78	Restaurant waiter	48
Farm owner and operator	76	Dock worker	47
Official of international labor union	75	Bartender	44
Electrician	73	Street sweeper	34
Trained machinist	73	Shoe shiner	33
Reporter on daily newspaper	71		

obtained in comparable surveys in these other countries. These correlations, which would likely be higher if the surveys had been more nearly comparable, show the striking uniformity of occupational prestige from country to country. As the data stand, they constitute a regularity to be explained, whether the explanation be in terms of a model of the economic structure together with the hypothesis that the economic structure generates such values, or in some other terms.

---

statistics, census data, and other quantitative tabulations constitute empirical generalizations. The criterion which has been applied and which excludes most such records is that data be not tied to a particular time and place, but rather be expressible in general terms, in a way that, for example, the U.S. voting statistics of 1932–1952 are not.

A second example of an empirical generalization is quite different from this, but similar to a number of others, in that it is a kind of *distributive* law, which concerns a frequency distribution along a continuum or among different classes. In this case, the generalization relates the *size* of "freely forming groups" to the *frequency* of occurrence of each size.

John James (1953) has observed in a number of public places (among city

Table 1.5

	Scores	Number of occupations compared*
Great Britain	.94	(24)
New Zealand	.97	(24)
Japan	.93	(25)
U.S.S.R.	.90	(10)
Germany	.96	(20)

* Because of different occupations in different studies, not all occupations were compared for each country.

pedestrians, in children's play groups, department stores, public markets, and at railroad depots and public beaches) the frequency of groups of various sizes. Summary Table 1.6 indicates the general relation between size and frequency. The fact that these data gathered in disparate situations show the same form of distribution suggests that a common process underlies the formation and dispersion of small groups of freely associating persons. What

Table 1.6

Group size	Number of groups observed	Per cent of total group
1	10,149	65.54
2	3,945	25.47
3	1,075	6.94
4	238	1.54
5	65	.42
6	14	.09
	15,486	100.00

this process is remains a matter for an explanatory theory to suggest. (See Chapter 11 for a theory to explain these data.)

Another example of a quantitative generalization is in form more like those laws one is familiar with in other sciences, but is still of the distributional variety like the one above. It is a generalization developed by Frederick Stephan and Elliott Mischler (1952), on the basis of data like those presented on page 14, which relate the *rank* of a group member (ranked in terms of amount of participation) and the *frequency* of participation. It is

$$p_i = ar^{i-1} \tag{3.1}$$

where p_i = proportion of total participations initiated by the ith member (ranked from high to low, excluding the leader);

r = an empirically determined (average) ratio of the ith member's participation to those of the $(i-1)$th member; and

a = an empirically determined coefficient, which is equal to the estimated value of p_1.

This generalization is meant to hold for small discussion groups from three to eleven members in size, excluding the leader (whose participation is not calculated from the above generalization, but is taken as given, so that $\Sigma p_i = 1 - p_L$ rather than 1.0), but with no single person giving a presentation; in other words, "free discussion" groups. It was developed from observations made upon a number of sessions of tutorial seminars at Princeton University, and has been found to fit also discussion groups of diverse types on which Bales has gathered data at Harvard.[29] The generalization is not applicable to *single* sessions, which show rather wide variability, but to averages for each rank over several sessions of groups of the same size. This averaging of data raises some question of whether the regularity can be in part explained as a simple statistical phenomenon which results from the averaging of data. This possibility, which has been investigated, will be discussed in a later section in this chapter, under "explanatory theories."

A second generalization is also presented by Stephen and Mischler, namely that r and a vary with n, the size of group (including the leader) being very nearly in accordance with[30]

$$r_n = .522 + .0172n \qquad (4 \leqslant n \leqslant 12) \tag{3.2}$$

$$a_n = \frac{234}{n+4} \qquad (4 \leqslant n \leqslant 12) \tag{3.3}$$

These are very pretty looking generalizations, stated in the form of algebraic equations with only a few parameters. Nevertheless, they, like all other numerical generalizations I know of in social science, have been verified over only a very small range of behavior. They could hardly be dignified by the term "law," yet they do represent a beginning in the direction of a law.

In investigations of other rank-frequency relations, I have found several

---

[29] This regularity exists even though the basic definition of an "act of participation" which was used for counting frequency of participation differed in the two studies.

[30] If $\Sigma p_i = 1$ rather than $1 - p_L$ where p_L is proportion of participation due to the leader, a could be determined from the relation $a = (1-r)/(1-r^n)$, together with eq. (3.2).

other phenomena to conform to this same exponential relation, which can be put in the form:

$$N_i = N_1 e^{-\alpha(i-1)} \tag{3.4}$$

where N_i = the frequency of occurrence of the ith-ranked item, and
     α = empirically determined parameter.

This is an alternative way of stating the Stephan-Mischler relation in (3.1). For the following sets of data, this equation holds, approximately, with the indicated values of the parameter:

    (a) Stephan's data:

$$N_i = N_1 e^{-1.1(i-1)/n} \tag{3.5}$$

where N_i = number of participations of the ith-ranked member, and
     n = number of persons in the group $(4 \leqslant n \leqslant 12)$.

    (b) The relative number of choices received in a sociometric choice situation, each member giving three choices (averaged over seven cottages within which choices were made, each having twenty-six members) (Moreno and Jennings, 1945):[31]

$$N_i = N_1 e^{-.119\ (i-1)} \tag{3.6}$$

where N_i = average number of choices received by the ith-ranking girl
            $(1 \leqslant i \leqslant 26)$, and
     $N_1 = 9.34$.

    (c) The relative sales of popular song records in the years 1947–1952 ranked weekly (Lowenthal, 1951):[32,33]

$$N_i = N_1 e^{-.094\ (i-1)} \tag{3.7}$$

where N_i = number of sales of ith-ranking record $(1 \leqslant i \leqslant 20)$, and
     N_1 = (unobtainable from published data).

    (d) The relative sales of fiction and nonfiction best sellers for 1949, ranked weekly (*Publishers' Weekly*, 1949):[34]

$$N_i = N_1 e^{-.207\ (i-1)} \tag{3.8}$$

where, for fiction,
     N_i = total sales of ith-ranking fiction title $(1 \leqslant i \leqslant 10)$, and
     N_1 = (unobtainable from published data);
and for nonfiction,
     N_i = total sales of ith-ranking nonfiction title $(1 \leqslant i \leqslant 10)$, and
     N_1 = (unobtainable from published data).

[31] This exponential relation holds only for the first twenty ranks out of the twenty-six.

[32] The records were ranked weekly, one ranking per month was sampled, and these twelve sets of data were combined by averaging for each rank.

[33] These data are better approximated if a coefficient $(i-1)/i^{.118}$ is applied to the right-hand side of the equation.

[34] Books were ranked weekly, one ranking each month was sampled, and these data were averaged for each rank.

This exponential relation, holding true for the particular content areas discussed above and presumably for others as well, is not very satisfying, for it suggests no explanation of why such a phenomenon occurs, nor does it allow one to presume easily just what scope it might have in terms of other content areas. Many *qualitative* empirical regularities in social behavior are "understandable," in the sense that our experience leads us to have a ready explanation at hand. When, for example, George Homans states the generalization, " . . . persons who interact frequently with one another tend to like one another" (1950, p. 111), most of us can very quickly offer an explanation for this regularity, based on our own experience and our introspection. Whether such "explanations" can form a useful foundation for social science is another question; the present point is that they set us at ease, while the distributive generalizations of the types discussed above leave us puzzled, disturbed, and sometimes resistant. Yet it is not the function of an empirical generalization to suggest its own explanation. Such generalizations as these must stand, puzzling as they are, and perhaps even irritating, until someone provides an explanation for them. The explanation may turn out to be trivial, or it may reveal social processes which were not at all previously evident.

A number of other social and nonsocial phenomena (e.g., number of cities of a given size class as compiled by Hammer (1951), follow a size-frequency or rank-frequency distribution curve somewhat similar to those presented above. Many of these are compiled by Zipf (1949); others are presented, together with an explanatory stochastic model, by Simon (1957).

The examples of quantitative generalizations presented in this section are weighted far too strongly in the direction of relating sizes or ranks and frequencies. Certainly this is not in the main stream of what we usually think of as fruitful research in social science. The reason that they are so prevalent in a discussion of quantitative generalizations seems to be this: It is only in these simple areas of counting numbers of persons or numbers of events of some sort that measurement which is both quantitative and generalizable beyond the specific situation has been carried out in sociology. Even within the limited area of measurement circumscribed by the procedure of counting, many measures are not at all generalizable beyond the immediate context (e.g., the number of people who answer Yes to a survey question is hardly a generalizable measure of behavior, unless the question itself concerns some general phenomenon).

The fact that this section is almost completely limited to these distributional phenomena certainly does not mean that *qualitative* empirical generalizations are not abundant in social science. Considerable progress, generally of the kind that Durkheim made in locating relevant variables, is being made without quantification of the sort discussed here (though much of this research does depend on statistical cross-tabulations to develop its qualitative generalizations) and by no means am I deprecating its importance.

At the same time, it seems far from necessary that quantitative generalizations be confined to such distributional phenomena as those prevalent in this section, even with our methods of measurement in their present undeveloped state. An example will show the kind of quantitative generalizations which could even now be developed in social science, and which may someday exist in abundance. This is a case which, with more effort, could be made into a useful and well-established generalization with very broad scope. It is the classic set of experiments of Asch, in which he measured the effect of group pressure in distortion of judgments (1951). The judgments were based upon visual perception of lines of unequal length, and a naive subject was asked to report his judgment[35] after a number of other subjects had reported their own judgments. These other subjects, preinstructed by the experimenter, sometimes reported the incorrect judgment, and were unanimous in this incorrect report. In many cases the naive subject was influenced by the unanimous but incorrect majority against the dictates of his senses. Asch was able to vary the discrepancy between the incorrect judgment and the correct one by varying the lengths of the lines, and he varied the size of the unanimous majority from three persons to sixteen. He found, in varying the latter, that a majority of size four was most influential, even slightly more so than larger majorities.

With this situation, Asch had all the basic ingredients necessary for the development of a quantitative generalization. The group size, the lengths of the lines, and the number of incorrect responses are all quantitatively measured. He stopped, however, and went on to other areas of work, because it was not at all his intent to establish a quantitative generalization. He is a social psychologist primarily concerned with understanding *why* and *how* persons are influenced by group pressures rather than measuring precisely the *extent* to which this influence occurs. Asch was concerned, as are many social psychologists and sociologists, with *locating* a variable affecting behavior rather than with measuring its effect.

But let us see just what would be necessary in order to extend Asch's work to obtain a generalizable quantitative result. The kind of quantification might take the following form:

$$p_d = f(s,x,y,z) \tag{3.9}$$

where p_d = probability of distortion of judgment in the direction of a group,

$\qquad s$ = group size,

$\qquad x$ = clarity of the stimulus,

$\qquad y$ = individual variables, and

$\qquad z$ = situational variables (kind of instructions, extrinsic reward for agreeing with group, etc.)

In order to specify this function, the following steps would be necessary:

---

[35] Three comparison lines were used to match against a standard line which was the same length as one of them. The required judgment was to pick out the line which matched the standard line.

(a) Experiments, tests, interviews, and other data necessary to locate the individual variables responsible for the widespread individual differences found. (For example, McClelland reports that interviews Asch made with subjects after the experiment show that "need for achievement" is strongly related to tendency to succumb to group pressure.) This would specify the equation $p_d = f_1(y)$.

(b) Further experiments in which experimental conditions other than the stimulus itself, such as instructions to the subject, previous relations with the members of the majority, etc., are varied. The ideal result would be one in which the resultant distortion was independent of a wide range of such conditions. Even if it were not, however, the environmental conditions could in this way be brought explicitly into the relationship, for these experiments would specify the function $p_d = f_2(z)$.

(c) Further experiments in which the clarity of the stimulus was varied in one direction until almost everyone agreed with the group when it was incorrect, and in the other until almost none agreed with it. This would specify the function $p_d = f_3(x')$, where x' is the clarity of the stimulus expressed in terms of the length of the line, distance from it, lighting conditions, etc.

(d) One added step, an important one, remains. As the stimulus variable, x', stands, it is tied specifically to the particular experimental situation. What is necessary is to translate this physical stimulus, using results of psychophysical experiments, into its equivalent in subjective perceptual experience, perhaps in terms of the psychophysicist's "just noticeable differences." In this way, the generalization is applicable to *any* visual perception, and if psychophysical measurement were more advanced, to other sensory perception as well. Without this step, which links up a psychophysical stimulus-response generalization with a social-psychological generalization, the relationship would remain of little value, bound to the particular kind of physical stimulus used in the experiment. With it, the generalization becomes one which shows the effect of social constraints in increasing the objective stimulus variation necessary to create a subjectively just noticeable difference.

This indicates the kind of steps which would be necessary to make a precise quantitative relation out of one social-psychological experiment which seems close to quantification. These steps are not simple ones, but long and difficult. Yet they would result in a very general relationship, one which could serve as a postulate in theories of group behavior, and one which would have great practical significance by showing the various implications of the group pressure phenomenon under varying conditions.

Since the preceding paragraphs were written, the Asch experiments have in fact been subject to mathematical treatment. The above discussion is left as it was to show the different directions which mathematical formalization might go. For Bernard Cohen (1963) has built a mathematical model for the Asch situation which conceives of the behavior as a stochastic "learning" process. The individual is in one of five states, which can be thought of as "definitely nonconforming," "tentative nonconforming," "undecided," "tentative conforming," and "definitely conforming." His past behavior in conforming or nonconforming, together with the felt rewards or punishments from the group, leads toward a "learning" of the group-reinforced response. Cohen's model fits experimental data quite well, and it is obvious from the data that the behavior may be conceived as a learning process rather than a static one as suggested in the above discussion.[36] Yet still remaining to be investigated are most of the suggestions above: effects of group size, individual variables, environmental variables, and a psychophysical definition of the stimulus to free the model from the particular experimental situation. Thus the two formulations almost walk past one another, the one suggested above missing the basic sociopsychological process involved, and the one carried out by Cohen neglecting the parameters which would give wider scope to the generalizations resulting from the model.

4. USE OF MATHEMATICS IN THEORY CONSTRUCTION[37]

The uses of mathematics discussed up to this point are subsidiary to theory construction. Measurements are the building blocks for laws or generalizations, and generalizations are the building blocks for theories. Of course, it is hardly this simple, for measurements (particularly measurements of disposition variables) are often prescribed by the theory within which they are to fit, and the kinds of generalizations one develops are often based on ideas about their relevance for some theory which one has in mind. Thus there is a considerable amount of interaction between these different uses of mathematics. Nevertheless, theory construction is the ultimate aim in terms of which the other uses must be finally judged. The power of mathematics in empirical science rests in its power as a language for expressing the relations between abstract concepts in a theory.

All theories may be thought of as consisting of a set of postulates, A, and a set of possible deductions from the postulates, B. The postulates often state a general structure of relations between properties, while the deductions consist of specific behavior of the objects with which the theory is concerned. The theory is thus a calculating device which allows one to say, "*If* postulates A are true (and certain initial conditions C obtain), *then* behavior B will result."

---

[36] However, a re-examination of Cohen's data indicates that if in fact a learning process was occurring, its effect was very small (Coleman, 1964). The principal variation is due to stable individual differences.

[37] In this discussion of mathematical theories, there will be no mention of statistical problems in fitting the data to the mathematical model. Nevertheless this is an important problem, one which must not be neglected when a rigorous test of a theoretical model is being made.

Theories vary in complexity according to the complexity of A, the set of postulates, and the difficulty in proceeding from the "if," that is, from the postulates A, to the "then," that is, to the deductions B.

Now it is useful to distinguish two kinds of theory-development in which the role of the postulates A and the deductions B is reversed. In *explanatory* use of theory, one starts with observed phenomena, B, and then devises an underlying "theory" composed of postulates A, which can explain the phenomena. The atomic theory of matter is a theory developed and used in this way.

A second kind of theory-development, however, might be called a *synthetic* use of theory. It is in response to a different question, What are the consequences of the joint occurrence of a_1, a_2, a_3? In the first approach, one tests the deductions, and thereby gives confirmation to the postulates; in the second approach, one tests the postulates themselves.[38] The theory of terrestial mechanics, which is simply a logically consistent conceptual system, together with the empirical generalization that acceleration due to gravity is constant for free-falling bodies, is this second sort of theory. The theory is a calculating device which allows knowledge of the postulates, A, to give knowledge of the consequences, B. As a different sort of example, the binomial distribution shows that *if* one had (a) n independent events, each with two possible outcomes and (b) each event with an identical probability, p, of outcome x, *then* the probability of k occurrences of outcome x is

$$Pr\{k \mid p, n\} = \binom{n}{k} p^k (1 - p)^{n-k}$$

Some might hesitate to call the Bernoulli model a "theory," since it is so unlike the explanatory theories of physics. Yet it is precisely the same sort of "if ... then ... " statement, differing only in the perspective of the investigator. In the first case, he asks, "What could have caused these phenomena, B?" In the second, he asks, "What are the joint implications of this set of conditions, A?" He may not even be concerned in this second case with knowing whether this configuration of conditions A *generally* holds, but only want to know what will result when and if they occur.

Although there is no logical difference between two kinds of theories, some theories are used in a primarily explanatory way, while others are used in a primarily synthetic way, because of our peculiar observational position. We do not directly observe the underlying entities and relations of statistical mechanics, but see only the behavior of gases. We do, however, directly

---

[38] An interesting example exists in sociology of confusion between these two approaches. Stewart Dodd (1955) carried out diffusion experiments in which he established by experimental fiat the conditions of interpersonal diffusion which give a logistic growth curve. Then he "confirmed the theory" by showing that a logistic growth curve did in fact occur. Dodd and his students have, however, done some good work with diffusion models (De Fleur and Larsen [1958]), and see references given in Dodd (1955).

observe the toss of a coin. Similarly, we can easily observe mass, length, and time, and by virtue of Galileo's postulate of constant gravitational acceleration, calculate the distance covered by a freely falling body.

James Clerk Maxwell, one of the founders of statistical mechanics, recognized this different perspective of ordinary mechanics and statistical mechanics. He compares the two perspectives (1877, pp. 121–122):

> The method of investigating the forces which act between bodies which was thus pointed out and exemplified by Newton in the case of heavenly bodies, was followed out successfully in the case of electrified and magnetized bodies by Cavendish, Coulomb, and Poisson.
>
> The investigation of the mode in which the minute particles of bodies act on each other is rendered more difficult from the fact that both the bodies we consider and their distances are so small that we cannot perceive or measure them, and we are therefore unable to observe their motions as we do those of planets, or of electrified and magnetized bodies.
>
> Hence the investigations of molecular science have proceeded for the most part by the method of hypothesis, and comparison of the results of the hypothesis with the observed facts.

Theories used primarily in one way or the other will be called "explanatory theories" or "synthetic theories" for convenience below, though it is important to recognize that this describes, not their logical character, but their common use.

It is important to recognize the difference between explanatory and synthetic theories. Explanatory theories, like statistical mechanics or the atomic theory of matter, take a number of known facts about the real world—that is, empirical generalizations or laws—and develop some explanatory scheme from which these generalizations may be deduced. Testing the theory becomes a task of re-examining the prior generalizations for consistency with the theory's predictions, as well as making new predictions and gathering data to test these.

This is the approach of which most of us think when we think of "theories" in science. It is the approach that is found in psychology, in atomic physics, in statistical mechanics. However, it is not the approach found in terrestrial mechanics or in servomechanism theory in electronics, and certain normative[39] theories in economics, like the theory of games and linear programming. There is no notion of "testing" such theories; it is only specific postulates which are tested. The theories are used in a synthetic way, taking a number

---

[39] A normative theory is one which prescribes behavior, in the sense that it says, "If these are your goals, then you must behave such-and-such to best realize them." It thereby acts as a calculating device for assessing the consequences of behavior in a complex situation, and allows selection of that behavior which best leads to the desired consequences. The postulates of such a theory are not descriptive statements of behavior, but are specifications of the conditions under which the behavior is to occur—the "rules of the game," so to speak.

of empirical generalizations or logical relations and instead of working "inward" to explain them, working "outward" by using them as postulates of a theory and studying their joint implications. They organize our immediately observable experience into larger systems of action which are beyond immediate observation. If, for example, there were theories of mass behavior based on well-confirmed social psychological laws, confirmed at the interpersonal level, these theories would be used in this synthetic fashion. Such theories, then, use empirical generalizations as postulates from which to derive implications, while the explanatory theories use generalizations as implications from which to infer a set of postulates. It is sometimes true that in the construction of synthetic theories, observations exist at the level of the deductions as well as at the level of the postulates. The essence of these theories, however, is that the postulates are constructed on the basis of their known correspondence with actual events, rather than solely on the basis of their utility in explaining other events.

Most sciences rely primarily on one or the other type of theory, because of their peculiar relation to their subject matter. A nuclear physicist or a psychologist stands outside his subject, can only observe its gross behavior, and must devise logical constructs which explain this behavior. A meteorologist knows the laws which govern the behavior of gases, but must construct a synthetic theory from them to describe and predict the weather. Sociology, because of its very wide span of concern, from inside the individual to the organization of complete societies, must use both approaches to theory. It is difficult to predict which will be more important, but it appears that the former, explanatory theories, are more nearly the province of psychology, while it is the peculiar province of sociology to develop the synthetic theories.

4.1 Explanatory theories

4.1.1 *Within the individual.* In purely verbal explanation, every sociologist assumes certain explanatory constructs within the individual to help him explain individual behavior. We explain behavior in terms of motives, attitudes, goals, frustrations, needs, motives, and other constructs. Yet present-day sociologists are somewhat wary—and probably rightly so—of setting up a *formal* system of constructs inside the individual to account for behavior. Since W. I. Thomas, with his four basic "wishes," perhaps the only major sociologist to pose a systematic psychological theory has been Talcott Parsons, with his cognitive, cathectic, and evaluative modes of orientation, together with a number of other constructs (see Parsons, 1951, and Parsons and Shils, 1951). Neither Thomas' needs, however, nor Parsons' modes of orientation—nor for that matter, the constructs of earlier sociologists—have been formally or in any sense mathematically related to other psychological or behavioral entities. The closest approach that sociologists have made to mathematical theories of individual behavior lies in the attitude scaling techniques, with their (wholly implicit) theories about the relation of attitudes to behavior under certain stimulus conditions. (There is no rigorous line separating these techniques for inferring dispositional properties from theories of individual behavior; in a well-developed science, the techniques would be derivable from these behavior theories. Since this is not true in social science, the two can best be distinguished by their differing purposes: the measurement models for attitudes and other dispositional variables are designed to allow measurement of an underlying variable through its hypothesized relation to observed behavior. Usually this is done in order to predict other behavior, and often the "theory" on which it is based is left wholly implicit. Theories of action, on the other hand, are designed to explain parsimoniously a wide range of behavior.)

Among social psychologists and psychologists, mathematical theories of behavior have been abundant. Learning theory is probably the field in which work in mathematical theory has been most abundant (see Bush and Estes, 1959, for a representative sample of work being done). Until around 1950, mathematical learning theory developed in a tradition of deterministic models, either with a heavy component of substantive ideas incorporated (as in Hull, 1943, and Hull *et al.*, 1940) or with more parsimonious assumptions about internal processes (as in Thurstone, 1930). Since that time, a new development of stochastic learning theory has taken place, in which the individual at a given stage of learning is characterized by a certain probability of responding in one way or another. These models, stemming either from work by Estes and Burke (1955) or from work by Bush and Mosteller (1955) have used the mathematics of Markov processes, and have taken this mathematics about to the limits of its present development. Unfortunately, these limits occur before much substantive complexity has been incorporated, and as a consequence, the models are applicable only to extremely simple experiments.

A good example of a formal theory of behavior is that by Luce (1959) which begins from postulates about the conditions which choice behavior ought "reasonably" to fulfill. To state the matter loosely, the essential postulate might be termed "independence of the choice from irrelevant alternatives": if a person chooses A over B when C is present, he will choose A over B when C is not present. Luce shows that if this is true for a set of alternatives A, B, . . . (in a probabilistic sense, such that the statement above is in terms of relative probabilities of choosing A and B), then the choosing individual can be characterized by a set of quantities, v_i, one for each alternative. Each of these quantities, unlike probabilities of choice, is associated only with the particular alternative, and is independent of the set of alternatives. Also unlike probabilities, these quantities are unbounded above, so that they can take on any positive value. They have much the same substantive meaning as Hull's "habit strengths" associated with a response. This is a much more attractive prospect than that offered by the stochastic learning theories mentioned above. Those theories specify an individual's state only in terms of his probabilities of choice, and go no further "within" him; thus they form no basis on which to predict what would happen if two responses, both partially learned in separate experiments, now confront the chooser in a third experiment.

There are some formal and semiformal theories of individual behavior which have this general approach: They bring inside the individual the external environment to which he reacts, by positing a number of variables like motives, beliefs, goals, and other concepts largely derived from introspection. Lewin's topological field theory (1936) is an example. Such theories often remain completely "within" the individual, with no measurement prescriptions tieing this interlocking system of concepts to behavior or to the stimulus environment. Thus, there is seldom any indication of whether a "goal" is defined as that toward which the individual proceeds, or is defined independently of his actual behavior. If it is defined independently, what are the ways of recognizing what a subject's goal is? Or if the theory has a concept of "barriers" to action (as does Lewin's field theory), and the existence of such barriers is to be used in a particular case to explain why the individual took path B rather than path A, then it is important that the theory provide means for an independent definition of barrier. If it does not, then the theory cannot be tested. Without any prescription of how at least some of these concepts are measured, then the theories are little more than heuristic devices whereby each of us, by linking the theory up with the real world in whatever way we see fit, can explain behavior. This does not mean that such theories are not good theories; any one of them may be very good, but without explicit prescriptions for relating the internal, unobserved structure with observable events, it is impossible to confirm or disprove them. Lewin's field theory, E. C. Tolman's theory (as formulated in Parsons and Shils, 1951), the Parsons-Shils theory of action (in the same volume, 1951) are all theories which show this same defect, which is precisely the defect which *ad hoc* commonsense psychological explanations of behavior have. The task of setting down precisely the criteria which a psychological theory of action should meet has yet to be done, not to speak of the task of devising such a theory itself.

These explanatory theories at the individual level are mentioned only in passing, since our concern here is not with the use of mathematics in psychology, but with its use in sociology and social psychology.

4.1.2 *Explanatory theories on the group level.* Since much of our observation of social behavior is on the level of the individual or the small group, there is less explanatory than synthetic theory at the group level. There do exist many verbal theories about large-scale social organizations, such as Weber's theory of bureaucracy, Michels' theory of the shift of power from the many to the few in organizations, the theory of mass society, Marx's theory of capitalism, and others which begin with the aim of explaining a large-scale social configuration. But most of these should be considered synthetic theories, since the premises about subgroups and about behavior in certain status positions, etc., on which they are based are—to some degree, at least— themselves confirmed by observation.

Table 1.7

TO INDIVIDUAL

	Rank	1	2	3	4	5	6
	1		1238	961	545	445	317
	2	1748		443	310	175	102
FROM	3	1371	415		305	125	69
INDIVIDUAL	4	952	310	282		83	49
	5	662	224	144	83		28
	6	470	126	114	65	44	

There are a very few mathematical explanatory theories on the level of groups of which I am aware; I will present one example to give some indication of their general character. Robert Bales and co-workers presented an empirical generalization concerning the relative frequencies of participation in discussions by members of six-person discussion groups; see Table 1.7 (1951). Joseph Keller (1951) noticed that this matrix is nearly factorable into two vectors. That is, each cell x_{ij} can be stated as the product of two factors, a_i and b_j. This means that if each individual in the group were characterized by two numbers, a_i and b_i, the whole matrix of who-to-whom frequencies could be predicted. Keller factored the matrix, and got two factors with the following values (i.e., the matrix $C = A'B$, where A and B are vectors

$$A = \begin{pmatrix} 63.0 \\ 27.7 \\ 21.0 \\ 14.5 \\ 8.8 \\ 6.9 \end{pmatrix} \qquad B = \begin{pmatrix} 63.0 \\ 19.5 \\ 15.8 \\ 10.7 \\ 5.7 \\ 3.2 \end{pmatrix}$$

which, when multiplied, reproduce rather well the matrix in Table 1.6. Keller suggested that the A vector be considered as the individual's "initiation potential," and the B vector as his "reception potential." According to the theory, then, the relative number of participations from i to j is a product of i's initiation potential and j's reception potential.

Whether the two such attributes by which individuals can be characterized predict anything apart from their performance in this series of meetings is a question which has not yet been answered. A positive answer would be an aid to the theory of participation in small face-to-face groups; a negative answer would mean that Keller has done nothing more than reduce the thirty-six numbers to twelve parameters.

This example of an explanatory theory is admittedly not representative of the major work going on in social research and theory today. It is sufficient, however, to indicate the nature of such theories, and their relation to empirical data.

4.2 Synthetic theories

Here the group and individual levels will not be distinguished, for it is characteristic of many of these theories that they begin with postulates on the individual level and end with deductions on the group level.

Despite some similarities, the theories discussed here differ widely from one another. Some use qualitative generalizations rather than quantitative ones; some use differential equations while others use stochastic processes; some treat whole systems of behavior, others treat only small segments. The present discussion will attempt to indicate generally what these theories are like, what their proponents expect from them, and what role they might be expected to play in the future of social science.

4.2.1 *Diffusion theories*. There is a general class of theories which may be applied to the phenomenon of social diffusion: diffusion of a piece of information, of a technological innovation, of a belief, of an innovation in fashion, etc. These theories are applicable to situations in which each individual in a group can be characterized as having or not having the attribute being diffused. Complete diffusion in a group of a given size occurs when all individuals have the attribute.

These theories are structurally isomorphic with theories in other sciences, showing an identical mathematical form. It is the structural similarity of the phenomena, apart from their particular content, which allows this identical mathematics. The nature of the isomorphism will become evident upon examination of the particular theories. (Stochastic diffusion theories are examined in some detail in Chapters 10, 11, and 17.)

One of the simplest diffusion theories is one which, stated in words, says that the rate of propagation of the attribute (i.e., piece of information, behavioral innovation, belief, style) is proportional to the number of people who already have it. This would correspond, socially, to a situation in which each person received an attribute (say a message), and transmitted it to a given number of other persons per unit time, none of whom had heard the message before.

If we assume that the population is very large, so that a differential equation may be used, and if we let

x = the number of people who have the item at any one time, and
t = time,

then $\dfrac{dx}{dt}$ = the number of people getting the item per unit time.

and the theory says,

$$\frac{dx}{dt} = kx \qquad (4.1)$$

where k is the diffusion constant of proportionality. Expressed in integral form and letting $t = 0$ at $x = 1$, this is

$$x = e^{kt} \qquad (4.2)$$

This simple theory of diffusion is immediately recognizable as the exponential law of population growth. In place of the diffusion of an attribute to new persons is the birth of new persons into the population; analogous to the social situation in which each person who has the attribute transmits it to a constant number of new others per unit time is the genetic situation in which each pair of persons gives birth to a given number of others per unit time. The constant of proportionality represents the difference between the birth and death rates. In other sciences, the law represents still different phenomena: growth in size of certain organisms, the equation for continuously compounded interest in finance, and (with a negative growth exponent) the decay of radioactive substances, the rate of monomolecular reactions in chemistry, and the loss of body weight in a starving animal.[40]

The particular kind of mathematics used to represent these phenomena may be quite different from the above differential equation. A stochastic birth-death process (in which each person has only a *probability* rather than a certainty of propagating another per unit time) might have been used rather than the differential equation. There are, in fact, in all these diffusion theories, the two alternative mathematical representations, deterministic and stochastic. Some consequences of using one rather than the other will be discussed in Chapter 18. More important at the moment, however, is the structural isomorphism among these different areas of behavior and the two mathematical representations.[41]

Under social conditions with populations limited in size, the above assumptions about diffusion do not adequately represent what happens. A more realistic assumption is one which allows for a limited population, postulating that the rate of diffusion (or growth) is proportional to the number who already have the attribute *and* to the number who have yet to receive it. In terms of the social situation, each one who already has the attribute

---

[40] Ludwig von Bertalanffy (1950) discusses these isomorphisms in a general examination of isomorphic laws in science.

[41] In general, the stochastic models show a greater structural isomorphism with behavior than do deterministic ones. For certain problems, the points of difference make important differences in the deductions; for others, they do not. See Chapter 7 for a case in which there is an important difference in deductions.

transmits it to a constant proportion of others per unit time, but a certain proportion of these persons already have the attribute. Mathematically,

$$\frac{dx}{dt} = kx(N - x) \qquad (4.3)$$

or, letting $x = 1$ at $t = 0$,

$$x = \frac{Ne^{kt}}{N - 1 + e^{kt}} \qquad (4.4)$$

where N is the population size.

This equation is recognizable as the familiar logistic curve of population growth. In terms of population growth, the structurally isomorphic situation is that in which environmental conditions such as food restrict the maximum population to size N. By imposing such conditions upon insect populations, the predictions of this theory have been well verified. In chemistry, an auto-catalytic reaction—one in which the reaction product catalyses further reaction—fulfills the conditions of the differential equations, and the reaction proceeds in conformity with these predictions.

A third kind of diffusion is perhaps simpler than either of these: it postulates that all diffusion proceeds from a constant source independent of the number who already have the attribute. It posits a limited population, so that the number of new hearers per unit time is proportional to the total number who have not yet heard. Mathematically,

$$\frac{dx}{dt} = k(N - x) \qquad (4.5)$$

or, letting $t = 0$ when $x = 0$,

$$x = N(1 - e^{-kt}) \qquad (4.6)$$

where N is the population size.

In this case, there would be no isomorphic situation in population growth; in chemistry a reaction which depends upon a constant source of heat, externally supplied, is isomorphic to this. Many other situations also fit these postulates, for example, those situations in which propagation of information is from a single source constant over time—mass media propagation rather than interpersonal propagation.

It is easy to ask just how such idealized processes, and such "contentless" ones, may be useful in actual social theory or research. Fortunately, an example is at hand that shows an actual use which has been made of these diffusion theories in an applied research problem (Coleman, Katz, and Menzel, 1957). The general problem concerned the process of the adoption of a new drug by doctors in four midwestern communities. One variable which was found to play a very important part in the time at which the doctor introduced the drug was his integration or isolation in the local medical community, as measured by the number of times other doctors named him as a social friend or as a frequent fellow-discussant of medical cases. Those doctors who were highly integrated with their colleagues adopted the drug much more quickly—on an average, about four months sooner—than their socially or medically isolated fellows. Two alternative hypotheses appeared reasonable in explanation of the difference:

(a) The integrated doctors were different kinds of doctors on the whole, doctors who were more up-to-date and quicker to pick up new things. That is, the same traits which made them integrated made them quick to use new drugs.

(b) The integrated doctors were in a social position to learn about the drug and be persuaded to use it quickly, while the isolated doctors, out of contact with their fellows, had to depend upon advertising and the drug salesman to be persuaded to use the drug.

How can a choice be made between these hypotheses on the basis of the data? We reasoned as follows: if hypothesis (a) were true, and the difference in introduction were due to individual differences, then the process of diffusion would be much the same for the isolated and integrated doctors (probably some combination of the second and third diffusion processes above), and the resulting shapes of the cumulative curves of introduction should be roughly the same, differing only in the size of the parameter k. If, however, hypothesis (b) were true, then the very process of introduction should be different: the integrated doctors should be persuaded to use the drug by their colleagues who have already come to use it—a diffusion process in accordance with the logistic law; the isolated, in contrast, should be persuaded by the drug salesman and advertising, in accordance with the constant-source law discussed under the third diffusion process above.

When an attempt was made to fit theoretical curves to the data, the result shown in Figure 1.3 occurred: the logistic curve fitted reasonably well the curve for the integrated doctors, considering the inadequacy of the data, while the constant-source curve fitted reasonably well the isolates.[42] Thus hypothesis (b), which postulated social location rather than individual differences as the cause of the difference in drug introduction between integrated and isolated doctors, is confirmed, and hypothesis (a) is rejected. Here is one simple example, then, in which these theories of diffusion, which may seem too highly idealized for practical use, have served a very practical purpose.[43]

[42] There were several measures of integration; the one shown in Fig. 1.3 fits the theoretical curves better than the others, but they too tend to confirm hypothesis (b).

[43] No attempt was made to fit these curves closely to the data. Rather, restrictions were placed on the selection of parameters, so that any fit which resulted would allow greater confidence in the hypothesis. The value .16 was given to Y_2 and X_2 to approximate the data at $t = 2$; the only parameters selected with a view to fitting the later portions of the curve were k_1 and k_2.

These three "ideal types" of diffusion processes are only the best-known formal theories applicable to diffusion. Vito Volterra, a French mathematician, worked out in detail some theories of considerably greater complexity (1931). He applied these theories to population growth, all of them taking off from the basic exponential curve of eq. (4.2). He considers the case in which the environment varies slowly so that the constant k is a function of time. He considers also the case in which several different species are competing for the same food (in diffusion, several innovations competing for the same audience), as well as other variations, such as a predator-prey relation.

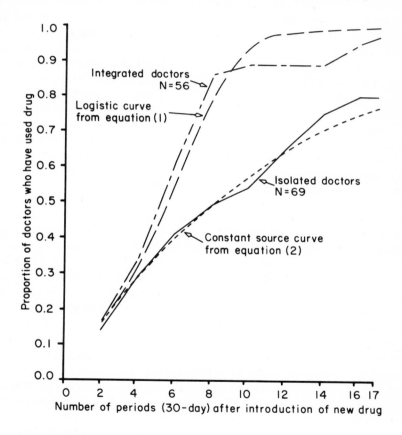

Figure 1.3. Cumulative Rates of New Drug Adoption by Integrated and Isolated Doctors in Four Midwestern Communities

Equations used:

$$X_{t+1} = X_t + k_1 X(1 - X) \quad \text{(integrated doctors)} \qquad (1)$$
$$Y_{t+1} = Y_t + k_2(1 - Y) \quad \text{(isolated doctors)} \qquad (2)$$

where $X_2 = Y_2 = .16$; $k_1 = .5$; $k_2 = .08$.

(See also H. T. Davis, 1960, for an extension of Volterra's work.) Another author, Anatol Rapoport, has considered various mechanisms for the spread of information in a population; he uses rather complicated stochastic models, however, which are somewhat harder to apply to data than are the ordinary deterministic equations discussed above (1953, 1954).

A number of other theories of the diffusion type recently developed in other areas than social science also are applicable to processes of diffusion and related phenomena. These are theories of epidemics, which use both deterministic and stochastic models for their representation (see Bailey, 1957). Though they have been developed for the study of the spread of contagious diseases, they seem equally applicable to the study of socially "contagious" phenomena, as are the diffusion laws discussed above. It seems only a matter of time until such social phenomena as the growth of fads and fashions, the spread of news, the growth of popular opposition to a public policy, the rise and fall of political demogogues, and other situations will be subject to analysis with the use of theories related to these diffusion-type theories.

These diffusion laws represent one kind of synthetic theory in social science. Their postulates can ordinarily be confirmed by direct measurement, leading one to predict that one or another characteristic curve of diffusion will occur.[44] There are numerous other kinds of these synthetic theories, however, as the examples below will indicate.

4.2.2 *Theories of marriage rules in kinship systems.* In primitive tribes with classificatory statuses and prescriptive marriage, the system of statuses can be described by two kinds of rules: a marriage rule and a descent rule. The marriage rule can be stated in terms of a husband-wife matrix of zeroes and ones (called W below), with rows representing husband's status and columns representing wife's status. Each row and each column have all zeroes except a single one, which indicates the status from which the spouse must come. Similarly, the descent rule may be described by a descent matrix (called C below), with rows representing the father's status group, and columns representing the child's. A one in row i and column j means that when the father is of status group i, the son's status group is j.

Following outlines proposed by R. R. Bush (see Kemeny, Snell, and Thompson, 1956), White (1963) has developed this approach in detail and applied it to describe the marriage and descent systems of certain primitive tribes. The allowable marriages with kin are given by the products of W and C matrices (and their inverses) that equal W. White shows that in some tribes,

---

[44] It should be noted, however, that in the applied example of drug introduction discussed above, the theories were used in part as explanatory theories. This example makes evident the fact that a theory is "explanatory" or "synthetic" only relative to the particular data at hand. Nevertheless, it is usually true that the same kinds of data are generally available with respect to a given theory.

the matrices are such that $W = C^{-1}WC$, that is, marriage is allowed with mother's $(C^{-1}W)$ brother's daughter (C). In others, the matrices are such that $W = C^{-1}W^{-1}C$.

This approach takes the extensive list of particular rules and shows the structure that generates them. It thus shows the implicit order that lies behind the apparently *ad hoc* rules, and allows comparison of such societies by the kind of order or structure that inheres in their marriage and descent rules.

4.2.3 *Qualitative postulate systems.* Herbert Simon (1957) has introduced a method of theory-formalization which seems to have some potentiality for social theory. Perhaps the most practicable feature of the method is its use of qualitative propositions of the sort which abound in social theory. Taking a set of such verbally formulated propositions, Simon states them mathematically, then (always working with a set which have a number of inter-dependencies between a few variables), he formulates the system of equations which represents them, and examines their deductions. An example will indicate the procedure.

George Homans has stated in *The Human Group* a number of propositions, of the order of:

> ... persons who feel sentiments of liking for one another will express those sentiments in activities over and above the activities of the external system, and these activities may further strengthen the sentiments of liking. (1950, p. 118.)

Simon takes the three basic ones of Homans' propositions (including the one stated above), and writes them symbolically thus:

$$\frac{dF}{dt} = f(I,F) \qquad \frac{\partial f}{\partial I} > 0; \frac{\partial f}{\partial F} < 0 \qquad (4.7)$$

(The change in friendliness in a group is an increasing function of the amount of interaction, I, carried on in the group, and a decreasing function of the existing level of friendliness, F.) Equation (4.7), together with the two other equations that follow, constitutes the system of behavior which Simon examines:

$$I = g(A,F) \qquad \frac{\partial I}{\partial A} > 0, \frac{\partial I}{\partial F} > 0 \qquad (4.8)$$

$$\frac{dA}{dt} = \Psi(A,F;E) \qquad \frac{\partial \Psi}{\partial A} < 0, \frac{\partial \Psi}{\partial F} > 0, \frac{\partial \Psi}{\partial E} > 0 \qquad (4.9)$$

where A is the number of different activities carried on by the group and E is the number of externally imposed activities. Taking these three equations together, it is possible to make certain deductions about the equilibrium points of the system, about the direction the system will move (i.e., the relative shifts in F, I, and A) when in a given position, and so on. These deductions are not powerful; they tell little about the resulting state of the system. But this reflects only the weakness of the postulates themselves, stated as they are qualitatively.

A thorough examination of this kind of theorizing in sociology is available (Coleman, 1960); it will not be discussed in detail here. However, since it is the one use of mathematics which can be directly applied to propositions from existing social theory, it may be useful to mention some of the restrictions upon it, together with the possible functions it can perform. First, some of the restrictions:

(1) The variables must constitute to some degree a "system" of behavior; that is, there must be interdependencies, with at least one "closed loop" or feedback. Otherwise, the propositions will remain a series of discrete propositions from which few or no deductions can be made.

(2) In order that the deductions be made by available mathematical techniques, the system must ultimately be reducible to two differential equations. Practically, this means that other relations (like eq. (4.8) above) must be stated in algebraic form, as equilibrium equations. Ordinarily one would write the fastest-acting relations as equilibrium equations, for they reach equilibrium most quickly; the two slowest would be stated as rate equations, that is, as differential equations like (4.7) and (4.9) above.

(3) A restriction is also imposed on the variables contained in the theory. Though it seems that the monotonicity restrictions are quite weak, they impose severe restrictions on the measurement of variables, particularly if the variables are group variables, aggregates of individual measures, as in the case of Homans' generalizations. There are various ways of getting around this difficulty for practical purposes, though the general problem remains.

In contrast to these limitations are some of the values of such formalization:

(1) Formalization of a verbal statement of the form, "X increases with increase in Y," makes one face the question of whether this statement is meant as mere correlation, both X and Y co-varying as a result of another variable, or as a real structural (i.e., causal) relation. Verbal theorizing allows much ambiguity in this.

(2) Other ambiguities in interpretation of the verbal generalizations are made explicit by formalization. Verbal statements easily hide ambiguity; mathematical ones do not.

It should be noted that the values (1) and (2) arise from a formalization of verbal generalizations without ever making deductions; they derive merely from setting down the generalizations in mathematical rather than verbal form. Carrying out deductions, however, adds these values:

(3) Inconsistencies or lack of independence between postulates is made

apparent in carrying out deductions. Given the state of chaos which much verbal social theory is in, this would be of considerable value.

(4) Implications of the postulates which could never be carried out mentally with verbal theories are possible once they are formalized. Thus the formalization helps us to see a little beyond our noses in examining implications which were not directly evident.

(5) Comparisons of theories with one another, as well as more precise comparison of theory with experiment, are possible as they never really are when a rather involved theory is stated in purely verbal terms.

Two of these three examples of synthetic theories, that is, diffusion theories and qualitative system theories, are only two cases among many possible theories in this general class. In particular, it seems that many social phenomena are amenable to treatment as *systems* of behavior, using models similar to those used in the study of economic systems and in the theory of servomechanisms. Particularly such areas of social life as political organization, which we describe in such systemic terms as "power equilibrium," "the flow of influence," "shifts of power," and "reciprocal influence," and so on, seem directly amenable to this kind of treatment. In the area of political organization, in fact, a good example of such work exists. Anthony Downs (1957) has conceived of the political system in a democracy much as an economic system: the parties compete for "customers" by offering "products" in the form of positions on issues which have a high utility for voters. A voter in turn selects that party whose positions on various issues imply highest utility for him.

An older example of a synthetic theory in the social sciences is Lewis Richardson's work on armament and arms races (1939). Richardson, noting that the armaments of nations seemed to show a high interdependence, developed a model to mirror this interdependence. The model derived from quite reasonable postulates about the reaction of each nation to armament of the other. The mathematics is that of simultaneous linear differential equations, and the quantities which are linked together by these equations are the values of military equipment of each of two opposing nations. Using data from periods both of arms build-ups and of disarmament, Richardson made serious and extensive attempts to show the fit of the model to such international relations. Yet perhaps because the model attempts to handle very simply a highly complex set of interdependencies, it can hardly be regarded as directly useful, either in theory or practice.

It seems possible that theories of this sort will be highly productive in the future. The major problems in the way of formulating such theories are evidently those of the conception and measurement of the quantities which serve as "currency" or as "forces" in these systems: power, influence, and the like. Both the practical problems of measurement and the very conceptualization (i.e., assuming ideal conditions for measurement) are formidable ones, to which no general solution appears readily available. (See March,

1955, Parsons, 1963, and Coleman, 1963, for discussions of the problem.)
It is likely that solutions will occur only through the theories themselves,
giving prescriptions for such measurement.

The examples and discussion in this section indicate the broad range of
synthetic theories in social science. It is true at present that most sociologists
are engaged in explanation: *why* does a given social configuration occur? or
why do a certain class of people behave as they do? Such pursuits are quite
important, and are the natural direction in which the scientist's curiosity
leads him. Yet sociology has a peculiar perspective, from which it can verify
postulates about individual behavior, but cannot easily follow the complexities
of the combinations and interrelations which produce large-scale social
phenomena. Under such conditions, it appears that sociology can profit
immensely from asking "What are the consequences?" instead of "Why?"
Having taken several postulates about individual behavior in an organization,
for example, then it may be extremely useful to ask what the joint implications
of these postulates are, and what they show when treated together as a
system (assuming that the postulates do cover a relatively closed area of
behavior). This approach has shown its merit in economics through such
methods as linear programming and the theory of games. It seems quite
likely that its merits in sociology are great, too, and that it will prove of
increasing value as more and more facility is gained in using it.

4.3 Other mathematical theories

Besides the explanatory and synthetic theories discussed above, there
are other theories or models which have a very elusive relation to the
real world. Some of these, oddly enough, are models developed for experiments; others are models which are not developed in conjunction with any
empirical data, and in many cases are little more than the product of an
imaginative mind. This is not to say, however, that such models are of no
use. I hope to indicate below ways in which they are valuable.

First, however, should be mentioned some experimental models. It is
sometimes felt by sociologists that experimentation is the research ultimate
to which sociology can and should aspire. This was explicitly stated, for
example, by a leading field researcher in a presidential address before the
American Sociological Society (Stouffer, 1953). This is a questionable thesis
in general, given the subject matter of sociology, but it is particularly questionable when one is developing a mathematical theory or model to represent
social phenomena. More specifically, it seems that under the following
conditions, the usefulness of such procedures seems particularly open to
question:

(a) First one develops a "mathematical model" to represent a social
process, say some small-group process. The model is one in which the
postulates are set down, and deductions are calculated from these postulates.

(b) Then a laboratory experiment is carried out, with one of the following two characteristics:

(1) All the postulates of the mathematical model are verified by fiat in setting up the social situation or conditions under which the experiment is carried out. (See Dodd, 1955, for an example of this. The experiment in this case was a demonstration of the logistic law of diffusion. The conditions of the experiment as set up confirmed the postulates of the logistic law, so that the resulting diffusion curve necessarily followed that predicted from these postulates.) In a case like this, the "experiment" becomes little more than a demonstration that one's mathematical calculations were correct when he made the deductions from the postulates of the model.

(2) All the postulates of the model are established in setting up the experiment except the one or two which represent some psychological process, rather than a social one. (See Leeman, 1952, for an example of this.) In this case, the "experiment," which gives actual results to compare with those predicted by the model, is nothing more than confirmation or rejection of the postulate about the psychological process. This is certainly a valid purpose if the psychological process necessitated the group situation as part of the conditions under which it is to hold. (The "group pressure" phenomenon studied in Asch's experiments is a good example of such a case. Another example, in which a model was set up, then an experiment carried out, is reported by Hays and Bush, 1954.) But if the psychological postulate is one which has little to do with social phenomena or with a group situation, then it might better be tested directly, without the trappings of a social situation, which confuse the issue. In the example of this procedure referred to above (Leeman), the one postulate tested by the experiment was a postulate about choice between two objects, when there were no real criteria for choosing between them, and no rewards or punishments for choosing one rather than another. If it is desired to examine such choice behavior, it could better be done with individuals, using a legitimate psychological model and experiment, rather than with groups in an illegitimate "sociological" model and experiment.

These examples illustrate a confusion between the two types of theory discussed here. In both cases, the postulates were confirmed by experimental fiat or could be directly tested. But the investigators, with a belief that "theory should be tested by experiment," felt constrained to set up experimental tests of the theory. Thus in fact their theories were of the synthetic variety, which required no social experimentation; but the theories were treated as explanatory ones, whose deductions must be tested against experiment.

There is another sort of theory which has a peculiar relation to the real world. Such theories are exemplified by Rashevsky's (1951), which have little attachment to actual (or even idealized) social phenomena (at the level either of postulates or of deductions). What value these theories has seems to lie in two areas:

(a) Mathematically expressed theories from physics, chemistry, genetics, economics, and other sciences may be useful for social science, either because of their *isomorphism* with social phenomena, which allows bodily transference of a mathematical apparatus, or because of their *suggestiveness* in indicating how mathematical theories may be constructed in social science. In precisely the same ways, the models which have been developed for social phenomena, but are without any roots in the real world, can be useful for the development of social theory. (See Coleman (1954) for an attempt to use some of Rashevsky's models in this way. This attempt itself, however, shows some of the same "detachment" from the real world that Rashevsky's models do.)

(b) The second value of such models is as training tools for mathematically inclined social scientists. If one holds in abeyance his questions about the model's applicability, and concentrates instead on the formal mechanism of the model, and on how this relates to the substantive postulates, he may learn much from such models. Since they are unconstrained by any correspondence to actual phenomena, they can exhibit many more variations in structure, and many more types of mathematics, than a similar set of models constructed to conform to actual or idealized social phenomena.

5. PREDICTION MODELS

There is one use of mathematics which has not been mentioned above. Sometimes mathematics is used in a particular situation in order to predict what will occur in a similar situation, with no pretensions that a theory is being developed. Direct extrapolation of a curve is the simplest example, and there are numerous variations. This use of mathematics is a kind of borderline area, between the uses of mathematics that I have taken for consideration, and the use of statistical inference, which I have excluded from consideration. A good example of a borderline case is that of item analysis (Solomon, 1961), which is used in psychological testing and in social surveys for extracting a subset of items which are about as good as the larger set in predicting some external criterion. Another borderline example is that of discriminant function analysis. Objects (e.g., individuals) are known to be in either of two classes, and there are numerous measures on each object which imperfectly correlate with class membership. Discriminant function analysis provides a minimum-error technique for classifying the objects.

Regression analysis is somewhat closer to the matters under consideration in this volume, because it is a method for estimating parameters in a causal relation (e.g., the parameters a and b in the relation $y = a + bx$). The methods for carrying out these analyses are simply applications of statistics; nevertheless, techniques have been developed particularly for such purposes. (In particular, Leo Goodman, 1959, presents methods for using ecological data in regression analysis for making inferences about individual behavior.)

More nearly within the scope of the mathematics I am examining comes a model like that of Anderson's (1954) Markov chain model for the study of changes in vote intention over the period of an election campaign. Using the data from a six-wave panel study (monthly interviews from May to October), Anderson fits a model which posits constant transition probabilities (from vote intention at one time to the next) for an individual. He shows that to fit such a model to these data, the campaign must be broken into two periods (May–July and July–October), and the second period has a time scale different from calendar time (i.e., changes from July to August, a one-month period, nearly equal changes from August to October, a two-month period). Thus Anderson uses a Markov chain model to investigate a given socio-psychological phenomenon; the model is a kind of extrapolation technique which predicts future position on a given attribute as a function of present and past position.[45]

This example shows the nature of these prediction models; a considerable amount of mathematics, of the kind Anderson used as well as other kinds, is useful in the fitting of such models. For the particular purposes of a given research problem, they may be quite valuable, though they make little pretense to constitute "theories."

6. CONCLUSION

I have attempted to show in this chapter primarily two things. The first is the diversity of uses of mathematics in sociology. In measurement, in the expression of empirical generalizations, as a language for theory, and in simple prediction, mathematics finds a place. It may be that at the present stage of sociology mathematics is of little use in one or another of these different ways; this should not keep us from putting it to work for social science in those areas where it can be of aid. In short, it is important to pick and choose in using mathematics for sociology, and not to become unrestrainedly enamored with it nor to reject it out of hand.

Second, I have attempted to put the use of mathematics in its proper perspective as a *tool* of social science rather than as an end in itself. It seems to me extremely important, if mathematics is to aid sociology, that social scientists who use it never lose sight of their substantive problem in the analysis of the mathematical problems to which it leads them. In examining the past uses of mathematics in sociology, few though they may be, it appears evident that the more important contributions have been made when men remained diligently in search of the answer to a sociological question rather than letting themselves be sidetracked to the study of a mathematical question (which often will long ago have been solved by a mathematician in any case).

---

[45] It is interesting to note that Marshall and Goldhamer, and Telser, use Markov processes as a model for generating a *measure*; Anderson uses the same model as a prediction device.

This does not mean that mathematical methods developed for other sciences or as exercises in pure mathematics are not of use; to be sure, they are the only sources of mathematics that we have. It is rather to say that the necessarily difficult task of developing mathematical sociology can best be performed when our concentration remains upon the sociological problem, and the mathematical tools remain means to an end.

CHAPTER 2

PROBLEMS OF QUANTITATIVE MEASUREMENT IN SOCIOLOGY

1. INTRODUCTION

Time and again the same obstacle has been evident in the path of quantification in social science: the lack of adequate measurement. In the discussion of quantitative generalizations in Chapter 1, the virtual absence of all else but distributional phenomena (which require only counting for their measurement) indicates the lack of quantitative measurement except in these simple cases. The paucity of quantitative theories, and the primitive nature of those which do exist, testify to the crippling effect of lack of measurement. Quantitative laws and theories seem to require more in the way of measurement than social phenomena are prepared to give. Even the weakest theories, those based on qualitative generalizations, impose measurement requirements which are seldom met by the kinds of measurements which exist today in social science.

Both sociologists and psychologists often point to the problem of measurement as a major stumbling block in the development of social science.[1] And of course sociology and psychology have had their share of cries for "operationalism" in measurement, though these cries have no more provided the key to fruitful measurement than have other watchwords.

Altogether, there seems to be considerable agreement that in faulty measurement lies a primary obstacle to social and psychological theory; at the same time, there seems to be no simple way around the obstacle.

What is it about quantitative measurement that is so crucial for theory-development? Essentially this: the power of a theory to provide precise and numerous deductions lies in its ability to carry out transformations—in fact, chains of transformations—upon the input data.

If these data are in the form of numbers, and maintain their properties as numbers after the transformations, then the powerful transformations of algebra, calculus, and matrix algebra can be carried out upon them. If the data do not obey these requirements, then these powerful tools are unusable. Thus the task of assigning numbers so that they meet these requirements is a crucial one for any science—and it is a task extremely difficult to meet in social science.

An example will indicate what it means to say that the tools of algebra are legitimately usable to transform the input data. Suppose a sociologist asks respondents to make pairwise comparisons of occupations in terms of prestige (not including all pairs, but only a subset). Suppose further he finds that the prestige relation is generally transitive. He then assigns the occupations numerals on the basis of the number of occupations they exceeded in prestige. Selecting four occupations, he would have:

Doctor	70	(high)
Salesman	40	
Bookkeeper	30	
Street cleaner	10	(low)

Now these numerals, assigned in terms of the criterion, "higher in prestige than," denote the result of an operation of paired comparisons, which is transitive. This means it *is* permissible to carry out this mathematical deduction:

$$\text{(a)} \quad 70 > 40$$
$$\text{(b)} \quad 40 > 30$$
$$\text{therefore} \quad 70 > 30$$

or "Doctor is higher in prestige than bookkeeper." That is, we can use very

---

[1] In psychology, the concern with quantitative measurement has been particularly great, beginning with psychophysics and spreading throughout the rest of psychology. See, for example, Bergmann and Spence (1951), Koch (1951), Gullicksen (1946), Reese (1943), Stevens (1955), Stevens and Galanter (1957), Torgerson (1958).

simple mathematics to deduce that doctors are ranked higher than book-keepers (70>30) if we know that doctors are ranked higher than salesmen (70>40) and salesmen are ranked higher than bookkeepers (40>30). However, it is *not* permissible to say that the prestige of a bookkeeper (30) plus the prestige of a salesman (40) equals the prestige of a doctor (70). The notion of "adding prestige" has no meaning in terms of the sociologist's instructions to the respondent, nor does it have meaning in terms of the respondent's behavior in comparing occupations. If, however, the numerals 10, 30, 40, 70 had been applied to these occupations in such a way that they fulfilled the properties of real numbers, then this deduction would be possible, and the notion of "adding" would be meaningful. If, for example, an econo-mist put beside these four occupations the numbers 10, 30, 40, and 70 as above, to represent the average weekly earnings in each occupation, then it would be perfectly permissible to make the deduction

$$30+40 = 70$$

i.e., the average weekly earnings of a doctor equals the sum of the average weekly earnings of a salesman and a bookkeeper. It is permissible because the resulting number has precise meaning to which a dimension may be attached. This number with a dimension is usable in that part of economic theory which deals with exchanges of commodities, or exchanges between money and commodities. The sum of $70 will buy equal amounts, independ-ently of whether it is in the hands of one man or in the hands of a two-man partnership.[2]

It is evident, then, that operations one may carry out with real numbers, and the criteria that those operations imply for measurement, bring about the fundamental problems in the theory of measurement. Once these criteria are set down, they form the basis from which all the measurement problems to be discussed[3] must begin.

2. CRITERIA FOR ORDINAL AND CARDINAL MEASUREMENT

There are three generally recognized levels of measurement, which Stevens (1951) calls ordinal, interval, and ratio scales.[4] Rather than treating these levels directly, it will be more useful to treat only the lowest (ordinal)

[2] For certain parts of economic theory, involving preferences for commodities and for money, certain operations with money are not allowable. For example, if a man has $2x$ dollars, the expenditure or gain of $1 will generally mean less to him than if he has only x dollars.

[3] Some of the applied problems to be dealt with toward the end of the chapter are exceptions to this.

[4] Coombs (1950) has devised a scale which establishes an order among intervals, which is a kind of intermediate point between ordinal and interval scales. But since our purpose is not completeness here, but rather to learn how social scientists may gain a foothold in quantitative measurement, this will not be discussed systematically.

and the highest (ratio or cardinal). It will then be possible to examine interval scales in terms of the criteria imposed upon these two types of measures.

The ground-breaking work on the theory of measurement was published by N. R. Campbell in 1928. His criteria have been taken over in the social sciences, first in psychophysics, then in the measurement of subjective utility under risk, and in other psychological measurements.[5] They have hardly reached sociology—that is, there seem to be no attempts to devise measures in sociology that fulfill criteria beyond those of ordinality. As will be evident later, this is not as poor a situation as it first appears to be. But in order to pass such a judgment, it is necessary first to examine the classical theory of measurement.

Two criteria for cardinal measurement have been generally recognized, following largely from Campbell's early work. These are analogous to the criteria which numbers must meet if they are to permit the operations of algebra. Only if those criteria are met can there be a true isomorphism between the mathematics and the theory, at the same time that the theory adequately corresponds to the real world. The theory is "caught in the middle," so to speak. On one side is the mathematics, which says that these measures must conform to the same criteria that real numbers conform to, if they are to reap the deductions that can be obtained with real numbers, using the operations of addition and multiplication. On the other side is the real world, which has its own ways of behaving, and refuses to be put into arbitrary categories.

The criteria imposed by the mathematics on a measure which ranges over objects or states x_i ($i = 1, 2, \ldots$), say $m(x_i)$, are as follows:

That the method of measurement assign a number $m(x_i)$ to object or state x_i on the basis of the following two operations, which impose restrictions upon the allowable numbers which can be assigned to the object:

Operation (1). A *comparison* between every two objects or states, x_i and x_j, which imposes an *order* restriction on assignment of numbers:

$$m(x_i) > m(x_j) \quad \text{or} \quad m(x_i) = m(x_j) \tag{2.1}$$

This first criterion merely establishes an ordinal scale, and must be supplemented by another for cardinality. The second criterion, which has caused much controversy and confusion in the theory of measurement, is usually stated something like this:

Operation (2). A method of *combination* of objects x_i and x_j must exist, such that it imposes a restriction upon assignment of numbers $m(x_i)$, $m(x_j)$, and $m(x_i \text{ comb. } x_j)$ to objects x_i, x_j, and $(x_i \text{ comb. } x_j)$ as follows:

$$m(x_i \text{ comb. } x_j) = m(x_i) + m(x_j) \tag{2.2}$$

[5] For some of the work in this area, see besides the references given earlier, Davidson, McKinsey, and Suppes (1955), Hempel (1952), Marshak (1954), Ramsey (1931), Suppes and Winet (1955).

It is this operation which transforms a property which *orders* objects into one which assigns them a *metric* or *quantity*. And it is this operation which most sociopsychological measurement procedures fail to meet. This has been the primary stumbling block for quantitative measurement in psychology and sociology. This second criterion will be examined shortly. First, however, it is useful to look at the implications of the first criterion, the comparison operation.

2.1 Ordinal measures and the comparison operation

The comparison operation (1) above establishes a "weak order" between the objects, or a "quasi-series," ordering the objects along some continuum without any notion of distance: in measurement of occupational desirability, "x_i being more desirable than x_j"; in measurement of mass, "x_i tipping the scales over x_j"; in measurement of temperature, "x_i making the mercury in a closed glass tube expand more than does x_j"; in the economist's measurement of utility, "x_i being preferred to x_j"; in measurement of attitudes, "person x_i being more favorable toward ——— than is x_j." All these comparisons are specific examples of operation (1), and all permit objects x_i and x_j to be assigned numbers $m(x)$ such that $m(x_i) > m(x_j)$ or $m(x_i) = m(x_j)$.

Note that if this comparison procedure is to permit assignment of numbers such that $m(x_i) > m(x_j)$ or $m(x_i) = m(x_j)$, then the comparison must fulfill certain criteria which the relations ">" and "=" between real numbers fulfill. It is here that the constraints of the empirical world enter, for it may be that a given comparison operation just does not fulfill these criteria.

The most important criterion which must be fulfilled is *transitivity*: if a comparison of x_i and x_j results in assignment of numbers such that $m(x_i) > m(x_j)$, and comparison of x_j and x_k results in assignment of another number $m(x_k)$, such that $m(x_j) > m(x_k)$, then comparison of x_i and x_k must be compatible with the previous assignment, which states that $m(x_i) > m(x_k)$. In simple terms, if doctors are rated more prestigeful than salesmen (and given prestige scores of 70 and 40 respectively), and salesmen are rated more prestigeful than street cleaners (who are given a prestige score of 10), then these scores imply that doctors (70) will be rated more prestigeful than street cleaners (10) when these two occupations are compared. If this is *not* so, then it is not permissible to assign numbers which establish an order relation, for there is no serial ordering of objects relative to the comparison in question. This is often illustrated by the moh scale of hardness for physical materials. Numbers are assigned on the basis of a "scratch" relation: if A will scratch B, then it has a higher number than B. But after the scale had been established, it was found that there were substances such that A scratched B, B scratched C, but C in turn scratched A. Insofar as this occurs, no ordering exists between objects with respect to hardness, and numbers cannot be assigned. Similar cycles occur in pecking orders among animals and humans (Landau,

1951, 1953). If A pecks B, and B pecks C, then it is sometimes true that A does not peck C, but is pecked by him. In such cases, the peck relation is not transitive, and numbers cannot be attached to individuals to represent the peck relation.[6]

A perfect Guttman scale (see p. 18) is an interesting case of dual measures meeting this criterion. Such a scale simultaneously gives a measure on individuals $m_1(x)$ and a measure on items $m_2(y)$. Suppose these numbers, m_1 and m_2, are assigned in order of scale position of persons (x_i), and items (y_j), such that $m_1(x_1) > m_2(y_1) > m_1(x_2) > m_2(y_2) \ldots > m_2(y_n) > m_1(x_{n+1})$ (where there are n items and more than n individuals). Then the properties of the order relation holds among individuals and among items, and between individuals and items, where the relation is interpreted as "is more positive than," "is taller than," or something else depending on the content of the items.[7]

It should be noted here that all physical or psychological comparison procedures have a certain degree of insensitivity or unreliability which may lead to inconsistencies.[8] Thus this insensitivity of the instrument (which is of course greater in the behavioral sciences than in classical physics) must be taken into account when judging whether any comparison operation gives rise to a valid weak order of the sort described above, with only errors due to unreliability, or whether there is no valid order at all.

This first measurement operation has imposed a certain restriction of the assignment of numbers to objects; but there are still infinitely many numbers which can be assigned to objects to fulfill the criterion. In the doctor-salesman-street cleaner prestige example, one could assign not only 70, 40, 10, but instead, 11, 8, 2, or 1.0, 0.99, 0.97, or any number of other combinations, so long as m (doctor) $> m$ (salesman) $> m$ (street cleaner). But this wide freedom in assigning numbers means that the operations of addition and multiplication cannot be carried out upon the numbers in order to make deductions. In order to allow these algebraic operations to be used in making deductions, the freedom in assigning numbers must be sharply restricted. As several authors have noted, if these algebraic operations are to be allowed, the freedom in assignment of numbers must be restricted by the relation, $m_2(x) = am_1(x)$, where $m_1(x)$ is a number assigned to an object on the basis of the measurement operation, a is an arbitrary scale constant, and $m_2(x)$ is

---

[6] It is legitimate to attach numbers to individuals to denote the numbers pecked. But then the relation is "A pecks more than B" rather than "A pecks B."

[7] A weak order is imposed on individuals and a strong order on items by this technique. Since there are many individuals with the same response patterns, many individuals will be assigned the same number, $m(x_i)$.

[8] For example, with any balance, one can carry out a series of weighings such that A balances B, which balances C, and then find that A and C do not balance. Upon weighing with a finer balance, it would be shown that A is slightly heavier than B, which is slightly heavier than C. Though each of these differences is below the sensitivity of the first balance, their sum is not, so that A registers heavier than C.

an alternative number assigned to the object. The transformation must be such that for all objects x, the *same* scale constant, a, transforms $m_1(x)$ into $m_2(x)$.

The problem, then, is in finding a measurement operation which will ensure that the assignment of numbers is restricted to this class. It is operation (2) above that is usually recognized as the one kind of operation that will fulfill this purpose, and allow the establishment of a cardinal measure. In contrast to the comparison operation, its implications are far from obvious. As a result, there has been a proliferation of attempts at quantitative measurement in various sciences, attempting to meet this criterion in diverse and often illegitimate ways. The operation will be examined in detail here, because quantitative measurement in social science depends upon a clear understanding of the constraints it implies and upon knowing whether this is the only measurement operation which imposes the necessary restrictions on the assignment of numbers.

2.2 Measurement of mass

The time-honored example used to illustrate the theory of measurement is that of mass. In measurement of mass, the comparison and combination operations are particularly well exemplified. Below, these two operations will be described, together with the validation required for each.

(1) *Comparison operation: Calibration*

A number of objects whose mass is to be measured are used together with a two-pan balance. Each pair of objects is compared by use of the balance. If the objects balance, then the two objects are assigned to the same equivalence class. If they do not, a "heavier than" relation is established between the two objects.

(2) *Comparison operation: Validation*

Between each pair of objects exists either an equivalence relation or a "heavier than" relation. If the "heavier than" relation does establish a weak order among the objects, then for every triplet, if A is heavier than B, and B is heavier than or equivalent to C, then A must be heavier than C. This test, carried out on the balance, constitutes the validation if it is met. We know, of course, from experience that the "heavier than" relation does generate a weak order.

(3) *Combination operation: Calibration*

(a) The set of equivalent objects at the low end of the "heavier than" order will be considered to have unit mass.

(b) Place in the left pan of the balance two of these objects; find another which balances these when placed in the right pan. Assign this and all others equivalent to it a mass of two units.

(c) Add to the two objects in the left pan a third object from the unit-mass equivalence class. When an object is found which will balance these objects when placed in the right pan, assign it and all others equivalent to it a mass of three units. Carry out the same procedure, assigning to an object a mass of four units, to one a mass of five units, and so on. (Not all objects can be assigned masses in this way, given a particular unit mass selected, but it is clear that the same procedure could in principle be repeated with arbitrarily small objects as units. See Campbell, 1928, pp. 16, 17 for a complete procedure.)

(4) *Combination operation: Validation*

Take an object which has been assigned a mass of two units; put it in the left pan together with an object from the original unit-mass equivalence class. *If* this balances the right pan which has in it an object which has been assigned a mass of three units, then this is one step toward validation. If it does not, this means that an object defined as having one unit of mass has a different effect on the balance when it is on the balance *alone* than when it is *combined with* an object of two units. That is, the change in total mass in a balance pan created by adding an object would not be independent of the amount of mass to which it is added. We know, of course, in the case of mass, that the assignment of numbers will be validated if the calibration has been carried out carefully. However, this is so only because nature provided a marvellous simplifying device. That is, the earth constitutes a great "force-source," so that the force between the bodies being balanced and the earth completely overpowers forces of gravitation among the bodies themselves. Were it not for this, the complexities in measurement of mass would parallel those in measurement of some concepts in social science.

The remainder of the validation would be carried out in a similar fashion. To the two-unit object would be added successively more of the unit-mass calibrating objects, balancing first against the four-unit object, then against the five-unit objects, and so on. Then other objects with varying weights would be used in the left pan.

2.3 The nature of the operation

This example of the measurement of mass is especially important, for it illustrates an important point that has often been overlooked in the theory of measurement, leading to the development of useless measures and foolish "operational definitions." This point lies in the nature of the comparison and combination operations. It is the special virtue of these operations that they embody two elements: (a) They constitute *behavior of the object itself*. The objects are placed on the scales, and it is *their* motion, or lack of it, that determines the assignment of numbers. (b) This behavior is precisely the same behavior which the theory is designed to explain. It is *motion*, not the ability of the objects to scratch one another, nor their ability to fit together (as in a jigsaw puzzle), nor any other quality.

This point is well illustrated in the history of temperature measurement. The British physicist William Thomson (Lord Kelvin) was dissatisfied with a measurement of temperature which depended on the thermal expansion of particular bodies such as mercury. He wanted to define a one-degree temperature change so that the *amount of mechanical work in a Carnot cycle* done by a decrease of one degree in temperature was independent of the level of temperature. That is, he wanted the scale to depend upon behavior of substances in the theory with which he was concerned, i.e., thermodynamics. The scale of temperature that resulted was nearly the same as temperature measured the old way; but the important point is that it might have been different—and if it had been, it would have been Kelvin's temperature that was useful in thermodynamics. (See Wightman, 1953, p. 284, for further discussion.)

This point is one which has been most frequently neglected, particularly by students of psychophysical measurement. In psychophysical measurement, there has been no behavior theory within which the resulting measure or concept is desgined to fit. Consequently, all sorts of psychologically irrelevant operations have been carried out by subjects in establishing psychophysical scales. The *reductio ad absurdum* is recent work carried out by Stevens and associates. A number of "ratio scales" were established for perceptual phenomena, by having the subject estimate the size, shape, loudness, etc., of objects or events in the physical world. These investigators carefully validated the comparison and combination operations involved; but the behavior by which the scales were established were merely judgments or estimates—not behavior relevant to psychological theory, nor even to classical psychophysics.[9]

More generally, the whole movement of "operationism," with its insistence on operational definitions of concepts, has overlooked this one most crucial point. It is not up to the whim of the investigator to determine what operation is to be used to establish a definition; the operation must constitute action on the part of the objects of the theory, and it must be the same action that the theory is about. Otherwise, it is to no avail to establish a cardinal measure, by even the most rigid adherence to Campbell's criteria of measurement. The measure will exist, to be sure, but it will be of no use.

It is worth while in this connection to note a discussion of the theory of

---

[9] The aim in classical psychophysics was a more fruitful one, even if confused by the problem of quantitative measurement. It was to assess the subjective impact of a physical stimulus. It is obvious that such measurement would be important for stimulus-response theories of behavior; but it has never been carried out in conjunction with these theories. Stevens, in his earlier work, has been an important contributor to the classical problems of psychophysics. Criticisms of the strategy of psychophysical measurement may be found in Mount (1956), who says, "A considerable part of the discussion in the literature has developed around a search for empirical operations. However, . . . no careful analysis has been made of the function that such operations would perform if they were discovered." See also Johnson (1945) and Comrey (1950).

measurement by a philosopher of science, Herbert Dingle (1950). Putting aside the classical criteria proposed by Campbell, and followed by theorists of measurement since that time, Dingle proposes that the one crucial criterion in measurement is that the resulting concept stand in "simple relation" to others in the theory. One way (but as subsequent sections will indicate, not the only way) to ensure that the concept does stand in a simple relation is to assign numbers according to the operations of comparison and combination stated earlier, *where the behavior involved is that central to the theory itself.*

It is useful, before proceeding, to restate the combination operation in a more fruitful way. A close examination of just what function this combination operation performs in the establishment of a scale shows essentially this: The previous comparison allows one to establish equivalences and relations of " $>$ " between given objects or given states of an object. The combination operation allows this comparison to be carried out between *different points* on a scale. It does this by "putting together" objects which have been found to be equivalent and comparing them with another object, using the same comparison process as before. The measurement of mass, for example, depends upon the feasibility of physically transferring an object from one pan of a balance to another. The measurement of length depends on the feasibility of taking two lines which have been visually compared side by side and found equal, putting them end to end alongside another line, and again visually comparing them to this other line. These considerations lead to a slightly different restatement of the combination operation, one which can be varied to cover the case of interval measurement.

The criterion can be stated thus: Given that one can establish equivalences between objects or states with respect to a particular comparison operation; then if it is possible to use the *same* comparison to establish equivalence between an object or state y on the one hand and two or more other objects or states, $x_1, x_2, \ldots, x_n$, on the other, so that

$$m(y) = m(x_1) + m(x_2) + \ldots + m(x_n) \qquad (2.3)$$

where $m(y)$ is the scale value assigned to object y and $m(x_i)$ are the scale values assigned to objects $x_1, x_2, \ldots, x_n$, then this will establish a metrical scale having a fixed zero point with respect to the given comparison operation.

The empirical criteria that must be met if the scale is to be valid can be stated quite simply. Suppose values are assigned to $m(u_1)$, $m(u_2)$, and $m(v)$ by comparison of u_1 with $x_1, \ldots, x_k$, comparison of u_2 with $x_{k+1}, \ldots, x_n$, and comparison of y with u_1, u_2, as follows:

$$m(u_1) = m(x_1) + m(x_2) + \ldots + m(x_k) \qquad (2.4)$$

$$m(u_2) = m(x_{k+1}) + \ldots + m(x_n) \qquad (2.5)$$

$$m(v) = m(u_1) + m(u_2) \qquad (2.6)$$

and if the number $m'(v)$ is assigned by comparison with x_1, x_2, ..., x_n, so that

$$m'(v) = m(x_1) + \ldots + m(x_n) \qquad (2.7)$$

then $m'(v)$ should equal $m(v)$. If it does not, a metrical quantity has not been established with respect to the given comparison operation.

An important point to remember is that the "combination operation" is simply the comparison operation by which equivalences and an order was established, with one variation: fortunate circumstance allows some kind of juxtaposition so that one point on the scale can be compared with another point on the scale, taken a times. This means that the comparison which could originally establish equivalence only between objects or states at the same point on the scale can now be used to "climb up" the scale, so to speak.

2.4 Interval measurement

Between ordinal and cardinal measurement stands interval measurement. The difference between it and the others can be stated as follows:

(a) Ordinal measurement restricts the assignment of numbers to all those that maintain the order relation established by the comparison operation. Formally, this implies that all alternative measures $m_j(x)$ must be related to one another by a monotonic transformation.

(b) Cardinal measurement restricts the assignment of numbers to all those that maintain the equivalences established by the combination operation. Formally, this implies that all alternative measures $m_j(x)$ must be related to one another by a scale constant.

(c) Interval measurement is cardinal measurement of the *intervals* separating two states of an object or two objects. Assignment of numbers to these intervals may be made via comparison and combination operations upon the intervals (or changes) between the states or objects, rather than upon the states or objects themselves. Formally, this implies that all alternative measures of the intervals $m_j(\Delta x)$ must be related to one another by a scale constant. This implies further that the measures of the concept or property itself, $m_j(x)$, must be related to one another by a linear transformation. Thus the zero point is arbitrary.

An example of interval measurement of utility under risk will illustrate the difference between cardinal measurement and interval measurement.

2.4.1 *Measurement of utility under risk.* An important concept in classical economic theory is that of utility. The "rational man's" preferences among various goods are based on the value or utility which he associates with these goods. The utility of goods thus acts as a "common denominator," which the economist can use to equate varying amounts of various goods. Now it turns out that the very concept of utility (in choice situations not involving risk) implies only an order relation, and not a metric. That is, in economic theory, there is a comparison operation by which goods can be ordered according to preferences, but there is no combination operation by which a quantitative measure can be attached to utility. Economic theory neither requires a cardinal measure of utility nor provides a means for its measurement.

However, in considering risky situations, where one is not certain whether he will get commodity A or commodity B, then the notion of "utility under risk" does have some of the properties of a quantitative measure. These properties are determined by the fact that the measurement of utility does not have to preserve information under all the operations of algebra, but only under the operations (a) of being multiplied by a number p_i between zero and one (a probability), and (b) of adding such products obtained in (a) subject to the restriction that $\Sigma p_i = 1$. Altogether, then, the numbers U_i assigned to the utility of objects must preserve the information in the following equation:

$$p_1 U_1 + p_2 U_2 + \ldots + p_m U_m = p_{m+1} U_{m+1} + p_{m+2} U_{m+2} \\ + \ldots + p_n U_n \tag{2.8}$$

where

$$\sum_{i=1}^{m} p_i = 1, \quad \text{and} \quad \sum_{i=m+1}^{n} p_i = 1$$

This equation provides both the restrictions which a utility measure should meet, and prescribes (in a general way) the comparison and combination operation necessary for measurement. The resulting measures will be that class of measures which will make eq. (2.8) invariant. Such measures turn out to have the same degree of restrictiveness as usual interval measures. That is, alternative measures of utility must be related by linear transformation. That a linear transformation does make eq. (2.8) invariant is verifiable by substituting in eq. (2.8) the quantity

$$U_i' = aU_i + b \tag{2.9}$$

If the transformation is permissible, then the substitution should preserve the equality.

$$\sum_{i=1}^{m} p_i (aU_i + b) \overset{?}{=} \sum_{i=m+1}^{n} p_i (aU_i + b) \tag{2.10}$$

$$a\Sigma p_i U_i + b \overset{?}{=} a\Sigma p_i U_i + b \tag{2.11}$$

Subtracting b from each side and dividing through by a results in the original eq. (2.8).

Two general methods for measuring utility by means of eq. (2.8) have been proposed, the first outlined by von Neumann and Morgenstern (1947), using various objective probabilities to calibrate different utility values,[10] and the second stemming from an idea of Ramsey's (1931) and developed by Davidson, McKinsey, Siegal, and Suppes (1955) which uses a single event, with (subjectively) equally probable outcomes.[11],[12] Neither of these will be treated in detail, but the second (which has been validated experimentally) will be outlined below. (See Davidson, Siegel, and Suppes (1955) for a complete procedure.)

(1) *Comparison operation*

A preference relation between all objects is established by asking the individual whether he prefers object x or object y for all pairs of objects (x, y). Transitivity can be tested with these data.

(2) *Combination operation*

(a) First an event with two outcomes is found such that the individual sees one outcome to be just as likely as the other in the following sense: If A_1 and A_2 are alternative choices, B and $\bar{B}$ are outcomes, and x and y are rewards which go with particular combinations of decision and outcome, he cannot decide between A_1 and A_2 (or chooses them equally often) in the following table, even though he values the reward x much more than he values y. (Intuitively, it is evident that if he felt B was more probable than $\bar{B}$, he would choose A_1, since he values x more than y.)

		Outcome	
		B	$\bar{B}$
Decision	A_1	x	y
	A_2	y	x

Then the following equation can be written, where p is the probability of outcome B and U_i is the utility associated with reward i:

$$pU_x+(1 - p)U_y = (1-p)U_x+pU_y$$

and the only value of p which will satisfy this equation (if $U_x \neq U_y$) is $p = 1/2$.

---

[10] Actually, the measurement procedure outlined by von Neumann and Morgenstern is derived measurement, for the measurement of probabilities is taken as given, and utilities are calculated from these probabilities.

[11] This latter method can also be used to measure the subjective probability attributed to an event. In the former method, it is assumed (though the assumption can be tested in validating the measure of utility) that subjective probabilities and objective probabilities are the same.

[12] For other work in this area see Marschak, who proposed a third method of measuring utility (1954), and Savage (1954). Mosteller and Nogee (1951) once carried out experiments calibrating a measure of utility using von Neumann and Morgenstern's method. However, they neglected any attempt at validation of the measure.

(b) Given this event with equally likely outcomes, then comparisons like the following can be made:

Outcome

	B	$\bar{B}$
A_1	x	y
A_2	v	w

Decision

and if the individual cannot decide, then

$$1\ U_x + 1\ U_y = 1\ U_v + 1\ U_w$$

or $$U_x + U_y = U_v + U_w$$

or $$U_v - U_y = U_x - U_w.$$

(c) By similar choice situations; objects z, a, and b are found such that (by the above procedure) the following relations hold:

$$U_v - U_y = U_z - U_x$$
$$U_v - U_y = U_a - U_z$$
$$U_v - U_y = U_b - U_a$$

etc.

In this way, objects w, x, z, a, b, . . ., all equidistant in utility, can be assigned utility values, starting from an arbitrary number, and continuing at equal intervals. In effect, the choice situation with outcomes B and $\bar{B}$ is exactly analogous to a special kind of balance in the measurement of mass, a balance in which only pairs of objects on one pan can be balanced against other pairs on the other pan. With such a balance, only interval measurement of mass could be carried out.[13]

(3) *Validation*

Once w, x, z, a, b, . . . have been assigned values, then this implies that in a number of other choice situations, the individual cannot decide, producing the following equalities:

$$U_x - U_w = U_z - U_x \qquad \text{(i.e., } \tfrac{1}{2} U_x + \tfrac{1}{2} U_x = \tfrac{1}{2} U_z + \tfrac{1}{2} U_w\text{)}$$
$$U_x - U_w = U_a - U_z$$
$$U_x - U_w = U_b - U_a$$
$$U_z - U_x = U_a - U_z$$
$$U_z - U_w = U_a - U_x$$

[13] It does seem reasonable to assign zero utility to the absence of reward, which could constitute one of the alternatives (say v) in the above paradigm. However, since zero utility plays no special role in the theory [see eq. (2.8)], such an assignment is unimportant.

If the individual cannot decide, and these (and other) equalities *do* hold, then the measure is validated. Such validation has been carried out (for 15 of 19 subjects) by Davidson, Siegal, and Suppes (1955).

2.5 Derived measurement

A great deal of space was devoted in the above pages to the examination of a very strict approach to measurement. However, once one has established a link between a theory and the real world through one or two measurements, he can use the theory itself to give him measures of other quantities. For example, having measures for length, a physicist can define a concept like volume, and then using it, together with the measure for mass, define a concept of density (the mass of an object divided by its volume), and so on. Physicists have called these concepts "derived," in contrast to the fundamental measures discussed above, which depend on no previous quantitative measurement. That is, once we have validated the use of real numbers for one (or a few) concepts in a theory, then we may use the algebraic relations of which the theory is composed to obtain other measures.

However, this is more easily said than done. It has sometimes in science taken a stroke of genius to realize that a quantity could be *measured* through its hypothesized relations to other concepts. The concept of force in mechanics is perhaps the best example of this (see Wightman, 1953). Galileo posited the qualitative relation between the mass of a body, the force applied to it, and motion of the body. That is, Galileo believed something like the following: When force is applied to a body, it accelerates. When the same force is applied to a larger body, it accelerates more slowly. Yet it took Newton to define explicitly the concept of force and to propose that the amount of force be measured on the basis of the amount of motion (i.e., acceleration) it produced in a body of a given mass. That is, through the simple equation

$$F = ma \qquad\qquad (2.12)$$

Newton defined a quantitative concept of force in terms of mass, distance, and time, three already measured concepts. He could not, of course, have proposed just any equation instead of (2.12); the empirical validity of his theory depended upon the particular form of the relation that he did propose. Yet the major step forward was one of transforming a qualitative relation to a quantitative one, defining the hypothesized concept of force in terms of the already measured ones of mass and acceleration.

It may be important for the development of quantitative social theory to realize that the distinction between "fundamental" and "derived" measurement is nowhere near so sharp as is generally believed. Both are derived from the theory, but in different ways. The measurement of mass derives from the conception that the ability of a body to move a lever is proportional to its mass, which means that the ability of bodies of equal mass to move a lever will be equal (i.e., they will balance).[14]

The major difference between such measures and the "derived" measures like force is this: The "derived" measures derive from algebraic relations in the theory between concept and an already cardinally measured concept. The "fundamental" measures derive from essentially *qualitative* aspects of the theory, which establish a peculiarly fortunate situation in which the operations of comparison and combination can be carried out. (Whether these operations are empirically validated is another question, one which concerns the validity of the theory.)

3. ARE THE CLASSICAL CRITERIA NECESSARY?

To this point our attention has been restricted to ideas taken from one area of science, classical mechanics. While many behavioral scientists would assent to these criteria, their day-to-day behavior in the manipulation of numbers contradicts this assent. Are all these activities invalid, or are the criteria discussed above more narrow than need be?

To answer this, it is useful to examine some examples. First, consider a ridiculously simple case: the behavior of a coin, thrown n times, turns up heads k times. If these are independent throws, and are performed under the same conditions, the coin behaves according to a series of n Bernoulli trials. It is possible to form an estimate of the parameter p of the binomial distribution by forming a ratio, k/n. It is similarly possible to use the binomial distribution, involving numerous addition and multiplication operations upon k and n, to obtain the probability that a given p would result in k successes in n trials.

In this case, there were no "comparison" and "combination" operations to form the measures k and n on the coin's behavior. They were obtained by simple counting, just as are many quantitative data in social science. Yet they were operated upon by the operations valid for real numbers; and the results of these operations provide correct deductions. No one would refuse to accept these operations as legitimate. Even if someone did so, his position would be untenable, because the use of the operations is repeatedly confirmed by the empirical correctness of the deductions.

Now consider another case. Physical chemists, studying the movement of colloidal particles, have devised a stochastic theory (Chandrasekhar, 1954) which takes as data the number of particles within a given area at one point in time, and the number per unit area over the whole plane of observation, and correctly predicts the expected number to be found in the same area

---

[14] It is irrelevant here that mass (or weight) was measured before the existence of the theory. The important point is that the measurement could be derived from the conceptions of the theory, even if no prior measurement existed.

after any given period of time. In this theory, the data used are numbers of particles, and the deductions concern numbers of particles. Again the predictions are correct. But even if they were not, most of us would intuitively feel, as in the case of coin tossing, that the fault did not lie in the illegitimate use of the operations of addition and multiplication on the observed numerical data, but in an error in the form of the theory.

Now suppose we consider an example not quite so obvious. Population genetics includes detailed mathematical theories which use as data the number of persons with certain phenotypic traits (e.g., blood types). (See Li, 1955.) The behavior to which its deductions lead also concern the number of persons with particular phenotypic traits, at a later time. To move from data to deduced behavior, the theory relates the phenotypic data to numbers of genes, and then via the mechanisms of genetic selection in mating, translates this into numbers of future phenotypic types. Again, no one would say that these quantitative data were being illegitimately subject to the operations of addition and multiplication.

These examples have perhaps belabored the obvious. Nevertheless, *why* are these measures, formed by counting, exempt from the criteria discussed earlier? And if they are theoretically useful measures, why are not all numbers formed by counting in social behavior useful also?

But are these measures really exempt from the earlier criteria? The numbers are formed by an implicit comparison operation, leading to the assessment that all events or observations in a given class (i.e., all trials) were equal relative to the behavior under question. There is also an implicit combination operation, in which the combination of the first and second trial is given a number (two) equal to the sum of the numbers (ones) given individually to the trials. That is, there is an implicit assumption of no interaction between trials, or an implicit assumption that an experiment of n trials will give an expected result no different than the *sum* of the expected results in experiments of m and r trials, respectively, where $m + r = n$.

For neither the comparison operation nor the combination operation is there an empirical validation that the operation fulfills the necessary requirements. The operation is carried out by fiat, so to speak, by the investigator's counting, rather than by behavior of the objects themselves (e.g., behavior of matter on a scale, expansion of mercury in a glass tube, or behavior of individuals in response to a stimulus). The important consequence of this difference is that there *can* be no validation of the assignment of a measure in the measurement operation itself, since it is the investigator, rather than the behavior of the objects themselves, who establishes an equivalence between events and combines them by adding. The validation, in theories of this sort, lies in a very different place, in a comparison of the theory's deductions with the data to be predicted. That is, do the objects behave according to the predictions of a theory which establishes given equivalence classes, and combines them by counting?

For example, consider an application of the binomial distribution to responses of a set of individuals who differed widely in their underlying probabilities of response. Since these underlying probabilities are not known to the investigator, he counts all responses as equal, whether they derive from an individual with probability .9 or from an individual with probability .05. Applying the binomial distribution as if all had the same underlying p, he arrives at an estimate of the variance of k, the number of successes. (The estimate is $k(1 - k/n)$.) Then he carries out the same experiment a number of times, and he finds peculiarly that the actual variation among the k's obtained in different experiments is much less than his calculated variance would predict.[15] That is, his theory does not fit because he applied it to a situation in which the assignment of ones was not legitimate. Some successes came from individuals who had a high probability of success, and some from those who had a low probability, while the theory allows one to treat as equal only successes coming from individuals with the same underlying p.

This simple example illustrates the fundamental difference between two kinds of theories in their approach to validation. In the type represented by classical mechanics there is validation in the measurement operations themselves. In the other, represented by Bernoulli trials or population genetics, the investigator postulates a particular assignment of numbers, and the postulate is tested only by test of the theory's deductions. If he has established equivalence classes in such a way that all elements identified as equivalent are in fact equivalent in those aspects of their behavior treated by the theory, then the theory will be confirmed; if not, the theory will be disconfirmed. In some cases, it is obvious from the physical structure of the research that postulates are confirmed. For example, in throws of a coin, it is evident that the probability of success is equal on each trial and that the trials are independent. When the behavior concerns persons, however, some of the postulates are usually in doubt, and a test of the theory's deductions is required in order to know whether the assignment of numbers was legitimately made.

In Chapter 18, a general class of "sometimes-true" theories, which includes probability models, and most of the models presented in this book, is dis-

---

[15] This can best be seen intuitively by looking at the extreme case, where half the individuals had a probability of 1.0, and half had a probability of 0. In that case, there would be no variability at all in k, the number of successes, in different experiments with n trials. But the estimate of the variance from any experiment would be $.25n$, leading to a prediction of a high variation among the k's. The correct estimate of the variance in this case would depend upon a knowledge of the underlying p's, and would be the sum of n binomial variances, each with a different probability of success, p_i:

$$\frac{1}{n} \text{ var } (k) = \sum_{i=1}^{n} p_i(1 - p_i) = \Sigma p_i - \Sigma p_i^2$$

As the variation between different p_i's is greater, Σp_i^2 is greater, and thus var (k) is smaller. [See Feller (1957, p. 216) for a discussion of this problem.] This fact is used, in Chapter 12, to study the variation among individuals in underlying probabilities.

cussed. These sometimes-true theories are examples of this second type of theory. They are not based on some immutable concept such as "mass"; rather, they assume a particular structure of behavior at the micro-level, and generate mathematically the consequent behavior at the macro-level. When the structure of behavior at the micro-level is widely variable, as in the case of social systems, the theories are of the "sometimes-true" sort. When the structure of behavior at the micro-level is fixed, as in genetic selection in mating, or as in statistical mechanics, then the theories are not "sometimes true," but either true or false, depending upon the correctness of the postulates at the micro-level.

4. WHEN ARE THE TWO TYPES OF THEORIES APPLICABLE?

For mature sciences, whose theoretical structure is well laid, such matters as these are of interest only to philosophers of science. But in sciences that are engaged in laying such theoretical foundations, the matter leads to important strategic questions. In sociology, for example, are we best advised to find some comparison and combination operations to measure "cohesiveness," "prestige," and other such concepts, or are we better advised to build models based on simple counting? In psychology as well, the issue arises: will the quantitative measures of behavior be established through measurement validation, or through numbers formed by mere counting, supported by validation of the theory?

Some of the kinds of behavior with which we are concerned almost naturally come to us in quantitative form. This is most true for the sociologist, dealing with numbers of people carrying out a given behavior, or numbers of people in a given situation. For such behavior (for example, most of the behavior discussed in the remaining chapters in this book), it seems most reasonable to use counting, together with theory-validation, rather than to use measurement validation. It may very well be that most such theories will not be valid at first (e.g., all stochastic theories which assume individuals to have the same underlying transition probabilities or transition rates). Nevertheless, this strategy suggests that they may be made valid by establishing more refined equivalence classes. For example, a theory that combined the change models of Chapter 5 with the individual variability models of Chapter 12 would begin to approximate reality more closely than either alone. Such a model is partially developed in Chapter 13.

This strategy may invite easy assent; but its implications go against much current work in sociology. It says, in effect, that it is not theoretically fruitful to develop such concepts as cohesion, prestige, and the like, to "measure" them, and then to establish relations between them (e.g., "The higher the prestige of a group, the greater its cohesion"). But it says more than this: it says that to devise a measure of concepts like "amount of cohesion," *even* by use of the classical criteria for cardinal measurement, rather than usual methods of index construction, will not be the most fruitful procedure.

However, this judgment would be different where it is extremely difficult to set up equivalence classes of independent events or actions, and thus difficult to establish numbers by counting. When the behavior is essentially *qualitative*, then classical measurement is necessary. For example, in classical mechanics, without the measurement of mass, behavior of objects was wholly qualitative: "The heavier an object, the more speed it will impart to another object upon impact"; "The larger of two objects of the same substance is the heavier"; "The heavier an object, the more work it can do in moving other objects via a lever." Without quantitative measurement of mass, distance, and time, such behavior was destined to remain wholly qualitative. There are no equivalence classes of independent actions or events that can be added to form numbers. Quantitative measurement, by means of the classical operations of comparison and combination, was necessary if the theory was to consist of something more than qualitative relations of more or less. Objects differed very much in their behavior, and it turned out that a large part of that difference could be accounted for by differences in mass (or at the same distance from earth's center, weight), and treating the objects as equivalent *except for* differences in mass. Thus the equivalence class, which already exists for Bernoulli trials or in population genetics, must be established through classical measurement in the case of the mechanics of motion. If it had been possible to count the number of protons and neutrons in each material object (or even the number of molecules, for substances of the same composition), then such measurement would have been unnecessary. Counting would have served the same purpose, because each unit that was counted (each proton or neutron) was the same in those aspects of its behavior covered by the theory, and any object containing the same *sum* of protons and neutrons behaved the same.

Thus the question of whether the classical operations of cardinal measurement are necessary for theory-construction resolves to a question of the kind of behavior under study. If, as in the case of individual behavior, it concerns qualitative variability of behavior among different indivisible objects (e.g., individuals), then the classical measurement operations must come into play, to create equivalence classes among these differently behaving objects. But, as indicated in Section 2, it is crucial that these operations involve that behavior which the theory is about, rather than some arbitrary "operational definition." Otherwise, one finds himself in the absurd position that psychophysical measurement has ended in: measurement which fulfills the classical conditions, but with respect to a comparison operation unrelated to behavior of psychological interest.

Thus, for example, measurement of attitudes or values cannot be carried out by mere counting, because the behavior they help determine is qualitative: acting in direction A or B, acting with greater or less intensity, preventing the action of another, etc. Section 2 has indicated how cardinal scales have been so devised in other areas.[16] Similarly, a sociological concept such as the prestige of an individual or an activity may be subject to measurement operations other than mere counting. An example of how this might be done is carried out in the appendix to this chapter.

5. DISPOSITION PROPERTIES AND INDEX FORMATION

"Theoretical" concepts in present-day sociology are terms like anomie, morale, integration, segregation social isolation, mobility, social status, social class, and many others; they have the status of theoretical concepts largely because we use them as crude explanatory variables in understanding why some phenomenon occurs or does not occur. For example, Durkheim used the concepts of egoism (i.e., social isolation or lack of a socially shared purpose) and anomie (i.e., normlessness) to explain the incidence of suicide; social psychologists (Cartwright and Zander, 1953, p. 73) use the concept of cohesiveness to explain why some groups work well together and accomplish a lot, while others do not; Parsons (1951, p. 259) uses the concepts of activity-passivity, conformity-alienation, and orientation toward objects vs. orientation toward norms to explain eight kinds of conforming and nonconforming behavior. The list of such work could be greatly extended.

These concepts are used not only in an explanatory way, but truly as intervening variables, which may be *caused* by numerous factors, and in turn have numerous *consequences*. Durkheim, for example, saw egoism not only as resulting in high suicide rates, but also as caused by certain religious norms, certain kinds of family life, and certain kinds of political systems. The function of intervening variables (or disposition variables as they are sometimes called), is that they serve as a link between numerous sources and numerous consequences. The concept of "social isolation," for example, is used by Faris and Dunham (1939) to link up a number of factors (lonely childhood, deafness, disfiguring physical defects, certain kinds of living in a city, introversion) in a causal relationship with schizophrenia. Other authors have used the concept to link up those (and other) causes with various other consequences (see Davis, 1947, and Wood, 1953).

Thus the concept of "social isolation" plays much the same role for some sociologists that "temperature" does for chemists. As one variable characterizing the state of a physical body, temperature can be raised by numerous concrete means (putting a burner under the object, rubbing it with another object, compressing it, if it is a gas, and so on). At the same time, a rise in temperature has numerous concrete consequences (ice melts, water boils, chemical reactions take place, fluids like mercury expand, sand fuses into glass, and so on).

[16] See also Section 8.3 of Chapter 6.

It is true, however, that although such concepts as social isolation are related to numerous concrete causes and consequences, they are not linked to other theoretical concepts as is the concept of temperature. We seldom have a theoretical framework within which our concepts are related, so they ordinarily still have only the role that temperature and pressure did before such investigators as Boyle and Gay-Lussac established the relation of pressure, temperature, and volume of a gas. That is, our concepts serve as an explanatory link between *particular* manifest phenomena just as temperature serves as an explanatory link between such particular phenomena as heating water on a stove or a campfire, and the water's boiling. But they are not related to other *general* concepts as temperature is related to pressure, volume, heat, energy, and other concepts in thermodynamics, for we have no theories in which such general concepts play a part.

Concepts like temperature are ordinarily measured by using a convenient manifestation of one of the general theoretical relationships of which they are a part. The general relation between the volume of a fluid and its temperature, a relation which is manifested in the expansion of mercury, provides one means of measuring temperature. The general relation between the temperature of a solid and its liquefaction as manifested in the melting of clay cones in a kiln provides another means. For social behavior, lacking such general relations of our concepts to other theoretical concepts, we ordinarily measure our concepts by using simply the particular manifestation in which they play a part. A classic example is the measurement of group cohesiveness by Lippitt and White in their study of authoritarian and democratic group atmospheres (1939). In each group, they recorded the number of times the word "I" was used and the number of times "we" was used. Their measure, or index of cohesiveness, was the ratio of the number of "we's" to the number of "I's."

Such index formation is not fundamental measurement of the kind discussed earlier. Nor does it have the status of measures formed by counting in such models as a binomial distribution, for there is no theory or model to provide a validation test. Nevertheless, it represents the present state of most measurement in sociology, and must do until some means of fundamental measurement exists for these disposition concepts, or until explicit models are constructed in which they play a part.

With this as the situation, there are still several notions which can be used to make our measurement more likely to produce generalizations from which theories may be built. These notions are the *degrees of freedom* of a set of observations from which an index is to be constructed; the *area of ambiguity* between two or more indices constructed from the same set of observations; and the *dimensional specification of meaning* of an index. The first two of these have been treated in detail by Lazarsfeld and Barton (1951), and will be mentioned only sketchily here; the third will be treated in more detail.

Index construction can be divided into two steps: a decision about *what observations* are to be used to measure the concept, and a decision about how they are to be *combined*. To measure racial segregation in a city, one has to decide whether to use census tract statistics, block statistics, house-by-house information, or some other data. Having decided this, one still is faced with a hundred or even a thousand numbers, which must somehow be combined to give one number representing the degree of racial segregation in the town. However, in much index formation, one has only two or three such numbers which must be combined. The number of these is the number of degrees of freedom contained in the data. Because these observations can be combined in numerous ways (since there is more than a single degree of freedom), of which several may appear equally reasonable, the possibility of ambiguity in the ordering of two objects exists. If a precise theory existed, then there would be no question about how these observations were to be combined to give the single measure; in the absence of such a theory, ambiguity does exist.

Table 2.1

Occupation	Proportion of persons in the occupation x_i	Proportion of fathers in the occupation whose sons are in same occupation y_i
1. Professional	.053	.284
2. Semi-professional	.030	.175
3. Proprietor, manager, official	.063	.165
4. Clerical and sales	.221	.423
5. Skilled	.218	.324
6. Semi-skilled	.276	.436
7. Unskilled	.070	.282
8. Protective service	.023	.087
9. Personal service	.034	.100
10. Farming	.011	.043

The existence of such ambiguity, and the ways in which it can be resolved, can be illustrated by the concept of "occupational mobility." Suppose we have information about the proportion of people in an occupation and the proportion whose fathers were in the same occupation, for the occupational categories listed in Table 2.1.[17]

These are derived from the table of occupational mobility in Chapter 1 (Table 1.3) in the following way:

[17] See Chapter 14, Section 5, and Leo Goodman (1963b) for application of an explicit mathematical model for generational mobility, an approach quite superior to index-construction of the sort described here, which proceeds without such a model.

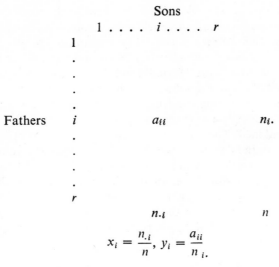

$$x_i = \frac{n_{.i}}{n}, \; y_i = \frac{a_{ii}}{n_{i.}}$$

The problem is, then, to calculate for each occupation, a measure of the rate of occupational mobility from father to son. This means there are two degrees of freedom for each measure; because there are two, the data of Table 2.1 may be represented in a two-dimensional space, as in Figure 2.1.

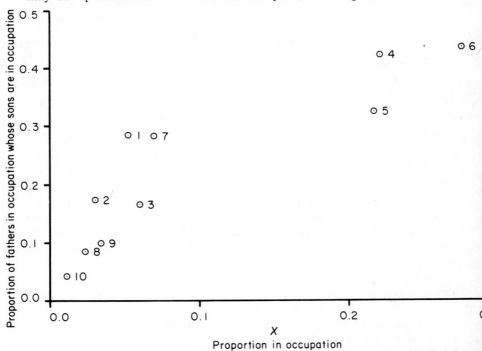

Figure 2.1

The construction of an index is tantamount to dividing up this space by isometric lines (lines of equal occupational mobility). One such index, representing one way of dividing the space is, algebraically,

$$m_1 = x - y$$

Most people will protest—and with good reason—that this combination does not at all reflect what is meant by occupational mobility. For example, it shows farming as having a higher mobility than any other occupation though 68% of their fathers were also farming, higher than any other group (see Table 1.3 of Chapter 1).

It is of course foolish to expect some such arbitrary combination of x and y to produce a measure of occupational mobility. But what about the two following combinations, which divide up the space in the two ways shown by Figure 2.2. Both appear quite reasonable in the way they rank these occupations, though they do rank them differently.

$$m_2 = \frac{x}{y} \tag{5.1}$$

$$m_3 = \frac{1-y}{1-x} \tag{5.2}$$

Upon examination, both these indices seem to reflect occupational mobility reasonably well. Yet they produce the two differing sets of lines shown in Figure 2.2. And the two orderings of occupations are considerably different. It is precisely here that the notion of "area of ambiguity" enters. Consider, for example, the two lines passing through the point representing farming, labelled 10 in Figure 2.2. The areas between these lines, OAB and OCD, are the areas of ambiguity for this point with respect to these two indices. Any occupation falling within these areas will be ranked higher than farming by one index, and lower than farming by the other. In the area OAB lie points 3, 4, 5, 6, 8, and 9, representing most of the labor force. These are ranked *above* farming in occupational mobility by the m_2 index and *below* farming by the m_3 index. Thus six out of the nine other occupations fall in the areas of ambiguity for farming. This fact, and more generally the large differences in slope between the isometric lines for the two indices, means that the two indices give quite different results when applied to a set of occupations. Only if the slopes of two indices were precisely the same so that the lines did not cross, would there be no area of ambiguity for a given point. In terms of the formulae for the indices, this means that the only allowable differences between two indices is a linear transformation. That is, the index

$$m_4 = \frac{a(1-y)}{1-x} + b \tag{5.3}$$

(where a and b are arbitrary) will create no areas of ambiguity with the formula

$$m_3 = \frac{1-y}{1-x} \qquad (5.4)$$

for it involves simply a shift of scale and position of the isometric lines, and not a shift of slope.

Thus we are forced to the conclusion that in order to preserve mono-

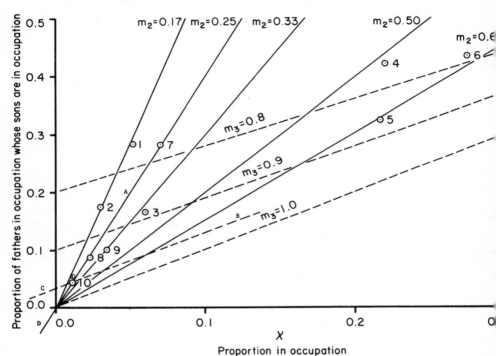

Figure 2.2

	Occupation	Ranking by	
		m_2	m_3
1.	Professionals	9	9
2.	Semi-professional	10	6
3.	Proprietor, manager, official	4	4
4.	Clerical and sales	3	10
5.	Skilled	1	5
6.	Semi-skilled	2	7
7.	Unskilled	8	8
8.	Protective Service	6	2
9.	Personal Service	5	3
10.	Farming	7	1

tonicity of a measure which is combined from a number of numerical components, formulae for combination can differ by no more than a linear transformation.

However, suppose that two methods of combination are not related by a linear transformation as are m_3 and m_4; yet it is impossible to decide which reflects better the meaning of the concept. Suppose, for example, it were impossible to say whether m_2 or m_3 better represented what one meant by occupational mobility. What can one do if it is still desired to develop some generalization of the form "As attribute x in an occupation increases, the occupational mobility of the occupation will increase"?

If it is impossible to decide between m_2 and m_3, then the only alternative left is to restrict the generalization to those sets of occupations which are ordered alike by the two measures. That is, the generalization would be restricted to those occupations which were not in one another's areas of ambiguity. This is not a happy solution, of course; yet it is no different from what has happened in science generally. Generalizations or laws when first introduced are usually quite restricted in scope; only as the science progresses, with improvements in measurement and elaboration of the laws, is the scope gradually broadened.

Thus a restriction in scope of the generalizations in which the concept plays a part is one solution to the problem of ambiguity between two indices. Another is to study more carefully just what the meaning and implications of the two indices are, together with the nature of the generalizations which it is hoped to develop. Such a study will often show clearly that one index does reflect accurately the intended meaning of the concept, while the other does not. It is here that dimensional specification of the meaning of an index becomes useful, and even necessary.

Every number which constitutes a component of an index has a definite meaning which derives from the operations used to form it. This is the *dimension* associated with the number. For example, the x-values in Table 2.1 have the dimension

$$x_i = \frac{n_{.i}}{n} = \frac{\text{number of sons in occupation } i}{\text{total number of sons in all occupations}} \tag{5.5}$$

while the y-values have the dimension

$$y_i = \frac{a_{ii}}{n_{i.}} = \frac{\text{number of sons in occupation } i \text{ whose fathers are in occupation } i}{\text{total number of fathers in occupation } i} \tag{5.6}$$

Any index number, then, which is some combination of these two numbers, will have a dimension which is the corresponding combination of the dimensions of the two numbers. The index m_3, for example, is

$$\frac{1-y}{1-x} = \frac{\dfrac{n_{i.} - a_{ii}}{n_{i.}}}{\dfrac{n - n_{.i}}{n}} = \frac{\dfrac{\text{number of fathers in occupation } i \text{ whose sons shifted}}{\text{total number of fathers in occupation } i}}{\dfrac{\text{number of sons in occupation other than } i}{\text{total number of sons (or fathers)}}} \quad (5.7)$$

As it stands, this dimension for m_3 has little intuitive meaning. However, further examination makes the meaning more evident. The numerator can be stated as: "the proportion of fathers in occupation i whose sons have shifted to another occupation." When this proportion is one, all sons will have shifted out of the occupation; when it is zero, all sons will have stayed in the occupation. It can thus be considered a measure of the *actual mobility* from the father's occupation. But this must be standardized by taking into account the *expected* mobility. The most reasonable basis for expectation is to assume independence between father's and son's occupations. If this assumption is made, then the expected mobility from occupation i is simply the proportion of all sons' jobs which are not in occupation i. This turns out to be the dimension of the denominator $(n - n_{.i})/n$, of the fraction.

Thus the dimensions of the index m_3, which look formidable in eq. (5.7), turn out to be, in abbreviated form

$$m_3 = \frac{\text{actual mobility from occupation } i}{\text{expected mobility from occupation } i} \quad (5.8)$$

This appears to be a quite reasonable definition of mobility from an occupation. Further analysis would show that this index has desirable properties: it is zero when all sons stay in the occupation; it is one when the mobility from the occupation is exactly what would be expected if a son were no more likely to go into his father's occupation than other sons were to go into it. An examination of the other index, m_2, would not show such an intuitively appealing meaning, nor such desirable properties. Its abbreviated dimensions are

$$m_2 = \frac{\text{expected stability in occupation } i}{\text{actual stability in occupation } i} \quad (5.9)$$

It is evident that this is not what we mean by occupational mobility. A similar dimensional specification of other indices of mobility which are based on these data and which appear reasonable would show that few, if any, come as close to what is meant by occupational mobility as does m_3. Thus there is good reason for using it and rejecting other possible combinations of the data as measuring something different. This does not ensure, of course, that this measure will prove relevant for a generalization or a theory, while others are not relevant. However, by matching up, in as careful a fashion as possible, the meaning of occupational mobility as a theoretical concept with the dimensions of the index used to measure it, the likelihood of finding invariant relations and of obtaining theoretical relevance is immensely increased.

The case of occupational mobility provides a good example of this. Until recently, occupational mobility figures for various countries were almost completely noncomparable, simply because *no one* had reported their data in terms of an index of the form of m_3. Almost all studies used an index of the form $1 - y$, and few reported original data, to allow computation of comparable measures. [See Goldhamer's introduction in Rogoff (1953) for a discussion of this.] Once measures of the form of m_3 were used, it was possible both to begin to explain rates of occupational mobility (see Rogoff, 1953, p. 15) and to find surprising cross-national invariances in patterns of mobility (see Lipset and Rogoff, 1954).

This "dimensional specification" is deceptively elementary. It is no more than a rational procedure for what we do mentally in constructing measures of the concepts which play a part in our research and theory. But without an explicit procedure for analyzing the meaning of an index through specifying its dimensions, it is easy to be fooled by intuitively appealing indices. The point is that our intuitions and our vague mental manipulations of the dimensions of measurements are notably inaccurate; to substitute an explicit procedure will ensure that our indices keep closely to the meaning we intend them to have. (See Bridgman, 1922, and Duncan, 1953, for further discussion of dimensional analysis.)

In construction of indices as measures of sociological concepts, then, there are a number of problems and at the same time certain techniques for alleviating them. The basic problem is that no direct method of measurement exists for these concepts, either through comparison and combination operations, through counting, or through derived measurement. Without this, and without even an explicit theory showing their relations to other concepts, it becomes necessary to use particular manifestations, and to combine these observations in some way which we feel accurately reflects the concept. In constructing an index, the precise specification of its dimensions will often aid in narrowing down the reasonable indices to one or two. Beyond this, the "area of ambiguity" of the remaining indices can be examined, excluding those cases where ambiguity exists. The remaining cases will be ranked alike by the two (or more) indices, so that generalizations of the form "As x increases, y increases" may be developed.[18]

One final caution must be added in a discussion of index construction. The construction of an index involves a loss of information, for two or three or more numbers are combined to result in a single number. Because information is lost, it is important to make certain that the gains resulting from use of the index justify its use. Oftentimes the "theoretical" concept for which the index is constructed is so ill-defined and ambiguous as to render an index of

---

[18] In Chapter 14, a superior approach to index construction, based on the use of an explicit model designed to reflect behavior, is discussed.

it less valuable than any one of the components which make up the index.

An excellent example of this occurs with indices of social stratification in voting studies. A number of studies report the relationship of "social status" to voting for political parties of the left and right. The indices of social status are ordinarily *ad hoc*, varying from study to study, both in the basic observations on which they are based and on the way these observations are combined. As a result, these studies are nearly useless for comparison purposes and for establishing useful generalizations. If the relations of the various components to voting were given, the gain would be a great one, for these components are such important variables in their own right as income, occupation, and education. Such variables play an important part in the workings of society; they are related to others, and have meanings which become lost if they are compressed in some *ad hoc* way into an index of "social status."

This caution against overeager development of composite indices cannot be made too strong. Too often our hope of producing an index to stand as a measure of some abstract concept leads us to neglect or obscure those very concepts which are most firmly rooted in measurement.

6. GROUP AND INDIVIDUAL VARIABLES

One important measurement problem in sociology concerns the two levels on which sociologists must work: the level of the individual and that of the group. We have *observations* at two levels, *concepts* at two levels, and *relationships* at two levels. Furthermore, it is often necessary to shift back and forth: measuring group-level concepts from individual data; or inferring individual relationships from group-level relations.

One of the major problems, but one which extends over into the others, is the *aggregation* problem, the problem of relating observations on individuals to group-level concepts. Suppose we want to develop a generalization of the general order of "As the cohesiveness of a group increases, its productivity will increase." That is,

$$\frac{\partial p}{\partial c} > 0 \qquad\qquad (6.1)$$

where $\qquad\qquad p$ = productivity of the group,
$\qquad\qquad\qquad c$ = cohesiveness of the group.

Suppose further that the experience which prompts such a generalization is the fact that people work harder toward a goal when they feel more strongly about the goal. Our reasoning goes this way: Feelings of closeness or cohesiveness toward a group of which one is a member makes an individual feel more strongly toward the group goal. On the individual level, this means that the closer an individual feels toward a group, the harder he works toward the group goal.

What problems are there, then, in going on to make the corresponding group-level statement about cohesiveness and productivity? Under certain ideal conditions, there may be no problem at all. For consider the individual proposition (which we now assume to be correct):

$$\frac{\partial p_i}{\partial c_i} > 0 \tag{6.2}$$

Now suppose all individuals in a group, $1, 2, \ldots n$, increase their feelings of closeness toward the group from time 1 to time 2. That is, for all individuals i,

$$c_{i2} > c_{i1}$$

Then, because of eq. (6.2), which holds for each individual,

$$p_{i2} > p_{i1}$$

If the group's productivity is a simple sum of individual productivity, then

$$p_2 = \Sigma p_{i2} > \Sigma p_{i1}$$

or $p_2 > p_1$. More generally, so long as the group's productivity varies directly with each individual's productivity (i.e., where $\frac{\partial p}{\partial p_i} > 0$), then it is necessarily true that $p_2 > p_1$ when $p_{i2} > p_{i1}$ for all individuals. Thus under these ideal circumstances, that is, when:

(a) the same group is being compared over time,
(b) all individuals' feelings of closeness shift in the same direction, and
(c) group productivity is an increasing function of individual productivity,

then the group-level generalization equation, (6.1), is logically implied by the individual-level generalizations, eq. (6.2).

But if circumstances are *not* so ideal, no statement can be made on the group level. For example, if different groups are compared, rather than the same group over time, individual productivity p_i might be quite differently related to feelings of closeness, c_i, due to different group structures or differing values in the two groups. Secondly, even if the same group were compared over time, but one c_i shifted down rather than up between time 2 and time 1, then it is impossible to say that the over-all productivity increased. This one person may be the group leader, who is crucial to group productivity or have some other key role in affecting productivity. His decreased cohesiveness could more than offset the increased cohesiveness of the others. Finally, it is obvious that if one member's productivity contributes *negatively* to the group productivity (e.g., the harder he works, the more he gets in the way of others), then an increase in his cohesiveness may offset the increased productivity due to the increased cohesiveness of the others.

This case, however, has concerned only the situation in which the functions were left unspecified. If individual cohesiveness and productivity are measured as cardinal or interval measures, if the functions relating individual cohesiveness and productivity are known, and if the functions relating individual to group productivity are known, then some kind of group-level generalization is always possible, not just under the ideal conditions (a), (b), and (c) above. The problem then is only one of logical transformations from the individual-level generalizations to the group-level ones. However, it is important to note that the group-level generalization will not in general be one involving group-level concepts of cohesiveness and productivity. So long as the functions differ for different individuals, then an aggregate generalization cannot be stated. The example below will show this in detail. If, in a two-person group,

$$p_1 = \alpha c_1 + \beta \tag{6.3}$$

$$p_2 = \gamma c_2 + \delta \tag{6.4}$$

$$p = \eta p_1 + \xi p_2 \tag{6.5}$$

then it is not possible to write a function, $p = f(c)$, such that c is an aggregate (scalar) measure of cohesiveness, and that this function preserves all the information which is contained in eqs. (6.3), (6.4), and (6.5).[19] Instead, the group-level generalization must take the form of a relationship between vectors rather than one between scalar quantities:

$$\begin{pmatrix} p_1 \\ p_2 \end{pmatrix} = \begin{pmatrix} \alpha c_1 + \beta \\ \gamma c_2 + \delta \end{pmatrix} \tag{6.6}$$

and

$$p = \eta p_1 + \xi p_2 \tag{6.7}$$

This result means that the group-level generalization is no more compact nor convenient than the individual-level one, for it is simply the same generalization in slightly different notation. More generally, what this means is that when individual-level generalizations are fully specified, and the concepts are cardinal or interval measures, then it is only possible to write the equations as a "group-level" generalization by maintaining the separate equations, written in vector notation. The group-level concepts are *not* scalar quantities aggregated from individual measures, but are vector quantities.

But now consider what we ordinarily do in forming group-level concepts from individual observations and in developing group-level generalizations. We usually simply add up some measures on individuals, get an aggregate measure, and then relate this aggregate measure to another aggregate

---

[19] It is trivially true, of course, that if $c = g(x)$, where $x = \eta(ac_1 + \beta) + z(\gamma c_2 + \delta)$, then this preserves the information in the original equation. But this means that $x = p$, and $g = f^{-1}$, so that c would no longer be an aggregate measure of cohesiveness, but depends upon the relations of individuals' cohesiveness to productivity.

measure. For measurement of group cohesiveness, a common procedure is to add up the number of sociometric choices made to persons within the group, divide this by the total number of sociometric choices, and consider this ratio a measure of "group cohesiveness." (See, for example, Gross and Martin, 1952.) Other techniques are more sophisticated than this, but most of them involve some addition operation. Now we have already seen that this addition operation assumes cardinality of the individual measures; but this assumption is met as long as the individual measures are formed by counting. A much more serious problem is the question of just what rationale exists for such addition in view of the fact that such an aggregate measure cannot allow one to reproduce the individual-level generalization, as the preceding discussion shows. Unless some rationale exists for addition, that is, *unless the addition operation corresponds to some social phenomenon*, then the group-level concept has no meaning other than as a kind of aggregate psychological concept. And as an aggregate psychological concept, its usefulness can be seriously questioned. It does not allow reproduction of the individual-level relationships, so it has little cause for existence unless it enters into some group-level relationship which is not derivative from the individual-level one. But if this is to occur, then the concept should have meaning as a group-level concept. This means that the addition operations by which it was constructed should correspond to some social phenomenon.

An example from thermodynamics should make the problem clear. Thermodynamics can be very instructive here, because a two-level situation occurs there as well. Thermodynamic variables, such as heat content, entropy, temperature, pressure, and specific heat, are aggregate measures for which molecular-level concepts exist in statistical mechanics. The concept of temperature, for example, is simply an aggregate measure representing the mean of the distribution of velocity among molecules. The temperature of a gas can be derived logically if only the mean velocity of molecules in the gas is known—or, conversely, the mean molecular velocity can be derived if only the temperature is known.[20]

If it is possible to have such meaningful and useful aggregate concepts as temperature in thermodynamics, as simply the sum or average of molecular-level measures, then shouldn't it be just as possible in sociology? The answer is in general No,[21] and there appear to be two reasons:

(a) One reason has to do with the *invariant form* of the distribution of velocity in a gas. The distribution is approximately a normal distribution, with a variance which is determined by the mean. Therefore, to specify the mean velocity of the molecules (or, alternatively, the temperature of the gas),

[20] The relation is $\bar{c} = \sqrt{8RT/M}$, where $\bar{c}$ is the mean velocity, M is the molecular weight of the gas, R is the molar gas constant, and T is Absolute temperature.

[21] Though the general answer is no, there are specific cases which are possible. These will be mentioned shortly.

is to specify the complete distribution.[22] It is obvious that in sociological phenomena, the distribution of individual attributes takes various forms, and can hardly be characterized by a single parameter. The only time that the distribution can be characterized by a single parameter is when the individual attribute is dichotomous, like a vote, or a suicide, or a marriage. In this case, a single number representing *proportion* or *rate* does fully characterize the distribution. (This special case will be mentioned in more detail below.)

(b) Perhaps more important than the invariance of the distribution of velocity is the *simple homogeneous structure* of relations among molecules. Molecules as conceived of by thermodynamic theory can be fully characterized by individual variables: velocity, spatial position, etc. There are no particularized relations between them, as there are, say, in gravitational theory. In the theory of gravitation, two bodies have a definite effect on one another as a function of their masses, their velocities, and their distance. As a result of this network of relations, it is very difficult to calculate the relative motions of three or more bodies. In contrast, the absence of such relations among molecules means that the molecules in a gas can be considered as a truly aggregate body; though they interact, it is not in accordance with some complicated or nonhomogeneous structure, but in accordance with random interactions among elements of a homogeneous mass. It is because of this that it is meaningful to construct aggregate concepts simply by addition or averaging. In gases at equilibrium, the velocities and other attributes of molecules always relate to one another in this same random way.

Now if individuals in groups behaved in this way, so that no structure of relations evolved other than random interactions, then they too could be considered a truly "aggregate body" for the purpose of group-level concepts and laws. But of course individuals do not act randomly with respect to one another. They form attachments to certain persons, they group together in cliques, they establish institutions, which are essentially formalized sets of special relations. In short, the very essence of society is a nonrandom structure of some sort.

The situation is not quite so gloomy, however. For if the characteristics of a social structure are investigated, then the structure can be systematically taken into account in the development of theory (see, for example, Chapter 17). Sometimes the technical complications in taking it into account are great; yet the necessity for doing so is clear. As a matter of fact, it is precisely *because* there is some varying structure of relations between individuals that sociology has a reason for existence. Sociology would otherwise be nothing more than an "aggregate psychology," as thermodynamics is an "aggregate statistical mechanics," and would be concerned only with distri-

---

[22] The invariance of the distribution is a result of the fact that only equilibrium states are considered. Thermodynamics is concerned only with equilibrium phenomena, not with rates of change.

butions of motives, needs, beliefs, and so on. Many sociologists today, in fact, forget that sociology is different from aggregate psychology and base their "sociological" explanations on such distributions,[23] or even worse, upon some modal psychological trait, neglecting even the variations. Similarly, the social psychological propositions of the cohesiveness-productivity type discussed earlier are of this aggregate psychology variety, completely neglecting the phenomena of structure, and extrapolating, as it were, from individual feelings, motives, and needs, to some "group-level" feelings, motives, and needs. That such an extrapolation is illegitimate has been indicated by the preceding discussion.

However, under very special conditions, such "aggregate psychology" can be legitimately carried out. Suppose, for example, we want to develop a generalization relating two *rates* of behavior, as follows:

$$s = f(d) \tag{6.8}$$

where
$$s = \text{suicide rate in a society, and}$$
$$d = \text{divorce rate in the society.}$$

This is a generalization on the level of the group or society, and both these variables are group-level concepts, for they characterize the society itself. Now if the individual-level generalization is of the following form:

Pr {suicide, given divorce} > Pr {suicide, given continued marriage}
then the group-level generalization follows directly, with only the restriction that it is used for changes in the same society over time rather than comparison between societies. This is restriction (a) on p. 87; restrictions (b) and (c) are no longer necessary because the individual-level measures of divorce and suicide are fully expressed by the group-level measures.[24] That is, there is no question of how the individual-level concepts combine to produce the group-level concept. To look at it another way, the generalization expressed in eq. (5.17) is not a generalization about some group-level phenomenon, but an aggregate generalization about behavior of individuals. It is, in other words, a legitimate generalization in aggregate psychology.[25] It is obvious, however, that only when the individual variables are dichotomous attributes can such a parallelism occur between the individual-level generalization and the group-level one without making the group-level variables vector quantities. Otherwise, information is lost in moving from the individual to the group

[23] The very method of survey research in sociology has greatly increased this difficulty, for by collecting data from a "sample" of persons, it explicitly overlooks the relations between persons. Only recently has survey research taken these relations into account by "saturation sampling" and incorporating questions about social relations in the interview (see Coleman, 1958).

[24] This assumes that there is no "contextual effect," i.e., that the divorce rate in a society does not affect the probability of suicide among nondivorcees.

[25] However, it should be recognized that the reference class for the assignment of probability is not different observations on the same individual, but observations on a large class of individuals.

level. There would be a many-one correspondence between variations in the individual measures and variations in the group level. For example, if x is a group-level concept formed by aggregating x_1 and x_2, individual-level variables, as follows,

$$x = x_1 + x_2$$

then a two-unit increase in x may correspond to a two-unit increase in x_1 (or x_2) or to a one-unit increase in x_1 and a one-unit increase in x_2, or to numerous other combinations. If an equivalence between such different individual-level changes is to be made, then it should be made explicitly, for it necessarily assumes something about the structure of relations between individuals in the group.[26]

APPENDIX—MEASUREMENT OF PRESTIGE

The concept of "prestige" of an individual or activity is an interesting one, for it is based upon the orientation of a number of persons toward the activity or person, yet is a concept characterizing the activity or person itself.

First of all, it is useless simply to set down a name such as "prestige," no matter how respectable a sociological concept, and then proceed to devise a measure of it. Rather, the first step is to ask either or both of two questions: (a) how, in the implicit theory in which prestige is to play a part, is behavior affected by it? or (b) what, in the implicit theory, are the ways in which prestige is gained or lost?

Only if one of these questions is answerable, can legitimate operations be devised for an ordinal, interval, or cardinal scale of prestige. For it is one of these relations itself which must provide the operation. And only if the question is answerable in such a way that some behavior beyond comparison is implied will the resulting measure be more than an ordinal one. For example, the economists' concept of utility under conditions of certainty, since it is always associated with a particular amount of a good, implies no behavior beyond comparison, and can become nothing more than an ordinal measure.

Suppose our interest is with the way that prestige structures in a social system act as motivating devices, to generate association structures, and to motivate people into various activities. Then we may choose to answer the first question above, saying that the definition of "prestige of person i in the eyes of j" within our theory is "that which makes individual j want to associate with individual i." Essentially two paths are open: (a) to set up a "counting" model which would take numbers as input data and provide as output a measure of the tendency to associate with others; or (b) to set up a comparison (and possibly combination) procedure based upon the definition of

---

[26] Or else it assumes, as in thermodynamics, that there are constraints on the system so that the distribution of changes is fixed.

prestige. The first procedure would not provide a validation of the measure except through a test of the theory; the second would provide direct validation.

For the first procedure, we suppose (using the methods of Chapters 4 and 5) that this tendency constitutes a transition rate, a_i, in the direction of associating with person i, with random shocks ε_i, in the opposite direction; then if n_i are the number of persons who associate with i, $a_i/\varepsilon_i = n_i/(n - n_i)$. Finally, if we hypothesize that the random shocks ε_i are the same for all persons i, the measure of prestige a_i for person i is given (relative to ε_i) by the above equation. Sociometric data of association would provide the necessary numbers n and n_i. It should be clear, however, that the measure is in no way validated as a cardinal measure. Use of over-time data would be necessary to validate that the prestige attributed to i, a_i, was the same for all potential associates, that the random shocks, ε_i, were the same for all persons i.

If we choose the second alternative, to provide a comparison procedure for ordinal prestige, or a comparison and combination procedure for cardinal prestige, then our procedure could be as follows:

(1) Observe all persons in the dilemma of choosing between association with every two persons, and record with whom he chooses to associate.[27]

(2) These data would be tested for ordinality by testing the transitivity of pairwise choices. It would be possible also to test whether i's prestige was in the same ordinal position for all j's. (However, with this measurement procedure, it is possible to obtain a separate measure of the prestige of i in the eyes of each j.)

(3) If the quantity of prestige that persons 1, 2, ..., n have in the eyes of j governs only choices among them as single individuals, then these can be nothing more than an ordinal measure—since j's behavior, as governed by the theory, covers nothing beyond ordinal comparisons of individuals.

However, if the quantity of prestige also governs choice among *groups* of individuals, then a cardinal measure is possible. Suppose the theory postulates that his choices among different groups depends on the average prestige of the members. Then we observe or ask him his choice among different pairs of groups, composed of persons whose ordinal position has already been determined.

(4) Taking these data, we would proceed as follows: assume the existence of quantities p_i, the prestige of person i (in j's eyes). Let

$$ p_k = \frac{1}{m} \sum_{i=k_1}^{k_m} p_i $$

[27] Alternatively, because verbal responses probably reflect desires as directly or more directly than actual behavior, we could ask him in a questionnaire to choose between persons in terms of his desire to associate with them. Note, however, that we would *not* ask him to name "who has the higher prestige." The reason is important: his conception of who has high prestige plays no role in the theory. In contrast, his desires to associate with others are an intrinsic element in the theory.

for group k, of m members. Then if $p_k > p_h$, let $\delta_{kh} = 1$; otherwise $\delta_{kh} = 0$. Now if, in the empirical test, group k is desired over h, let $x_{kh} = 1$; otherwise let $x_{kh} = 0$.

Then the problem is to assign numerical values to the individual p_i's such that the quantity

$$\sum_k \sum_h x_{kh}\delta_{kh} \tag{A.1}$$

is maximized. The first variable, x_{kh}, is derived from the empirical test; the second, δ_{kh}, derives from the particular assignment of values for p_i. This is not an easy task, though it is an interesting one. It is near to a linear programming task, because numbers p_i are assigned so as to satisfy (insofar as possible) a set of inequalities; that is,

$$\frac{1}{m} \sum_{i=k_1}^{k_m} p_i > \frac{1}{n} \sum_{i=h_1}^{h_n} p_i$$

for all pairs of groups k and h, in which group k is preferred to h.

If there are many groupings of persons among which preferences are made, then the possible assignment of numbers is narrowly restricted. Obviously, however, if there are only a few persons altogether, and thus a few combinations, there is "looseness" in the allowable assignment of numbers to the p_i, and the resulting assignment is only an approximation to cardinality.

(5) Validation of this measure as a cardinal measure would occur immediately if the quantity (A.1) were at its potential maximum—that is, if it were possible to assign numbers to p_i such that δ_{kh} was one whenever x_{kh} was one, and zero otherwise. This validation would mean that this person was behaving as if each other person had a value p_i, and each grouping of persons had a value $p_k = \dfrac{1}{m} \sum\limits_{i=k_1}^{k_m} p_i$. In the absence of such perfection, it

would be necessary to test in some fashion for systematic error. (For example, perhaps this person is behaving as if p_k is equal to the *sum* of p_i, rather than the *average*. If that were so, large groups would be chosen much more often than predicted by *any* assignment of numbers to p_i.)

It is important to note what measurement does in this case: it takes behavior that is essentially *qualitative* (that is, choice of one individual over another, or one group over another), and creates from this behavior a quantitative number which will account for it, i.e., correctly predict it. However, it should be pointed out that neither the procedure for optimally assigning numbers to maximize (A.1), nor a validation test which examines systematic error exists. These are interesting and complicated mathematical problems. It is evident that if quantitative measures based on methods other than counting are to be developed, procedures to solve these two types of problems are necessary.

CHAPTER 3

MATHEMATICS AS A LANGUAGE FOR RELATIONS BETWEEN VARIABLES

Sociologists have often been led to comment upon the no-man's-land which separates social theory from social research. Robert K. Merton, for example, in his essay on the contribution of research to theory (1949) says:

> On the one hand, we observe those sociologists who seek above all to generalize, to find their way as rapidly as possible to the formulation of sociological laws. Tending to assess the significance of sociological work in terms of scope rather than the demonstrability of generalizations, they eschew the "triviality" of detailed, small-scale observation and seek the grandeur of global summaries. At the other extreme stands a hardy band who do not hunt too closely the implications of their research but who remain confident and assured that what they report is so. To be sure, their reports of facts are verifiable and often verified, but they are somewhat at a loss to relate these facts to one another or even to explain why these, rather than other, observations have been made. For the first group the identifying motto would at times seem to be: "We do not know whether what we say is true, but it is at least

significant." And for the radical empiricist the motto may read: "This is demonstrably so, but we cannot indicate its significance." (p. 83.)

This was written about 1945, but conditions have changed very little. Researchers plod on, often ignoring the complexity of behavior in their task of finding simple isolated relations, while discursive theory soars ever higher, constructing more and more elaborate verbal systems to describe behavior. At best, these verbal systems have provided us with a vivid heuristic image of a system of behavior in operation, at worst they have led us into flights of fancy and ever further into a morass of words. And in any case, they are hardly translatable into research terms. Yet if our discursive theory is often too broad to be usable, our research is often so pedestrian that it offers no aid to the theorist. Ordinarily concerned with single relations inferred from correlations, most social research fragments behavior, leaving it like Humpty Dumpty, never to be put together again.

One of the values of mathematics as a language for science is its tendency to bring together research and theory. It forces the theorist to examine just what he does mean, and to set it down in unambiguous form. Thus his propositions are out in the open, so to speak, not hedged about with equivocation and ambiguity. At the same time, mathematics forces the researcher to state his research results in terms which are of potential relevance to theory. It may be of help to see first how such a language is useful for both theory and research in other sciences. Two simple examples, one from early mechanics and one from economics, should indicate the usefulness of a mathematical language.

1. MECHANICS

Galileo, who has been called the father of the science of mechanics, is remembered primarily for his discovery that the acceleration of a freely falling body is constant, and independent of mass. Here is the way he says it (in the words of one of the speakers of his dialogues):

> At present it is the purpose of our author merely to investigate and to demonstrate some of the properties of accelerated motion (whatever the cause of this acceleration may be)—meaning thereby a motion, such that the momentum of its velocity goes on increasing after departure from rest, in simple proportionality to the time, which is the same as saying that in equal time-intervals the body receives equal increments of velocity; and if we find the properties which will be demonstrated later, are realized in freely falling and accelerated bodies, we may conclude that the assumed definition includes such a motion of falling bodies and that their speed goes on increasing as the time and the duration of the motion. (Galileo, 1638.)

In what appears today as rather clumsy language, Galileo is saying that the rate of increase of velocity per unit time for falling bodies is constant;

i.e., the acceleration is constant. The algebraic notation by which we express such a general relation was not in use in Galileo's time; he was forced to use awkward verbal expressions, or nearly equally awkward geometry, unless he had particular numbers at hand as the result of an experiment. The value of an algebraic expression as a "shorthand" for such statements is evident when we can write Galileo's statement as follows:

$$a = g \tag{1.1}$$

$$\frac{dv}{dt} = g \tag{1.2}$$

where g is a constant, a is acceleration, v is velocity, and t is time measured from point of rest.

Certainly the rise of mechanics depended very greatly on the use of such mathematical formulae to replace verbal statements like those of Galileo's speaker. A random page of any modern text in the mechanics of rigid bodies would indicate just how hopeless it would be to express mechanics in any less formal and rigorous language. Simple though the discovery of Galileo is, its expression in ordinary literary language, or even in the geometry that Galileo often used for his proofs, is difficult; modern mechanics would be inconceivable in such languages.

2. MATHEMATICS AS A LANGUAGE FOR ECONOMICS

Economists have long had a mathematical theory for the effect of demand on the price of a good. The example below shows the relation of demand to price in its simplest form. Stated in words, the relation is

(a) The demand of consumers for a good decreases as
the price goes up; it increases as the price goes down.

Stating the relation mathematically gives the following equation, letting q represent quantity bought, and p represent price:

$$\frac{dq}{dp} < 0 \tag{2.1}$$

Making an arbitrary assumption that the decrease of quantity per unit increase in price is constant gives

$$\frac{dq}{dp} = b \quad (b < 0) \tag{2.2}$$

where b is a constant representing the effect of one unit of price (e.g., one dollar) on demand. Its dimensions are

$$\frac{\text{change in goods bought}}{\text{change in price}}$$

(Equation (2.2) assumes for simplicity of exposition that the decrease in demand per unit is constant over the whole price range. Though this is ordinarily not a reasonable assumption, it is sometimes useful for the restricted price range in which the supply-demand system remains.)

Integrating eq. (2.2) gives

$$q = a + bp \qquad (2.3)$$

where a represents the demand at a zero price. The graphical form of this equation is given in Figure 3.1.

This relationship between quantity and price says that if one knows the price of a good, he can immediately determine, from the graph or from the equation, just how much of the good will be bought. This formulation, however, obscures a dynamic element implicit in the theoretical statement (a) above. The statement implies that if the demand has adjusted to a given

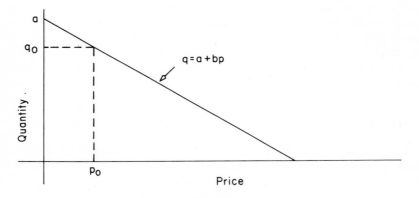

Figure 3.1

price (i.e., is on the line $q = a + bp$ in Figure 3.1), and then the price is suddenly changed, the demand will readjust to come back to the line, at the new price. If the price is at p_0, then q_0 goods will be bought. Then if the price is increased for some reason to p_1, the quantity will subsequently reduce to q_1. If the price should be decreased, the quantity bought will in turn increase. In other words, if the price is changed in any way to displace the system from this line, then the quantity bought will adjust to the new price level. This movement over time to bring the quantity bought back "into line" with price, or into equilibrium, is illustrated graphically in Figure 3.2. If the price is displaced by some external cause either to a higher price (p_1) or to a lower price (p_2), the demand changes to send the system back to this line.

This discussion implies more than eq. (2.3), for it concerns *time*, and time has not entered the mathematical formulation at all. Equation (2.3) is a static formulation, and constitutes a statement of the *equilibrium* value of q as a function of p. What about the *change* of q, dq/dt, when there has been a disturbance in price? The theoretical statement (a) implies that this is zero when $q = a + bp$, negative when q is greater than this, positive when q is less than this, or

$$\frac{dq}{dt} = 0 \qquad \text{(when } q = a + bp\text{)} \tag{2.4}$$

$$\frac{dq}{dt} > 0 \qquad \text{(when } q < a + bp\text{)} \tag{2.5}$$

$$\frac{dq}{dt} < 0 \qquad \text{(when } q > a + bp\text{)} \tag{2.6}$$

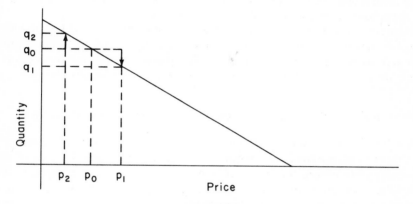

Figure 3.2

The simplest assumption is that dq/dt is proportional to the distance of q from the equilibrium line, or

$$\frac{dq}{dt} = k(a + bp - q) \tag{2.7}$$

where k is a positive constant. Its dimensions are:

$$\frac{\text{change in quantity}}{\text{time} \times \text{units of quantity from the equilibrium line}}$$

Equation (2.7), then, expresses the dynamic effect of price on quantity, and constitutes a mathematical formulation of the verbal theoretical statement in (a) above. This formulation has, of course, made two assumptions which were not implied in the theoretical statement: that the (equilibrium) variation in demand with variation in price is constant; and that the rate of change of demand in moving back to the equilibrium line is proportional to the distance from it. These are simple linearity assumptions. It is a simple linear differential equation, which has taken the vague language of the theorist and put it in precise terms which the economic researcher can understand and test.

These two examples, from mechanics and economics, indicate the utility of mathematics as a language for scientific theory. But how does this relate to empirical research? Can the researcher, equipped with tools for quantitatively measuring distance and time, or quantity and price, fit his results with the theoretical formulations?

If he can carry out controlled experiments, as is possible in mechanics, then he has no difficulty in testing eq. (1.2) or (2.3) or (2.7) and obtaining a numerical estimate for the constant g (in eq. 1.2) or a and b (in eq. 2.3) or k (in eq. 2.7). The equations and definitions themselves indicate the experimental tests necessary to confirm them, and once confirmed, prescribe the operations necessary to estimate the constants.

However, when precisely controlled experimentation is not possible, then the researcher must resort to other techniques. In particular, the technique of regression analysis incorporates precisely the same conception of relations between variables as do the theoretical formulations above.

3. EMPIRICAL INVESTIGATIONS AND REGRESSION ANALYSIS

Starting from the other direction—with quantitative empirical data rather than theoretical propositions—requires a different approach. Instead of a qualitative proposition, there is a set of data, say for example, a number of observations of price and for each observation of price a corresponding observation of quantity of goods bought. These data can then be plotted on the familiar scatter diagram, as for example in Figure 3.3.

The technique of regression analysis brings these data into correspondence

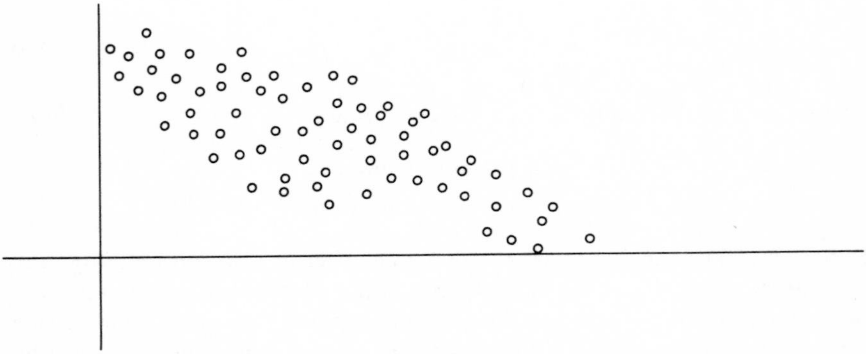

Figure 3.3

with equations like those of the preceding section. For the regression of q on p, an equation of the following form is assumed:[1]

$$q = a + bp + \varepsilon \qquad (3.1)$$

where $b =$ the slope of the regression line,

   $a =$ the q-intercept of the line, and
   $\varepsilon =$ a random variable with variance σ_ε^2 and mean zero.

This equation for the regression of q on p constitutes the same structural equation, using the same mathematics, as the theoretical relation expressed in eq. (2.3). The one addition is an error term, ε, to account for the deviations of the data from the regression line. If the data are widely scattered from the line of best fit, then the variance of ε is high, and the relation between p and q rather tenuous. If the points cluster closely around the line, the relation between p and q is quite strong.

Since eq. (3.1) differs in this one respect from the theoretically derived equation (2.3), then it is important to see the interpretations of this "error" term. Some interpretation is needed if the empirical equation is to be brought into correspondence with the mathematical model which serves as a language for theory—that is, eq. (2.3) and the related equations. There are two basic interpretations of this error term in a regression equation; they have been called the "error-in-variable" approach and the "error-in-equation" approach (Kendall, 1952). The first assumes that the error arises in measurement; that the "true" quantity and price have a fully determinate relation as expressed in eq. (2.3), but that the process of measurement has introduced error. Economists have often used this approach to examine in detail the problem of identification of parameters of models of supply and demand. See also Koopmans and Reiersøl (1950).

The second approach assumes that the measurement is correct but that the equation is incomplete or incorrect—that demand, for example, is a function of other variables besides price, which move the system away from a determinate quantity-price line. The true equation, according to this approach, might be something like this:

$$q = b_1 p + b_2 x + b_3 y + b_4 z + \ldots + a^* \qquad (3.2)$$

where b_1, b_2, b_3, b_4, . . ., a^* are constants, and $x, y, z, \ldots$ are other relevant variables. These other variables of the system, $x, y, z, \ldots$, being unmeasured, contribute to the variance of q which shows up as "error variance," σ_ε^2, in eq. (3.1). According to this approach, random changes in these other implicit variables impart "random shocks" to the dependent variable, throwing it out of equilibrium with the explicitly measured independent variable (in this

---

[1] See Hald (1952) or Kendall (1952) for an exposition of the methods of regression analysis discussed here. These are standard techniques and will not be repeated here.

case p), and producing some scatter around the regression line as shown in the scatter diagram of Figure 3.3. Then either slowly or quickly the independent variable in the equation pulls the dependent one back to the regression line. This assumption is completely in accord with the theoretical equation (2.7), which expresses the movement of q back to the equilibrium line after having been moved away.

This assumption of an incomplete equation and consequent "random shocks" naturally leads to the attempt to take into explicit account some of these "errors" or "shocks" by introducing other variables as determinants of the dependent variable. Looking back at eq. (3.2), we see that this means measuring variables x, y, or z, or all of them, and then finding the parameters of the regression equation

$$q = b_1 p + b_2 x + b_3 y + b_4 z + a^* + \varepsilon' \tag{3.3}$$

where ε' is again a random variable with mean zero and variance $\sigma_{\varepsilon'}^2$. The aim in introducing x and y and z depends on how much a theorist the researcher is. They may be introduced because they play a part, in precisely the way specified in eq. (3.3), in his theory. Or he may introduce them for the directly practical aim of ending up with an error variance $\sigma_{\varepsilon'}^2$, much smaller than the error variance σ_{ε}^2, in the initial two-variable equation. The new equation, eq. (3.3), is a multiple regression equation; the computed coefficients tell just how highly related each of the independent variables is to the dependent variable when each of the others is held constant.

In summary, then, the language of differential equations and algebraic equations serves both theory and research in sciences which are built upon continuous variables, and helps to bring theory and research together by leading them to "speak the same language." It is true, of course, that the gap between theory and research is not so easily spanned as this oversimplified exposition suggests. The regression equations must make some very strong assumptions which are often not met in practice, and which would confound the investigator attempting to build theory from the ground up by utilizing regression equations.

A simple example will illustrate some of the difficulties which might arise by this kind of "brick-by-brick" approach to theory. Suppose that early mechanics had developed by the use of regression equations. Suppose, specifically, that an investigation had been carried out relating the length of *time* a body had fallen through air and the *velocity* it attained. The relation in mechanics is that the velocity attained is equal to the acceleration due to gravity times the time the object has fallen, or

$$v = gt \tag{3.4}$$

where g is the acceleration due to gravity. Now if there has been numerous investigations involving different-sized bodies, different velocities, and bodies with differing densities, the investigators would have ended with numerous pairs of observations (v_i, t_i), which they would locate on a scatter diagram in order to find the line of best fit. But in every case, and especially for high velocities (i.e., objects which fell a great distance) and low-density objects (i.e., feathers), the observed velocity would fall considerably below that which the theoretical equation (3.4) predicts. The resulting regression equation might have ended up including other variables, such as mass or density of the object; and there would have been indications that at high velocities the relation of velocity to time was not even linear. The reason, of course, would be air resistance, which has different effects as a function of the density of the object, its shape, its velocity, and other things. The regression equation would of course have been empirically correct, but it wouldn't have corresponded to the simple velocity-time relation which served as the basis for Galileo's remarkable contribution to the science of mechanics. They might even have served to confound the issue, by bringing in too soon a factor— i.e., air resistance—which was irrelevant to the fundamentals of mechanics. Such a possibility is pointed out by Ernst Mach, the physicist and philosopher of science:

> . . . the task of the early investigators who lay the foundations is quite a different one from that of their successors. The former have to seek out and establish the weightiest facts only, and to do this, as history teaches, calls for more intelligence (*Geist*) than is generally believed. (Mach, 1897.)

Thus, as this example from mechanics illustrates, even though the mathematical language is the same, in any science there is still a gap between equations and parameters generated directly by empirical regression techniques and those developed with the aid of theoretical considerations. In particular, three important assumptions are made when regression analysis is used to induce causal or theoretical relations:

(a) It is assumed that the structural equation is theoretically correct (i.e., the variables are linearly related, and the dependent variable in the regression analysis is in fact the dependent variable in the causal relation). This means that one should have an *a priori* assumption as to what the structural relation is—which variable affects the other, and whether the effect is linear or not; it is possible to carry out regression analyses assuming various kinds of nonlinear relations—but the point is that the mathematical structure of the equation must be decided in advance; the regression analysis only tells the coefficients once this structure is assumed.

(b) Other variables which affect the dependent variable are assumed to be uncorrelated with the independent variable. (If this assumption is not true, as often it is not, then the observed relation may be a spurious one because of the effect of other variables not taken into account. It is to reduce this difficulty that more variables are added and multiple regression is used.)

(c) The parameters of the equations are alike or nearly so for all units on which observations are made. Otherwise a broad scatter will show up on a scatter diagram, indicating little or no relationship, when there may in fact be a strong relationship, but different parameters for different units.

These assumptions are important, for they are inherent limitations on cross-sectional investigations which take observations on many units, each at only one point in time. When the data can be extended to over-time observations, so that one is no longer dependent on regression analysis, then these assumptions are sharply reduced.

4. CONCLUSION

These two examples, from mechanics and economics, indicate the utility of the mathematics of ordinary algebra and calculus as a language for scientific theory. Why, then, isn't it possible for sociological theory to do as so many other sciences have done, and use this language too?

A closer look at these examples indicates one of the fundamental problems: from where does the social scientist get quantitatively measurable variables (i.e., concepts) which can serve as distance, mass, and time do for the physicist or quantity and price do for the economist? At present, he does not get them at all; and indications are that he will not, except in very special cases. Chapter 2 indicates the kind of conceptual rigor and empirical precision upon which useful quantitative measurement depends.

Thus we cannot simply adopt this mathematics which has proved so eminently successful for so much of science. Because behavior is usually expressed in qualitative terms—agreeing or disagreeing, liking or disliking, going to the left or to the right, quitting school or continuing, marrying or not marrying—any mathematical language which can serve for social science must in some fashion mirror this discrete, nonquantitative behavior.

CHAPTER 4

A MATHEMATICAL LANGUAGE FOR RELATIONS BETWEEN QUALITATIVE ATTRIBUTES

1. THEORY AND RESEARCH IN SOCIOLOGY: LACK OF A MATHEMATICAL LANGUAGE

A short example in social theory and research will show the way in which the lack of quantitative variables inhibits the kind of merging of theory and research illustrated above in economics and mechanics. The example from theory is one familiar to many sociologists: a proposition from George Homans' *The Human Group* (1950) about the dependence of *sentiments* which persons have toward one another upon their *interaction* or association with one another. The proposition, as Homans states it, is: "If the interactions between the members of a group are frequent in the external system, senti- ments of liking will grow up between them" (p. 112). This is not a high-level theoretical explanation of behavior. It is an induction from experience—from his own experience and from the studies he focusses on in his book. It is somewhat embarrassing, in fact, to call this a "theoretical relationship" because it is little more than descriptive of things that we see every day. In this respect, however, note that the other examples, from mechanics and economics, were no less simple and descriptive.

The difficulty, of course, in proceeding on to a mathematical model of this relation, as with the other two examples, is that the variables are not quantitative: "liking one another" may be meaningful to us as social scientists and as persons; but it is not embedded within a theory which lends it the criteria for quantitative measurement, nor is it directly accessible to such measurement, as are distance, time, price, and quantity. "Frequency of interaction" allows counting, and thus apparent quantification, but the question of comparability of a few long interactions with many short ones makes even this apparent quantification problematic.

In sum, the concepts or variables of this relation are simply not amenable to the framework of algebraic and differential equations into which the previous relations were cast. Thus we proceed in sociology (and usually in psychology too) by leaving the relation on the verbal level, thereby reducing any possibility of its being incorporated into a system of relations. (To be sure, Homans begins to examine in conjunction pairs of relations in his verbal theory; but beyond this simple pairwise examination, the matter gets too complex, and out of hand.)

So this is where the theory remains. What about the research results? How far do they move toward a merging with the theory? This is difficult to answer, because research results take such different forms. The research results which Homans examines before arriving at the proposition are mostly qualitative, showing how continued association of men on a job or boys in a neighborhood creates strong personal ties which were not there initially. Much other data from all sorts of sources may bear indirectly on the proposition. For example, it has long been known that workers and employers in small shops are more likely to have positive sentiments toward one another, less likely to have mutual antagonism, than in large plants. The interpretation, of course, is that there is higher interaction between employer and employee in the small shops than in the large one.

The best kind of confirmation of the proposition would of course be to examine many groups over time, to see just what does happen to peoples' feelings for one another as they come into interaction through some external constraint. However, often such over-time analysis is impractical, and the investigator is forced to substitute cross-sectional data, and to carry out statistical analyses, just as the economist is forced to use statistical analysis of cross-sectional data in his investigations of demand and price, or supply and price. The difference, of course, is that the economist has two quantitatively measurable variables, price of goods and quantity of goods, while the sociologist has "liking" and "interaction," neither of them quantitatively measurable. What happens in such a situation, of course, is that we use observation and interview to measure interaction and friendship in a qualitative way, say as dichotomous attributes, and then cross-tabulate these attributes, in the usual kind of statistical tabulation. A typical example may be drawn from a study of printers, each of whom in the course of an interview was asked who his closest friend was among other printers. Some printers named another in the same shop; some named a man who was outside the shop. One of the factors affecting interaction on the job, and thus (according to Homans' proposition) the likelihood of friendship developing, is the kind of work in which printers were engaged. Table 4.1 shows the tendency of linotype operators and handmen to have their closest friend in the same shop.

As this table shows, having one's closest friend in the shop is related to working as a handman. In Homans' terms the type of work is the "external system" which imposes a high or low rate of interaction upon the persons subject to it. It is evident, in looking back at his proposition, that these data, in conjunction with prior knowledge that a handman's job allows more on-the-job interaction than does a linotype operator's, do support it. There are the usual problems of interpretation, just as there are with regression

Table 4.1

	Handmen (more interaction)	Linotype operators (less interaction)
Closest friend in shop	.60	.49
Closest friend outside shop	.40	.51
(Total number)	(106)	(144)

analysis, but let us assume that no selective factors were involved, and that the correlation represents an actual effect of interaction upon friendship.

So far, this is fine; but just as the theory is able to go no further than the verbal language toward a precise *model* of the relationship, the empirical results progress no further than this toward a model, that is, toward a merging with the theory. This is usually the state at which research rests, for the investigators have documented their point, and have little need to go further. One reason for this, of course, is that there is not much generality to the particular classifications used: having "closest friend in shop" and "type of job" are not general concepts, but are classifications specific to this situation. Another reason, however, is that there is no mathematical language for theory which would help relate the specific classifications to general concepts of "interaction" and "friendliness." That is, there is no model for dichotomous attributes analogous to that of differential equations and algebraic equations for quantitative variables. There are various measures of association of one sort or another, but none which derive from a conception of the causal relationship acting through time. It is precisely this lack which the model to be presented hopes to overcome—not in any patchwork or approximate way, but *as a model which has precisely the characteristics for problems involving discrete states that the usual differential-equations model has for problems involving continuous variables.* In fact, the model to be presented goes one step further: it is a stochastic or probabilistic model, so that the external "shocks" to the system are an intrinsic part of the model, and not something tacked on at the end, as they ordinarily are with differential or algebraic equations reflecting relations between continuous variables. In addition, the model is intrinsically dynamic: causes are conceptualized in terms of the changes they bring about. One of the primary aims in its development has been to tie together conceptually our notions of behavior over time and the static cross-tabulations which constitute much of our research.

2. CONTINUOUS-TIME, DISCRETE-STATE MODEL WITH RANDOM SHOCKS

To start out very simply, let us first consider the case of a single dichotomous attribute, such as having "closest friend in shop" or having "closest friend outside shop," in the example of the preceding section. When asked who his closest friend is, the individual can be in one of two states: a state leading him to name as his closest friend a man in the shop (state 1) or one leading him to name someone else (state 2).[1]

Now if we think of what happens over time among the persons in each of these two states, the most natural notion is that of transitions continuously occurring between these states. If, for example, these same people were interviewed a second time, some who had been in state 1 would now be in state 2, and vice versa. Pictorially, it might be represented as follows:

State 1 (having closest friend in shop)

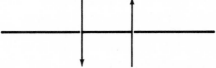

State 2 (having no closest friend in shop)

Or it might be represented as the usual fourfold table of "turnover" on the next page (Table 4.2) would show it (using hypothetical numbers).

Now it seems obvious that if we conceive of *change* occurring in both directions between the two times as a function of various unknown attributes, then the most appropriate mathematical model to represent this change is a continuous-time, discrete-space stochastic process. In other words, there is

---

[1] This statement belies a vagueness in the connection between underlying state and overt response. The connection is discussed explicitly in Chapters 12 and 13. In the present models we will assume a perfect correspondence between underlying state and overt response.

a continual likelihood of change between the two states culminating in the
overall change shown in Table 4.2.

Such continuous-time stochastic processes act a little differently from the
more familiar discrete-time stochastic processes which are characterized by
transition probabilities for moving from each state to each other state.
There are some treatments of continuous-time discrete-state processes in
texts on probability (see Doob, 1953; Feller, 1957; Bharucha-Reid, 1960;
Bartlett, 1955; Takacs, 1960), though they have been less fully treated than
discrete-time processes.[2]

Although these processes have had relatively little attention in social
science, it is important, for reasons which will become obvious in Section 4,
that they, rather than the usual discrete-time Markov chains, be taken as
the foundation of what is to come. Applications of these models, or their
deterministic counterparts, have, of course, been numerous in other branches
of science, and two of these applications will be discussed briefly a few pages
hence.

Table 4.2

		TIME II		
		Yes	*No*	
	Yes	125	25	150
TIME I				
	No	25	50	75
		150	75	225

Now going back to the example of having one's closest friend in the shop,
this continuous-time model says that "random shocks" would provide a
general migration from each state to the other. If these random shocks
are serially uncorrelated, then the probability of a person's moving at any
instant of time is constant.[3] In any small interval of time dt, the probability of
moving from state 1 to state 2, given that the individual is in state 1, is a
constant multiplied by dt, $q_{12}dt$. Similarly, the probability of his moving from
state 2 to state 1 if he is in state 2 is a constant multiplied by dt, $q_{21}dt$. (This
constant, which will be labelled q_{ij} throughout these chapters, is usually called
a transition intensity in the literature on probability, but the term "transition
rate" seems a more felicitous expression and will be used here.) From this,
we can write an equation for the rate of change in the probability that he is
in state 1:

---

[2] I am deeply indebted to Richard Savage for helping me through Doob's difficult
treatment, and for his aid in acquainting me with these models.

[3] See Appendix 1 to this chapter for a discussion of this model as a stochastic process,
and its relation to a discrete-time Markov process.

$$dp_1 = -q_{12}p_1\,dt + q_{21}p_2\,dt$$

$$\frac{dp_1}{dt} = -q_{12}p_1 + q_{21}p_2 \tag{2.1}$$

This stochastic process is specified for an individual. In most cases, however, we will be dealing with aggregates of individuals, and except where otherwise indicated, we will assume that each individual is governed by the same transition rates. This means that for n individuals, there are n independent identical processes. Multiplying eq. (2.1) by n, we get an equation expressing the sum of the n independent processes:

$$\frac{dnp_1}{dt} = -q_{12}np_1 + q_{21}np_2 \tag{2.2}$$

If p_i is the probability of being in state i, characterizing each individual, then np_i, or n_i, is the expected number of individuals in that state. Ordinarily, data will be such that they can be interpreted as estimates of n_1 and n_2. Thus from this point, we will deal with equations for the expected values, and speak loosely of "numbers of persons." In Chapters 10 and 11, stochastic models for groups of n persons will be examined, and at that point, the distribution around this expected value is examined.

In order to examine more closely just what this process implies, let us consider a system with only the one-way process from state 1 to state 2:

$$\frac{dn_1}{dt} = -q_{12}n_1 \tag{2.3}$$

An intuitive idea of q_{12} can be seen as follows: If there were 1000 persons whose closest friend is in their shop at time zero, and each has a probability of .001 of shifting out of this state within a period of time Δt, then we would expect to see .001 × 1000, or one person shift during that period of time Δt. If there were 10,000 persons initially in state 1, then we would expect to see about .001 × 10,000, or ten persons shift during that time. (The number actually shifting would be subject to random variation, which is discussed in Chapter 10, but this variation will be disregarded for the time being, as mentioned above, so as to focus only on the expected number shifting.)

If persons were observed continuously, so that the number shifting in any interval of time could be counted, and if the number in the state were replenished by transition in, so that it remained constant, then the transition rate q_{12} could easily be estimated. For, dividing eq. (2.3) through by n_1, and replacing the derivatives by differences gives

$$\frac{\Delta n_1}{n_1\Delta t} = -q_{12} \tag{2.4}$$

and if n_1 is constant throughout the time interval through which the differences are taken, then this equation, which is simply a restatement of the equation defining the process, may be used to estimate q_{12}. The number Δn_1 is the number who shift from state 1 to state 2 in the interval of time Δt.

This transition rate, q_{12}, is the fundamental parameter in these continuous-time processes, somewhat analogous for the continuous-time stochastic process to the transition probability in the usual discrete-time process.[4] The nature of the process is best seen by calculating what happens over time. Suppose that in a system governed by eq. (2.3) there are at time zero n_{10} occupants in state 1, and we wish to find out just how many of these occupants will still be in state 1 at the end of time t. Then by definition of the process,

$$\frac{dn_1}{dt} = -q_{12}n_1 \tag{2.5}$$

That is, the (expected) decrease in the number of occupants per unit time is equal to the transition rate multiplied by the number of occupants left in that state at that time. Integrating this equation over the time interval 0 to t will give the number of original occupants still left, n_{1t}, relative to the number who were initially there, n_{10}.

Integrating eq. (2.5) over the interval 0 to t gives[5]

$$\int_{n_{10}}^{n_{1t}} \frac{dn_1}{n_1} = -\int_0^t q_{12}\,dt \tag{2.6}$$

$$\ln\frac{n_{1t}}{n_{10}} = -q_{12}t \tag{2.7}$$

Or, taking antilogarithms of both sides and letting $p_t = n_{1t}/n_{10}$, the expected proportion of original occupants left at time t, we obtain

$$p_t = e^{-q_{12}t} \tag{2.8}$$

If we know q_{12}, then the expected proportion p_t for any time period t can be calculated by use of eq. (2.8). Or if, conversely, we have an estimate of p_t, eq. (2.8) can be used to estimate q_{12}.

Returning to the example used earlier, we recall that there are shifts in *both* directions. In such a situation one can ask another very different question: what is the equilibrium distribution, that is, the number in state 1 and the number in state 2 at equilibrium? For there will be some point at which the expected flow between states in one direction equals that in the other. This is the point of aggregate equilibrium, in which any individual may shift from one state to another, but the distribution remains the same. This is a

[4] The directly analogous quantity in a continuous-time process to the p_{ij}'s of a discrete-time process is another quantity, derived from the q_{ij}'s. See Appendix 1 to this chapter.

[5] The symbol "ln" will be used in place of $\log_e$, since all logarithms in this book are natural logarithms, to the base e.

frequently occurring situation in surveys, and is illustrated by the hypothetical "turnover table" of Table 4.2, earlier in the chapter.

In a two-state process with two-way flow, each individual is characterized by two transition rates, q_{12} and q_{21}, the transition rate out of state 1 into state 2, and the transition rate out of state 2 into state 1, respectively. Then if there are n_1 and n_2 persons at any time in states 1 and 2, respectively, the (expected) number leaving state 2 and entering state 1 during any time dt is $q_{21}n_2 dt$, while the number leaving state 1 and entering state 2 is $q_{12}n_1 dt$. The rate of change in n_1 (i.e., in the number of persons whose closest friend is in their shop) and in n_2 (the number whose closest friend is not in their shop) is described by eq. (2.9):

$$\frac{dn_1}{dt}(= -\frac{dn_2}{dt}) = q_{21}n_2 - q_{12}n_1 \qquad (2.9)$$

That is, first the net gain by state 1 is equal to the net loss by state 2. This gain (or loss) by state 1 is equal to the number *entering* per unit time ($q_{21}n_2$) minus the number *leaving* ($q_{12}n_1$). When there are only two states to the system, as in this case, the rate-of-change equation for each state includes only the shifts across one boundary; when there are more states, as in most of the models to come, the relation becomes more complicated.

The behavior of such a process over time may be seen by integrating eq. (2.9) to find the expected number in state 1 at any time, n_{1t}. This integration, carried out in Appendix 2 to this chapter, results in the following expression for n_{1t}:

$$n_{1t} = n\frac{q_{21}}{q_{21} + q_{12}}(1 - e^{-t(q_{21} + q_{12})}) + n_{10}e^{-t(q_{21} + q_{12})} \qquad (2.10)$$

where $n = n_1 + n_2$ (constant over time), and
n_{10} = number in state 1 at time zero.

The change in n_{1t} over time is exemplified in Figure 4.1, which shows the graph of n_{1t} under two extreme conditions: when everyone is initially in state 2 ($n_{10} = 0$), and when everyone is initially in state 1 ($n_{10} = n$). Whichever of these initial conditions exists, there is a regular change through time leading to the same asymptote. If the initial state were somewhere between these two, then the graph of n_{1t} would lie somewhere between the two extreme curves shown in Figure 4.1.

The equilibrium value of n_{1t} may be seen from either of two relations. First, looking at eq. (2.10), and letting $t \to \infty$, then eq. (2.10) reduces to

$$n_{1\infty} = n\frac{q_{21}}{q_{21} + q_{12}} \qquad (2.11)$$

Alternatively, the equilibrium state may be found by considering the differential equation (2.9). Equilibrium comes when the number of persons shifting

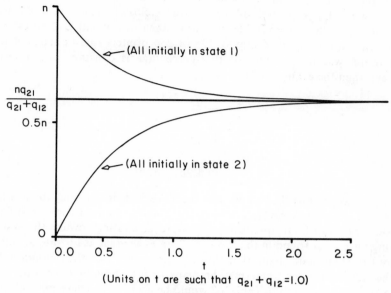

(Units on t are such that $q_{21} + q_{12} = 1.0$)

Figure 4.1

from state 1 to state 2 equals the number shifting from state 2 to state 1, so that eq. (2.9) reduces to

$$\frac{dn_1}{dt} = 0 \qquad (2.12)$$

When this is so, then

$$0 = q_{21}n_{2e} - q_{12}n_{1e} \qquad (2.13)$$

where n_{ie} is the number of persons in state i at equilibrium; or

$$\frac{n_{1e}}{n_{2e}} = \frac{q_{21}}{q_{12}} \qquad (2.14)$$

or

$$\frac{n_{1e}}{n_{1e} + n_{2e}} = p_e = \frac{q_{21}}{q_{12} + q_{21}} \qquad (2.15)$$

That is, the expected proportion of persons in state 1 at equilibrium, p_e, is given by the ratio of transition rates shown on the right side of eq. (2.11) or (2.15). This quantity, p_e, can also be thought of as the probability, for a given individual, that he will be found in state 1, or the expected proportion of time that he spends in state 1.

Thus if one knows the q_{ij}'s for a system like this, he can predict the state of aggregate equilibrium, as indicated in eq. (2.15). On the other hand, if one knew p_e, the proportion of persons whose closest friend was in the shop, and this proportion were stable over time, then this would give an estimate of the ratio of q_{ij}'s. For example, 135 of 250 printers questioned said their best friend was in the shop. If this percentage is constant over repeated surveys, then the estimate of the ratio of q_{ij}'s is

$$\frac{135}{115} = \frac{q_{21}}{q_{12}}$$

$$= 1.2$$

or

$$q_{21} = 1.2q_{12}$$

That is, if we assume that all printers are alike in their tendency to have their closest friend in the shop (q_{21}) or in their tendency to have their closest friend outside the shop (q_{12}), then everyone's rate of shifting toward the state of having his closest friend in the shop is 1.2 times as great as his rate of shifting away from this state. Note that this says nothing about the *absolute* values of the transition rates; there may be many or few shifts in a given period of time. Over-time data as in Table 4.2 would be necessary to determine absolute sizes of q_{ij}'s. Cross-sectional data can at best tell only the *relative* sizes of the rates, and this under the assumption of aggregate equilibrium.

It is evident, of course, that an assumption that all printers are alike in their tendency to have their closest friend on the job is not true. There are many attributes—attitudes of shopmates, chances for interacting with them on the job and off, chances for interacting with nonshopmates, and others—which affect their friendships. Thus if the model is to be of use, it must be elaborated to take into account these determining variables—or, rather, these determining attributes, since most of them are not numerically measurable, but are only discrete attributes. It is such an elaboration which brings us into the kind of problems with which much of social theory and social research are concerned. However, before developing these models, it will be helpful to review two of the many uses that this type of model has had in other branches of science. These examples should illustrate both the model's simplicity and its broad applicability.

3. EXAMPLES OF USE OF CONTINUOUS-TIME, DISCRETE-STATE MODELS

3.1 Chemical reactions

Chemistry is one science that, like sociology, is often concerned with discrete states rather than continuous variables. Many chemical problems concern chemical reactions, that is, movement between two states, or equilibrium between two (or more) states. Since these reactions are at the atomic or molecular level, the movement between states is a movement of very large numbers of particles (i.e., atoms, molecules). As a consequence, the classical chemical equations are not concerned with the stochastic properties of the process, and are simply equations for expected values. Modern physics and chemistry must, however, be concerned with the stochastic nature of the process.

Consider a very simple one-way chemical reaction, such as the decomposition of a gas:

$$A \rightarrow B$$

where A is the initial gas, B is the decomposition product(s). If the reaction is a simple one, without complex intermediate steps, then the rate of the reaction is directly proportional to the concentration, C, of the reacting substance:

$$\frac{dC}{dt} = -kC \tag{3.1}$$

that is, the rate of decrease in concentration of the reacting gas is proportional to its concentration at that time. The parameter k, called the specific reaction rate of the reaction, is precisely analogous to the transition rate, q_{ij}, discussed above. The equation for finding the amount of reacting substance left after time t is given by integrating eq. (3.1):

$$\int_{C_0}^{C_t} \frac{dC}{C} = -\int_0^t k\,dt \tag{3.2}$$

$$\ln\frac{C_t}{C_0} = -kt \tag{3.3}$$

or

$$C_t = C_0 e^{-kt} \tag{3.4}$$

where C_0 is the initial concentration of the reactant and C_t is the concentration after time t. This example is the simplest kind of problem in chemical kinetics; most reactions are more complicated than that of eq. (3.1). However, this simple case illustrates how basic this continuous-time discrete-space model in its deterministic form is for chemical kinetics.

Another large class of problems in physical chemistry besides reaction rates (i.e., chemical kinetics) is that of chemical *equilibria*. Suppose the reaction in the preceding case were a reversible one:

$$A \rightleftharpoons B$$

Then one would be concerned not only with the rate at which the reaction occurred, but also with the concentrations of the two substances at equilibrium. If the specific reaction rate in the forward direction is k, and in the backward direction k', then the equation which characterizes the changes in concentration of the two substances is

$$-\frac{dC_A}{dt} = \frac{dC_B}{dt} = kC_A - k'C_B \qquad (3.5)$$

where C_A and C_B are the concentrations of the two substances at any time. At equilibrium, the changes in concentration are by definition zero, so that

$$0 = kC_A - k'C_B \qquad (3.6)$$

or

$$\frac{C_{Ae}}{C_{Be}} = \frac{k'}{k} \qquad (3.7)$$

where C_{Ae} and C_{Be} are the concentrations of A and B at equilibrium. The ratio k'/k for the reversible reaction is usually treated as a single constant,

$$\frac{k'}{k} = K$$

These illustrations of very simple problems in physical chemistry and the kinds of equations developed to deal with them indicate the broad applicability of the model introduced earlier. It is of course true that physical chemists, dealing with aggregates of billions of molecules, did not need to make their model a stochastic one, and could always treat the phenomena as determinate; we, on the other hand, cannot make such an assumption but must at some points take into account random variability.[6] Despite this difference, the fundamental elements of the model are alike, and stand in contrast to the models of relations between continuous variables discussed earlier, and also in contrast to the discrete-time stochastic models.

3.2 The Poisson process

A second example of the use of models of this general sort is the Poisson process. It has been used to account for such disparate phenomena as the clustering of German V-2 bomb hits in London and the clustering of bacteria in sections of a Petri dish (see Feller, 1957, p. 150). Its derivation is rather simple, and goes somewhat as follows:

(a) Assume that there is a large number of individuals (or city blocks,

---

[6] For certain problems in physical chemistry, such as the decomposition of a radioactive substance, the stochastic nature of the process must be taken into account. Also there are numerous recent problems, such as the movement of colloidal particles in and out of an observed area, in which the process must be treated as a stochastic one. Models of Brownian motion are of this same sort, except that they are continuous-time, *continuous-space* stochastic processes. See Chandrasekhar (1954) for a presentation of many of these models.

or square sections in a Petri dish, etc.) and a certain kind of event which can happen to them (e.g., be kicked by a mule, be hit by a V-2 bomb, be occupied by a bacterium). The states of these individuals or city blocks, or sections, may be labelled 0, 1, 2, ..., representing the number of events which have occurred to the unit in question (the individual, or city block, etc.). Initially each unit is in state 0, and is subject to the possibility of a recurrent event.

(b) The likelihood of this event happening in any unit of time is alike for all these individuals or other units, and can be estimated by the total number of events which occurred over the span of time divided by the number of individuals to which the event happened. The resulting parameter is the transition rate q_{ij} (though here the subscripts can be dropped, since q_{ij} is identical for all states i and j).

(c) After the event occurs to an individual, putting him in a new state, he is immediately subject to the same chance of a new event, with no delay.

Given these assumptions, one can calculate the expected proportion of persons to whom no events have occurred, those to whom one event has occurred, and so on. The calculation will not be carried out here (see Chapter 10), but the basic equations governing the process are of the same general form as eq. (2.1):

$$\frac{dp_0}{dt} = - qp_0 \tag{3.8}$$

$$\frac{dp_i}{dt} = - qp_i + qp_{i-1} \quad (i > 0) \tag{3.9}$$

The equation for p_i resulting from these assumptions is the familiar Poisson distribution:

$$p_i = \frac{(qt)^i e^{-qt}}{i!} \tag{3.10}$$

where p_i = probability of an individual's being in state i at time t (or expected proportion of individuals in state i at time t); and
i = number of events which have occurred to individual (i = 0, 1, 2, . . .).

The Poisson process gives rise to a multistate model, and in other ways is not directly analogous to the basic two-state model considered here. However, in the conception of the movement across each boundary, and the transition rate governing this movement, the two processes are alike.

These two examples, chemical reactions and the Poisson distribution, indicate the wide scope of the continuous-time discrete-space process; it has had a long and honorable history in other branches of science as well. It seems likely that models based on this process will become of central importance to mathematical theory in sociology and psychology.

4. RELATIONS BETWEEN DICHOTOMOUS ATTRIBUTES: THE PARTITIONING OF q_{ij}

In the example of having "closest friend in the shop" discussed earlier, persons were characterized only in terms of the two mutually exclusive states. For such a model to deal with Homans' proposition, or the printer data, it must take into account *causal relations* between attributes, that is, the *effect* of one attribute on another. These effects are conceived to occur through the fundamental governing quantity in the process, the q_{ij}'s. In the absence of any classification of individuals beyond that on the dependent attribute, the transition rate q_{ij} is conceived to be a "random shock," due to all the various factors which have some effect on this dependent attribute. Some of these factors, say $x, y, z, \ldots$, have their effect in moving the individual from state 2 to state 1; others, say $u, v, w, \ldots$, have their effect in moving him from state 1 to state 2.

The transition rate is assumed to be a summation of all the shocks due to the various factors which act in that direction. Or, from another perspective, the transition rate q_{ij} is *partitioned* into the effects due to all the factors which move the individual from state i to state j. To state it formally,

$$q_{21k} = \alpha_x x_k + \alpha_y y_k + \alpha_z z_k + \ldots + \varepsilon_1' \tag{4.1}$$

where q_{21k} = transition rate from state 2 to state 1 for individual k ($q_{21k} \geqslant 0$).

$\quad x_k$ = the value of factor x for individual k; when x is an attribute, as in all cases to be considered until Chapter 8, x_k is either zero or one, the presence or absence of the attribute.

$\quad \alpha_x$ = the effect of attribute x in moving the individual from state 2 to state 1; ($\alpha_x \geqslant 0$).

$\quad \varepsilon_1'$ = the random shocks due to factors not explicitly considered, factors other than $x, y, z, \ldots$, ($\varepsilon_1' \geqslant 0$).

Similarly for q_{12k}:

$$q_{12k} = \beta_u u_k + \beta_v v_k + \beta_w w_k + \ldots + \varepsilon_2' \tag{4.2}$$

where the definitions are analogous to those above.[7]

---

[7] It should be noted here that it is possible for some of the same factors to affect both transition rates. Attribute x may have a nonzero coefficient α_x and a nonzero coefficient β_x. If the attribute, for example, is "being in the same school," and the dependent attribute is "liking," then there may be effects in both directions. Being in the same school tends, through some mechanisms, to make a person like the other; through other mechanisms, it tends to make him dislike the other. As the dependent and independent attributes become more abstract, more nearly theoretical concepts, their effects will tend to be in one direction only. In empirical investigations with cross-sectional data, the effects on the two transition rates are not separately identifiable, so that only the net effect in one direction will be considered, assuming that the attribute has an effect only in one direction.

Another contingency often arises, in which a classification occurs where state i of the

This partitioning of q_{ij} is clearly an assumption about the way in which the effects of attributes combine to produce an over-all transition rate. As will be evident in the development of the model, this assumption corresponds to our usual intuitive feelings about the way in which effects of attributes combine. In some cases, however, effects combine multiplicatively, both in our theoretical conception and in the empirical data, and those cases will be examined in the next chapter.

5. EFFECT OF ONE INDEPENDENT ATTRIBUTE IN THEORETICAL PROPOSITIONS AND EMPIRICAL DATA

Equations (4.1) and (4.2) give the underlying effects which together produce the total transition rates. But in both theoretical investigations and empirical ones, the supposedly causal attributes explicitly considered are only a small subset of all those which affect the dependent attribute. Thus, often only one or two independent attributes are explicitly considered, and the effects of the rest are incorporated into the random shock. For the Homans' proposition about the effect of interaction upon friendship, there is only one independent attribute. In that case, the general equations (4.1) and (4.2) take the following form:

(a) For individuals ($k = 1$) in interaction with the person in question,

$$q_{211} = \alpha + \varepsilon_1 \qquad \text{(toward liking the person)} \qquad (5.1)$$
$$q_{121} = \qquad \varepsilon_2 \qquad \text{(toward not liking the person)} \qquad (5.2)$$

(b) For individuals ($k = 2$) not in interaction with the person in question,

$$q_{212} = \qquad \varepsilon_1 \qquad \text{(toward liking the person)} \qquad (5.3)$$
$$q_{122} = \qquad \varepsilon_2 \qquad \text{(toward not liking the person)} \qquad (5.4)$$

The *effect* of interaction upon friendship, as specified in the proposition, occurs via the coefficient α; the effects of all other factors are lumped into ε_1 and ε_2.

This formalization does more than simply translate Homans' theoretical proposition; it is equally at home with the qualitative empirical data of sociological research. For example, consider the data from the printer study, mentioned earlier in the chapter. These data exemplify the kind of data to which Homans' proposition should apply. In these data, the type of job becomes an indicator of more interaction or less, through external knowledge

---

independent attribute has an effect on q_{12}, and state j has an effect on q_{21}. In that case, the attribute affecting q_{21}, say u, is the same attribute as that affecting q_{12}, say x, but with a negative orientation. For example, suppose the independent attribute is religion, with only the two classifications, Protestant and Catholic. If Protestantism adds to q_{12}, while Catholicism adds to q_{21}, then the attribute x (for q_{12}) is one if Protestant, zero if Catholic, while u (for q_{21}) is one if Catholic, zero if Protestant. Such cases will be discussed when they arise in examples.

that the job of a handman allows more interaction than that of a linotype operator. The model is as diagrammed in Figure 4.2, where the transition rates q_{ij} are partitioned as for the Homans' proposition, eqs. (5.1)–(5.4).

Given the conceptualization, then it is possible to estimate the parameters α, ε_1, and ε_2 from data. There are essentially three kinds of data: the cross-section data of a survey; data at two or more discrete points in time; and continuous observation over time. The first situation, using a cross-sectional survey, occurs in the present example, shown in Table 4.1. The implicit assumption ordinarily made in interpreting such data is that they exhibit

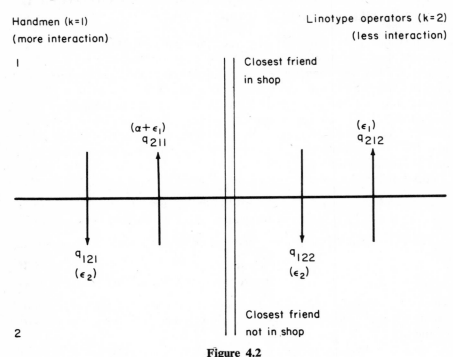

Figure 4.2

aggregate equilibrium; thus, as discussed in Section 2, $n_1 q_{12} = n_2 q_{21}$ for both sets of persons ($k = 1$ and $k = 2$). Using the partitioning of q_{ij}'s given in eqs. (5.1)–(5.4), the following equations are obtained:

(a) for $k = 1$ (more interaction),

$$\varepsilon_2 n_{1e} = (\alpha + \varepsilon_1)n_{2e} \tag{5.5}$$

(b) for $k = 2$ (less interaction),

$$\varepsilon_2 n_{1e} = \varepsilon_1 n_{2e} \tag{5.6}$$

For both groups, estimates of p_e are obtained from Table 4.1. Therefore, by solving eqs. (5.5) and (5.6) for the relative values of α, ε_1, and ε_2, in terms of n_{1e} and n_{2e}, these parameters of effect and random shock may be estimated. There are several ways of expressing the resulting estimates of α, ε_1, and ε_2: expressing two in terms of the third, or expressing the value of each relative to the total of all three. The latter method will be used, giving estimates of three quantities, $\alpha/(\alpha + \varepsilon_1 + \varepsilon_2)$, $\varepsilon_1/(\alpha + \varepsilon_1 + \varepsilon_2)$, and $\varepsilon_2/(\alpha + \varepsilon_1 + \varepsilon_2)$, which sum to 1.0. Using the notation

$$p_{1e} = \frac{n_{1e}}{n_{1e} + n_{2e}} \qquad (k = 1)$$

$$p_{2e} = \frac{n_{1e}}{n_{1e} + n_{2e}} \qquad (k = 2)$$

gives

$$p_{1e} = \frac{\alpha + \varepsilon_1}{\alpha + \varepsilon_1 + \varepsilon_2} \tag{5.7}$$

$$p_{2e} = \frac{\varepsilon_1}{\varepsilon_1 + \varepsilon_2} \tag{5.8}$$

With eqs. (5.7) and (5.8), each of the desired quantities may be obtained in terms of the p_{ke}'s, which are estimated by the data:

$$\frac{\alpha}{\alpha + \varepsilon_1 + \varepsilon_2} = \frac{p_{1e} - p_{2e}}{1 - p_{2e}} \tag{5.9}$$

$$\frac{\varepsilon_1}{\alpha + \varepsilon_1 + \varepsilon_2} = \frac{p_{2e}(1 - p_{1e})}{1 - p_{2e}} \tag{5.10}$$

$$\frac{\varepsilon_2}{\alpha + \varepsilon_1 + \varepsilon_2} = 1 - p_{1e} \tag{5.11}$$

Thus the effect of the independent attribute (type of job, used as an indicator of interaction) on the dependent one (closest friend in shop) is given by eq. (5.9); the random shock toward state 1 (closest friend outside shop) is given by eq. (5.10); and the random shock toward state 2 (closest friend outside shop) is given by eq. (5.11). Using the estimates of p_{1e} and p_{2e} from Table 4.1, we obtain

$$\frac{p_{1e} - p_{2e}}{1 - p_{2e}} = .22 \qquad \text{(effect of independent attribute)}$$

$$\frac{p_{2e}(1 - p_{1e})}{1 - p_{2e}} = .38 \qquad \text{(random shocks toward state 1)}$$

$$1 - p_{1e} = .40 \qquad \text{(random shocks toward state 2)}$$

Because these parameters are given relative to their sum, they add to 1.0.

Thus each of the resulting estimates can be viewed as that part of the total variation in p_e attributable to each of the three causes: the independent attribute, and the unexplained or random shocks in the two directions.[8]

5.1 A different assumption about the kind of effect

In the above discussion, it is assumed that the independent attribute has an effect in only one direction. However, in many instances, it would be assumed that the two states of the independent attribute both have effects, but in the opposite direction.[9] For example, in response to the following question, asked in a study of the social system of the high school,

"If you had a chance for two similar jobs, one in this town, and one in another town the same size but in another state, which would you take?"

it was found that boys more often wanted to take a job in their home town than did girls (Coleman, 1961, p. 124). In this case, it is reasonable to assume, from the following data,

	Boys	Girls
This town	75.5%	61.9%
Other town	24.5	38.1
Number of cases	(4020)	(4134)

that the transition rate toward "this town" was increased for boys, *and* that the transition rate toward "other town" was increased for girls. This may or may not be empirically true (as could be determined by over-time data), but the model should not exclude this possibility. In terms of the fundamental assumption of this model,

	Dependent attribute	Independent attribute
State 1	This town	Boy
State 2	Other town	Girl

the equations which partition the q_{ij}'s become

$$q_{21k} = \alpha_x x_k + \varepsilon_1 \tag{5.12}$$

$$q_{12k} = \beta_u u_k + \varepsilon_2 \tag{5.13}$$

---

[8] It is interesting to note that Hovland's "index of effectiveness," developed for examining the effect of experimental films and correcting for the ceiling effect, is precisely the same as the measure of effect of eq. (5.9). (See Hovland, Lumsdaine, and Sheffield, 1949, Appendix.) See also Chapter 6 below.

[9] If the two states are exhaustive, then when they both have effects in the *same* direction, this reduces to the case examined before, with the parameter α equal to the difference between the two effects.

where x_k and u_k are the same attribute, sex, oriented in opposite directions:

$$x_1 = 1 \quad \text{and} \quad u_1 = 0 \quad \text{(boy)}$$

$$x_2 = 0 \quad \text{and} \quad u_2 = 1 \quad \text{(girl)}$$

A diagrammatic representation of the model (after dropping subscripts on α_x and β_u) is shown in Figure 4.3.

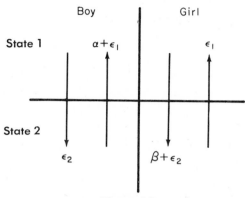

Figure 4.3

With over-time panel data, it is possible to obtain independent estimates for each of the four q_{ij}'s, and thus separate estimates for the two random shocks ε_1 and ε_2, and the two parameters of effect, α and β.[10] However, with cross-sectional data, this is not possible, and one must make some assumption to reduce the parameters of effect from two to one. The reasonable assumption is that $\alpha = \beta$, so that the model becomes that represented by Figure 4.4. The measure of α, ε_1, and ε_2 relative to the total of $\alpha + \varepsilon_1 + \varepsilon_2$ becomes somewhat different than before. The left side of Figure 4.4 is as before (see Figure 4.3), so that, as in eq. (5.7),

$$p_{1e} = \frac{\alpha + \varepsilon_1}{\alpha + \varepsilon_1 + \varepsilon_2} \tag{5.14}$$

where p_{1e} is the proportion of those in state 1 of the independent attribute (e.g., boys) in state 1 of the dependent attribute ("this town"). However, the corresponding proportion for the other side of the independent attribute (girls) is this time

$$p_{2e} = \frac{\varepsilon_1}{\alpha + \varepsilon_1 + \varepsilon_2} \tag{5.15}$$

[10] It is alternatively possible that for one of the states of the independent attribute (e.g., girls), there are added transition rates in *both* directions, and random shocks for the other state of the independent attribute. If, for example, girls shifted back and forth more frequently in both directions than did boys, this would be the case. In terms of the partitioning equations, (5.12) and (5.13), this means that $\alpha_x = 0$, but that u_k takes on values of, not zero and one, but some fraction and one.

In this case, the measure $\alpha/(\alpha + \varepsilon_1 + \varepsilon_2)$ is obtained merely by the difference between the proportions:

$$\frac{\alpha}{\alpha + \varepsilon_1 + \varepsilon_2} = p_{1e} - p_{2e} \qquad (5.16)$$

while the random shocks are

$$\frac{\varepsilon_1}{\alpha + \varepsilon_1 + \varepsilon_2} = p_{2e} \qquad (5.17)$$

and

$$\frac{\varepsilon_2}{\alpha + \varepsilon_1 + \varepsilon_2} = 1 - p_{1e} \qquad (5.18)$$

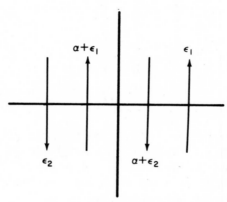

Figure 4.4

Thus if the underlying theoretical ideas correspond more to the "opposing effects" of this section, then the measures given in eqs. (5.16), (5.17), and (5.18) are appropriate. If they correspond more to the "presence or absence" of an effect, then the measures given earlier in eqs. (5.9), (5.10), and (5.11) are appropriate.[11] In the present example, using eqs. (5.16–5.18), we have

$$\frac{\alpha}{\alpha + \varepsilon_1 + \varepsilon_2} = .755 - .619 = .136 \qquad \text{(effect of sex)}$$

$$\frac{\varepsilon_1}{\alpha + \varepsilon_1 + \varepsilon_2} = .619 \qquad \text{(random shocks toward "this town")}$$

$$\frac{\varepsilon_2}{\alpha + \varepsilon_1 + \varepsilon_2} = 1 - .755 = .245 \qquad \text{(random shocks toward "other town")}$$

When there are two or more independent attributes, an excess of data

---

[11] Further examination of the alternative models is made in Chapter 6.

exists (e.g., a second attribute adds only one new parameter, but two new p_{ke}'s; a third adds only one more parameter, but four more p_{ke}'s; etc.). Such multivariate problems require special techniques for efficient use of the data; they will be examined in Chapter 6.

However, extension in another direction is important here. To this point, effects have always been from the "independent" attribute to the "dependent" one; yet in much social theory and research, *both* variables affect one another.

6. TWO-ATTRIBUTE SYSTEMS

The preceding examination considered only a two-state process, consisting of changes in one attribute. The independent attribute was introduced merely to classify individuals into subclasses for whom the transition rates were different. Yet it is only a short step from this to a process which mirrors the interdependence of two attributes. This requires only that we reverse the roles of the independent and dependent attributes, recognizing that attribute x not only affects y, but may change itself, and may even be affected by y. The result is a four-state system with nonzero transition rates on both attributes, as shown in Figure 4.5.

If there is an effect of each attribute on the other in the positive direction, then the q_{ij}'s are partitioned as follows:

(a) For changes in attribute y,

$$q_{21} = \alpha + \varepsilon_1 \qquad \text{(effect of } x_+ \text{ on } y \text{, plus random shock toward } y_+\text{)} \quad (6.1)$$

$$q_{12} = \qquad \varepsilon_2 \qquad \text{(random shock toward } y_-\text{)} \qquad\qquad\qquad\qquad (6.2)$$

$$q_{43} = \qquad \varepsilon_1 \qquad \text{(random shock toward } y_+\text{)} \qquad\qquad\qquad\qquad (6.3)$$

$$q_{34} = \qquad \varepsilon_2 \qquad \text{(random shock toward } y_-\text{)} \qquad\qquad\qquad\qquad (6.4)$$

(b) For changes in attribute x,

$$q_{31} = \beta + \eta_1 \qquad \text{(effect of } y_+ \text{ on } x \text{, plus random shock toward } x_+\text{)} \quad (6.5)$$

$$q_{13} = \qquad \eta_2 \qquad \text{(random shock toward } x_-\text{)} \qquad\qquad\qquad\qquad (6.6)$$

$$q_{42} = \qquad \eta_1 \qquad \text{(random shock toward } x_+\text{)} \qquad\qquad\qquad\qquad (6.7)$$

$$q_{24} = \qquad \eta_2 \qquad \text{(random shock toward } x_-\text{)} \qquad\qquad\qquad\qquad (6.8)$$

Such a system expresses the pair of qualitative statements,

$$x \text{ affects } y \text{ positively,}$$
$$y \text{ affects } x \text{ positively;}$$

or the roughly equivalent statements:

$$\text{As } x \text{ increases, } y \text{ increases,}$$
$$\text{As } y \text{ increases, } x \text{ increases.}$$

This is, of course, not the only configuration of effects possible; the general partitioning of the q_{ij}'s shown in eqs. (4.1) and (4.2) can take several forms other than that specified by eqs. (6.1)–(6.8). Some of these forms will be mentioned briefly in the subsequent chapters.

Such a two-attribute system is well exemplified by the propositions about interaction and friendship stated by Homans. In addition to his proposition about the effect of interaction upon friendliness, he says, in continuing the same sentence quoted on p. 103, "... and these sentiments will lead in turn

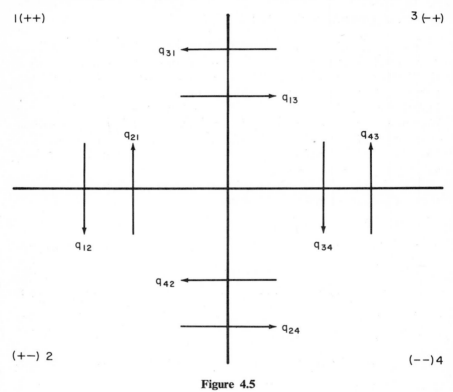

Figure 4.5

to further interactions, over and above the interactions of the external system" (p. 112). If interaction is attribute x and sentiments of liking, or friendliness, is attribute y, then this proposition implies that β is not zero in eq. (6.5). The random shocks η_1, are, in Homans' terms, the effects of the "external system" in imposing interactions, and β brings about further interactions when there are sentiments of liking (y_+).

Thus Homans' propositions imply a system of relations such as given by eqs. (6.1)–(6.8). The two parameters of effect, α and β, are the effects of interaction upon liking and liking upon interaction, with which Homans' propositions are concerned. In the absence of these parameters, the system would simply reduce to that shown in Figure 4.6.

It is not self-evident, but can easily be shown, that in this case there would be no relationship between liking and interaction at equilibrium. The

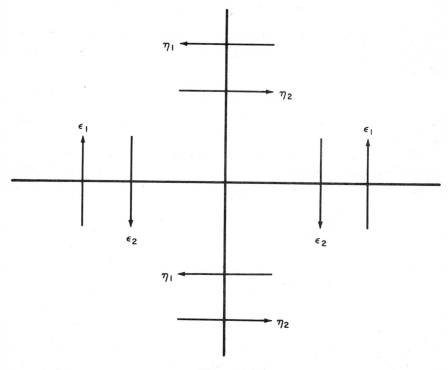

Figure 4.6

transitions between liking and not liking are independent of interaction, and the transitions between interaction and no interaction are independent of liking. If there were 1,000 people altogether, they might distribute themselves as in Table 4.3. If this were the distribution, with no correlation, then it

Table 4.3

		INTERACTION		
		Yes	No	
	Yes	60	140	200
SENTIMENTS OF LIKING				
	No	240	560	800
		300	700	1000

would be possible to estimate from the marginals the relative sizes of the random shocks to and from liking, and the relative sizes of those to and from interaction.[12] In this case,

$$\frac{\varepsilon_1}{\varepsilon_2} = \frac{200}{800} = \frac{140}{560} = \frac{60}{240} = .25$$

That is, the random shocks provided by the "external system" toward sentiments of liking are only .25 as great as those away from sentiments of liking. Similarly,

$$\frac{\eta_1}{\eta_2} = \frac{300}{700} = \frac{240}{560} = \frac{60}{140} = .43$$

The random shocks toward interaction are only .43 as great as those away from interaction.

However, suppose, in accordance with Homans' propositions, the distribution were as shown in Table 4.4. Here there is a positive correlation.

Table 4.4

		INTERACTION		
		Yes	No	
SENTIMENTS OF LIKING	Yes	110	90	200
	No	190	610	800
		300	700	1000

It might seem that we could estimate the relative values of ε_1 and ε_2 and of η_1 and η_2 as before, together with values of the effect parameters, α and β. However, this can no longer be done without ambiguity, simply because not enough information exists. There is no way of telling which variable affects the other; only that the variables are "correlated." It is of course possible to calculate a "measure of the relationship"; correlation coefficients are designed for this purpose.[13] However, no correlation coefficient can separate out from this table the effects of liking on interaction and the effects of interaction on liking.

[12] The lack of relationship shown in Table 4.3 does not explicitly imply a lack of effect. It is consistent with a system of wholly random shocks, and inconsistent with the model of effects given in eqs. (6.1)–(6.8). However, another set of effects, for example with x affecting y positively and y affecting x negatively, would be consistent with the lack of relationship shown in Table 4.3.

[13] Existing measures of association for dichotomous attributes do an exceedingly poor job of providing a measure of the over-all relation, if the relation is conceived as resulting from effects of the attributes on one another. This is one point which the present model can help remedy.

It is quickly evident that one cannot extricate the separate effects of two attributes which are interlocked in a system simply by use of these cross-sectional data. For example, both the following underlying systems could generate Table 4.4.

Model A (effect of interaction only)	Model B (effect of liking only)
$\varepsilon_1 = .010$	$\varepsilon_1 = .100$
$\varepsilon_2 = .123$	$\varepsilon_2 = .400$
$\eta_1 = .030$	$\eta_1 = .020$
$\eta_2 = .070$	$\eta_2 = .196$
$\alpha = .087$	$\alpha = 0$
$\beta = 0$	$\beta = .498$

Since either of these models will reproduce the data shown in Table 4.4, it is obviously impossible to use these data to decide how much interaction is affected by liking and vice versa. What is necessary in such a case is to examine changes over time. Heuristically, if we see that many people who at time zero are in state 2 (interaction, no liking) change to state 1 (interaction, liking) at time t, then we would decide that interaction does in fact tend to bring about liking. If we saw that people in state 3 tended to move to state 1 by time t, then we would say that liking does tend to bring about interaction. With numerical data, we could in fact estimate the parameters α and β, as well as the random shocks.

Thus over-time data become of crucial importance in extricating the effects of interdependent attributes bound together in a system. This is true of both continuous variables and dichotomous attributes. Economists and statisticians have made some attempts to draw such inferences from cross-sectional data when the variables are continuous, by observing the patterns of deviations from a straight-line relationship, but these attempts have met with no conspicuous success. And, as the example above indicates, such an attempt is impossible when the attributes are dichotomous. The next chapter will introduce such over-time considerations indicating how these data can be used to estimate parameters which are not identifiable on the basis of cross-sectional data alone.

APPENDIX 1—THE RELATION OF DISCRETE-TIME MARKOV PROCESSES TO THE CONTINUOUS-TIME PROCESS

A stochastic process is characterized by two kinds of probabilities: the probability at time t of *being in* state i, s_{it} and the probabilities of *going from* state i to state j, p_{ijt}. If the process is stationary, as are the ones considered in this chapter (but not in some of the other chapters), then p_{ijt}, the transition probabilities, are independent of t, and can be written p_{ij}. In the most familiar stochastic processes, the transitions occur at discrete time intervals. Such a process, with p_{ij}'s independent of t, is called a Markov chain. In a Markov chain with four states, the probability of being in state 1 after one time interval is given by

$$s_{11} = p_{11} s_{10} + p_{21} s_{20} + p_{31} s_{30} + p_{41} s_{40} \qquad (A.1)$$

That is, the probability of being in state 1 at time 1 is given by the probability of being in each state at time zero together with the transition probabilities of going from each state i to state 1. The system is characterized by four equations like eq. (A.1), one for each state. These four equations can be written in matrix notation as below; S is a column vector of state probabilities, s_{it}, and P is a matrix of transition probabilities, p_{ij}.[14]

$$S_1' = S_0' P \qquad (A.2)$$

$$
\begin{pmatrix} S_{11} \\ S_{21} \\ S_{31} \\ S_{41} \end{pmatrix}'
=
\begin{pmatrix} S_{10} \\ S_{20} \\ S_{30} \\ S_{40} \end{pmatrix}
\begin{pmatrix}
P_{11} & P_{21} & P_{31} & P_{41} \\
P_{12} & P_{22} & P_{32} & P_{42} \\
P_{13} & P_{23} & P_{33} & P_{43} \\
P_{14} & P_{24} & P_{34} & P_{44}
\end{pmatrix} \qquad (A.3)
$$

In such processes as this, the state of the system after a number of time periods is obtained by successive multiplication of the vector of states, S, by the transition matrix, P. For example, after five time periods, the state of the system would be found by using the fifth power of the transition matrix:

$$S_5' = S_0' P^5 \qquad (A.4)$$

If the processes discussed in this chapter were of this sort, with transitions operating at discrete time intervals, then they would be characterized by equations like eq. (A.2). Fortunately for some generalizations of the process to be discussed in later chapters, the processes do not act at discrete time intervals, but continuously through time. Thus these equations are not directly applicable. Instead, transition rates, q_{ij}, which are instantaneous

---

[14] A knowledge of matrix algebra is not required for following this discussion. It is only necessary to recognize matrix notation and to know what matrix multiplication is. Capital letters, such as S and P, are used to represent vectors and matrices. A prime ($'$), as found in eq. (A.2), means that before multiplication the rows and columns of the vector or matrix are interchanged. Matrix multiplication is the multiplication of each element in the row of the matrix or vector on the left with the corresponding element in the column of the matrix or vector on the right. The element in the new product matrix takes its row and column positions from the positions of the row and column which went to make it up. An example is

$$
\begin{pmatrix} a_{11} & a_{12} \\ a_{21} & a_{22} \end{pmatrix}
\begin{pmatrix} b_{11} & b_{12} \\ b_{21} & b_{22} \end{pmatrix}
=
\begin{pmatrix} a_{11}b_{11} + a_{12}b_{21} & a_{11}b_{12} + a_{12}b_{22} \\ a_{21}b_{11} + a_{22}b_{21} & a_{21}b_{12} + a_{22}b_{22} \end{pmatrix}
$$

rates of transfer, are defined for such a continuously acting system, and the equation analogous to (A.1) above is

$$\frac{ds_1}{dt} = q_{21}s_2 + q_{31}s_3 + q_{41}s_4 - (q_{12} + q_{13} + q_{14})s_1 \qquad (A.5)$$

where the subscript t is dropped from the s_{it}'s.

It might be parenthetically noted that many applications of Markov chains which use the discrete-time model are really processes which act continuously through time and would thus be more accurately described by the continuous-time model. In some processes, such as the ones under discussion in this chapter, use of the discrete-time model would lead to such problems as to finally break down altogether. It is likely that numerous processes which are not amenable to treatment with the discrete model can be handled well with the continuous one.

For a continuous-time process, the quantities directly analogous to the transition probabilities, p_{ij}, are transition probabilities $p_{ij}(t)$ which are a function of the time interval. That is, $p_{ij}(t)$ is the probability that, given an individual is in state i at time zero, he is in state j at time t. It can be shown (Doob, 1953, p. 236) that if these probabilities are a function only of the time interval t, they have the properties of transition probabilities in a Markov chain. Note that this transition probability, $p_{ij}(t)$ is conceptually different from the p_{ij}'s of the discrete model, for $p_{ij}(t)$ in effect sums up all the various paths by which the individual may have come from i to j, and all the times between zero and t at which jumps might have been made. Thus the $p_{ij}(t)$'s are not "fundamental" quantities for the continuous-time process, as are the p_{ij}'s for the discrete process, but are a result of the operation of q_{ij}'s over the period of time t. But how are the q_{ij}'s, which are instantaneous rates of transfer between states, related to the $p_{ij}(t)$'s? As Doob shows (p. 239) the q_{ij}'s are the derivatives of the $p_{ij}(t)$'s with respect to t as t approaches zero:

$$\lim_{t \to 0} \frac{p_{ij}(t)}{t} = \frac{dp_{ij}(0)}{dt} = q_{ij} \quad i \neq j \qquad (A.6)$$

The one exception is in the case of the diagonal elements, $p_{ii}(t)$, which represent the probability of being in state i at time t, given that one was in the same state at time zero. In that case,

$$\lim_{t \to 0} \frac{1 - p_{ii}(t)}{t} = \frac{-dp_{ii}(0)}{dt} = q_{ii} \qquad (A.7)$$

where q_{ii} is the sum of all the rates of shift out of cell i, that is,

$$q_{ii} = -\sum_{j \neq i} q_{ij} \qquad (A.8)$$

These equations show the relation of the $p_{ij}(t)$'s to the fundamental quantities governing the process, the q_{ij}'s.

We can see the relation between this continuous-time process and a discrete-time process in another way, by starting with a discrete-time process, and then letting the number of discrete-time periods within a given time span t approach infinity, while the probability of a jump on any one time period approaches zero.

Let us consider the simplest case, with a two-state Markov process (discrete-time) in which $p_{21} = 0$. Then

$$s_{11} = (1 - p_{12})s_{10} \qquad (A.9)$$

where s_{1i} is the probability of being in state 1 at period i. Similarly,

$$s_{12} = (1 - p_{12})s_{11}$$
$$= (1 - p_{12})^2 s_{10} \qquad (A.10)$$

and after n time periods,

$$s_{1n} = (1 - p_{12})^n s_{10} \qquad (A.11)$$

Then $(1 - p_{12})^n$ can be expanded, thus:

$$(1 - p_{12})^n = 1 - np_{12} + \frac{n(n-1)p_{12}^2}{2!} - \frac{n(n-1)(n-2)p_{12}^3}{3!} + \ldots \qquad (A.12)$$

And if we let n approach infinity and p_{12} approach zero in such a way that np_{12} remains finite and equals a constant, $q_{12}t$, then

$$(1 - p_{12})^n \rightarrow 1 - q_{12}t + \frac{(q_{12}t)^2}{2!} - \frac{(q_{12}t)^3}{3!} + \ldots \qquad (A.13)$$

$$\rightarrow e^{-q_{12}t}$$

or

$$s_{1n} = s_{1t} = s_{10}e^{-q_{12}t} \qquad (A.14)$$

By taking logarithms we obtain

$$\ln \frac{s_{1t}}{s_{10}} = -q_{12}t \qquad (A.15)$$

Next, differentiating gives

$$\frac{ds_1}{s_1} = -q_{12}\, dt \qquad (A.16)$$

and transposing results in

$$\frac{ds_1}{dt} = -q_{12}s_1 \qquad (A.17)$$

Thus if we take the discrete-time process in eq. (A.9) to the limit by dividing the time interval into an infinite number of periods, we obtain the corresponding continuous-time process.

APPENDIX 2—PROJECTION OF n_{1t} IN A TWO-STATE SYSTEM

Equation (2.9) is integrated as follows: First, since n_2 as well as n_1 is a function of t, $n - n_1$ is substituted for n_2 in eq. (2.9), since n is constant over time. Thus,

$$\frac{dn_1}{d\tau} = (n - n_1)q_{21} - n_1 q_{12} \tag{A.18}$$

$$\frac{dn_1}{nq_{21} - n_1(q_{21} + q_{12})} = d\tau \tag{A.18'}$$

Integrating over the time period 0 to t, gives

$$\int_{n_{10}}^{n_{1t}} \frac{dn_1}{nq_{21} - n_1(q_{21} + q_{12})} = \int_0^t d\tau \tag{A.19}$$

$$\frac{1}{q_{21} + q_{12}} \ln \left| \frac{nq_{21} - n_{10}(q_{21} + q_{12})}{nq_{21} - n_{1t}(q_{21} + q_{12})} \right| = t \tag{A.20}$$

or taking antilogarithms of both sides, we have

$$\left| \frac{nq_{21} - n_{10}(q_{21} + q_{12})}{nq_{21} - n_{1t}(q_{21} + q_{12})} \right| = e^{t(q_{21} + q_{12})} \tag{A.21}$$

The absolute value signs may be removed from eq. (A.21), since n_{1t} is a function of the other variables, and its value will be such as to make the left-hand quantity positive. The absolute value signs express the fact that if n_{10} is greater than its equilibrium value, n_{1t} will approach equilibrium from above, never going below it, while if n_{10} is less than its equilibrium value, which is $nq_{21}/(q_{21} + q_{12})$, n_{1t} will approach equilibrium from below. Removing the absolute value signs and solving eq. (A.21) for n_{1t} gives

$$n_{1t} = n\frac{q_{21}}{q_{21} + q_{12}} + \left(n_{10} - n\frac{q_{21}}{q_{21} + q_{12}} \right) e^{-t(q_{21} + q_{12})} \tag{A.22}$$

By rearranging terms, this becomes eq. (2.10).

CHAPTER 5

RELATIONS BETWEEN ATTRIBUTES: OVER-TIME DATA

1. INTRODUCTION TO OVER-TIME DATA: CONTINUOUS OBSERVATION

One of the primary aims in developing this continuous-time discrete-space model has been the desire to tie together the inferences about relationships which we make from cross-sectional data with the similar inferences we make from over-time data. The resulting model as presented above allows just such a tying-together: it is conceived in terms of processes operating over time, but it can equally mirror the states of aggregate equilibrium which our cross-sectional studies describe. Such a linkage is an important one, because all our analysis of "effects" of variables upon one another should ultimately be referable to the same theory about the processes involved, whether the data are cross-sectional or over-time.

The optimum kind of over-time data for our purposes would be continuous observation. Continuous observation would give directly the number of persons who had shifted within a given time interval from each state into each other state. For example, consider a simple two-state model with n_1 persons in state 1 at the start (time zero) and n_2 persons in state 2 at the start. If there were continuous observation of transitions, and if it were desired to estimate the transition rate from state 1 to state 2, it could be estimated directly by use of the following rate equation:

$$\frac{dn_{1t}^0}{dt} = - q_{12}n_{1t}^0 \tag{1.1}$$

where n_{1t}^0 is the number of original occupants of state 1 who remain at time t.

$$\ln \frac{n_{1t}^0}{n_{10}^0} = - q_{12}t \tag{1.2}$$

or

$$\ln p_{1t}^0 = - q_{12}t$$

where p_{1t}^0 is the expected proportion of original occupants of state 1 remaining at time t. If there were continuous observation, so that one could observe the number of original occupants who had made no transition at time t, then the quantity p_{1t}^0 would be directly observable at any time t, and the transition rate q_{12} could be immediately estimated. Besides allowing direct estimation of the transition rate, continuous observation would allow testing whether the continuous-time Markov assumptions actually fit the data, by estimating q_{12} at different intervals of time. The difficulty with observations at discrete points in time is that one can never know whether an individual who is in state 1 at both the first and second observations has remained there throughout the time period, or has taken two or more jumps—out of state 1, and then back again.

Although continuous-observation data is the optimum, ordinarily we must be content with observations at discrete points in time. For many practical problems this will still allow estimation of the transition rates, though not so directly as indicated above. The crucial variable in determining whether repeated observations will allow estimation of the transition rates (and thus of the effects of each attribute on the other) is the *spacing* of the observations.[1] Because most data are limited to repeated observations at discrete points in time, the discussion throughout most of this chapter will assume such data.

1.1 Notation

Notation here will be somewhat more extended than in the previous chapter, to maintain clarity and establish the correspondence between observed data and quantities in the model.

---

[1] For a general discussion of spacing of observations, see Simon (1957).

The observed quantities are as follows (assuming observations on the same individuals at two points in time):

$n_i.$ is the number giving response i at the first observation

$n_{.i}$ is the number giving response i at the second observation

n_{ij} is the number giving response i at the first observation
    and response j at the second observation.

In those cases where there are more than two observations on the same person, the number in states $i, j, \ldots, k$ at time points $t_1, t_2, \ldots, t_s$ will be labelled $n_{ij \ldots k}$. The numbers who have remained in state i through time t_m will be labelled $n_{i,m}$.

The quantities in the model that directly correspond to these observed quantities are as follows:

n_{i0} is the number in state i at time o

n_{it} is the expected number in state i at time t

n_{ijt} is the expected number in state i at time o and state j at time t.

In establishing a correspondence between observed data in a two-wave panel and the model, we use the observed data, $n_{.i}$, $n_{i.}$, and n_{ij}, as sample estimates of the expected values. Since the process is the sum of n identical and independent processes, these observed quantities are distributed binomially around the expected values.[2]

This correspondence also implies an identification of the state of the model with the response of the individual. This assumption will be discarded in the models of Chapter 13.

In obtaining approximate estimates of the values of q_{ij}, we will find it useful to define additional quantities that do not directly correspond to observed quantities, considering no jumps beyond the first:

$\overset{o}{n}_{it}$ is the number in state i at time o who have never left by time t. (As long as there is a transition into state i, this will be smaller than n_{iit}, which also includes occupants who have left and returned.)

$\overset{o}{n}_{ijt}$ is the number in state i at time o who made a jump to state j by time t. (This will in general be larger than n_{ijt}, since it includes those who have made further jumps and are no longer in state j at time t.)

In the exposition below, two methods will be given for estimating transition rates from two-wave panel data. One, which considers all possible jumps, will be called the "exact" method, since it employs the quantities n_{ijt}, which correspond directly to the observed data. The other, which considers only first jumps, will be called the "approximate" method, since it employs quantities $\overset{o}{n}_{ijt}$, which correspond only approximately to the observed data.

---

[2] Throughout these chapters, until Chapters 12 and 13, the assumption is made that all persons' transition rates are alike.

Both methods, of course, neglect sampling error, treating the observed data as expected values in the model.

2. "TURNOVER" IN A SINGLE ATTRIBUTE

Perhaps the simplest kind of over-time observation on the same people consists of two observations on one attribute. This gives tabulations of the sort shown in Tables 5.1 and 5.2. Table 5.1 is taken from a community study of voting in the 1948 presidential election (Berelson, Lazarsfeld, and McPhee, 1954) and Table 5.2 constitutes a control group in an experimental study of the effects of a transcribed orientation lecture upon soldiers in World War II (Hovland, Lumsdaine, and Sheffield, 1949, p. 299).

Table 5.1

		AUGUST, 1948, VOTE INTENTION		
		Rep.	*Dem.*	
JUNE, 1948, VOTE INTENTION	*Rep.*	429	32	461
	Dem.	38	142	180
		467	174	641

Table 5.2

ESTIMATES OF LENGTH OF PACIFIC WAR*

(SECOND QUESTIONNAIRE, 1 WEEK LATER)

		2 years or more	*1½ years or less*	
FIRST QUESTIONNAIRE, APRIL, 1945	*2 years or more*	53	12	65
	1½ years or less	9	107	116
		62	119	181

* This table is collapsed from the more extended tabulations in terms of half-year intervals presented in the source.

In both these turnover tables, there is not much shift between categories over time. And in both, there is near-stability in the aggregate, that is, in the marginal distributions. This suggests that in both cases, a state of aggregate equilibrium exists, with "random shocks" moving people from one state to another. In the first case, using only the marginal distributions in June (that is, not using the over-time data) we could estimate the relative sizes of these shocks:

$$\frac{q_{21}}{q_{12}} = \frac{n_1.}{n_2.} = \frac{461}{180} = 2.6 \tag{2.1}$$

where $n_1.$ = number of Republicans in June, and
$n_2.$ = number of Democrats in June.

However, when the internal changes are used, this allows an estimate of the absolute sizes of q_{21} and q_{12}. If the number of June Republicans who were still Republican at any time t between June and August are labelled n_{1t}^0, then the migration rate of these June Republicans into the Democratic camp is given by the equation

$$\frac{dn_{1t}^0}{dt} = -q_{12}n_{1t}^0 \tag{2.2}$$

Integrating this equation between the limits of time zero (June) and time t (August) gives

$$\ln \frac{n_{1t}^0}{n_{10}^0} = -q_{12}t \tag{2.3}$$

Since we know the value of n_{10}^0 (461 from Table 5.1) and can use n_{11} as a first approximation for n_{1t}^0 (429 from Table 5.1), this allows estimation of q_{12}:

$$q_{12} \approx -\frac{1}{t}\ln\frac{429}{461} = \frac{.072}{t}$$

If we measure time in terms of months, t is 2 (the two-month period between June and August interviews). Therefore $q_{12} = .036$ per month. Thus, on the basis of this estimate of q_{12}, for every person in the group at a given time, .036 persons per month migrated to the Democrats. A similar computation for migration of June Democrats into the Republican camp gives $q_{21} = .118$ per month.

Note that these data are treated just as in the continuous observation case of Section 1. This amounts to approximating the number who had remained Republican throughout the intervening period (n_{1t}^0) by the observed number who were Republican in both June and August. The errors resulting from this approximation will be discussed in Section 2.1 below, along with a method for exact estimation of the q_{ij}'s.

2.1 Exact estimates in two-state turnover

The procedure for estimating q_{12} and q_{21} given in eq. (2.3) is a general one useful for a multiple-state model. However, these estimates neglect all jumps beyond the first. Consequently, it is valuable, when possible, to give estimates that take all possible jumps into account. For a two-state model with panel data, this is possible without difficulty.

Turning back to eq. (2.10) of the preceding chapter (but using the notation of the present chapter), the equation can be written in two forms:

For those who start in state 1,

$$n_{11t} = n_{10}\frac{q_{21}}{q_{12} + q_{21}}\left(1 - e^{-t(q_{12}+q_{21})}\right) + n_{10}e^{-t(q_{12} + q_{21})} \tag{2.4}$$

For those who start in state 2,

$$n_{21t} = n_{20}\frac{q_{21}}{q_{12} + q_{21}}\left(1 - e^{-t(q_{12} + q_{21})}\right) + 0 \tag{2.5}$$

The data give sample estimates of n_{11t} and n_{21t} (n_{11} and n_{21}), and quantities by definition equal to n_{10} and n_{20} ($n_{1.}$ and $n_{2.}$). The first equation can be divided through by n_{10} and the second by n_{20}, and then the second can be subtracted from the first to give

$$p_{11t} - p_{21t} = e^{-t(q_{12} + {}_{21})} \tag{2.6}$$

or

$$q_{12} + q_{21} = -\frac{1}{t}\ln(p_{11t} - p_{21t}) \tag{2.7}$$

Substituting eqs. (2.6) and (2.7) into eq. (2.5) and simplifying (by using $p_{12t} = 1 - p_{11t}$) gives

$$p_{21t} = \frac{-q_{21}t}{\ln(1 - p_{12t} - p_{21t})}(p_{12t} + p_{21t}) \tag{2.8}$$

or, solving for q_{21},

$$q_{21} = p_{21t}\frac{-\ln(1 - p_{12t} - p_{21t})}{t(p_{12t} + p_{21t})} \tag{2.9}$$

Similarly, q_{12} equals p_{12t} times the fraction on the right. Since the panel data are direct sample estimates of the quantities in eq. (2.9), then they may be substituted to give

$$q_{21} = \frac{n_{21}}{n_{2.}}\frac{-\ln\left(1 - \dfrac{n_{12}}{n_{1.}} - \dfrac{n_{21}}{n_{2.}}\right)}{t\left(\dfrac{n_{12}}{n_{1.}} + \dfrac{n_{21}}{n_{2.}}\right)} \tag{2.10}$$

and similarly for q_{12}.

The estimates of q_{12} and q_{21} from Table 5.1 were .036 per month and .118 per month, respectively, by use of the approximate estimation with eq. (2.3). With the exact method,

$$q_{12} = \frac{32}{461} \; \frac{-\ln\left(1 - \dfrac{38}{180} - \dfrac{32}{461}\right)}{2\left(\dfrac{38}{180} + \dfrac{32}{461}\right)} = .041 \text{ per month}$$

and $q_{21} = .124$ per month.

The estimates of the transition rates have not been changed greatly, but it is interesting to note that the smaller has gained proportionately more (.041 / .036, compared to .124 / .118). The reason for this is that the larger transition rate, from state 2, sent back into state 1 some of those who migrated into state 2. These were not taken into account in the approximate method, which considered only one-jumps.

It is useful to compare the cross-sectional estimates (which give only the estimates of ratio q_{21}/q_{12}) from eq. (2.1) with the exact estimates from over-time data. These are as follows:

From cross-sectional data,

$$\frac{q_{21}}{q_{12}} = 2.6$$

From over-time data,

$$\frac{q_{21}}{q_{12}} = \frac{.124}{.041} = 3.0$$

These ratios differ somewhat. The over-time data estimates the transition to Republicans (state 1) to be slightly higher relative to the transition to Democrats than does the cross-sectional data. This is due to the slight trend toward the Republicans exhibited by Table 5.1. If the numbers of persons shifting in both directions had been exactly equal, then the cross-sectional data, representing a complete aggregate equilibrium, and the over-time data, would have given the same estimates.

The same near-equilibrium is evident in estimates of the length of the Pacific War shown in Table 5.2. The following estimates of q_{21} and q_{12} result from the approximate and exact methods [eqs. (2.3) and (2.10), respectively].

From cross-sectional data:

First questionnaire,

$$\frac{q_{21}}{q_{12}} = \frac{65}{116} = .56$$

Second questionnaire,

$$\frac{q_{21}}{q_{12}} = \frac{62}{119} = .52$$

From over-time data, using eq. (2.3) (approximate):

$$q_{12} \approx -\frac{1}{t} \ln \frac{53}{65} = .203 \text{ per week}$$

$$q_{21} \approx -\frac{1}{t} \ln \frac{107}{116} = .080 \text{ per week}$$

$$\frac{q_{21}}{q_{12}} \approx .39$$

From over-time data, using eq. (2.10) (exact):

$$q_{12} = \frac{12}{65} \frac{-\ln\left(1 - \dfrac{12}{65} - \dfrac{9}{116}\right)}{t\left(\dfrac{12}{65} + \dfrac{9}{116}\right)} = .214 \text{ per week}$$

$$q_{21} = \frac{9}{116} \frac{\ln\left(1 - \dfrac{12}{65} - \dfrac{9}{116}\right)}{t\left(\dfrac{12}{65} + \dfrac{9}{116}\right)} = .090 \text{ per week}$$

$$\frac{q_{21}}{q_{12}} = .42$$

Here a slight trend toward a shorter estimation of the war is evident in the data, and reflected in the discrepancy between the two cross-sectional estimates, and between these and the ratio of the over-time estimates. The ratio of the over-time estimates is identical to that which would be provided by the cross-sectional data after the system had reached the state of aggregate equilibrium toward which the data show it to be moving.

The cases above represent in a sense the sociologically and psychologically trivial situations: they treat only a single variable, on which the distributions remain nearly the same, with only a few internal shifts taking place. We are usually interested in *relations* between variables, and often interested in situations where there is some aggregate change, situations where there is a trend in one direction or the other. It is to the former of these more important cases that we turn next: relations between attributes.

3. AN INDEPENDENT AND DEPENDENT ATTRIBUTE: OVER-TIME DATA

The effect of a second attribute upon change in the first can be well illustrated by the experimental study mentioned above. One group of soldiers was exposed to a transcribed lecture program designed to convince them of the length and difficulty which lay ahead in the Pacific War. The control group, tabulated in Table 5.2 above, was not exposed to the program. Thus the independent variable is hearing or not hearing the program and the dependent variable is the change in prediction of the length of the war. The experimental group is shown in Table 5.3.

Table 5.3

CHANGES IN PREDICTION OF LENGTH OF PACIFIC WAR—
EXPERIMENTAL GROUP PREDICTION

		SECOND QUESTIONNAIRE, IMMEDIATELY AFTER PROGRAM		
		2 years or more	*1½ years or less*	
FIRST QUESTIONNAIRE, ONE WEEK	*2 years or more*	72	5	77
BEFORE PROGRAM	*1½ years or less*	48	80	128
		120	85	205

In this experimental group, much more change is evident than the "random shocks" found in the control group. The effect in the direction of predicting a longer war is quite evident. Between the two questionnaires, somewhat different effects were operative than before. Using the model of the preceding chapter, the transition rates would be as indicated in the following diagrams.

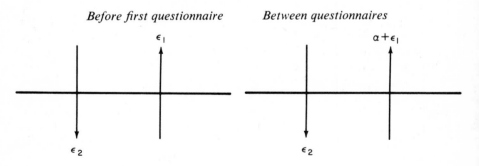

Before first questionnaire   *Between questionnaires*

The estimated ratio of the random shocks operating before the program is not far different from that estimated for the control group. This is to be expected, since they are random samples from the same population:

$$\frac{q_{21}}{q_{12}} = \frac{\varepsilon_1}{\varepsilon_2} = \frac{n_1.}{n_2.} = \frac{77}{128} = .60$$

However, the estimate of the transition rates operative over the period of the experiment is quite different:

By approximate method [eq. (2.3)],

$$\ln\frac{n_{11}}{n_{1.}} \approx \ln\frac{n_{1t}^0}{n_{10}^0} = -q_{12}t \tag{3.1}$$

$$q_{12} = \varepsilon_2 \approx -\frac{1}{t}\ln\frac{72}{77} = .066 \text{ per week}$$

$$q_{21} = \alpha + \varepsilon_1 \approx -\frac{1}{t}\ln\frac{80}{128} = .430 \text{ per week}$$

By exact method of eq. (2.10),

$$q_{12} = \varepsilon_2 = \frac{5}{77}\frac{-\ln\left(1 - \frac{5}{77} - \frac{48}{128}\right)}{t\left(\frac{5}{77} + \frac{48}{128}\right)} = .086 \text{ per week}$$

$$q_{21} = \alpha + \varepsilon_1 = \frac{48}{128}\frac{-\ln\left(1 - \frac{5}{77} - \frac{48}{128}\right)}{t\left(\frac{5}{77} + \frac{48}{128}\right)} = .493$$

COMPARISON OF THE EXACT OVER-TIME ESTIMATES FOR THE EXPERI-
MENTAL AND CONTROL GROUPS

	Control	Experimental	Difference
Shift to 2 + years (q_{21})	.090	.493	+.403
Shift to 1½ − years (q_{12})	.214	.086	−.128

The effect of the program as evidenced by these data was apparently to increase the transition rate toward prediction of longer duration of the war, and to reduce the transition rate toward predicting a shorter duration among those whose predictions were already higher. This appears inconsistent with the model presented above for the effects of such a stimulus. According to that model, the stimulus does not inhibit the random shocks acting in opposition to the stimulus. Its action is solely in adding to the random shocks which were already there. Thus the model of additive effects shown in the diagram above is consistent with the increase of q_{21} by .403 (thus yielding an estimate of α, the effect of the program, as .403); but it is not consistent with the decrease of q_{12} by .128. This result suggests that the model of an added effect α in the direction of the stimulus is not adequate to account for the effects of an experimental stimulus such as this.

However, further examination of the experimental situation shows a fact neglected above: the program's effects and the random shocks were not coincident in time. The random shocks acted over the period of a week, just as did those of the control group interviewed at an interval of a week. It was at the *end* of this week, immediately before the second interview, that the experimental group was given the program. The program could hardly have inhibited the random shocks which shifted people during the period of the week, because it occurred after they had already shifted.

In a more precise analysis of these data, it is necessary to use the transition rates estimated from the control group to estimate the number who moved during the period of the week. This makes it possible to estimate the actual condition of the subjects at the time of application of the stimulus. Use of these data show that at the end of the week, just prior to the program, the expected transition of the experimental group would have given turnover Table 5.4. This table indicates that the state of affairs at the time of the

Table 5.4

PREDICTED TURNOVER TABLE FOR EXPERIMENTAL GROUP BETWEEN
FIRST INTERVIEW AND BEGINNING OF EXPERIMENTAL PROGRAM

	2 years or more	1½ years or less	
2 *years or more*	63	14	77
1½ *years or less*	10	118	128
	73	132	205

program was not at all what had been assumed above. Twenty-four persons had defected from their initial positions. The estimate of the program's effect can be made by virtue of these assumptions: (a) The time period between the beginning of the program and the second interview (see Table 5.3) is short enough for the random shocks to be neglected (this is a reasonable assumption, for the period of time is at most a few hours compared to a week for which the random shocks were estimated). (b) All the effects of the program were toward predicting a longer duration of the war. This assumption is necessary because there is no turnover table between the estimated data at the beginning of the program and the actual data at the end.

Thus there is one parameter to calculate, q_{21} over the period of the program. The estimating equation is (2.10) which reduces, in this case of unidirectional transitions, to become identical to the approximate equation, (3.1). The estimate of n_2. is $118 + 14$, or 132. The estimate of n_{21} is given by Tables 5.3 and 5.4 $(48 - 10) + (14 - 5) = 47$. Thus:

$$q_{21} = \frac{47}{132} \frac{-\ln\left(1 - \frac{47}{132}\right)}{t\frac{47}{132}} = .440 \text{ per stimulus}$$

Alternatively, it is possible to obtain separate estimates of q_{21}, one based on the 118 who remained in state 2 up until the time of the program, and one based on the 14 who had moved to state 2 during the week before the program. These are

$$q_{21} = \frac{38}{118} \frac{-\ln\left(1 - \frac{38}{118}\right)}{t\frac{38}{118}} = .389 \text{ per stimulus}$$

$$q_{21} = \frac{9}{14} \frac{-\ln\left(1 - \frac{9}{14}\right)}{t\frac{9}{14}} = 1.03 \text{ per stimulus}$$

The difference between these estimates indicates that the ones who had shifted to state 2 during the week were more than three times as likely to shift to state 1 as the ones who had been and remained in state 2 until the program. That is, as one might expect, this is not a homogeneous system of persons. To look at it a little differently, it is possible to predict, on the basis of the program's effect on those initially in state 2, what its effect should be in "bringing back to the fold" the 14 persons who had strayed into state 2:

$$n_{21} = n_{20}(1 - e^{-q_{21}t}) = 14(1 - e^{-.389}) = 4.5$$

Thus, on the basis of the transition rate for those 118 persons who were originally in state 2, one would predict that there should be 4 or 5 persons of the 14 who had shifted to state 2 during the week via random shocks, who would be shifted back by the program. There were instead 9, showing the greater effect of the program on those who had originally been in state 1.

Note that in these estimates of q_{21} the value of t is not one week as before, but instead is the length of exposure to the stimulus. This also makes clear what was not evident in the earlier analysis: this transition rate is not directly comparable to the random shocks, because of the different times over which they are defined; and it is presumably not a permanent effect parameter added to the random shocks, but existed only during the period when the stimulus was applied. Section 5 examines this matter further, but at this point the question can be raised, Did the program act as a stimulus which provided a temporary α, a transition rate throughout the period of the program itself, or did it introduce a transition rate which is now permanently there? After the program, is the attitude characterized by the previous random shocks, ε_1 and ε_2 alone, or by a new transition rate toward state 1 of $\alpha + \varepsilon_1$? If the α were only temporary, acting through the period of the stimulus, then the opinion distribution should slowly regress to its previous equilibrium. It would be only a matter of time until the old distribution re-established itself again. On the other hand, the introduction of a permanent parameter, α, into the system, would lead to a new equilibrium, in which the proportion estimating a longer war would be much greater than it initially was.

A third questionnaire, at some interval of time after the program, would answer this problem. If the effect of the program was only to provide a temporary α, then a later observation should show an erosion of the short-term effect, in accordance with the transition rates ε_1 and ε_2. However, if the program permanently introduced an added transition rate, α, this third observation should show a continuing change in the direction of the longer expectancy of war. In neither case, however, would we expect the "effects" of the program as shown in the post-program questionnaires to be stable. They should either decrease or increase.

For this experiment, no third questionnaire was administered, so it is not possible to determine the nature of the program's effect—whether it was simply a direct stimulus, acting only through the period of time of the program, or whether it acted indirectly, introducing a permanent change in the transition rates. However, other experiments in this same series of studies did examine short-term and long-term effects of transcribed programs and films (one week and nine weeks after the experimental stimulus), with some interesting results. For some items, there was a usual erosion of effect over the nine-week period, indicating that the experimental stimulus had made its temporary impact, and then random shocks were bringing about a reversion to the earlier state. But with other items, there was a "sleeper" effect: little effect was evident one week after the stimulus, but there was a considerable effect after nine weeks. In terms of the interpretation of our model, the experiments did two very different things for the two sets of items: for some, it acted as a direct stimulus for change, a transition rate lasting only through the period of the film or program; for others it acted indirectly, by introducing a new transition rate into the system, and "leaving it there," so to speak, to work at its own speed in creating change.

But why should some items show one kind of effect, while others show a different effect? A glance at the items themselves suggests the answer: as the authors point out, it is the *factual* items, based on specific information in the films or transcriptions, for which the immediate effects take place; it is attitude items, especially the more general attitudes, for which the "sleeper effect" occurred.

These results suggest the following over-all effect of the films and transcriptions: they directly change the individual's state of factual information, his cognitive state; then this changed cognitive state in turn acts, through a period of time, to change the attitudes. Attitudes are generally more difficult to change than are informational states, for they seem held in place by some motivational elements. Perhaps what happens is that the new state of information is felt to be inconsistent with the attitude, and over a period of time this inconsistency is resolved. Part of the reduction in inconsistency might come by forgetting some of these new facts which are inconsistent with one's attitude, but part might come by a modification of the attitude itself. Thus as long as this new cognitive state remains (i.e., is not forgotten), the new transition rate, α, will remain.

4. OVER-TIME DATA WITHOUT INTERNAL CHANGES

In estimating the effects of the experiments above, it was assumed that "internal" changes, obtained by measuring the *same* persons at two points in time, were available. Thus, eq. (2.3) used such "internal" changes from Table 5.3 to estimate transition rates. However, in many cases such internal data do not exist. For example, in many of the War Department experimental communication studies from which this illustration was taken, a control-group design was used rather than a before-after design, giving no data on internal shifts. Table 5.5 illustrates this. These are all the data in existence; inspection

Table 5.5*

Responses to: "The reason Germany was not very successful in bombing British planes *on the ground* was that ..." (Correct answer to be checked: "The British kept their planes scattered at the edges of the fields.")

	Control group	Experimental group (film)
Per cent correct	21	78
Per cent incorrect	79	22
Number	(1050)	(1050)

* Hovland *et al.*, p. 39.

will show that they are analogous to the before-after marginals of Table 5.3 (before-control, after-experimental). But since the internal changes were used there to measure the effect, how can these data be used?

These data are precisely like the cross-sectional data discussed in the preceding chapter. The experiment vs. control condition is the independent variable, the response to the question is the dependent attribute. To be sure, there are not the usual problems of possible spuriousness that usually occur with field data, but this is a difference of interpretation of the resulting estimate, not a difference in the estimating procedure.

By means of the techniques discussed in Chapter 4, it is possible to measure the transition rate introduced by the film, either relative to the random shocks which were previously in existence (ε_1 or ε_2), or relative to the total transition rates ($\alpha + \varepsilon_1 + \varepsilon_2$).

$$\frac{\varepsilon_1}{\varepsilon_2} = \frac{n_{1.}}{n_{2.}} \tag{4.1}$$

where $n_{1.}$ is the number correct in the control group, and $n_{2.}$ is the number incorrect in the control group.

$$\frac{\varepsilon_1}{\varepsilon_2} = \frac{21}{79} = .27 \tag{4.2}$$

$$\frac{\varepsilon_1 + \alpha}{\varepsilon_2} = \frac{n_{.1}}{n_{.2}} \tag{4.3}$$

where $n_{.1}$ is the number correct in the experimental group, and $n_{.2}$ is the number incorrect in the experimental group.

$$\frac{\varepsilon_1 + \alpha}{\varepsilon_2} = \frac{78}{22} = 3.55 \tag{4.4}$$

Subtracting eq. (4.2) from (4.4) gives an estimate of α relative to ε_2:

$$\alpha = 3.28\varepsilon_2$$

Or, to get a measure of α relative to the total transition rates, as developed in the preceding chapter, we use eq. (5.9) of that chapter to obtain

$$\frac{\alpha}{\alpha + \varepsilon_1 + \varepsilon_2} = \frac{.78 - .21}{1 - .21} = .72$$

From these ratios, it is not possible to obtain estimates of the absolute values of α, ε_1, or ε_2, as it was when internal changes were known, but only the relative values.

It is important to note just what these estimates assume, and how such assumptions relate to those followed in the preceding estimation using change data. These estimates, based on the equilibrium equations of the model, assume that equilibrium exists in both cases. In the control case, presumably such an equilibrium does exist. But in the experimental case, it probably does not. As discussed in the preceding section, it is more likely that there is in process either a reversion to the pre-experimental distribution, or a continued shift to a new distribution even farther removed from the original one. Whichever subsequently would prove to be true (and a third questionnaire would be required to determine just which was true), the value of α as estimated from the equilibrium ratios of eqs. (4.1) and (4.3) will always be *less* than that estimated from internal changes with the same marginals. This is because the equilibrium ratios assume that a new equilibrium exists, whereas the estimates from internal changes assume that the new α is permanently there, and will establish a new equilibrium.

It is possible to approximate the estimation procedure used with internal changes by assuming that *net* changes in the distribution were also *gross* changes. In this example, we would assume the following:

BEFORE (CONTROL)

		Correct	Incorrect	
	Correct	.21	.57	.78
AFTER (EXPERIMENT)	Incorrect	0	.22	.22
		.21	.79	1.00

Using the procedures discussed in Section 3 above for estimating α from this "change" data, we obtain:

$$\alpha = \frac{-\ln\left(1 - \dfrac{n_{21}}{n_{2.}}\right)}{t} = \ln\frac{.22}{.79} = 1.28 \text{ per stimulus} \qquad (4.5)$$

This gives an estimate of the "net effect" of the film in terms of the model's parameter, α. This measure of effect cannot be compared to the other influences on the item. It can, however, be compared between items, to examine the relative effect of the experiment on different items.

Because of the lack of comparability within the item, it is probably better to make the other, equilibrium, assumptions of eqs. (4.1) and (4.3) to estimate the effectiveness of the experimental stimulus when no data on internal changes exist. But in using these equations a number of measures of the relative size of α are possible, as mentioned above. The most useful, for reasons discussed in Chapter 4, Section 5, is probably $\alpha/(\alpha + \varepsilon_1 + \varepsilon_2)$. It is interesting to examine this measure of effect in relation to the measure of effect which was used in these studies. The "effectiveness index" used by Hovland, Lumsdaine, and Sheffield was

$$E = \frac{p_{11} - p_{10}}{1 - p_{10}} \qquad (4.6)$$

where $p_{11} = \dfrac{n_{.1}}{n}$ ($n_{.1}$ = number "correct" in the experimental group), and

$p_{10} = \dfrac{n_{1.}}{n}$ ($n_{1.}$ = number "correct" in the control group).

Using the equilibrium assumptions, it is possible to relate p_{11} and p_{10} to the underlying parameters of this model:

$$p_{11} = \frac{\alpha + \varepsilon_1}{\alpha + \varepsilon_1 + \varepsilon_2} \tag{4.7}$$

$$p_{10} = \frac{\varepsilon_1}{\varepsilon_1 + \varepsilon_2} \tag{4.8}$$

Substituting in eq. (4.6) the equivalences shown in eqs. (4.7) and (4.8) and simplifying gives the following expression of E in terms of α and ε's:

$$E = \frac{\alpha}{\alpha + \varepsilon_1 + \varepsilon_2} \tag{4.9}$$

Thus the "effectiveness index" used in these studies is identical with the measure developed in the preceding chapter for the effect of an independent attribute on a dependent one, under equilibrium assumptions. For the example used, the value of this measure is

$$E = \frac{\alpha}{\alpha + \varepsilon_1 + \varepsilon_2} = .72$$

In sum, then, when "internal" shifts are not known, it is still possible to measure the effect of an experiment in terms of the parameters of this model; Hovland's "effectiveness index" is just such a measure. However, the measure remains a relative one: it gives the values of the effect parameter α relative to the random shocks which are operating to maintain a division on the item. And when the measure is viewed as a measure of the effect parameter, α, this implies the assumption that a new equilibrium has been reached, an assumption which is especially suspect in regard to the results of such experimental stimuli.

One of the questions which must always be asked of attempts to apply a mathematical model to a problem is this one: Just what has been gained by it? The preceding examination can provide a clear answer for this case: Once the effect of the experiment is viewed as an effect on the transition rates, rather than directly on the aggregate distribution, completely new problems are opened for investigation: Does the experiment provide a temporary α, or a permanent one? If the new transition rate acts only through the length of the stimulus what is the absolute size of random shocks returning the attitude to its old distribution? If a relatively permanent α has been instituted, just how permanent is it? Does it also act only over a relatively short period and then vanish, to allow the old distribution to reassert itself? If cognition is generally changed directly, by transitions during the stimulus, while attitudes are changed indirectly, by addition of a permanent parameter α, then what about the structural relation between cognition and attitudes within the individual? Could the models of cognitive states and attitude states be related in a fashion that would show such a structural relation and allow its empirical testing?

These are some of the questions which are raised when this model is applied to experiments like those of Hovland's. They provide a good illustration of one kind of value that mathematical models can have: to raise quite new questions for research, going beyond the original research aims. One of these questions, the last one raised about the relation between cognition and attitudes suggested by these data, will be explored a little way here; detailed exploration must remain for subsequent investigation.

5. POSSIBLE RELATIONS BETWEEN COGNITIVE STATES AND ATTITUDINAL STATES

One of Hovland's results mentioned earlier leads to some interesting speculations about the relations between changes in factual information and changes in attitudes. The relevant finding is this one: most changes in information seemed to take place immediately, while most changes in attitudes had a "sleeper" effect, showing more change rather than a regression as time went on. In the paragraphs above, it was suggested that this corresponded to two kinds of effects: in the first case, introduction of a direct effect, α, operating only over the period of the stimulus itself; and in the second case, an indirect effect: the stimulus does not directly provide a temporary parameter α, but rather has the effect of putting an individual into a state in which he has a new transition rate, α, which remains although the stimulus itself is gone. The question which can now be raised is this: Is there possibly some complementarity between these two types of changes? The following model suggests that there is.

Consider a strictly factual matter, one in which there are two states: knowing the correct answer or not knowing it. The item presented in Table 5.5 is a good example: The correct information is that the Germans' lack of success in bombing British planes on the ground was due to the scattering of planes at the edges of the fields. Any other answer to the question indicated that the person was in the "incorrect" state.

This item showed a great erosion over the nine-week period which measured the "long-term" effect. In contrast, the following item showed an increase in effect of the film over the nine-week period: "Do you think the British are trying to get others to do most of their fighting for them in this war, or do you think they are doing their fair share of the fighting?" (p. 42).

The over-all change toward a positive attitude toward British fighting was only 2% at the end of one week, but 14% at the end of nine weeks. This is a good example of the sleeper effect found in these studies.

Now consider the first question as an indicator of general knowledge about the Battle of Britain, and the second as an indicator of an attitude toward Britain's war effort in relation to our own. The proposed model is this simple one, with two attributes and four states. The attributes are knowledge of the Battle of Britain and attitude toward British fighting. The model is as diagrammed in Figure 5.1. The effect of the film, according to this model, was to temporarily introduce a transition rate β from a state of no knowledge (state 3 or 4) to a state of knowledge (state 1 or 2). According to this model, the film had no effect upon the transition rates between negative and positive attitudes. These depend rather upon whether one has knowledge about the Battle of Britain (states 1 and 2) or does not (states 3 and 4). In

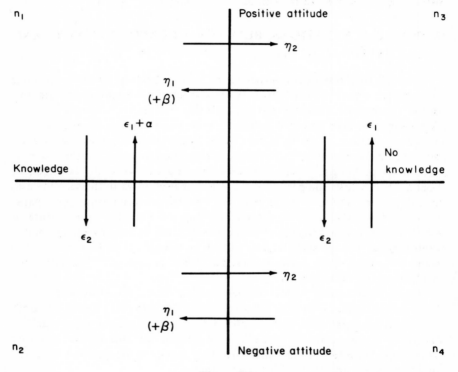

Figure 5.1

the former situation, there is an added effect parameter α, over and above the random shocks existing in the absence of knowledge. Very simply, the hypothesis is that it is not the film directly, but knowledge of the Battle of Britain which introduces an effect parameter into the transition rates between positive and negative attitudes. Since this knowledge remains after the film, the effect parameter, α, between the attitudinal states remains, for those persons who are in the knowledgeable state. Thus β lasts only during the period of the film itself, while α lasts as long as the knowledge remains.

This suggested model has a number of implications, some of which would be testable with further analysis of the same data, others requiring further experiments. Some of these implications are as follows:

(1) The attitudinal changes beyond the usual random shocks should not occur for the whole sample, but only for the persons who have made the cognitive change into the knowledgeable state.

(2) Those who were in the knowledgeable state *before* the experiment should even then have had an aggregate distribution of attitudes which is characteristic of this cognitive state—that is, they should already be characterized by a q_{21} of $\alpha + \varepsilon_1$, which characterizes others only *after* the film and their subsequent shift in knowledge.

(3) For these persons who were already in the knowledgeable state, the film should show no effect, just as for the persons who never made the cognitive shift as a result of the film.

(4) If several subsequent observations were made, it would be predicted that for those persons who forgot, shifting back to state 3 or 4, the effect parameter, α, for the attitude should no longer be operative.

Experimentally, this situation would be complicated by the fact that it is hard to know just what cognitive states a given attitude depends upon, if in fact the dependence does exist as suggested. However, this should not cause too much difficulty, since a given attitude may be dependent on several cognitive states, and show the above relationship with each of them.

Even beyond this model, there is probably another important effect which could be investigated with such experiments. Presumably the effect of knowledge about the Battle of Britain was due to a general strain toward consistency between cognitive and attitudinal states. This same strain should manifest itself in another way: by an effect upon the cognition. That is, those who have a negative attitude toward British fighting should have a higher transition rate toward forgetting the knowledge they had gained in the film (e.g., $q_{24} = \gamma + \eta_2$, rather than merely η_2). But such matters can only be mentioned here, and left to empirical investigation.

6. AN INDEPENDENT AND DEPENDENT ATTRIBUTE IN AN ONGOING SITUATION WITH OVER-TIME DATA

The example above has shown how the effects of an experimental stimulus upon a dichotomous attribute are described by this model when over-time data exist. An ongoing situation, however, is somewhat different. The independent attributes are not absent at one time and present at another, but are present at all times for some persons, and never for others. The effect parameters are not due to single events in time, and are not defined only over the period of those events, but are continuing, just as are the random shocks.

An example which illustrates some of these differences is given in Table 5.6 below.

6.1 The effect of ideological sensitivity upon knowledge of political issues

In a study of politics within a printers' union (Lipset, Trow, and Coleman, 1956), printers were divided into three groups: those high, medium, and low in "ideological sensitivity," that is, high, medium, and low in their attentiveness to political ideas. The men were asked at two points in time what one party's position was on the Taft-Hartley Act, as Table 5.6 indicates. Here the independent attribute is level of ideological sensitivity; for each of the three levels, the transition rates may be estimated. First, the cross-sectional data in January may be used to estimate ratios of transition rates in effect up until that time, and then the over-time data may be used to estimate the absolute values of transition rates in effect during the January to June campaign period.

Table 5.6

IDEOLOGICAL SENSITIVITY VS. CHANGES IN KNOWLEDGE OF PROGRESSIVE PARTY POSITION ON THE TAFT-HARTLEY LAW

		LEVEL OF IDEOLOGICAL SENSITIVITY								
		HIGH JUNE			MEDIUM JUNE			LOW JUNE		
		Correct	Incorrect		Correct	Incorrect		Correct	Incorrect	
JAN.	Correct	42	7	49	41	14	55	6	4	10
	Incorrect	8	18	26	31	75	106	12	57	69
		50	25	75	72	89	161	18	61	79

For those *high* in ideological sensitivity, the various estimates are:

(a) Using the cross-sectional marginals of January with eq. (2.1) gives an estimate of the ratio of the transition rates (assuming aggregate equilibrium):

$$\frac{q_{21}}{q_{12}} = \frac{49}{26} = 1.9 \tag{6.1}$$

(b) Using the panel data for those initially incorrect (state 2) with eq. (2.10) gives

$$q_{21} = \frac{8}{26} \frac{- \ln\left(1 - \frac{8}{26} - \frac{7}{49}\right)}{t\left(\frac{8}{26} + \frac{7}{49}\right)} = .41 \text{ for 5 months} \tag{6.2}$$

(c) Using the panel data for those initially correct (state 1) with eq. (2.10) gives

$$q_{12} = .19 \text{ per 5 months} \tag{6.3}$$

(d) The ratio of these last two estimates gives an estimate of the ratio of transition rates for comparison with (a) above:

$$\frac{q_{21}}{q_{12}} = \frac{.41}{.19} = 2.2 \tag{6.4}$$

These estimates indicate two things: first, both the cross-sectional data and the over-time data show that the transition rates toward correct knowledge are about twice as high as those away from it; and second, that the ratio of the rates before the campaign is not greatly different from what it is during the campaign. But as shown by the data for the other two groups (those medium and low in ideological sensitivity), this is not always true.

For those *medium* in ideological sensitivity the estimates corresponding to those above are

cross-sectional:

(a) $$\frac{q_{21}}{q_{12}} = \frac{55}{106} = .52$$

panel:

(b) $$q_{21} = .42 \text{ per 5 months}$$

(c) $$q_{12} = .37 \text{ per 5 months}$$

(d) $$\frac{q_{21}}{q_{12}} = \frac{.42}{.37} = 1.14 \tag{6.5}$$

For those *low* in ideological sensitivity:

cross-sectional:

(a) $$\frac{q_{21}}{q_{12}} = \frac{10}{69} = .14 \tag{6.6}$$

panel:

(b) $$q_{21} = .26 \text{ per 5 months} \tag{6.7}$$

(c) $$q_{12} = .59 \text{ per 5 months} \tag{6.8}$$

(d) $$\frac{q_{21}}{q_{12}} = \frac{.26}{.59} = .44 \tag{6.9}$$

First, it is useful to compare the transition rates from the over-time data.

These are

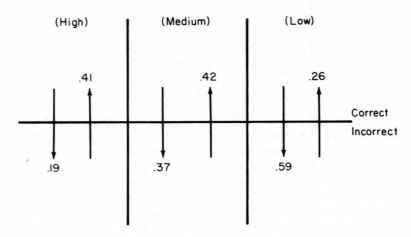

Both those of medium and of low ideological sensitivity show a considerable difference from the "highs." These transition rates may be compared to show the effects of ideological sensitivity, according to the panel data. The model of effects is

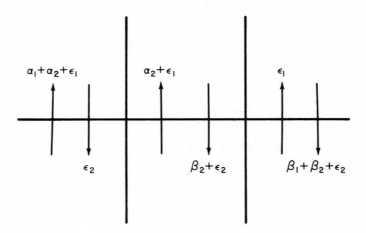

where ε_1 and ε_2 are the usual random shocks, and

α_1 = the added transition rate to "correct" for high ideological sensitivity relative to medium,

α_2 = the added transition rate to "correct" for medium ideological sensitivity relative to low,

β_1 = the added transition rate to "incorrect" for low ideological sensitivity relative to medium,

β_2 = the added transition rate to "incorrect" for medium ideological sensitivity relative to high.

These are estimated as follows:

$$\varepsilon_1 = .26 \quad \text{(to correct)}$$
$$\varepsilon_2 = .19 \quad \text{(to incorrect)}$$
$$\alpha_1 = -.01 \quad \text{(high relative to medium)}$$
$$\alpha_2 = .16 \quad \text{(medium relative to low)} \left.\right\} \text{(to correct)}$$
$$\beta_1 = .22 \quad \text{(low relative to medium)}$$
$$\beta_2 = .18 \quad \text{(medium relative to high)} \left.\right\} \text{(to incorrect)}$$

These are the effects through the five-month campaign period, as estimated from the panel data.

A direct comparison of the pre-campaign transition rates as estimated from the cross-sectional data, and the above during-campaign rates from the panel data, is given below.

RATIOS OF q_{21} TO q_{12}

	High	Medium	Low
Pre-campaign (cross-sectional):	1.9	.52	.14
During-campaign (panel):	2.2	1.14	.44

This comparison shows two interesting results: first, for all groups, the relative size of transition rates to "correct" are greater through the campaign than before the campaign period. But second, and more surprising, this gain is greatest for those medium and low in ideological sensitivity. The campaign has little effect for the knowledge of the "highs," but does have an effect in increasing the knowledge of the "medium" and "low" groups—presumably by increasing their transition rate to state 1 above its pre-campaign level.[3]

This example illustrates two kinds of "effects" of one attribute on another which can be found in over-time data: first, if a stable situation exists, and the dependent attribute is correlated with the independent one, then there will be a difference in transition rates for the two sides of the independent attribute, which can be thought of as an added transition rate due to the independent attribute. This effect is ordinarily exhibited both by the cross-sectional estimates and by the panel estimates. These effects will be evident even without any change away from aggregate equilibrium. However, a second effect is the disruption of aggregate equilibrium, as exemplified in

---

[3] This result is at variance with the usual finding, examined in Chapter 6, that the gain is greatest among those groups initially highest. The present result is more nearly like a regression effect. It may be due to regression toward the mean—for measurement of ideological sensitivity and of knowledge in January were based on attitude responses, and there may have been changes in the independent attribute as well as the dependent. This possibility makes necessary investigations like that of Section 7 below.

these data. The effect of some stimulus, the campaign in this instance, is to produce an added effect of the independent attribute. Here it was an effect in which the mediums and lows showed greater increments in their transition rates than the men high in ideological sensitivity.[4]

6.2 A caveat: unreliability of response

A strong note of warning must be added at this point. It would appear at first that inferences about the effect of attribute A upon B by examining the transition rates estimated from over-time data would be very solid inferences. But when there is aggregate equilibrium, an alternative hypothesis is also tenable: there is simply unreliability of response at each interview or observation, and this unreliability appears as spurious "changes" of position between the two interviews. Such unreliability would show a spurious effect of any attribute or variable which was correlated with the dependent response. Obviously it is important to decide whether an apparent effect is actually more than unreliability. Unfortunately, it seems impossible to determine this with two observations only, except indirectly, by using other items. However, adding a third observation, and comparing the changes between observations 1 and 2 with those between 1 and 3, allows a test between these alternative hypotheses. In brief, the comparison is this: if the "changes" between 1 and 3 are no greater in number than those between 1 and 2 or between 2 and 3, then this is simply unreliability of response; but if the "changes" between 1 and 3 approach the sum of the changes between 1 and 2 and between 2 and 3, then these are legitimate changes. The problem is somewhat more complicated than this, but we shall not go into it here. Chapters 12 and 13 will present a model involving unreliability of response. (See also Wiggins (1955) and Coleman (1964) for an examination of these problems of unreliability and change.)

6.3 The effect of professional orientation on doctors' adoption of a drug

Seldom in field work do we have systematic data on change over a number of observations. The following example indicates the kind of application of these models which such data would permit. It concerns the introduction by physicians of a new drug into their practices.[5] Six-day samples of doctors' prescriptions were taken in each of eight two-month (more exactly 56-day) periods following the drug's placement on the market. Forgetting for a moment the question of the effect of an independent attribute, we can see just how closely the data conform to the simple model with a constant transition rate q_{12}:

---

[4] As mentioned in the preceding footnote, this is not the usual case. See Chapter 6, Section 5.2, for this result.

[5] The research is that discussed briefly in Chapter 1.

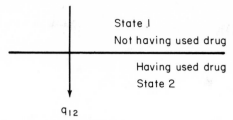

q_{12}

If n_{1t}^{0} is the expected number who have not used the drug at any time t, then according to this model,

$$\frac{dn_{1t}^{0}}{dt} = -q_{12}n_{1t}^{0} \tag{6.10}$$

or
$$n_{1t}^{0} = n_{10}e^{-q_{12}t} \tag{6.11}$$

or
$$\ln \frac{n_{1t}^{0}}{n_{10}} = -q_{12}t \tag{6.12}$$

The data are presented in Table 5.7, taking each 56-day period as a time interval of one unit. Now by using eq. (6.12), the successive values of $n_{1,t}/n_{1}$.

Table 5.7

t	$\dfrac{n_{1,t}}{n_{1\cdot}}$	t	$\dfrac{n_{1,t}}{n_{1\cdot}}$
0	1.00	5	.30
1	.85	6	.24
2	.69	7	.18
3	.50	8	.14
4	.34	9	.13
		($n_{1\cdot} = 125$)	

can be used to estimate q_{12}, since $n_{1\cdot} = n_{10}$ and $n_{1,t}$ is the observed datum for which the expected value is n_{1t}^{0}. Alternatively, a modification of eq. (6.12) can be used, as follows, since the time intervals are always one:

$$\ln \frac{n_{1t}^{0}}{n_{1,t-1}^{0}} = -q_{12} \tag{6.13}$$

Using eq. (6.13) and the observed data $n_{1,t-1}$, we obtain the following estimates for q_{12}:

0–1	.163		5–6	.223
1–2	.209		6–7	.288
2–3	.322		7–8	.251
3–4	.386		8–9	.074
4–5	.126			

If each of these estimates is weighted by the number of cases in the nonusing

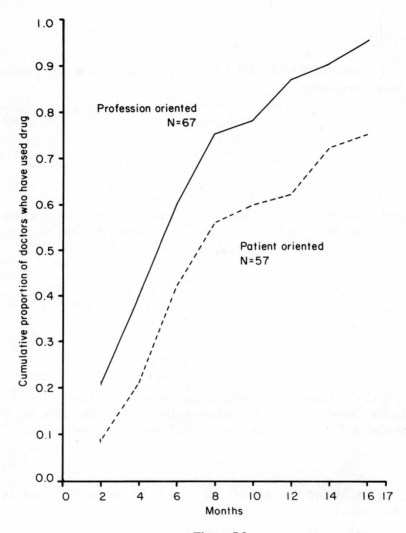

Figure 5.2

state at the beginning of the period, a weighted average for q_{12} (.234) can be obtained which is near to the best estimate.[6]

It seems apparent, from the list of q_{12}'s above that the values of q_{12} do change from one time period to the next. They first increase, then decrease, again, perhaps because of seasonal variations, perhaps owing to other factors. As suggested in Chapter 1, there is considerable evidence in this study to suggest that other factors were responsible. It appeared that the very process of adoption differed for the doctors who were socially integrated and those who were socially isolated, following a "snowball" course for the former and keeping a constant transition rate for the latter. As intimated in Chapter 1, it appeared that among the integrated doctors, the transition rate for each nonusing integrated doctor was augmented whenever a colleague began to use the drug, so that $q_{12} = kn_{2t}$ (where n_2 is the number who have already used the drug). In contrast, the isolated doctors appeared to follow the constant-rate process, uninfluenced by their colleagues' use of the drug.

An attitude of these doctors measured in an interview indicates how the model of independent attribute and dependent attribute applies to this case. The doctors were classified into "patient-oriented" and "profession-oriented" on the basis of their responses to a question about the criteria for judging a "good doctor" in their community. It turned out that the patient-oriented were consistently lower in their change from not using to using than were the profession-oriented, as shown by Figure 5.2. The model for this is the familiar one with a random shock for all the doctors, together with an added effect parameter for those who were oriented to the profession. For the patient-oriented,

$$\frac{dn_{1t1}}{dt} = -\varepsilon n_{1t1} \tag{6.14}$$

where n_{1t1} is the proportion of those in category 1 (patient-oriented) who have not yet used the drug. For the profession-oriented,

$$\frac{dn_{1t2}}{dt} = -(\alpha + \varepsilon)n_{1t2} \tag{6.15}$$

[6] The equation used in arriving at the over-all estimate is

$$q_{12\ av.} = \sum_{t=1}^{8} \frac{q_{12t}n_{1t}}{\sum_{t=1}^{8} n_{1t}} = .234.$$

The "best" estimate in a case like this is one which minimizes the sum of squared deviations of the observed from the estimated value n_{1t}/m_0, obtained from the over-all estimate for q_{12}. Another "best" estimate, and one which for many reasons would be preferable, is one which minimizes χ^2. The general problem of probability distributions of the parameters of these models is treated in Chapters 10 and 11, though the problem of statistical estimation is not treated in this book.

where n_{1t2} is the proportion of profession-oriented doctors who have not yet used the drug. By use of the integrated forms of these equations, estimates of ε for each time period and α for each time period can be found, as illustrated in the accompanying tabulation.

t	$\dfrac{n_{1t1}}{n_{101}}$	ε_t	$\dfrac{n_{1t2}}{n_{102}}$	$\alpha + \varepsilon_t$	α_t
0	1.00		1.00		
1	.91	.094	.79	.236	.142
2	.79	.142	.60	.275	.133
3	.58	.309	.40	.405	.096
4	.44	.277	.25	.470	.193
5	.40	.095	.22	.128	.033
6	.38	.051	.13	.526	.475
7	.28	.305	.10	.263	−.042
8	.25	.113	.04	.916	.803
	($N = 57$)	.175	($N = 67$)	.332	.157

Weighted averages of ε and α, obtained as indicated in the footnote on page 159, are .175 and .157. The data show, of course, the same over-all variations in transition rate as those discussed earlier. But apart from these deviations due to other variables like social integration, the model seems to fit the data reasonably well, showing an effect parameter for the profession-oriented doctors which remains roughly constant throughout the time period.

The next step in the development of an adequate model for these data is quite obvious: to set up a multivariate model, in which the effects of various attributes could be separated out. In other words, we would like to get a measure for the effect of profession-orientation apart from the effect of social integration, and apart from the effects of numerous other attributes, such as journal readership, which happens to be another attribute highly related to the doctor's date of introducing the drug into his practice. But such multivariate analysis requires systematic examination, and will be deferred until Chapter 6, where it is treated in some detail.

Before leaving this example, another variation of the model will serve to show how the particular form of the data determines the kind of model applied. In the above applications, the data were derived from the proportion who *had used* the drug by a particular time period. Suppose we think instead, now, of the proportions of doctors who *are using* the drug at any given time period. With this change, the states of the model change, and the model becomes a two-directional one. See the diagram on page 161.

The question now is, What is the most reasonable assumption about the transition rates, q_{12} and q_{21}? We have already seen that the transition rate from the state of not having used the drug to the state of having used it varied with different time periods in the way indicated above. It would seem, however, that the most reasonable, or at least the simplest, expectation for the transition rate toward use of the drug at any particular time would be constant, *for those who have already used the drug*. It would be a kind of random shock, dependent on the number of patients who were ill at that time, and upon other similarly fluctuating variables. The transition rate away from the drug's use should also be a random shock. That is, if these doctors, having once begun to use the drug, did not change in their likelihood of using it,

State 1

Prescribing the drug within a six-day period

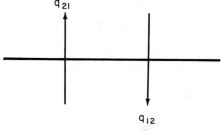

q_{21}

q_{12}

Not prescribing drug

State 2

then the transition rates q_{12} and q_{21} should simply be two random shocks, independent of the particular time period. On the other hand, if the doctor's use of the drug increased after he had begun to use it or if he became disenchanted and began to cut down on his prescriptions, this should show up in systematic changes in q_{12} and q_{21} over time.

The model, then, is one of the following sort:

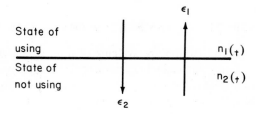

ϵ_1

State of
using $n_1(t)$

State of
not using $n_2(t)$

ϵ_2

where $n_{(t)}$ ($= n_{1(t)} + n_{2(t)}$) is the number who have used the drug *before* period t, and $n_{1(t)}$ is the number of these doctors who are using it at period t. Furthermore, we will assume that the frequency of such shocks is high, so that we can assume aggregate equilibrium at each observation, despite the new entrants into the system. Table 5.8 shows how the estimates of the relative values of ε_1 and ε_2 change from period to period. These figures show that, except for the first time period, the simple assumption of no change, once the drug was introduced into practice, accounts reasonably well for the data. The doctors did not, apparently, either greatly expand their use of the drug, once begun, nor slowly drop it from their practice. Other data in the original study, which examine the use of this drug relative to use of its competitors, indicate that the doctors did give it a larger place in their practice as time passed after its introduction. However, this effect occurred largely in the first two time periods (the first four months), which is consistent with the above results. See the original study (Coleman, Katz, and Menzel, 1957) for details.

This final example from the study of doctors' introduction of drugs indicates how the model is completely contingent upon the form of the data. Certain processes went into effect when the drug came on the market; the

Table 5.8

	$n(t)$ number having used before period t	$n_1(t)$ number of those using at period t	$\dfrac{\varepsilon_1}{\varepsilon_1 + \varepsilon_2}$
0	0	0	—
1	0	0	—
2	15	7	.47
3	31	21	.68
4	50	34	.68
5	66	39	.59
6	70	46	.66
7	76	57	.75
8	82	55	.67

model should mirror these processes, but in doing so, its states are determined by the form of the data, not by the social processes in their pristine state.

7. TWO-ATTRIBUTE SYSTEMS WITH OVER-TIME DATA

It is in the attempt to analyze systems of interdependent attributes that over-time data become particularly important. If two attributes are correlated in a cross-sectional study, then this tells us only that they are related, nothing about which affected the other, as Section 6 of the preceding chapter illustrated.

Figure 5.3 shows the diagram of effects and random shocks for such a system. This is a model in which, for both attributes, there is the presence or absence of an effect, not the opposing effects discussed in Section 6.2 of the preceding chapter. In the case of opposing effects, the transition rates into state 4 would be $\phi + \eta_2$ and $\beta + \varepsilon_2$ rather than merely the random shocks ε_2 and η_2. As will be evident, the data from a two-wave panel not only can separate out the effects of the two attributes, but also can show whether there are presence-absence effects as in the diagram, or opposing effects. In estimating the parameters, effects can be assumed in both directions. If β and

ϕ turn out to be zero or near zero, then the effects are of the presence-absence sort. Otherwise, they are in both directions.

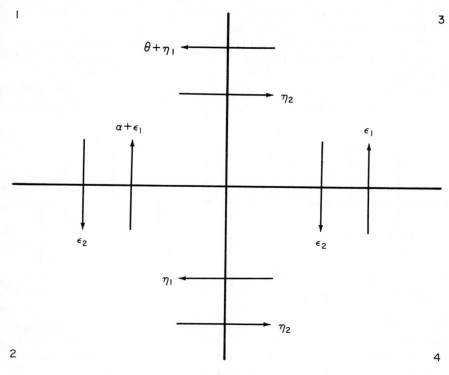

Figure 5.3

7.1 Estimation of parameters and the problem of multiple jumps

It is useful first to look at the problem of multiple jumps intuitively. Suppose that between one interview and the next, many people made this double shift: $++ \longrightarrow +- \longrightarrow --$; or this four move-shift: $++ \longrightarrow +- \longrightarrow -- \longrightarrow -+ \longrightarrow ++$. If either of these shifts did occur frequently, then the method of estimating parameters used in this chapter could lead to gross error. For these shifts would appear to be: $++ \longrightarrow --$ and $++ \longrightarrow ++$, respectively. All the intermediate moves would be undiscovered, since the two observations catch only the first and final state. To put it diagrammatically, consider the difference between the two situations pictured here, representing the shifts of a single individual relative to two interviews. On the left, in Figure (a), is a case in which the moves are infrequent enough, relative to the period between interviews, for a single jump to be bracketed by the interviews. Before the first interview, the individual had been shocked out of state 1 into state 3, $+ + \longrightarrow - +$; then the first interview catches him while he is in state 3; and the second interview catches him after his next move, to state 4, $- -$. If all individuals are like this, there is no difficulty of analysis because only a single move has been made between the two interviews.

But the diagram on the right, Figure (b) poses a much tougher problem, because there are four shifts between interviews, and there is no way of knowing what four shifts there were, or even that there were four shifts rather than none at all. It is because of such "hidden shifts" involved whenever the two observations bracket more than a single jump that the method

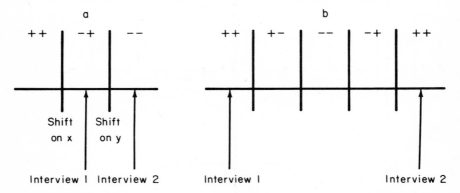

used above for estimating parameters is faulty. It is obvious that the analysis used there would break down if, for many people, more than one shift occurred between interviews. If by the second interview an unknown number c of the persons who shifted from i to j move elsewhere, then the observed number n_{ij} is not equal to the total number of shifts from i to j, but is equal to this number minus c. Yet there are many situations in which it is virtually impossible to bracket only one shift with two observations. Suppose, for example, that the correlation at aggregate equilibrium is quite high; as indicated earlier, this means that the amount of time an individual spends in states 1 or 4 (states of "consistency" between the two attributes) relative to the time he spends in states 2 or 3 (states of "inconsistency" between the two attributes), is given by $(n_1 + n_4)/(n_2 + n_3)$. Thus the time line of an individual would be something like this:

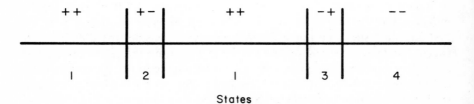

States

This would result in two things: first, not many cases of $+ -$ or $- +$ would occur in the first interview, since so few people are in an inconsistent state at any given time;[7] and second, when a shift out of equilibrium did occur between interviews, it would very often be followed by a shift back to equilibrium before the next interview. The sixteen-fold table resulting from the two observations might look as in Table 5.9. The table shows many shifts from $+ \; + \longrightarrow - \; -$ and many from $- \; - \longrightarrow + \; +$, without showing the intermediate shifts. A method of estimation that neglects this would give quite incorrect estimates of q_{ij}. The exact method of estimation would, with such a table showing almost no correlation, indicate that it is impossible to separate out the different q_{ij}'s—the interviews are too widely spaced. In data somewhere between this and the earlier tables with low frequency of jumps, the exact methods would correctly estimate the q_{ij}'s, and the approximate methods would be grossly incorrect. Thus it is of real practical importance to find exact methods of analysis.

Besides this kind of high correlation situation, there are other situations

Table 5.9

			II				
			(1)	(2)	(3)	(4)	
			+ +	+ −	− +	− −	
	(1)	+ +	250	10	10	205	475
I	(2)	+ −	10	2	3	10	25
	(3)	− +	10	3	2	10	25
	(4)	− −	205	10	10	250	475
			475	25	25	475	1000

in which the assumption of a single jump is unreasonable. It may be impossible, for example, to know *a priori* the rates of shift so as to find a safe interobservation period. Or, as in most panel studies which contain many items, a single time period may be imposed on a number of variables which have widely varying transition rates. In such cases, only a few relations, those which met the single-jump assumption, could be analyzed.

For these reasons, then, the models become much more useful when this restriction is removed, and the exact methods applied, as was done with the two-state models. Yet it should be emphasized, as mentioned above, that if

[7] This excludes the possibility that the individuals interviewed are nearly all in an inconsistent state at the same time, and are all caught at this time. In some situations, however, where an event throws many people into inconsistency at once, this possibility may be a practical one. Or in some cases, many people are inconsistent because the relation is not "geared in" (i.e., the effect parameter is small), but events are expected which will "gear in" the relation and shift people into consistency. Such situations have been utilized in panel studies of political campaigns and sales campaigns.

there are too many "hidden" jumps, then so much becomes hidden that little can be inferred from the data beyond what is learned from cross-sectional data. The situation is like one of trying to measure a precision part with an ordinary ruler; the scale is not calibrated finely enough to catch the deviations which are important.

7.1.1 *Approximate transition rates.* In this section, the approximate estimation method, assuming only one jump, will be derived. It can be used quite simply by hand, while the exact method requires extensive calculation and is best carried out on a computer. The results of the exact method are presented in subsequent examples, along with those of the approximate method.

In order to obtain estimates of the parameters of effect and random shock, it is necessary first to estimate each total transition rate q_{ij} from the data. This cannot be done via the equation used earlier for the two-state model, because there are transitions out of each state i into *two* other states, not merely one.

We begin as before by considering separately the "tagged" original occupants of state i. The total expected flow out of i for these original occupants is

$$\frac{dn_{it}^0}{dt} = -(q_{ij} + q_{ik})n_{it}^0 \tag{7.1}$$

In such continuous-time processes, q_{ii} is defined as the negative sum of the transition rates out of state i, in this case $-(q_{ij} + q_{ik})$. Then the equation for this total transition rate is given as in the two-state models, by integrating eq. (7.1) to give

$$q_{ii} = \frac{1}{t} \ln \frac{n_{it}^0}{n_{i0}^0} \tag{7.2}$$

To separate out the components of q_{ii}, we set up equations similar to (7.1), but for the expected flow of i's original occupants into the adjacent states j and k:

$$\frac{dn_{ijt}^0}{dt} = q_{ij}n_{it}^0 \tag{7.3}$$

$$\frac{dn_{ikt}^0}{dt} = q_{ik}n_{it}^0 \tag{7.4}$$

These equations cannot be directly integrated as was (7.1), but can be combined to give a ratio of q_{ij} and q_{ik}:

$$\frac{dn_{ijt}^0}{dn_{ikt}^0} = \frac{q_{ij}}{q_{ik}} \tag{7.5}$$

Multiplying through by dn_{ikt}^0 and integrating gives

$$n_{ijt}^0 - n_{ijo}^0 = \frac{q_{ij}}{q_{ik}}(n_{ikt}^0 - n_{iko}^0) \tag{7.6}$$

Since n_{ijo}^0 and n_{iko}^0 are zero, this gives

$$n_{ijt}^0 = \frac{q_{ij}}{q_{ik}} n_{ikt}^0 \tag{7.7}$$

This is an important result, for it states that whatever the relative sizes of the transition rates from one state into two others, the relative rates of evacuation into these states is at all times proportional to the sizes of the transition rates. This is true at the very beginning stages of the evacuation, and it is true when the evacuation is complete. It may be put in a slightly different form:

$$q_{ijt} = \frac{n_{ijt}^0}{n_{ijt}^0 + n_{ikt}^0}(q_{ij} + q_{ik}) \tag{7.8}$$

The result may be generalized beyond two states to give the general result:

$$q_{ij} = \frac{-n_{ijt}^0}{\Sigma n_{ijt}^0} q_{ii} \tag{7.9}$$

But since the sum of all first migrations into adjacent states, Σn_{ijt}^0, is equal to the total first migrations out, $n_{io}^0 - n_{it}^0$, then

$$q_{ij} = \frac{-n_{ijt}^0}{n_{io}^0 - n_{it}^0} q_{ii} \tag{7.10}$$

This result, together with eq. (7.2), gives q_{ij} in terms of n_{io}^0, n_{it}^0, and n_{ijt}^0:

$$q_{ij} = \frac{-n_{ijt}^0}{(n_{io}^0 - n_{it}^0)t} \ln \frac{n_{it}^0}{n_{io}^0} \tag{7.11}$$

Equation (7.11) gives q_{ij} in terms of the number of no-jumps (n_{it}^0) and the number of first migrations into state j, (n_{ijt}^0). The panel data n_{ii} and n_{ij} do not correspond to this, but can be used as first approximations, as was done in earlier sections, to estimate the q_{ij}'s. After estimation of the q_{ij}'s, then these may be used to estimate the components which make them up, the random shocks and effects, by use of the equations below (which assume the more general case of opposing effects):

$q_{12} = \varepsilon_2$	$q_{21} = \alpha + \varepsilon_1$
$q_{13} = \eta_2$	$q_{24} = \phi + \eta_2$
$q_{43} = \varepsilon_1$	$q_{31} = \theta + \eta_1$
$q_{42} = \eta_1$	$q_{34} = \beta + \varepsilon_2$

Example: Membership in Leading Crowd and Attitude Concerning It

In a study of the social system of adolescents in ten high schools (Coleman, 1961), all students were asked in a questionnaire several questions about the "leading crowd." They were asked whether they were in it, whether they wanted in, what it took to get in, who were prominent members of it, and several attitudes toward it. One of the latter questions (Y) was an agree-disagree question phrased:

"If a fellow wants to be part of the leading crowd around here, he sometimes has to go against his principles."

It might be expected that responses to this question will be affected by one's

Table 5.10   (Girls only)†

			MAY, 1958				
			(1)	(2)	(3)	(4)	
	x		+	+	−	−	
		y	+	−	+	−	
	(1)	+ +	484	93	107	32	716
OCTOBER, 1957	(2)	+ −	112	110	30	46	298
	(3)	− +	129	40	768	321	1258
	(4)	− −	74	75	303	536	988
			799	318	1208	935	3260

† Member of leading crowd: (+) (attribute *x*); Disagree that one goes against principles: (+) (attribute *y*).

self-perceived position in or out of the leading crowd; and in turn, it might be that this attitude about the leading crowd's behavior might influence one's willingness to be a member, and thus his self-perceived membership. Self-perceived membership was measured by question X:

Are you a member of the leading crowd?

Using these two questions at two points in time, it is possible to study the effect of each attribute on the other.[8] The data are as indicated in Table 5.10. Use of eq. (7.11) with these data allow estimation of the q_{ij}'s, and in turn estimation of the effects and random shocks. In the table, membership

[8] This is a rather elliptical statement, for it is presumably not the response to question X that affects question Y eight months later, but rather the underlying attribute of which X is an indicator.

in the crowd and a favorable attitude toward it (disagreement with the question) are labelled " + ." The estimation of approximate values for the q_{ij}'s proceeds as follows, using eq. (7.11), substituting n_{12}, n_{11}, and $n_{1.}$ from Table 5.10 for n_{ijt}^{0}, n_{it}^{0}, and n_{i0}^{0}, respectively, and letting $t = 1$ for simplicity:

$$q_{12} = \frac{-93}{716 - 484} \ln \frac{484}{716}$$

Using similar substitutions from Table 5.9 and solving, we obtain eight values of q_{ij}. Estimates from the exact method are included at the right.

$q_{12} = .157$	$q_{12} = .271$
$q_{13} = .181$	$q_{13} = .237$
$q_{43} = .410$	$q_{43} = .568$
$q_{42} = .101$	$q_{42} = .169$
$q_{21} = .594$	$q_{21} = .790$
$q_{24} = .244$	$q_{24} = .337$
$q_{31} = .130$	$q_{31} = .159$
$q_{34} = .323$	$q_{34} = .474$

The accompanying figure locates these transition rates on the diagram

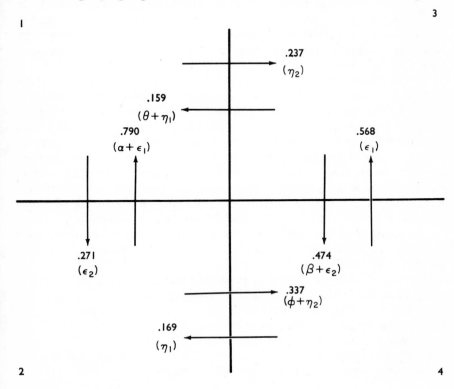

representing states on the two attributes. They are, together with the random shocks,

approx.	exact	approx.	exact
$\varepsilon_1 = .410$	.568	$\alpha = .184$	.222
$\varepsilon_2 = .157$	.271	$\beta = .166$	.203
$\eta_1 = .101$	.159	$\theta = .029$	$-.010$
$\eta_2 = .181$	.237	$\phi = .063$	.100

(The exact estimates show the effect θ to be acting from state 4 to 2, with the 3–1 transition rate consisting only of the random shock, η_1.)

The effects of attribute y (crowd against principles) on x (member of crowd) are given by θ and ϕ; the effects of x on y are given by α and β. It is evident x has a reasonably large effect on y in both directions. That is, self-perceived membership in the crowd brings a girl to feel that it doesn't lead a person against her principles ($\alpha = .222$) and perceived nonmembership brings a girl to feel that it *does* lead a person against her principles ($\beta = .203$). The latter effect is considerably stronger than the former when measured against the random shocks in the two directions (.271 to .568).

The attitude has a much smaller effect on perceived membership in the leading crowd, in one direction, and an essentially zero effect ($-.010$) in the other. Those who feel one must go against her principles tend slightly to leave the leading crowd, in perception or in fact ($\phi = .100$), but those who believe in the purity of the crowd are no more likely to see themselves in it eight months hence.

In this example there was a reasonably large number of jumps beyond the first. As a consequence, the estimates from the exact method are considerably different from the approximate estimates. A large component of this error is simple underestimation of the q_{ij}'s, but there is some differential under-estimation of different rates. This leads in one case to a different inference about the effects (by the approximate method, θ is .029 in the expected direction; by the exact method, it is .010 in the direction against expectations). As the results of this example suggest, when the values of n_{ij} in the reverse main diagonal are large enough to suggest a sizable proportion of jumps beyond the first, it is important to use the exact method outlined in Section 8.

To see how closely the model fits the data, the q_{ij}'s have been used (following a method outlined in Section 9) to regenerate the data. The results are shown in Table 5.11.

The eight transition rates were previously calculated using the cell values other than the main diagonal and reverse-diagonal ones. Consequently, either the main diagonal or the reverse diagonal should be examined to test the fit. The calculated values in the reverse diagonal are all the result of jumps beyond the first, so that the test is a rather severe one. These seem relatively close to the values in the data, and indicate a rather good fit.

An interesting comparison is possible by examining the boys' responses to these same questions. Table 5.12 gives these, using the same labelling.

Table 5.11

CALCULATED VALUES FOR THE EMPIRICAL
DATA OF TABLE 5.10, USING EXACT q_{ij}'s

1	477.9	92.9	107.0	38.2	716.0
2	111.9	113.2	27.0	45.9	298.0
3	129.0	36.5	771.6	320.9	1258.0
4	56.5	74.9	302.9	553.7	988.0
	775.3	317.5	1208.5	958.7	3260.0

Table 5.12 (Boys only)

MAY, 1958

			(1)	(2)	(3)	(4)	
	x		+	+	−	−	
		y	+	−	+	−	
(1)	+	+	458	140	110	49	757
(2)	+	−	171	182	56	87	496
(3)	−	+	184	75	531	281	1071
(4)	−	−	85	97	338	554	1074
			898	494	1035	971	3398

OCTOBER, 1957

Application of eq. (7.11) as before gives the approximate estimates, and application of the method of Section 8 gives exact estimates.

$$q_{12} = \frac{-140}{757 - 458} \ln \frac{458}{757}$$

	approx.	exact			approx.	exact
$q_{12} =$	.234	.431		$q_{21} =$	.546	.797
$q_{13} =$	.184	.267		$q_{24} =$	.278	.415
$q_{43} =$	.430	.701		$q_{31} =$	.239	.323
$q_{42} =$	.123	.208		$q_{34} =$	.365	.581

Comparison shows that as before the effects are all in the expected directions. They are, together with random shocks,

	approx.	exact			approx.	exact
$\varepsilon_1 =$	.430	.701		$\alpha =$	.116	.096
$\varepsilon_2 =$	.234	.431		$\beta =$	.131	.150
$\eta_1 =$	.123	.208		$\theta =$	.116	.115
$\eta_2 =$	.184	.267		$\phi =$	.094	.148

The configuration of effects for boys is somewhat different from that for girls. There is not the clear-cut dominance of self-perceived membership in the crowd over attitude about the crowd's behavior. The strongest effects relative to the random shocks are the effect of a positive attitude toward the crowd's behavior on locating oneself within the crowd ($\theta = .115$), and the effect of a negative attitude in moving out of the crowd ($\phi = .148$). The one effect which is considerably smaller for the boys than the girls is the effect that being a member has on leading one to believe the crowd is all right ($\alpha = .222$ for girls, .096 for boys).

It would be useful to project this system of attributes into the future, to examine its expected configuration at a later period. The methods producing this are given in Section 9 below. The results of the projection forward for one school year are given in Table 5.13, together with the regenerated

Table 5.13

a. CALCULATED VALUES FOR THE EMPIRICAL DATA OF TABLE 5.12, USING EXACT q_{ij}'s

1	451.0	139.8	110.0	56.2	757.0
2	170.8	187.4	51.0	86.9	496.0
3	183.9	57.4	548.9	280.7	1071.0
4	94.7	96.9	337.7	544.8	1074.0
	900.4	481.5	1047.5	968.6	3398.0

b. PROJECTION FORWARD ONE SCHOOL YEAR

1	340.5	147.3	154.1	115.1	757.0
2	182.6	113.0	97.6	102.9	496.0
3	248.6	110.2	402.0	310.2	1071.0
4	195.8	121.3	368.1	388.8	1074.0
	967.4	491.8	1021.7	917.0	3398.0

c. SUMMARY OF CHANGES

| | TIMES | | | |
	I	II	IIcalc.	IIIcalc.
Proportion in leading crowd	.37	.41	.41	.43
Proportion with positive attitude	.54	.57	.57	.59
Relation between attributes	.14	.18	.18	.20

data using the calculated transition rates. Again, the fit seems reasonably good, in comparing the regenerated data with the actual data. The projection shows that membership in the leading crowd is slowly increasing (states 1 and 2), and that positive attitudes about its behavior (states 1 and 3) are slowly increasing. In addition, the relation between membership and attitude is slowly increasing. (The relation is calculated using the equation derived in Chapter 12, eq. 4.9. This is shown in Table 5.13c.)

7.2 Two-attribute systems with different configurations of effect

In this section, two kinds of effects of attributes upon each other are examined: effects of each attribute in the positive direction only (from states 2 and 3 into state 1) and effects of each in two directions (from the two "inconsistent" states, 2 and 3, into both 1 and 4). These, however, are not the only configurations of effect in two-attribute systems, and it is useful to point out the other possibilities. The different possibilities correspond, in a rough way, to the analogous situation in a linear system of relations between two continuous variables. There, depending on the values of the coefficients in the relations, the system may behave in different ways, three of which are shown here.

Saddle points (unstable equilibrium points):

a

Stable and unstable focal points:

b   c

Stable and unstable nodal points:

d   e

One class of two-attribute systems may be labelled "consistency" processes of various sorts. This includes the two types examined above. Figures

5.4 and 5.5 gives the types of consistency and nonconsistency systems, together with short descriptions. The diagrams show arrows for the "effect" transition rates only, the random shocks being left implicit.

Figure 5.4. Consistency systems

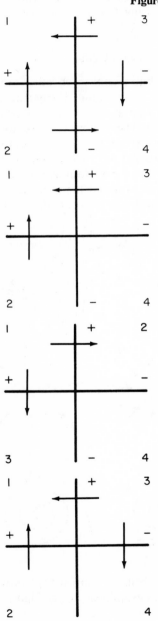

Consistency system in which both attributes have effects on both positive and negative sides. States 1 and 4 are "consistent" states.

Consistency system with effects in positive direction only. This is appropriate when attributes consist of "presence" or "absence," and presence of one induces presence of other.

Consistency system with effects only when both attributes are present. This is appropriate when two attributes are not compatible, and each can continue to exist only in absence of other. For instance, in example of knowledge about Battle of Britain and negative attitude toward British (see Sections 4 and 5), if the presence of both these attributes is labelled state 1, the effects might be such as to induce a shift away from negative attitude or away from knowledge.

Consistency system in which one attribute has effects on both positive and negative sides, while other has effect only when attribute is present. For example, campaigning for a candidate leads to liking him (from state 3 to state 1), while liking him leads to campaigning (2 to 1), and not liking him leads to not campaigning (3 to 4).

Figure 5.5. Nonconsistency systems

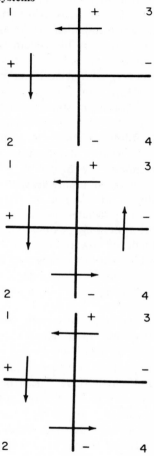

Negative reinforcement system. Presence of one attribute (*y*) induces the presence of a second attribute (*x*), which then leads to absence of first. *Example:* Cohesion in a group leads to success (from state 3 to 1); success leads to lack of cohesion (1 to 2).

Mutual negative reinforcement. The + + and − − states (1 and 4) induce a shift in attribute *y*, while the + − and − + states (2 and 3) induce a shift in attribute *x*. The typical resulting behavior is periodic. Example: Hunger leads to eating (from state 3 to 1); eating leads to nonhunger (1 to 2); nonhunger leads to noneating (2 to 4); noneating leads to hunger (4 to 3).

Presence of one attribute (*y*) induces the presence of another (*x*), which leads to absence of first, which in turn leads to absence of second. Example: Liking a person (*y*) leads to association with him (from state 3 to 1); the (unsuccessful) association leads to disliking him (from state 1 to 2); disliking him leads to non-association (from state 2 to 4).

These various configurations of effect for two-attribute systems indicate the wide range of work which remains to be done. The discussion in this chapter has only begun to scratch the surface; a wide range of systems awaits investigation.

7.3 A reinterpretation of consistency models

There are some grounds for suggesting a somewhat different model than one in which particular attributes *affect* one another. Such a model pushes explanation back one step, and offers an answer to the question: What is the fundamental mechanism of effect? or What is the conceptual model through which one attitude affects another?

Because of this, the interpretation below is an appealing one: First, in considering two cognitive or attitudinal states (e.g., the cognitive state of knowledge about the Battle of Britain, and the attitudinal state of negative attitude toward British fighting), there is no notion whatsoever of effect of either on the other. There are only random shocks into and out of the state, determined by the general stability of the attitude or cognition.[9] Thus in a two-attribute system, there are two random shocks for each attribute (ε_1, ε_2) and (η_1, η_2), but no effect parameters.

How, then, does the appearance of effect come about, with many persons in a consistent state, and few in an inconsistent state? These attitudinal and cognitive states are in some fashion guides to action. Suppose they operate as follows: From time to time, exogenous events focus a person's attention upon a given action-situation (e.g., in the Battle of Britain example, a friend mentions the British in conversation, inviting a response). Attitudes and cognitive states are associated with this action-situation, and when this focussing of attention occurs, then *and only then* do the random shocks operate for these associated attitudes. Now, if these attitudes both lead to the same response (e.g., expressing to the friend one's liking of the British), the tendency toward that response will be a strong one, and it will be quickly made, thus releasing the attention that was directed toward this action-situation. However, if the attitudes lead to conflicting responses, the individual cannot quickly make a response, and his attention must remain focussed on this action-situation. The longer the focus, and thus the longer the random shocks have to operate, the more likely will there be a shift from this state. Thus the states that lead to conflicting responses (inconsistent states) will tend to have few persons remaining in them, while the states in which the attitudes reinforce one another will tend to have persons move into them and remain there. The stronger the response tendencies toward one response, the less time the individual has to move into another state, and consequently, the more nearly it becomes an absorbing state for him.

This model may be diagrammed for the two-attribute case (using the Battle of Britain as an example), including:

(a) the movement from a "free-attention" state into the state where attention is directed toward this action-situation. This is presumed to be due to exogenous events, such as the conversation discussed earlier.

(b) the movement from the attention state back into a free-attention state, accomplished by taking action toward this situation.

The rate of movement into the attention-state is independent of whatever attitudinal state one is in; but the rate out is governed by the rate of response, which differs for each attitudinal state. If there is no knowledge of the Battle of Britain and a negative attitude (state 4 in the diagram), the rate is δ; if there is no knowledge and a positive attitude (state 3) the rate of movement

---

[9] Elsewhere, in Chapters 12 and 13, this stability is interpreted as the number of action-elements conditioned onto a particular object, or cognitive elements associated with a given cognition.

toward a (different) response is γ, roughly the same size as rate δ; if there is a positive attitude together with knowledge (state 1), the rate is α, larger than γ since the attitude is reinforced by knowledge; and if there is a negative attitude together with knowledge (state 2), these two lead to inconsistent responses, and thus a *small* response rate, β, smaller than either γ or δ, and much smaller than α.

The transitions between states 1, 2, 3, and 4 are not shown here, but they are, as discussed earlier, simply random shocks.

Now the virtue of this model, relative to the previous conception, is that it does not impose a psychologically vague notion of effects. The "effects" come about, rather, as a consequence of the reinforcing or conflicting tendencies to action (i.e., to attention-reduction) deriving from the two attitudes. To be sure, the mechanism through which such tendencies occur is unspecified, but the explanation has been carried one step further.

This model illustrates the need for detailed psychological experimentation in order to learn just how attitudinal and cognitive states become consistent, and how they relate to action. It would not be simple to test whether behavior is consistent with this model, but it would be possible to do so. For example,

Free attention state

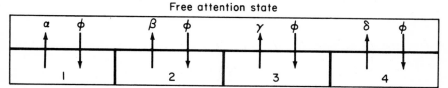

Attention directed toward British fighting

persons who were seldom confronted with an action-situation involving this topic would remain in inconsistent states, while according to the other model, they should continue to move toward consistency; or if persons were artificially prevented from taking action, and then attention was forced to remain focussed upon this topic, there would be as much movement out of consistent states as out of inconsistent ones (see Festinger, 1957, and Lawrence and Festinger, 1962, for related experiments).

There will be no attempt to apply this model to data, for the appropriate data to distinguish it from the "interdependent effects" model do not exist. For attitude-change data of the sort found in panel surveys or most experiments, the model discussed earlier is fully appropriate. Even if a mechanism like this is operating, that model provides a concise specification of the "effects" generated by this process.

8. EXACT ESTIMATES FOR TRANSITION RATES IN MULTI-STATE SYSTEMS

The above use of a four-state system with transition rates between adjacent states is one of a general class of multi-state systems with transition

rates among some or all pairs. The estimation method given below is appropriate for this general class of models when there are two-wave panel data or,
more generally, two observations on each unit separated by a fixed interval
of time. For concreteness, a four-state system will be used in deriving the
estimate.

If the times of the two observations are labelled 0 and t, then in solving
for the q_{ij}'s, we use the following equation (see Doob, 1953, p. 240):

$$N'(t) = N'(0)e^{Qt} \tag{8.1}$$

where $N(t) = \begin{pmatrix} n_{1t} \\ n_{2t} \\ n_{3t} \\ n_{4t} \end{pmatrix}$

$$Q = \begin{pmatrix} q_{11} & q_{12} & q_{13} & q_{14} \\ q_{21} & q_{22} & q_{23} & q_{24} \\ q_{31} & q_{32} & q_{33} & q_{34} \\ q_{41} & q_{42} & q_{43} & q_{44} \end{pmatrix}$$

where q_{ii} is defined as $q_{ii} = -\sum\limits_{j \neq i} q_{ij}$.

The symbol t is a scalar multiplier of Q, so that each element of Q is multiplied
by t.

Equation (8.1) gives the distribution at any time t if we know the initial
distribution, $N(0)$, and the values of q_{ij} for Q. The exponential of the matrix
is defined as

$$e^{Qt} = I + Qt + \frac{Q^2 t^2}{2!} + \frac{Q^3 t^3}{3!} + \dots \tag{8.2}$$

Having estimates of the values of the q_{ij}'s, it is possible to use eq. (8.2) to
calculate, to any desired degree of accuracy, e^{Qt}. This is a matrix which,
substituted in eq. (8.1), will allow an estimate of N_t in terms of the initial
state, $N(0)$.

However, eq. (8.1) and eq. (8.2) can also be used to estimate the values
of q_{ij}, given the observations at two points in time. Considering only the
subsample n_{i0}, then the vector $N(0)$ becomes $(n_{10}, 0, 0, 0)$ for the case $i = 1$,
in a system of four states. For such a subsample n_{i0}, the elements in the
vector $N(t)$ are $n_{i1t}, n_{i2t}, n_{i3t}, n_{i4t}$, since the subsample consists only of those
who began in state i. The equation for each element of this vector is, from
eq. (8.1) and (8.2), an infinite series whose first terms are as in eq. (8.3).

$$n_{ijt} = n_{i0}\left(\delta_{ij} + t\,q_{ij} + \frac{t^2}{2!}\sum_k q_{ik}\,q_{kj} + \frac{t^3}{3!}\sum_k \sum_m q_{ik}\,q_{km}\,q_{mj} + \dots\right) \tag{8.3}$$

where δ_{ij} is the kronecker delta, one when $i = j$, zero otherwise.

For a system of w states with transition rates from all states into all other states, there are $w(w-1)$ independent transition rates (the q_{ii}'s are a function of the q_{ij}'s), and in a w-state turnover table, there are $w(w-1)$ degrees of freedom. When $w = 4$, there are twelve independent n_{ij}'s, given the values of $n_i.$. Thus the q_{ij}'s may be estimated so as to exactly reproduce the data (except for certain special cases to be discussed later). Alternatively, as in the estimations carried out here, certain q_{ij}'s may be arbitrarily set to zero on theoretical grounds, and the others estimated subject to these constraints.

To carry out the estimation, first let the units of time be such that $t = 1$. Then, divide eq. (8.3) by n_{io} and transpose terms to give eq. (8.4). The term δ_{ij} vanishes if we consider only q_{ij} where $i \neq j$.

$$q_{ij} = \frac{n_{ijt}}{n_{io}} - \frac{1}{2}\sum_k q_{ik}q_{kj} - \frac{1}{3!}\sum_k\sum_m q_{ik}q_{km}q_{mj} - \cdots \quad (i \neq j) \qquad (8.4)$$

Eq. (8.4) may be used in an iterative procedure, letting the q_{ij} in the $r+1$ iteration be calculated by using the values of q_{ij} from the rth iteration on the right. The data corresponding to n_{ijt} and n_{io} are n_{ij} and $n_i.$ from the turnover table. In the first iteration, the values of q_{ij}'s on the right are set equal to zero. Thus if $q_{ij}^{(r)}$ is the value of q_{ij} from the rth iteration, the iteration equation is:

$$q_{ij}^{(1)} = \frac{n_{ij}}{n_{i.}} \qquad (8.5)$$

$$q_{ij}^{(r+1)} = \frac{n_{ij}}{n_{i.}} - \frac{1}{2}\sum q_{ik}^{(r)}q_{kj}^{(r)} - \frac{1}{3!}\sum\sum q_{ik}^{(r)}q_{km}^{(r)}q_{mj}^{(r)} - \cdots \qquad (8.6)$$

The series is carried out in each iteration until the next term is less than some preassigned threshold value. The iteration is carried out until all values of $q_{ij}^{(r+1)}$ differ by less than some threshold of accuracy from the values of $q_{ij}^{(r)}$. The iteration is tedious to carry out by hand, so that use of an electronic computer is desirable. A program written in Fortran which carries out the iteration efficiently is appended to this chapter as Appendix 2.

For certain types of data, the iteration does not converge. It appears that these are the cases in which the data used in estimation are incompatible with the model. The most obvious incompatibility is one in which for some state i, $n_{ii}/n_i.$ is less than some $n_{ij}/n_j.$ for some state j. This means that there is a negative relationship between the two observations. The continuous-time model when carried from $t = 0$ to $t \to \infty$, will only produce a decreasing positive relation between the two observations, finally reducing to a zero relation, but never a negative relation.

An approximate fit can be obtained by truncating the series after a fixed number of terms. In the example used in Section 9, such truncation was necessary after 11 terms, to produce convergence.[10]

In the case where a restriction is placed on certain parameters, a test of the fit of the model can be obtained. In the case of two-variable dichotomous systems, for example, the restriction is that q_{14}, q_{23}, q_{32}, and q_{41} are all zero. The iteration may be carried out by arbitrarily setting the values of these q_{ij}'s to zero in each iteration, and using only the data corresponding to the non-zero q_{ij}'s. Then after regenerating a set of calculated data from these q_{ij}'s, the calculated data may be tested for deviation from the actual data by a χ^2 test of fit. (Since the model consists of a set of n identical and independent processes, and the calculated values n_{ijt} are expected values of random variables produced by such processes, this test is appropriate.) The "exact" estimations used in Section 7 and the example below are carried out by

Table 5.14†

			WAVE II				
	x		+	+	−	−	
	y		+	−	+	−	
	x	y					
	+	+	307	12	20	23	362
WAVE	+	−	6	5	1	18	30
I	−	+	104	9	25	25	163
	−	−	51	112	27	888	1078
			468	138	73	954	1633

† x = attitude, y = usual brand.

restricting the values of q_{14}, q_{23}, q_{32}, q_{41} to zero, and using the computer program from Appendix 2.

Example

In the use of this model for examining the effects upon sales of a favorable attitude toward the brand, data were obtained at two points in time, five months apart, on a grocery item. Questions were asked at the two waves about whether it was the respondent's "usual brand," and about what brands he felt were among the best. Table 5.14 presents data for one brand, with

[10] One criterion that may be used in determining how many terms to include before truncating is to carry out estimates of q_{ij}'s using 3, 4, . . . terms, and after each estimate projecting over the period of the panel to produce a set of calculated values for the table of n_{ij}'s. Then a criterion of fit, such as the sum of squared deviations of the calculated from actual, may be applied. As the number of terms used in the iteration increases, this fit should first improve, then worsen. After the fit begins to worsen, the iterations can be stopped, and the q_{ij}'s which gave best fit can be used.

the largest share of the market. The q_{ij}'s were estimated by the iterative procedure of eq. (8.6) and found to be

$$
\begin{array}{ll}
q_{12} = .077 & q_{31} = 1.509 \\
q_{13} = .130 & q_{34} = .345 \\
q_{21} = .453 & q_{42} = .268 \\
q_{24} = 1.552 & q_{43} = .058
\end{array}
$$

Effects were estimated as follows:

$\alpha_1 = .268$ preserving effect of attitude on usual brand
$\alpha_2 = .395$ generating effect of attitude on usual brand
$\beta_1 = 1.422$ preserving effect of usual brand on favorable attitude
$\beta_2 = 1.241$ generating effect of usual brand on favorable attitude

8.1 An alternative method of estimating values of q_{ij}

Estimates of the transition rates may also be made by another method, for which I am indebted to M. Tainiter (1962). From the above discussion, it should be evident that

$$P_t = e^{Qt} \tag{8.7}$$

where P_t is the matrix of transition probabilities for a discrete-time process over the period t, embedded within the continuous process. (P_t is defined by an equation similar to eq. (8.1), $N'(t) = N'(0)P_t$, and the equality of P_t to e^{Qt} follows from this definition.)

By taking logarithms of both sides, eq. (8.7) can be put in the form

$$\ln P_t = Qt \tag{8.8}$$

The logarithm of a scalar, x, $0 < x < 2$, can be expressed as a power series

$$\ln x = (x-1) - \tfrac{1}{2}(x-1)^2 + \tfrac{1}{3}(x-1)^3 - \ldots \tag{8.9}$$

The logarithm of a transition matrix may be expressed in the same way, and thus evaluated.

$$\ln P_t = (P_t - I) - \tfrac{1}{2}(P_t - I)^2 + \tfrac{1}{3}(P_t - I)^3 - \ldots \tag{8.10}$$

The difference, $P_t - I$ amounts to the matrix of transition probabilities with main diagonal elements, p_{iit}, replaced by $1 - p_{iit}$. The series (8.10) converges whenever all the main diagonal entries, $1 - p_{iit}$, are less than .5 (i.e., this is a sufficient condition for convergence), which heuristically is the case of less than half the occupants of any given state moving from that state over the time period t.

Thus by evaluating the power series (8.10), it is possible to estimate the matrix Qt, of which the elements are q_{ijt}. This calculation can be done more readily by hand than can the previous procedure, and thus is preferable, except under one circumstance: when, as in the case of this chapter, certain elements of the Q matrix are arbitrarily designated to be zero (or some other value), and it is desired to estimate Q under this constraint. The iterative procedure discussed earlier allows such constraints to be imposed and the Q matrix to be estimated subject to these constraints. In all cases where the constraints are not imposed for which eq. (8.10) converges, the iterative procedure should also converge to the same value. In examples in which both procedures have been used, they have given the same values of q_{ij} as estimates.

9. PROJECTION OF THE SYSTEM FORWARD IN TIME

In many applications of a model like this, it is of interest to project the system forward, to examine the state of the system at some future point in time. If the future points in time are integral multiples of the time period between the two interviews, this may be done simply by treating the values $n_{ij}/n_i.$ as transition probabilities in a discrete-time Markov process, and taking the matrix to that power representing the integral number of time periods to the projection. For example, if we desire to project the system forward to t_m, where $t_m = mt$, and m is an integer, then

$$N'(t_m) = N'(0)e^{Qmt}$$
$$= N'(0)e^{Qt}e^{Qt}e^{Qt} \ldots e^{Qt} \tag{9.1}$$

where the product includes m identical terms e^{Qt}, or

$$N'(t_m) = N'(0)(e^{Qt})^m \tag{9.2}$$

But in a discrete-time Markov process, the state at time t is given by

$$N'(t) = N'(0)P \tag{9.3}$$

where P is the matrix of transition probabilities. If one is given the panel table between times 0 and t giving values n_{ij}, then the elements of P, the transition probabilities, may be estimated by $p_{ij} = n_{ij}/n_i.$. Obviously, $P = e^{Qt}$, and thus $N(t_m)$ may be found by

$$N'(t_m) = N'(0)P^m \tag{9.4}$$

The equation that may be used to project the internal cell frequencies, n_{ijt}, is

$$n_{ij} = n_i.[p_{ij} + \Sigma_k p_{ik}p_{kj} + \Sigma_{k_1}\Sigma_{k_2} p_{ik_1}p_{k_1 k_2}p_{k_2 j} + \Sigma_{k_1} \ldots \Sigma_{km-1} p_{ik_1}p_{k_1 k_2} \cdots p_{km-1 j}] \tag{9.5}$$

This simple projection from the transition matrix is of course appropriate only for the case of unconstrained q_{ij}'s. When the model is specified, so that q_{14}, q_{23}, q_{32}, q_{41} are zero, then it is necessary to project from the estimated values of q_{ij}, as described in eq. (8.3).

It is interesting that eq. (9.5) is similar to a truncated form of the projection equation using the q_{ij}'s, if p_{ii} is taken as $1 + q_{ii}$ in the first term for n_{ii}, and elsewhere p_{ij} is taken as q_{ij}. This, of course, derives from the fact that q_{ij} is the limiting form of p_{ij}, when the time interval approaches zero, and thus the number of time periods between zero and t approaches infinity.

If, however, it is desired to project forward to any point in time, then this may be done directly by use of eq. (8.3).[11] An example of results of projection using eq. (8.3) is given in the second example of Section 7.

APPENDIX 1—CALCULATION OF $_3n_{2131t}$

Throughout this chapter, it has been assumed that the data at hand were the number of individuals who began (at time zero) in state i and ended (at time t) in state j. For some purposes, however, it may be of interest to calculate the expected number who have followed a particular path between origin and destination. Consequently, an example of such a calculation is carried out here: the expected number who, during time t, take exactly three jumps, $2 \to 1 \to 3 \to 1$. This member will be labeled $_3n_{2131t}$ (the leading subscript 3 representing the number of jumps involved). In the calculation, we let $q_i = - q_{ii}$ for simplicity of notation.

The calculation proceeds in four steps: (1) calculating n_{2r} (the number remaining in state 2 until time r), where r refers to a variable time between 0 and s; (2) calculating $_1n^0_{21s}$, where s refers to a variable time between 0 and τ; (3) calculating $_2n_{213\tau}$, where τ refers to a variable time between 0 and t; and, finally, (4) calculating $_3n_{2131t}$.

(1) First we use eq. (7.2) in exponential form, to calculate n_{2r}:

$$\frac{n^0_{2r}}{n_{20}} = e^{-q_2 r} \qquad (A.1)$$

(2) Now to carry out step 2, consider the total length of time zero to s. If an individual is to start out at state 2 at time zero, make one jump to state 1, and be in 1 at time s, there are three events which must occupy this time: (stay in 2 until time r), (jump from 2 to 1 at time r), (stay in 1 from time r to s). The number of individuals carrying out these three events is n^0_2 multiplied by:

$$(e^{-q_2 r}) \qquad \times \qquad (q_{21}) \qquad \times (e^{-q_1 (s-r)})$$
$$\text{(stay in 2)} \qquad \text{(jump to 1)} \qquad \text{(stay in 1)}$$

But since r can vary from zero to s, the total number of individuals following this path is

[11] Care must be taken in numerical techniques designed to carry out this projection, when the time period over which the projection is made is large. Because q_{ii} is negative, alternate terms of eq. (8.3) tend to be of differing signs but sometimes very large in magnitude. It is sometimes easier to determine a time period $\varDelta t$ such that every point to which a projection is made is an integral multiple of $\varDelta t$. Then generate the transition matrix $P = e^{q \varDelta t}$, and use eq. (9.5) for projecting.

$$n_{21s}^0 = n_{20}^0 \int_0^s e^{-q_{2}r} q_{21}^{-q_1(s-r)} dr \qquad (A.2)$$

or,

$$\frac{_1 n_{21s}^0}{n_2^0} = \int_0^s e^{-q_{2}r} q_{21} e^{-q_1(s-r)} dr \qquad (A.3)$$

Integrating gives

$$\frac{_1 n_{21s}^0}{n_2^0} = \frac{q_{21}}{q_1 - q_2}(e^{-q_{2}s} - e^{-q_{1}s}) \qquad (A.4)$$

Equation (A.4) gives the value of $_1 n_{12s}^0$ in terms of the transition rates.[12]

(3) By use of the same reasoning as in step 2, we obtain

$$\frac{_2 n_{213\tau}}{n_2} = \int_0^\tau \frac{_1 n_{21s}}{n_2} q_{13} e^{-q_3(\tau-s)} ds \qquad (A.5)$$

Substituting the right side of eq. (A.4) into eq. (A.5) and integrating, we obtain

$$\frac{_2 n_{213\tau}}{n_2} = \frac{q_{21}q_{13}}{q_1 - q_2}\left[\frac{e^{-q_{2}\tau} - e^{-q_{3}\tau}}{q_3 - q_2} - \frac{e^{-q_{1}\tau} - e^{-q_{3}\tau}}{q_3 - q_1}\right] \qquad (A.6)$$

(4) Following this same reasoning, we obtain

$$\frac{_3 n_{2131t}}{n_2} = \int_0^t \frac{_2 n_{213\tau}^0}{n_2^0} q_{31} e^{-q_2(t-\tau)} d\tau \qquad (A.7)$$

Substituting the right side of eq. (A.6) into eq. (A.5) and integrating, we obtain

$$\frac{_3 n_{2131t}^0}{n_2^0} = q_{21}q_{13}q_{31}\left[\frac{e^{-q_{2}t} - e^{-q_{1}t}}{(q_1 - q_2)^2(q_3 - q_2)} + \frac{e^{-q_{3}t} - e^{-q_{1}t}}{(q_2 - q_1)(q_3 - q_2)(q_1 - q_3)}\right.$$
$$\left. + \frac{e^{-q_{3}t} - e^{-q_{1}t}}{(q_2 - q_1)(q_3 - q_1)^2} + \frac{t}{(q_2 - q_1)(q_3 - q_1)}\right] \qquad (A.8)$$

An alternative calculating procedure for any path, however complicated, is to use the infinite series of eq. (8.3), excluding all products of q_{ij}'s that do not conform to the indicated path. Thus in the sixth term of the infinite series, the product $q_{21}\ q_{11}\ q_{11}\ q_{13}\ q_{31}$ would be allowed in calculating $_3 n_{2131t}$, since it conforms to the indicated path, while $q_{21}\ q_{13}\ q_{31}\ q_{13}\ q_{31}$ would not, since it includes two extra jumps.

[12] For the special case in which $q_2 = q_1$, eq. (A.4) is indeterminate. In that case, the integration of eq. (A.3) gives

$$\frac{_1 n_{21s}}{n_2^0} = q_{21}s e^{-q_{1}s}$$

The same problem holds in each of the steps below, if $q_1 = q_2$, $q_2 = q_3$, or $q_1 = q_3$.

APPENDIX 2

```
C       ITERATIVE SOLUTION OF Q(I,J) IN NXN TABLE AND PROJECTIONS
C       MAXIMUM N IS 30, MAXIMUM FOR READ-IN FORMAT IS 12, FOR OUTPUT 16
C       CUT IS INPUT CONSTANT FOR SIZE OF LAST TERM IN SERIES E.G. .00001
C       NPROB IS INPUT CONSTANT, NUMBER OF SEPARATE PROBLEMS
C       MM IS INPUT CONSTANT, MAXIMUM NUMBER OF TERMS IN EACH ITERATION
C       NTOT IS INPUT CONSTANT, MAXIMUM NUMBER OF ITERATION CYCLES FOR QIJ
C       N IS INPUT CONSTANT, SIZE OF MATRIX
C       NTM IS INPUT CONSTANT, NUMBER OF TRANSITION MATRICES TO BE MADE
C       T(I) ARE INPUT CONSTANTS, TIME PERIODS OF TRANSITION MATRICES
C            EXPRESSED RELATIVE TO INITIAL TIME SPAN AS UNIT
C       LAST T, T(NTM), MUST BE 1.0
C       ISQ(I,J) IS MATRIX OF ZEROES AND ONES, ONES ONLY WHERE WHERE
C            POSITIVE Q(I,J)S ARE DESIRED
C       R(I,J) IS INPUT TABLE OF DATA WITH ROW SUMS
C       FIRST OUTPUT IS Q(I,J)S IF ITERATION CONVERGES
C       SECOND OUTPUT IS TRANSITION PROBABILITIES FOR PERIODS REQUESTED
C       THIRD OUTPUT IS REGENERATED DATA
C       FOURTH OUTPUT IS INPUT DATA
        DIMENSION FM(5), FN(3)
        DIMENSION R(30,30), RC(30,30),Q(30,30,2),P(30,30,2),T(30),
       1ISQ(30,30)
C       READ IN CONSTANTS
        READ INPUT TAPE 5,4, CUT,NPROB,MM,NTOT
        READ INPUT TAPE 5,10,N
        READ INPUT TAPE 5,10,NTM
        READ INPUT TAPE 5,1,(T(I),I=1,NTM)
        DO 25 I=1,N
        READ INPUT TAPE 5,11, (ISQ(I,J),J=1,N)
     25 CONTINUE
        M=N+1
        CTT =400.*CUT
        DO 61 NN=1,NPROB
C
C       READ IN INPUT DATA FOR PROBLEM NN
        DO 26 I=1,N
        READ INPUT TAPE 5,95, (R(I,J),J=1,M)
     26 CONTINUE
C
C       SET UP INITIAL VALUES FOR Q(I,J)
        IP=1
        IT=2
        DO 21 I=1,N
        Q(I,I,IP)=0.
        DO 21 J=1,N
        IF (I-J) 20,21,20
     20 CONTINUE
        IF (ISQ(I,J)) 22,24,22
     24 CONTINUE
        Q(I,J,IP)=0.
        GO TO 21
     22 CONTINUE
        Q(I,J,IP) =R(I,J)/R(I,M)
        Q(I,I,IP) =Q(I,I,IP)-Q(I,J,IP)
     21 CONTINUE
        WRITE OUTPUT TAPE 6,14
        DO 27 I=1,N
        WRITE OUTPUT TAPE6,12, ((I,J),J=1,N)
     27 CONTINUE
C
C       GO INTO ITERATION CYCLES
        DO 44 NCY=1,NTOT
        DO 51 I=1,N
        IA=1
```

```
      IB=2
      DO 82 J=1,N
      Q(I,J,IT) =R(I,J)/R(I,M)
      P(I,J,IB) =Q(I,J,IP)
   82 CONTINUE
C
C     START LOOP WHICH ADDS A TERM TO SERIES ON EACH CYCLE
      DO 83 L=2,MM
      FL=L
      DO 85 J=1,N
      P(I,J,IA)=0.
      DO 86 K=1,N
      P(I,J,IA) =P(I,J,IA) + P(I,K,IB)*Q(K,J,IP)/FL
   86 CONTINUE
      Q(I,J,IT) =Q(I,J,IT) - P(I,J,IA)
   85 CONTINUE
      ITEMP =IB
      IB=IA
      IA=ITEMP
      DO 87 J=1,N
      TEMP =P(I,J,IB)*P(I,J,IB)
      IF (TEMP-CUT) 87,83,83
   87 CONTINUE
      GO TO 89
   83 CONTINUE
C
C     EXIT FROM SERIES IF NO CONVERGENCE
      WRITE OUTPUT TAPE 6,9,L
   89 CONTINUE
      DO 52 J=1,N
      IF (I-J) 50,53,50
   50 CONTINUE
      IF (ISQ(I,J)) 52,53,52
   53 CONTINUE
      Q(I,J,IT)=0.
   52 CONTINUE
   51 CONTINUE
      DO 31 I=1,N
      Q(I,I,IT)=0.
      DO 31 J=1,N
      IF(I-J) 32,31,32
   32 Q(I,I,IT) = Q(I,I,IT) - Q(I,J,IT)
   31 CONTINUE
      ITEMP =IT
      IT=IP
      IP=ITEMP
      DO 41 I=1,N
      DO 41 J=1,N
      TEMP = (Q(I,J,IT) - Q(I,J,IP))**2
      IF (TEMP-CTT) 41,44,44
   41 CONTINUE
      DO 28 I=1,N
      WRITE OUTPUT TAPE 6,13,NCY, (Q(I,J,IP),J=1,N)
   28 CONTINUE
      GO TO 60
   44 CONTINUE
C
C     EXIT FROM ITERATION IF ITERATION FAILS TO CONVERGE
      DO 128 I = 1,N
      WRITE OUTPUT TAPE 6,13,NCY, (Q(I,J,IP), J = 1,N)
      WRITE OUTPUT TAPE 6,13,NCY, (Q(I,J,IT), J = 1,N)
  128 CONTINUE
      GO TO 61
```

```
   60 CONTINUE
C
C     BEGIN TO REGENERATE TRANSITION PROBABILITIES AND INPUT DATA
      DO 29 IV=1,NTM
      IA=1
      IB=2
      DO 79 I=1,N
      DO 79 J=1,N
      P(I,J,IB)=0.
      RC(I,J   )=0.
   79 CONTINUE
      DO 77 I=1,N
      IA=1
      IB=2
      P(I,I,IB)=1.
      RC(I,I   )=1.
      RC(I,M   )=1.
      DO 75 L=1,MM
      FL=L
      DO 74 J=1,N
      P(I,J,IA)=0.
      DO 71 K=1,N
      P(I,J,IA)= P(I,J,IA) + P(I,K,IB)*Q(K,J,IP)*T(IV)/FL
   71 CONTINUE
      RC(I,J   )=RC(I,J   ) + P(I,J,IA)
   74 CONTINUE
      ITEMP=IB
      IB=IA
      IA=ITEMP
      DO 81 J=1,N
      TEMP = P(I,J,IB)*P(I,J,IB)
      IF (TEMP-CUT) 81,84,84
   81 CONTINUE
      WRITE OUTPUT TAPE 6,92,I,L
      GO TO 77
   84 CONTINUE
   75 CONTINUE
      LM=L-1
      WRITE OUTPUT TAPE 6,9,LM
   77 CONTINUE
      DO 68 J=1,M
      RC(M,J   )=0.
      DO 68 I=1,N
      RC(M,J   )=RC(M,J   ) + RC(I,J   )
   68 CONTINUE
C
C     OUTPUT TRANSITION PROBABILITIES
      WRITE OUTPUT TAPE 6,94,T(IV)
      DO 29 I=1,M
      WRITE OUTPUT TAPE 6,91,          I,(RC(I,J   ),J=1,M)
      PUNCH 1, (RC(I,J),J=1,M)
   29 CONTINUE
C
C     OUTPUT REGENERATED DATA
      DO 67 I=1,N
      RC(I,M   )=R(I,M)
      DO 67 J=1,N
      RC(I,J   )=RC(I,J   )*R(I,M)
   67 CONTINUE
      DO 63 I=1,N
      RC(I,M   )=R(I,M)
   63 CONTINUE
      DO 65 J=1,M
```

```
      RC(M,J    )=0.
      DO 65 I=1,N
      RC(M,J    ) = RC(M,J    ) + RC(I,J    )
   65 CONTINUE
      DO 30 I=1,M
      WRITE OUTPUT TAPE 6,93,          I,(RC(I,J    ),J=1,M)
   30 CONTINUE
C
C     OUTPUT INPUT DATA
      WRITE OUTPUT TAPE 6, 8, (I,I=1,N)
      DO 33 I=1,M
      WRITE OUTPUT TAPE 6,5,   I,(R (I,J),J=1,M)
   33 CONTINUE
   61 CONTINUE
      CALL EXIT
    1 FORMAT (2X7F10.4)
    2 FORMAT (I4,3X,16F7.3)
    3 FORMAT (5A6)
    4 FORMAT (F9.8,I3,3I4/(1X10F5.1))
    5 FORMAT (I4,(3X,12F10.4))
    7 FORMAT (// 1X,11HCALC P, N ,(I6,12I10))
    8 FORMAT (//   11H ACT N(I,J),(I6,12I10))
    9 FORMAT (5XI3, 20H  CYCLES NOT ENOUGH   )
   10 FORMAT (I2)
   11 FORMAT (30I1)
   12 FORMAT (16(I6,I1),7X)
   13 FORMAT (3XI4,(16F7.3))
   14 FORMAT (7H1Q(I,J) )
   91 FORMAT (I4,(3X,12F10.4))
   92 FORMAT (25H NUMBER OF TERMS FOR I =  ,I2,4H IS , I2)
   93 FORMAT (I4,(3X,12F10.4))
   94 FORMAT (/7H TIME = ,F10.4)
   95 FORMAT (12F6.0)
C     SAMPLE DATA
      END
*     DATA
.000001    1  51 100      CUTOFF, NPROB,NTOT,NT
   4   N
   3   NTM
      2.       3.5       1.             T(1),T(2),T(3)
0110
1001
1001
0110
   484.    93.   107.    32.   716.
   112.   110.    30.    46.   298.
   129.    40.   768.   321. 1258.
    74.    75.   303.   536.   988.
```

CHAPTER 6

MULTIVARIATE
ANALYSIS

It is paradoxical that models for representing relations between continuous variables are so much further developed than are their analogs for relations between attributes. It is paradoxical because the latter relations are so much simpler, and cannot exhibit many of the special features (nonlinearity, etc.) which are found in relations between continuous variables.

Nowhere is this difference in simplicity better manifested than in multivariate analysis. When two continuous variables are treated as independent variables in relation to a third which is taken as the dependent variable, the total amount of data is enormous. It consists of a trivariate frequency distribution, each unit characterized by three numbers which locate it in three-dimensional space. In contrast, two independent dichotomous attributes in relation to a third dependent one generate only eight possibilities, the cells of an eightfold table, rather than the infinity of points in a three-dimensional space.

Yet in spite of this greater simplicity of attribute data, multivariate analysis is far better developed for continuous variables. For example, the technique of multiple regression for continuous variables allows a reduction of the vast complexity of the data to a single predictor equation in which each independent variable is allocated only one coefficient. It is possible, when using cross-sectional data, to analyze the effects of several independent variables upon a dependent one, to express the results in terms of the several regression coefficients (or alternatively, partial correlation coefficients). These coefficients express the amount of relation of each variable to the dependent one, holding constant all the others.

There have been some efforts, however, to provide a basis for multivariate analysis of dichotomous attributes. Robert Somers (1959) starting with Kendall's τ for the case of tied ranks, has developed measures of "partial τ," that is, measures of the effects of an attribute when the effects of others are partialled out. Fred Schreier (1957) has also developed a set of similar measures, with special attention to nonadditive relations. In addition, standard techniques of analysis of variance for m factors, each at two levels, may be applied to multivariate analysis with m independent attributes (see Maxwell, 1961). This technique gives identical procedures to those discussed in portions of the present chapter. Some work has also been carried out using analysis of variance techniques, but with transformed variables. A good treatment of this may be found in Maxwell. Recently, also, computer techniques have been developed for multivariate analysis with dichotomous attributes or ordered variables (Cooley and Lohnes, 1962, Morgan et al., 1962, Wilson, 1963). These approaches (which lead in somewhat different directions from the present one) make a start on the problems of multivariate analysis with dichotomous attributes.[1] Yet the usual procedure for multivariate analysis of attribute data remains as always: We lay out in tabular form the data in its full grandeur, then examine the percentages in the dependent attribute among the various classifications. An example from *The American Soldier* (Stouffer, 1949, vol. I, p. 323) will illustrate. Soldiers were asked whether they wanted to use their civilian occupational skills in the Army. A little less than half said they would prefer to use these skills in the Army. In an effort to learn why some men did and others did not want to use their civilian skills, the authors examined several background and status characteristics. Table 6.1, including noncoms vs. privates, aged over 25 vs. under 25, and having a high-school vs. a grade-school education, was presented in the analysis.

By careful inspection of this table it is possible to see that education, age, and being a noncommissioned officer all show a positive relation to the dependent variable when the others are held constant. Sometimes such an inspection is aided by one or another technique: nonparametric statistics, such as a sign test, in which the number of positive and number of negative percentage differences between pairs of classifications are counted; or a table of differences, presenting the percentage differences between pairs of classifica-

---

[1] See also an elaboration of a general algebra of dichotomous systems (Lazarsfeld, 1961).

tions in more easily assimilable form. But these techniques are merely crutches to aid our careful inspection.

Why the need for such a "careful inspection" of the data in their raw form? This is hardly an analytical tool of great power and accuracy, particularly when careful inspections by two persons might lead them to the opposite conclusions. In analyzing relations between continuous variables, we would hardly treat—even if we could—the full multivariate distribution to a "careful inspection." We would carry out a multivariate analysis which led to regression coefficients or partial correlation coefficients.

Table 6.1

RELATION OF ARMY RANK, AGE, AND EDUCATION TO DESIRE TO USE CIVILIAN SKILLS
IN SERVICE

	PRIVATES				NONCOMS			
	25 −		25 +		25 −		25 +	
	Grade	High	Grade	High	Grade	High	Grade	High
Per cent	32	44	45	56	37	46	40	58
Number	(147)	(210)	(142)	(133)	(70)	(170)	(83)	(125)

With these things in mind, it is now possible to state the intention of the present chapter—to develop a technique for multivariate analysis of attribute data which allows expression of the relations in terms of a single parameter for each independent variable. The model of the previous chapters lays the foundation for such a technique, for it restates the manifest relation between attributes in terms of underlying parameters of effect and random shock. The technique is implicit in the development of the preceding chapters, but its practical importance for data analysis warrants the special attention of a separate chapter.

At the very outset it is necessary to recognize that something must be lost in any such data-reduction as is proposed here. Analysts of attribute data are usually well aware of this, and sometimes use it as a justification for the "careful inspection" of the total data rather than a more highly formalized technique. Several things are lost, for example, by multiple regression analysis of continuous variables. There is usually an assumption of a linear relation between each independent variable and the dependent one (though particular nonlinear assumptions are possible also); and there is often an assumption of no interaction between the independent variables in their effects. The answers to such complaints of lost data and obscured effects are two: First, any analytical procedure, and in fact the very data-collection procedure, involves reduction of the data, abstraction of some aspects to the neglect of others, and there is no reason to balk at this point in the procedure. Second, it is much easier to examine the degree to which the data do depart from linearity and the amount of interaction effects they do contain *after* an analysis which makes these assumptions than before.

After a regression analysis, for example, it is possible to examine the systematic departures of the data from the regression equation. Later in the chapter it will be evident that this second argument is equally strong with attribute data and constitutes a major attraction for using the proposed technique with attribute data, for the departures of data from prediction are quite easily examined.

1. DEVELOPMENT OF THE MODEL FOR THREE ATTRIBUTES

We begin with the fundamental equation for partitioning the transition rate, as discussed in Chapter 4, Section 4. The dependent attribute is dichotomous, having states 0 and 1, as are the independent ones. The states of the independent attributes are so labelled that state 1 of x, y, z, ..., is the state assumed to have an effect toward state 1 of the dependent attribute, by contributing to q_{01}, and state 0 of x, y, z, ..., has an effect toward state 0, by contributing to q_{10}. (This labelling would seem to be an initial restriction, but in fact, is not. It is only done so that the effect components in the resulting transition rates are in fact positive.) The transition rate from state 0 to 1 of the dependent attribute thus has components contributed by each attribute which is in state 1. For an individual who is characterized by x_1, y_1, and z_1 the transition rate $q_{01;xwz}$ would be

$$q_{01;111} = \alpha_x + \alpha_y + \alpha_z + \varepsilon_1 \tag{1.1}$$

If any of these attributes were in state 0, the corresponding component of the transition rate would vanish.

Correspondingly, for an individual characterized by x_0, y_0, and z_0, the transition rate in the opposite direction, $q_{10;xyz}$, would be

$$q_{10;000} = \beta_x + \beta_y + \beta_z + \varepsilon_2 \tag{1.2}$$

If any of these attributes were in state 1, the corresponding component would vanish.[2]

Thus in the initial example in Table 6.1, "wanting to use one's civilian skills" is state 1, while "not wanting to use them" is state 0; x_1, y_1, and z_1 are having a high-school education, being over 25, and being a noncom, respectively; and x_0, y_0, and z_0 are a grade-school education, being under 25, and being a private. For a single independent attribute, high-school vs. grade-school education, the model would look like this:

---

[2] In terms of the fundamental equation in Chapter 4, for partitioning the transition rate, this case corresponds to the one mentioned in the footnote, where state i of the independent attribute has an effect on one q, and state j has an effect on the other. In the fundamental equation, this is expressed by having the attribute that contributes a β to the second transition rate be identical, but with the opposite orientation, to the attribute that contributes an α to the first.

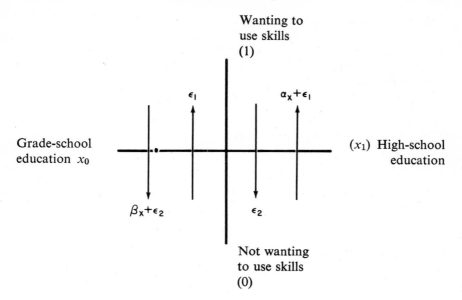

As mentioned in preceding chapters, this gives four parameters (three independent ones since cross-sectional data allow only identification of their relative sizes) while there are only two independent pieces of information. As a consequence, some simplifying assumption must be made. In some cases in Chapter 4 we assumed a one-way effect so that $\beta = 0$. In other cases we assumed a two-way effect with both effects equal: $\alpha_x = \beta_x$. Here the latter assumption will be used, with a section later (Section 6) indicating how the former would be used.

For the example above, with three independent attributes, the partitioning of the transition rates $q_{01;xyz}$ is as follows (using eqs. (1.1) and (1.2), together with the assumption that $\beta_j = \alpha_j$ for all independent attributes j). The eight classifications of Table 6.1 are listed in left-to-right order.

Cell 000 (grade school, 25—, private)

$$q_{10;000} = \alpha_x + \alpha_y + \alpha_z + \varepsilon_2 \qquad (1.3)$$
$$q_{01;000} = \varepsilon_1$$

Cell 100 (high school, 25—, private)

$$q_{10;100} = \alpha_y + \alpha_z + \varepsilon_2$$
$$q_{01;100} = \alpha_x + \varepsilon_1$$

Cell 010 (grade school, 25+, private)

$$q_{10;010} = a_x + \alpha_y + \varepsilon_2$$
$$q_{01;010} = a_y + \varepsilon_1$$

Cell 110 (high school, 25+, private)

$$q_{10;110} = \qquad\qquad \alpha_z + \varepsilon_2$$
$$q_{01;110} = \alpha_x + \alpha_y \qquad + \varepsilon_1$$

Cell 001 (grade school, 25−, noncom)

$$q_{10;001} = \alpha_x + \alpha_y \qquad + \varepsilon_2$$
$$q_{01;001} = \qquad\qquad \alpha_z + \varepsilon_1$$

Cell 101 (high school, 25−, noncom)

$$q_{10;101} = \qquad \alpha_y \qquad + \varepsilon_2$$
$$q_{01;101} = \alpha_x \qquad + \alpha_z + \varepsilon_1$$

Cell 011 (grade school, 25+, noncom)

$$q_{10;011} = \alpha_x \qquad\qquad + \varepsilon_2$$
$$q_{01;011} = \qquad \alpha_y + \alpha_z + \varepsilon_1$$

Cell 111 (high school, 25+, noncom)

$$q_{10;111} = \qquad\qquad\qquad \varepsilon_2$$
$$q_{01;111} = \alpha_x + \alpha_y + \alpha_z + \varepsilon_2$$

For every classification by the three independent attributes there are the three effect parameters, α_x, α_y, and α_z, and two random shocks, ε_1 and ε_2, one in each direction. The difference among the classifications lies in the direction in which the effect parameters operate, as indicated by the diagram.

The five parameters as defined are

α_x = effect of education,

α_y = effect of age,

α_z = effect of Army rank,

ε_1 = random shock due to other variables in the direction of wanting to use skills, and

ε_2 = random shock due to other variables in the direction of not wanting to use skills.

Equations (1.3) specify the transition rates in terms of the hypothesized underlying parameters of effect and random shock. To estimate these parameters by use of the observed proportions in state 1 for each classification, it is necessary to relate the transition rates to the proportions. As in Chapter 4, we assume statistical equilibrium (an assumption which survey analysis implicitly makes when it studies relations between attributes). This implies the following equality (for a given classification):

$$n_1 q_{10} \quad = n_0 q_{01} \qquad (1.4)$$

or

$$\frac{n_1}{n_1 + n_0} = \frac{q_{01}}{q_{01} + q_{10}} \qquad (1.5)$$

and $n_1/(n_1 + n_0)$ is the proportion in state 1 on the dependent variable.

In this chapter, a slight change in notation for these proportions will be used. A subscript $(1, 2, 3, \ldots, n)$ will be used to refer to each of the independent attributes; a subscript for a given attribute will appear for those classifications in which that attribute is in state 1. Thus when attributes x, y, and z are in state 1 (as in the far right-hand cell of Table 6.1), the proportion in state 1 on the dependent attribute will be labelled p_{123}; when only attribute x is in state 1, the proportion will be labelled p_1.

For a three-attribute dichotomous case, as in Table 6.1, the proportions positive would be labelled: $p_.$, p_1, p_2, p_{12}, p_3, p_{13}, p_{23}, p_{123}, reading from left to right in the table.

Thus, using eq. (1.5) and eq. (1.3), it becomes possible to relate the parameters of effect to the observed data. Estimates of each of the proportions in the initial table can be written in terms of the parameters of the model:

$$p_.^* = \frac{\varepsilon_1}{\alpha_x + \alpha_y + \alpha_z + \varepsilon_1 + \varepsilon_2} \tag{1.6}$$

$$p_1^* = \frac{\alpha_x + \varepsilon_1}{\alpha_z + \alpha_y + \alpha_z + \varepsilon_1 + \varepsilon_2}$$

$$p_{123}^* = \frac{\alpha_x + \alpha_y + \alpha_z + \varepsilon_1}{\alpha_x + \alpha_y + \alpha_z + \varepsilon_1 + \varepsilon_2}$$

where the asterisk indicates that the p_i's are not actual data, but estimated p_i's which would be generated by the parameters once they were obtained.

The problem, then, of a technique for analyzing the relations of x, y, and z to the dependent attribute lies in the problem of estimating the five parameters α_x, α_y, α_z, ε_1, ε_2 (four independent ones) with the eight pieces of independent information shown in Table 6.1. There is an excess of data, and one way of resolving such an excess is by the method of least squares. This is not the only method, but the criterion which it meets seems a reasonable one: it gives that set of parameters which will generate a set of estimates (p_i^*) whose sum of squared deviations from the actual data (p_i) is minimum.[3]

First of all, the notation may be simplified. Since the denominators of eq. (1.6) are identical, the sum of all five parameters, we may divide through by this sum to get standardized parameters which add up to 1.0. Call these a_1, a_2, a_3, r, and s, in place of α_x, α_y, α_z, ε_1, and ε_2, respectively. Then eq. (1.6) becomes

$$p_.^* = + r \tag{1.7}$$

$$p_1^* = a_1 + r$$

$$p_2^* = a_2 + r$$

$$p_{12}^* = a_1 + a_2 + r$$

[3] The question of weighting, and the question of what variables we want to minimize the sum of squared deviations from, will be treated shortly.

$$p_3^* = a_3 + r$$

$$p_{13}^* = a_1 + a_3 + r$$

$$p_{23}^* = a_2 + a_3 + r$$

$$p_{123}^* = a_1 + a_2 + a_3 + r$$

The method of least squares consists of finding min $\Sigma(p_i - p_i^*)^2$ and successively minimizing this sum of squared deviations with respect to each of the different components of p_i^*. This may be done in each case by taking the first derivative with respect to that component and setting it equal to zero. Then the resulting four simultaneous equations (one each for a_1, a_2, a_3, and r) may be solved for a_1, a_2, a_3, and r. The fifth component, s, may be found by subtracting the others from one, since the sum of the five is one. By first replacing p_i^* by its components in the sum of squares, then taking the first derivative with respect to a_1, a_2, a_3, and r, setting the results equal to zero, and simplifying, we get four equations, which may be solved for a_1, a_2, a_3, and r to give

$$a_1 = \frac{1}{4}(p_1 + p_{12} + p_{13} + p_{123} - p. - p_2 - p_3 - p_{23}) \qquad (1.8)$$

$$a_2 = \frac{1}{4}(p_2 + p_{12} + p_{23} + p_{123} - p. - p_1 - p_3 - p_{13}) \qquad (1.9)$$

$$a_3 = \frac{1}{4}(p_3 + p_{13} + p_{23} + p_{123} - p. - p_1 - p_2 - p_{12}) \qquad (1.10)$$

$$r = \frac{1}{4}(2p. + p_1 + p_2 + p_3 - p_{123}) \qquad (1.11)$$

and s is found by the fact that all sum to one:

$$s = 1 - a_1 - a_2 - a_3 - r \qquad (1.12)$$

Alternately, s can be found by taking $1 - p_i$ as the observation, turning the whole least-squares procedure around, working with the transition rates into state 0. This gives the following estimation equation for s, which gives identical results to eq. (1.12), and may be used as a computational check:

$$s = \frac{1}{4}(4 - 2p_{123} - p_{23} - p_{13} - p_{12} + p.) \qquad (1.13)$$

All these results are found to be surprisingly simple. Each of the effect parameters is found merely by adding all the p_i's to which this parameter contributes, subtracting the equal number of p_i's to which it does not, and dividing by four. It is simpler to think of the equations for a_1, a_2, and a_3 as the average of four differences: the differences between pairs of proportions

which are alike except that the parameter in question is present in one and
absent in the other [see eq. (1.7)].

$$a_1 = \frac{1}{4}[(p_1 - p.) + (p_{12} - p_2) + (p_{13} - p_3) + (p_{123} - p_{23})] \qquad (1.14)$$

$$a_2 = \frac{1}{4}[(p_2 - p.) + (p_{12} - p_1) + (p_{23} - p_3) + (p_{123} - p_{13})] \qquad (1.15)$$

$$a_3 = \frac{1}{4}[(p_3 - p.) + (p_{13} - p_1) + (p_{23} - p_2) + (p_{123} - p_{12})] \qquad (1.16)$$

Put in this form, the equations for isolating the effect of each variable are
not much different from the heuristic procedure we carry out when in a
higher-order cross-tabulation we take a "mental average" of the differences
between adjacent cells. The equation for the random shock, r, cannot be put
in quite such intuitively appealing form, but is almost as simple as that for
a_1, a_2, and a_3.

Example: Effect of education, age, Army rank on attitude toward civilian
skills

For the example given at the beginning of this chapter, a_1, a_2, a_3, r, and s
may be found as follows:

$$a_1 = \frac{1}{4}(.44 - .32 + .56 - .45 + .46 - .37 + .58 \qquad)$$

$$= .125 \quad \text{(effect of education)}$$

$$a_2 = \frac{1}{4}(.45 - .32 + .56 - .44 + .40 - .37 + .58 - .46)$$

$$= .100 \quad \text{(effect of age)}$$

$$a_3 = \frac{1}{4}(.37 - .32 + .46 - .44 + .40 - .45 + .58 - .56)$$

$$= .010 \quad \text{(effect of rank)}$$

$$r = \frac{1}{4}[(2 \times .32) + .44 + .45 + .37 - .58]$$

$$= .330 \quad \text{(random shock toward using civilian skills)}$$

$$s = 1 - .125 - .100 - .010 - .330$$

$$= .435 \quad \text{(random shock away from using civilian skills)}$$

Check: $s = \frac{1}{4}[4 - (2 \times .58) - .40 - .46 - .56 + .32]$

$$= .435$$

These five values show the relative sizes of the partial relationship of education, age, and Army rank upon wanting to use civilian skills in the Army, together with the sizes of the random shocks (or unexplained variation) in each direction. It is evident that most of the variation is unexplained, and that Army rank explains almost none of it, while age and education explain some.

These measures may be directly employed to reproduce the p's, which will show just how close the predicted values p_i^* are to the actual values p_i.

	$p.$	p_1	p_2	p_{12}	p_3	p_{13}	p_{23}	p_{123}
p_i (actual)	.32	.44	.45	.56	.37	.46	.40	.58
p_i^* (estimated)	.33	.46	.43	.56	.34	.47	.44	.57

The deviations are fairly small and seem to show no consistent pattern. The estimates from the model provide a good fit to the data.

However, in some cases the deviations of actual from estimated can in itself provide an analytical tool of some value. A good illustration is another taken from *The American Soldier* (vol. 1, p. 554).

Example: Effect of race, present camp, origin, upon desired camp location

The dependent attribute is naming a camp in the North or South as the preferred one. The independent attributes are race (Negro-white), region of origin, and location of present camp. Table 6.2 gives the results, tabulated as proportion naming a Southern camp.

Table 6.2

	NORTHERN MEN				SOUTHERN MEN			
	NORTHERN CAMP		SOUTHERN CAMP		NORTHERN CAMP		SOUTHERN CAMP	
	Negro	White	Negro	White	Negro	White	Negro	White
	($p.$)	(p_1)	(p_2)	(p_{12})	(p_3)	(p_{13})	(p_{23})	(p_{123})
Proportion naming a Southern camp	.085	.145	.222	.369	.414	.628	.819	.905

The partitioning of the transition rates is exactly as in eq. (1.7). Using eqs. (1.8) to (1.12), the parameters of the model are

$a_1 = .127$ (effect of race)

$a_2 = .261$ (effect of present camp)

$a_3 = .486$ (effect of region of origin)

$r = .012$ (random shock due to other variables in southern direction)

$s = .114$ (random shock due to other variables in northern direction)

In this example, quite in contrast to the preceding one, almost all the variation in the dependent attribute is accounted for by the independent attributes used in the analysis. Only a total of .126 of the variation remains unexplained.

However, if the predicted p_i^* are calculated and compared with the actual p_i, interesting departures from the assumptions of the model are revealed:

	$p.$	p_1	p_2	p_{12}	p_3	p_{13}	p_{23}	p_{123}
p_i (actual)	.085	.145	.222	.369	.414	.628	.819	.905
p_i^* (estimated)	.012	.138	.273	.400	.498	.625	.759	.886
$p_i - p_i^*$	.078	.007	$-.051$	$-.031$	$-.084$	.003	.060	.011

The greatest deviations (deviations of .05 or greater) are for $p.$, p_2, p_3, and p_{23}. Two, $p.$ and p_{23}, are in the direction of more naming a southern camp than the model predicts, while two, p_2 and p_3, are in the direction of fewer naming a southern camp than the model predicts. All four groups are Negroes, and the deviations are not quite as one would expect. It is not the northern Negroes who especially shy away from a southern camp, nor is it the reverse, southern Negroes wanting especially to get out of the South. The Negroes who choose a southern camp less often than the model predicts are those who have had experience in both places: southern Negroes who are presently in a northern camp (p_3), and northern Negroes who are presently in a southern camp (p_2). Those who choose a southern camp more often than the model predicts are Negroes with experience in only one place: either southerners in a southern camp (p_{23}) or northerners in a northern camp ($p.$).

This example illustrates well just how a model such as this one can lead to findings that were never evident before. If, instead of stopping after measures of effect are calculated, we let these lead us into a further analysis of residues, that is, deviations from predicted values, then results can emerge which were quite obscured by the over-all tendencies in the data. By setting up an explicit model, we factor out these major overriding tendencies and allow the residual differences between groups to become manifest. Later, of course, a more complicated model can be developed to these deviations explicitly into account. Failing that at present, this "method of residues" seems a most promising tack.

2. THE GENERAL EQUATIONS FOR m DICHOTOMOUS INDEPENDENT ATTRIBUTES

In Section 1, the case of three independent attributes was examined. The general equations for any number of independent dichotomous attributes follow the same pattern. In the three-attribute case, each measure of effect was an average of differences between the condition in which this attribute is absent, and the condition in which it is present. If weighting is not done, then this is a simple average; if weighting is done, it is a weighted average.

If there are m independent attributes altogether, then there are, altogether 2^m p's. For any given attribute i, there are, therefore, half this many pairs, 2^{m-1}, to be averaged. If the index c signifies a particular combination of the other dichotomies (e.g., state 1 on attributes 2, 3, 5, 8, m, and state 0 on all others, excluding the one in question), then there are 2^{m-1} such combinations, and the proportion difference for each combination is $p_{ic} - p_c$. The equations for the effects of attribute i are

$$a_i = \frac{1}{2^{m-1}} \sum_{c=1}^{2m-1} (p_{ic} - p_c) \qquad (2.1)$$

or, if we let $2^{m-1} = v$,

$$a_i = \frac{1}{v} \sum_{c=1}^{v} (p_{ic} - p_c) \qquad (2.2)$$

For two independent attributes, there are two comparisons on each; for three, there are four comparisons; for four, eight comparisons; and so on.

The residual effects or random shocks in the same direction as the effects, r, is also found by a general formula, but one less simple. It is found, as in the three-attribute case in the example above, by solving the set of least squares equations for r after minimizing with respect to each of the effect parameters and r. The general equation for m independent attributes is

$$r = \frac{1}{2^m} \left\{ (m+1)p. \quad + (m-1) \sum_{i=1}^{m} p_i \quad + (m-3) \sum_{j=i+1}^{m} \sum_{i=1}^{m} p_{ij} \right.$$

$$+ (m-5) \sum_{k=j+1}^{m} \sum_{j=i+1}^{m} \sum_{i=1}^{m} p_{ijk} \quad + \ldots +$$

$$+ [m - (2m-3)] \sum_{k=m-1}^{m} \ldots \sum_{i=1}^{m} p_{ij\ldots k}$$

$$\left. + [m - (2m-1)] p_{12\ldots m} \right\} \qquad (2.3)$$

where $p_{ij}\ldots$ is that proportion for which attributes $i, j, \ldots$ are in state 1. For the 1, 2, 3, and 4 attribute cases, this reduces to

$$r_1 = p. \qquad (2.4)$$

$$r_2 = \frac{1}{4}(3p. + p_1 + p_2 - p_{12}) \qquad (2.5)$$

$$r_3 = \frac{1}{8}(4p. + 2p_1 + 2p_2 + 2p_3 - 2p_{123}) \qquad (2.6)$$

$$r_4 = \frac{1}{16}(5p. + 3\sum_{i=1}^{4} p_i + \sum_{j=i+1}^{4}\sum_{i=1}^{4} p_{ij} - \sum_{k=j+1}^{4}\sum_{j=i+1}^{4}\sum_{i=1}^{4} p_{ijk} - 3p_{1234}) \qquad (2.7)$$

The number of terms in each of the summations in eq. (2.3) is given by the number of combinations of m things taken u at a time, where u is the number of effects operative. There are $\binom{m}{1} p_i$'s, $\binom{m}{2} p_{ij}$'s, $\binom{m}{3} p_{ijk}$'s, and so on.

The general equation for s is found directly from eq. (2.3), by considering that s plays precisely the same role for $1 - p$ that r plays for p, and that the effects which contribute to a given $1 - p$ are all those which do not contribute to the corresponding p. Thus corresponding to p. for r in eq. (2.3) would be $1 - p_{ij \ldots m}$. If we use this substitution in eq. (2.2) and reverse the order of terms, the equation for s becomes

$$s = \frac{1}{2^m} \left\{ 2^m - (1 - m)p. - (3 - m) \sum_{i=1}^{n} p_i - (5 - m) \sum_{j=i+1}^{m} \sum_{i=1}^{m} p_{ij} + \ldots \right.$$

$$\left. - (m - 1) \sum_{k=m-1}^{m} \ldots \sum_{i=1}^{m} p_{ij \ldots k} - (m + 1)p_{12 \ldots m} \right\} \qquad (2.8)$$

For the special cases of 1, 2, 3, and 4 attributes, the equation reduces to

$$s_1 = 1 - p_1 \qquad (2.9)$$

$$s_2 = \frac{1}{4}(4 + p. - p_1 - p_2 - 3p_{12}) \qquad (2.10)$$

$$s_3 = \frac{1}{8}(8 + 2p. - 2p_{12} - 2p_{13} - 2p_{23} - 4p_{123}) \qquad (2.11)$$

$$s_4 = \frac{1}{16}(16 + 3p. + \sum_{i=1}^{4} p_i - \sum_{j=i+1}^{4} \sum_{i=1}^{4} p_{ij} - 3 \sum_{k=j+1}^{4} \sum_{j=i+1}^{4} \sum_{i=1}^{4} p_{ijk} - 5p_{1234})$$

$$(2.12)$$

3. SAMPLING VARIATIONS AND THE PROBLEM OF WEIGHTING

It is implicitly assumed above that we place the same confidence in each p_i. While this may be so for very large samples, one certainly would not have the same confidence in a p_i based on 20 cases as in a p_i based on 200 cases. Ordinarily, in fact, we would have about the same amount of confidence in each original *observation*, not in each p_i. If that were so, then the confidence we would have in the precision of each p_i would be inversely proportional to the variance of that p_i. Or, to put it a little differently: the aim is not simply to get parameters which will most closely reproduce the original p_i's. The aim is to estimate, in as reliable a fashion as possible, the parameters of effect of attributes x, y, and z, and the size of the unexplained variation in the dependent variable r. To do this, it is necessary to pay less attention to deviations which the estimates may have from p_i that have high variances. The question is how best to do this.

In ordinary regression analysis it sometimes happens that one hypothesizes nonlinear regression of a particular sort which can be put in the form $f(y) = a + bx$. To do this and still minimize the sum of squared deviations from the original observations y, rather than from $f(y)$, is possible through a special weighting procedure for the transformed variables (see Deming, 1948). This problem is much like the present one, and it would seem that the solution is directly applicable here. However, for several reasons it is not. Note first that in each of equations (1.8)–(1.11) some terms are positive while others are negative. This means that a direct weighting of p_i's could produce some very odd results. If, for example, $p_.$, p_2, p_3, and p_{23} all happened to have high weights because there were many cases in these cells, then this could make a_1 negative, by upweighting all the p_i's which were negative in the estimation of a_1. Obviously such a weighting procedure introduces more than a weighting, and could hardly be used.

There is an even more fundamental objection which applies to *any* weighting procedure. It can be formulated as follows. The model whose parameters are being estimated is one which, in effect, partitions each proportion into a number of additive components. Deviation of the observed data from the model can be due to one of two sources: (a) the model is appropriate for the population as a whole, but sampling variations produce deviations in the observed data; or (b) there are systematic effects of other factors, which means that the deviations would remain, whatever the sample size.

Any method of weighting the observed proportions implicitly assumes that all deviations are due to sample size, (a) above. This assumption can be shown, in specific instances, to be extremely untenable. Consider, for example, a case in which there were two independent dichotomous attributes, with $p_.$ and p_1 based on 10,000 cases, and p_2 and p_{12} based on 1,000,000 cases. If differential weightings were applied in the estimate of a, then the $p_1 - p_.$ difference would count for much less than would $p_{12} - p_2$. But it can easily be shown that sampling variation could have caused only the most minute imprecision in p_1 and $p_.$ (in 99 such samples out of 100, p_1 would be closer than $\pm .015$ to the population value). Beyond this range of imprecision, the sampling-variation hypothesis becomes untenable, and the $p_1 - p_.$ difference should count just as much as does the $p_{12} - p_2$ difference.

This is a fundamental difficulty with weighting procedures in any regression analysis. However, in dealing with dichotomies, one can estimate the variance of the individual observation [the estimate is $p_i(1 - p_i)$], and thereby show the size of the deviation that could reasonably have been produced by sampling variation.

The ideal procedure for this estimation would not be weighting at all; it would consist of the following steps:

(1) Consider each observed proportion, p, to be a population probability.
(2) For each p, draw a "sample value," $\hat{p}$, using the sample size on which p_i was based, and estimate the parameters of the model (a_i's, r, and

s), using the unweighted estimating procedures discussed in Section 2 above.

(3) Carry out step 2 a number of times.

(4) Average the resulting estimates of the parameters.

This procedure would take into account the imprecision of observed p's due to sampling variation, but would not allow sample size to have the undue effect it can have in any weighting procedure.

In the absence of machine procedures for carrying out the above steps or others which would have the same effect, it seems most reasonable to proceed as follows:

(a) Whem sample sizes for all p's are large, reject the hypothesis that deviations of p's from the model are due to sampling variation, and disregard the slight imprecision in the p's produced by sampling variations. This implies use of the direct, unweighted estimating equations, (2.1) for a_i and (2.3) for r.

(b) When sample sizes for some p's are small, accept the hypothesis that deviations of the p's from the model are due to sampling variation, and use a weighting procedure.

3.1 Weighting procedure

In carrying out weighting to estimate the parameters of effect, it seems reasonable to weight each difference upon which the estimate is based [see eq. (1.14)] according to our degree of confidence about its precision. This weighting is by the inverse of the variance of the difference.

Let the difference be labelled $p_{ic} - p_c$ for the general case (as in Section 2 above), with the subscript c referring to a particular combination of other effects, and the subscript i referring to the presence of the effect in question. Then the estimate of the variance of this difference is the sum of the estimates of the variances of p_{ic} and p_c (since p_{ic} and p_c are independent random variables). The latter variances are

$$\hat{\sigma}_{p_{ic}}{}^2 = \frac{p_{ic}(1 - p_{ic})}{n_{ic}} \tag{3.1}$$

$$\hat{\sigma}_{p_c}{}^2 = \frac{p_c(1 - p_c)}{n_c} \tag{3.2}$$

where n_{ic} and n_c are the number of cases on which p_{ic} and p_c are based. Then $\hat{\sigma}_{ic}{}^2$ can be expressed as the sum of the variances of p_{ic} and p_c, thus:

$$\hat{\sigma}_{ic}^2 = \hat{\sigma}_{p_{ic}}^2 + \hat{\sigma}_{p_c}^2 \tag{3.3}$$

Each difference is then weighted by the inverse of this variance, and the over-all result is divided by the sum of the weights to obtain the estimate of a_1:

$$w_{ic} = \frac{1}{\hat{\sigma}_{ic}^2} \tag{3.4}$$

$$a_i' = \frac{1}{\Sigma_{w_{ic}}} \sum_{c=1}^{2m-1} w_{ic}(p_{ic} - p_c) \qquad (3.5)$$

The problem of estimating r when there is weighting remains unsolved, and appears especially difficult. In the absence of a solution, the best procedure is probably to use the unweighted procedure for estimating r. An alternative procedure is to substitute the various values of a_i and p in eq. (1.7) and then obtain an average r from these equations.

3.2 Mixed weighted and nonweighted estimates

Often in multivariate analyses a situation exists which is a kind of mixture between the case where weighting is inappropriate and the case where weighting is appropriate. That is, all but two or three of the p's are based on a large enough number of cases to be rather precise, allowing one to reject the hypothesis that their deviations from the model are due to sampling variation. Differential weighting for these p's is thus inappropriate. However, a few of the p's may be based on a small number of cases, say 25, or even 10. For the differences in which these p's play a part, one would not want to reject the hypothesis that deviations are due to sampling variation.

In such a case, one would want a mixed procedure, including differential weights for the differences involving small-sample p's but no differential weights for those involving large-sample p's. A reasonable procedure here is to assign some arbitrary sample size to all the p's whose sample sizes are large enough to reject the sampling-variation hypothesis, and to carry out a weighting procedure in conjunction with the actual sample sizes for the small-sample p_i's. Equation (3.3) would then be used to obtain the weights for each difference, as in the ordinary case of weighting, and eq. (3.5) to obtain the measures of effect.

The question remains, How small should sample sizes be before one accepts the sampling-variation hypothesis, and proceeds with weighting? It is probably best, in the absence of a truly correct procedure, to use a rule of thumb, somewhat as follows. Consider, first, the standard deviation of a difference $p_{ic} - p_c$ based on sample sizes of about one hundred, when p_{ic} and p_c are in the range of 0.3 to 0.7. By eq. (3.3), the variance of this difference will be about 0.005, and the standard deviation about 0.07. This means that if new values of p_{ic} and p_c were drawn, only about three times out of ten would the difference between them deviate from the observed difference more than about 0.07. That is, the estimate of a_i based on $p_{ic} - p_c$ would remain within a range of $(p_{ic} - p_c) \pm 0.07$ seven times out of ten. So long as we are interested principally in values of a_i which are considerably greater than 0.07, say 0.2 or greater, and are interested only in relatively large differences between a_i and a_j, then deviations of this size are unimportant That is, sample sizes of one hundred or larger for each of the p's could produce sampling variations only so small that they would not affect the results in which we were interested. Thus in order to allow the other type of deviations, not due to sample size, to have their legitimate influence on a_t, we would decide not to carry out weighting.

If we were concerned with much smaller a_i's and smaller differences between a_i's, then a larger sample size than one hundred would be necessary as the dividing line between weighting and nonweighting. If, on the other hand, a deviation of less than 0.07 seven times out of ten is more restrictive than necessary for the problem at hand, then a smaller sample size than one hundred would become the dividing line. For example, a sample size of fifty would give a deviation of less than 0.10 from the true value of $p_{ic} - p_c$, seven times out of ten.

3.3 Significance tests for effect parameters

In many investigations, it is desirable to test the hypothesis that an effect parameter is greater than zero, or to carry out some other statistical test upon it. In order to do this, it is necessary to know the sampling distribution of the a_i. These may be easily obtained from the fact that the p's, of which they are linear combinations, are binomially distributed.

Returning to eq. (2.2),

$$a_i = \frac{1}{v} \sum_{c=1}^{v} (p_{ic} - p_c)$$

Since p_{ic} and p_c are independently binomially distributed, their difference is approximately normally distributed with variance equal to the sum of their variances. Furthermore, for the same reason, the sum of these differences is approximately normally distributed with variance equal to the sum of the separate variances. But this sum is va_i (where v is the number of differences that are summed, in the case of m dichotomous attributes, 2^{m-1}). Thus,

$$\text{var}(va_i) = \sum_{c=1}^{v} (\hat{\sigma}_{p_{ic}}^2 + \hat{\sigma}_{p_c}^2) \tag{3.6}$$

This is simply the sum of the variances of all p's, since every p enters once in calculation of a_i. Thus eq. (3.6) can be rewritten as

$$\text{var}(va_i) = \sum \hat{\sigma}_{p_j}^2 \tag{3.7}$$

or

$$\text{var}(va_i) = \sum_j \frac{p_j(1 - p_j)}{n_j} \tag{3.8}$$

where the summation extends over all p_j's that enter into the calculation of a_i.[4] In the cases considered so far, with m dichotomous independent variables,

---

[4] This method of estimating the variance of a linear combination of proportions is proposed by Goodman (1961), who shows that it has a smaller variance around the true variance than a previous method of calculating the variance, known as the Stouffer-Dorn-Tibbets method, based on an average of the p's.

this is all 2^m p_j's for each a_i. In other cases, such as the ordered attributes of Section 4 below, not all p_j's will enter the calculation of each a_i.

If the sum of these estimates of variances for m attributes is labelled $\hat{\sigma}^2_m$, then the variance of each a_i is given from eq. (3.8):

$$\text{var}\,(va_i) \;=\; \hat{\sigma}^2_m \tag{3.9}$$

or

$$v^2\,\text{var}\,(a_i) = \hat{\sigma}^2_m \tag{3.10}$$

or, dividing through by v^2, and representing var (a_i) by $\hat{\sigma}^2_{a_i}$, we obtain

$$\hat{\sigma}^2_{a_i} = \frac{\hat{\sigma}^2_m}{v^2} \tag{3.11}$$

In the case of m dichotomous attributes, eq. (3.11) is a sum of 2^m variances of p's, divided by $(2^{m-1})^2$, or 2^{2m-2}:

$$\hat{\sigma}^2_{a_i} = \frac{\hat{\sigma}^2_m}{2^{2m-2}} \tag{3.12}$$

Each a_i has the same estimated variance, since each p_j enters once into the calculation of each a_i. The probability that a_i could have been zero or negative in the population can then be tested by finding

$$u_i = \frac{a_i - 0}{\hat{\sigma}_{a_i}} \tag{3.13}$$

where u_i is the standardized normal deviate. The probability that a value of u_i as great as that found could have occurred by chance may be determined from a table of the standardized cumulative normal distribution.

The example of Table 6.1, where the effects of education, age, and rank on wanting to use civilian skills were calculated, will serve to indicate how this estimate of the variance of a_i may be used to give significance tests or confidence levels for a_i. The values of a_i are

$$\begin{aligned}
a_1 &= .125 \quad &&\text{(effect of education)}\\
a_2 &= .100 \quad &&\text{(effect of age)}\\
a_3 &= .010 \quad &&\text{(effect of rank)}
\end{aligned}$$

To test the chance that a_1 might be zero in the population, we first calculate its variance, using $\hat{\sigma}^2_{p_j} = p_j(1 - p_j)/n_j$:

$$\hat{\sigma}^2 = \frac{.32 \times .68}{147} = .00148 \qquad \hat{\sigma}^2_3 = \frac{.37 \times .63}{70} = .00333$$

$$\hat{\sigma}^2_1 = \frac{.44 \times .56}{210} = .00117 \qquad \hat{\sigma}^2_{13} = \frac{.46 \times .54}{170} = .00146$$

$$\hat{\sigma}_2^2 = \frac{.45 \times .55}{142} = .00174 \qquad \hat{\sigma}_{23}^2 = \frac{.40 \times .60}{83} = .00289$$

$$\hat{\sigma}_{12}^2 = \frac{.56 \times .44}{133} = .00185 \qquad \hat{\sigma}_{123}^2 = \frac{.58 \times .42}{125} = .00195$$

Then, following eq. (3.12), the estimate of the variance of a_i is one-sixteenth the sum of these eight variances. Thus:

$$\hat{\sigma}_{a_i}^2 = \frac{1}{16}(.00148 + .00117 + .00174 + .00185 + .00333 + .00146$$

$$+ .00289 + .00195)$$

$$= .00099$$

and the standard deviation is

$$\hat{\sigma}_{a_i} = .0315$$

The probability that each a_i might be zero in the population is given by the test of eq. (3.13),

$$u_i = \frac{a_i - 0}{\hat{\sigma}_{a_i}}$$

giving

$$u_1 = \frac{.125}{.0315} = 3.97$$

$$u_2 = \frac{.100}{.0315} = 3.17$$

$$u_3 = \frac{.010}{.0315} = 0.32$$

From tables of the cumulative normal distribution, this gives

$$\text{pr}\{a_1^* \leqslant 0\} < .0001$$

$$\text{pr}\{a_2^* \leqslant 0\} = .0008$$

$$\text{pr}\{a_3^* \leqslant 0\} = .37$$

where a_i^* are the population parameters corresponding to a_i. These probabilities show clearly that one is on safe grounds in supposing that the first two effects (those of education and age) were not a consequence of chance, while the third (that of Army rank) could easily have been so.

In the case where weighting is carried out by the inverse of the variance of $p_{ic} - p_c$, to give a_i, then the variance of each weighted difference may be calculated from eqs. (3.4) and (3.5) to give

$$\hat{\sigma}_{a'_i}^2 = \frac{1}{\sum_c w_{ic}} \qquad (3.14)$$

This variance estimate may be used, in conjunction with the value of a_i', to carry out tests like that in eq. (3.13). Thus the test for the chance that a_i' will be zero in the population becomes extremely simple. The value a_i' is found by summing the weighted differences and dividing by the sum of the weights. The quantity u_i $[u_i = (a_i' - 0)/(\hat{\sigma}_{a'_i})]$ is found by dividing the sum through by the square root of the sum of the weights. The ease of this calculation, once one has the a_i', is shown by recalculating the example of Table 6.1 for the weighted estimates of effect, a_i'. For the first attribute, education, we first calculate

$$w_{1.} = \frac{1}{\hat{\sigma}_1^2 + \hat{\sigma}_.^2} = \frac{1}{.00148 + .00117} = 377$$

$$w_{12} = \frac{1}{\hat{\sigma}_{12}^2 + \hat{\sigma}_2^2} = 278$$

$$w_{13} = \frac{1}{\hat{\sigma}_{13}^2 + \hat{\sigma}_3^2} = 209$$

$$w_{123} = \frac{1}{\hat{\rho}_{123}^2 + \hat{\rho}_{23}^2} = 203$$

and

$$\Sigma w_{1c}(= \frac{1}{\hat{\sigma}_{a'_1}^2}) = 377 + 278 + 209 + 203 = 1067$$

Then a_1 is found by calculating the weighted differences, $w_{ic}(p_{ic} - p_c)$, summing them, and dividing by the sum of the weights:

$$a_1' = \frac{1}{1067}[377(.44 - .32) + 278(.56 - .45) + 209(.46 - .37)$$
$$+ 203(.58 - .40)]$$

$$= \frac{131.2}{1067} = .123 \qquad \text{(effect of education)}$$

The quantity u_1 for testing the probability that this value is greater than zero is then merely

$$u_1 = \frac{131.2}{\sqrt{1067}} = 4.02$$

$$\text{Pr}\{a_1^* \leqslant 0\} < .0001$$

For the second attribute, age, the calculations are

$$w_{2.} = \frac{1}{\hat{\sigma}_2^2 + \hat{\sigma}_.^2} = 310$$

$$w_{21} = \frac{1}{\hat{\sigma}_{12}^2 + \hat{\sigma}_1^2} = 331$$

$$w_{23} = \frac{1}{\hat{\sigma}_{23}^2 + \hat{\sigma}_3^2} = 161$$

$$w_{213} = \frac{1}{\hat{\sigma}_{123}^2 + \hat{\sigma}_{13}^2} = 293$$

$$\Sigma w_{2c} \quad \left(= \frac{1}{\hat{\sigma}_{a'_2}^2}\right) = 1095$$

$$a'_2 = \frac{1}{1095}[310(.45 - .32) + 331(.56 - .44) + 161(.40 - .37)$$

$$+ 293(.58 - .46)]$$

$$= \frac{120.0}{1095} = .110 \qquad \text{(effect of age)}$$

$$u_2 = \frac{120.0}{\sqrt{1095}} = 3.63$$

$$\Pr\{a_2^* \leqslant 0\} < .0005$$

For the third attribute, Army rank, the calculations are

$$w_{3.} = \frac{1}{\hat{\sigma}_3^2 + \hat{\sigma}_.^2} = 208$$

$$w_{31} = \frac{1}{\hat{\sigma}_{13}^2 + \hat{\sigma}_1^2} = 380$$

$$w_{32} = \frac{1}{\hat{\sigma}_{23}^2 + \hat{\sigma}_2^2} = 216$$

$$w_{312} = \frac{1}{\hat{\sigma}_{123}^2 + \hat{\sigma}_{12}^2} = 263$$

$$\Sigma w_{3c}\left(= \frac{1}{\hat{\sigma}_{a'_3}^2}\right) = 1067$$

$$a'_3 = \frac{1}{1067}[208(.37 - .32) + 380(.46 - .44) + 216(.40 - .45)$$

$$+ 263(.58 - .56)]$$

$$= \frac{12.46}{1067} = .012 \qquad \text{(effect of Army rank)}$$

$$u_3 = \frac{12.46}{\sqrt{1067}} = 0.38$$

$$\Pr\{a_3^* \leqslant 0\} = .35$$

As these calculations indicate, there is considerably more labor in calculating the weighted a_i''s than in calculating the unweighted a_i's; but this extra labor gives immediately the value of u_i as well, to allow a test that the population value is greater than zero. The variance of the weighted a_i''s will always be less than (or at most, equal to) the variance of the unweighted a_i's. In this case, the variance of all the unweighted a_i's was .00099, while the variance of the weighted a_i''s were .00094, .00091, and .00094, respectively (1/1067, 1/1095, and 1/1067). This does not ensure, however, that the values of u_i for tests of significance will always be higher for the weighted a_i''s, although that was true in this example. Because of fluctuations in $p_{ic} - p_c$, the value of a_i' may be below the value of a_i, and far enough below to overcome the effect of the lower variance.

3.4 Effect of the number of classifications on the variance of a_i

One of the difficulties in extending multivariate analysis lies in the decreasing number of cases in any cell. This decrease in number of cases is often the reason for stopping in a multivariate analysis, rather than proceeding to higher-order classifications. Any given proportion p_i is based on such a small number of cases that it may be highly unstable. But the above analysis suggests that the use of measures of effect a_i may partially overcome this difficulty. For as the number of cases on which each p_i is based decreases, the number of p_i's increases, as a partial compensation. In fact, two important results stem from this approach, showing that the variability of a_i is not affected by the number of independent attributes used in classification, and the variability of a_i' is not affected by this nor heavily influenced by variations in the number of cases in each cell:

(1) *Using the unweighted estimates, a_i, then if each p_i is based on the same number of cases, the estimate of the variance of a_i is independent of the number of independent attributes, and has an upper bound at $1/n$, where n is the total sample size.*

If weighted estimates, a_i', are used, then this result becomes much stronger:

(2) *Using the weighted estimates, a_i', then if both proportions, p_{ic} and p_c, in each comparison $p_{ic} - p_c$ are based on the same number of cases, the estimate of the variance is independent of the number of independent attributes and has an upper bound at $1/n$, where n is the total sample size.*

Furthermore, if there is an imbalance in the number of cases n_{ic}, on which p_{ic} is based, and n_c, on which p_c is based, then the maximum possible effect on the variance of a_i' is to reduce the effective sample size for the above upper bound by some fraction of $n_{ic} + n_c$. The maximum fraction of this subsample lost is $1 - 4p^0q^0$, where p^0 is the proportion $n_{ic}/(n_{ic} + n_c)$, and q^0 is the proportion $n_c/(n_{ic} + n_c)$. Thus if within this comparison, there are 100 cases, divided 90 : 10, the maximum number of cases lost in this comparison is $100 [1 - 4 \times .9 \times .1] = 64$, and this comparison contributes at least 36 effective cases for reduction of the total variance of a_i. Variations in sample size between different comparisons, $p_{ic} - p_c$, bring about no reduction in the effective number of cases.

These results mean that the major factor controlling the variance is the *total* sample size, and that for any size sample, a higher-order classification is just as feasible as a low-order one. Furthermore, the variance is not highly affected by what would seem to be large variations in number of cases in different cells. In the preceding example, the total number of cases was 1080. Thus if all cells had equal numbers of cases, the upper bound on the variance would be 1/1080. The number of cases in cells ranged from 210 down to 70; but the effect on the variance of the unweighted a_i was merely to reduce the 1080 to 1000 ($= 1/\hat{\sigma}_{a_i}^2$); and the comparable numbers for the weighted a_i were 1067, 1095, and 1067. If any one cell had been reduced to zero cases, the total decrease in the effective sample size for a_i would have been the number of cases in the other cell being compared with it, in this example, 210 or less.

The results above are obtained as follows: For the unweighted a_i, $\hat{\sigma}_{a_i}^2$ is $1/2^{2m-2}$, times the sum $\Sigma\hat{\sigma}_{p_j}^2$ and each $\hat{\sigma}_{p_j}^2$ is $p_j(1 - p_j)/n_j$ [see eqs. (3.8) and (3.12)]. But the maximum that $\hat{\sigma}_{p_j}^2$ can reach occurs when p_j is .5, and this maximum is $1/4n_j$. If all n_j are equal, then they are equal to $n/2^m$, where m is the number of independent attributes. Thus the maximum variance of any one p_j is

$$\frac{1}{4n_j} = \frac{1}{4n/2^m} = \frac{2^{m-2}}{n}$$

The maximum of the sum of these variances (of which there are 2^m in number) is $2^m(2^{m-2}/n)$, or $2^{2m-2}/n$. But the estimate of the variance of a_i is $1/2^{2m-2}$ times this sum, so that

$$\hat{\sigma}_{a_i}^2 \leqslant \frac{1}{2^{2m-2}}\left(\frac{2^{2m-2}}{n}\right)$$

or

$$\hat{\sigma}_{a_i}^2 \leqslant \frac{1}{n} \tag{3.15}$$

if all n_j are equal. If the n_j are not equal, then the variance tends to be dominated by the smallest n_j. In that case, an upper bound for the estimate of the variance can be easily calculated as

$$\hat{\sigma}_{a_i}^2 \leqslant \frac{1}{2^m n_j^*} \tag{3.16}$$

where n_j^* is the smallest n_j. That is, the effective n for calculating an upper bound on $\sigma_{a_i}^2$ is reduced from the total sample size to 2^m times the smallest

n_j. In the example above, this is $8 \times 70 = 560$. A more proximate upper bound may be found by greater calculation, taking into account each n_j:

$$\hat{\sigma}^2_{a_i} \leqslant \frac{1}{2^{2m}} \Sigma \frac{1}{n_j} \qquad (3.17)$$

However, this variance can become quite large if there are a few nearly empty cells, as there tend to be in a large multivariate analysis. It is the weighted case which is valuable here, because a nearly empty cell effectively "takes away cases" only from its companion in the difference $p_{ic} - p_c$, and not from other cells.

The upper bound for the estimate of the variance of a_i' in the weighted case is found by examining each weight:

$$w_{ic} = \frac{1}{\hat{\sigma}^2_{ic} + \hat{\sigma}^2_c}$$

$$= \frac{1}{\dfrac{p_{ic}q_{ic}}{n_{ic}} + \dfrac{p_c q_c}{n_c}}$$

This weight is minimum when p_{ic} and p_c are both .5, so that

$$w_{ic} \geqslant \frac{1}{\dfrac{1}{4n_{ic}} + \dfrac{1}{4n_c}}$$

or

$$w_{ic} \geqslant \frac{4n_{ic}n_c}{n_{ic} + n_c} \qquad (3.18)$$

In the case where $n_{ic} = n_c$, then

$$w_{ic} \geqslant n_{ic} + n_c \qquad (3.19)$$

Since the estimate of the variance of a_i is the inverse of the sum of the weights, then

$$\hat{\sigma}^2_{a_i'} \leqslant \frac{1}{\displaystyle\sum_{c=1}^{2m-1} (n_{ic} + n_c)}$$

and

$$\hat{\sigma}^2_{a_i'} \leqslant \frac{1}{n} \qquad (3.20)$$

when $n_{ic} = n_c$ for each comparison.

When n_{ic} is not equal to n_c, then the effective reduction in n for use in eq. (3.20) can be found by use of eq. (3.18). Multiplying numerator and denominator of (3.19) by the total number of cases in this comparison,

$n_{ic} + n_c$, and using p^0 and q^0 for $n_{ic}/(n_{ic} + n_c)$ and $n_c/(n_{ic} + n_c)$, we get

$$w_{ic} \geqslant (n_{ic} + n_c)4p^0q^0 \qquad (3.22)$$

Thus instead of contributing $n_{ic} + n_c$ cases for eq. (3.21), this comparison contributes (at least) $(n_{ic} + n_c)4p^0q^0$. Thus the effective number of cases "lost" is $(n_{ic} + n_c)(1 - 4p^0q^0)$. If p^0 is very far from .5, this will be a large fraction of $n_{ic} + n_c$; but even for fairly large variations from .5, this fraction lost is not exceedingly great. For example, if the split is .80 : .20, the fraction lost is only .36 of the total $n_{ic} + n_c$. As indicated earlier, if the split is .90 : .10, the fraction lost is .64. The most important point, however, is that this effective "loss" of cases is only within this comparison. There may be a wide range of variation in sample size among different comparisons without affecting the variability of a_i.

4. INDEPENDENT ATTRIBUTES WHICH ARE ORDERED OR UNORDERED CLASSIFICATIONS OF THREE OR MORE CLASSES

4.1 Ordered classes

As often as not, an independent attribute in an investigation is not an attribute at all, but an ordered variable with three or more positions. For example, there might have been three age groups or three categories of education, or four levels of Army rank in the first example. It is generally the case that independent variables are less often dichotomies than is the dependent behavior or attitude. The latter may more often be a "natural dichotomy" (answering Yes or No, taking the left or the right path, voting or not voting) than the former, which are often background or status variables of a diverse sort.

The example below, taken again from *The American Soldier* (vol. 1, p. 528), will indicate how the basic least-squares equations are modified in such a case. After the example, the general equations will be given.

Example: Effect of attitude toward racial separation, region of origin, and education on wanting to be in combat outfit

Here education is not dichotomized, but trichotomized, separating those with no high-school education, those with some high-school education, and those who had graduated from high school. The dependent variable was the answer to a question "If it were up to you, what kind of an outfit would you rather be in?" and the positive (or state 1) response was "a combat outfit." The sample consisted of Negro soldiers in March 1943. These soldiers were classified by education (grade school, some high school, and finished high school), region of origin (North-South), and attitude toward racial separation in the Army (for separation and against). The results were as indicated in Table 6.3.

Table 6.3

	GRADE			SOME HIGH			HIGH				
	SOUTH		NORTH		SOUTH		NORTH		SOUTH		NORTH	
$p.$	p_1	p_2	p_{12}	p_3	p_{13}	p_{23}	p_{123}	p_{33}	p_{133}	p_{233}	p_{1233}
For	*Ag.*	*For*	*Ag.*	*For*	*Ag.*	*For*	*Ag.*	*For*	*Ag.*	*For*	*Ag.*
sep.	*sep.*	*sep.*	*sep.*	*sep.*	*sep.*	*sep.*	*sep.*	*sep.*	*sep.*	*sep.*	*sep.*

Proportion choosing combat											
.09	.13	.14	.19	.15	.16	.25	.30	.17	.21	.28	.31

The model includes the following effects (stated in terms of the standardized coefficients:

a_1 = effect of attitude toward racial separation,
a_2 = effect of region of origin,
a_3 = effect of some high-school education relative to grade-school education,
$a_{.3}$ = effect of completing high-school education relative to some high-school education,
r = random shocks in direction of combat, and
s = random shocks away from combat.

These effects act as follows in the twelve cells of Table 6.3:

$p.$	p_1	p_2	p_{12}
r	$a_1 + r$	$a_2 + r$	$a_1 + a_2 + r$
p_3	p_{13}	p_{23}	p_{123}
$a_3 + r$	$a_1 + a_3 + r$	$a_2 + a_3 + r$	$a_1 + a_2 + a_3 + 1$
p_{33}	p_{133}	p_{233}	p_{1233}
$a_3 + a_{.3} + r$	$a_1 + a_3 + a_{.3} + r$	$a_2 + a_3 + a_{.3} + r$	$a_1 + a_2 + a_3 + a_{.3} + r$

As this tabulation indicates, the effect of each gradation of education is considered relative to the gradation below it, so that the total effect of a high-school education is $a_3 + a_{.3}$. (See Section 4.2 for a direct calculation of the total effect.)

The least squares solution for this model gives estimates which, as before, are the average of pairwise differences between p's. The equations are

$$a_1 = \frac{1}{6}[(p_1 - p.) + (p_{12} - p_2) + (p_{13} - p_3) + (p_{123} - p_{23})$$
$$+ (p_{133} - p_{33}) + (p_{1233} - p_{233})] \quad (4.1)$$

$$a_2 = \frac{1}{6}[(p_2 - p.) + (p_{12} - p_1) + (p_{23} - p_3) + (p_{123} - p_{13})$$
$$+ (p_{233} - p_{33}) + (p_{1233} - p_{133})] \qquad (4.2)$$

$$a_3 = \frac{1}{4}[(p_3 - p.) + (p_{13} - p_1) + (p_{23} - p_2) + (p_{123} - p_{12})] \qquad (4.3)$$

$$a_{.3} = \frac{1}{4}[(p_{33} - p_3) + (p_{133} - p_{13}) + (p_{233} - p_{23}) + (p_{1233} - p_{123})] \qquad (4.4)$$

The equations for the two measures for the ordered attribute, a_3 and $a_{.3}$, are identical to those of a three-attribute dichotomous model, for each gradation of the ordered variable is in effect a dichotomy acting in conjunction with two other dichotomies. The equations for the measures for the dichotomies, in contrast, are like those for a four-attribute model, but with two missing comparisons—those in which the second gradation of the ordered variable appears without the first gradation. As will be evident below, this "mixture" between a three-attribute model and a four-attribute model shows up in the equations for r and s.

The data of the example in eqs. (4.1)–(4.4) give the following estimates:

$a_1 = .037$ (effect of attitude toward racial separation)
$a_2 = .093$ (effect of region of origin)
$a_3 = .078$ (effect of some high-school education relative to grade-school education)
$a_{.3} = .028$ (effect of completing high-school education relative to some high-school education)

Solution of the least squares equations gives this expression for r:

$$r = \frac{1}{12}(5p. + 3p_1 + 3p_2 + p_{12} + 2p_3 + 2p_{33} - 2p_{123} - 2p_{1233}) \qquad (4.5)$$

and for s:

$$s = \frac{1}{12}(12 + 2p. + 2p_3 - 2p_{123} - 2p_{12} - p_{33} - 3p_{133} - 3p_{233} - 5p_{1233}) \qquad (4.6)$$

Substitution of the data from the example into eqs. (4.5) and (4.6) gives

$r = .073$ (random shocks in direction of combat)
$s = .707$ (random shocks away from combat)

The equation for r is a mixture between r_4 and r_3, as is evident by comparison with eqs. (2.6) and (2.7). All the p's with no subscript 3 referring to the ordered variable enter into this equation as they would in r_4 [see eq. (2.7)]. All the p's with a subscript 3 enter as they would in r_3 [(see eq. (2.6)], if the subscript 33 is treated as referring to a new attribute, comparable to 1, 2, and 3 in eq.

(2.6). The equation for s is derived from that for r by the substitutions indicated in Section 2 of this chapter.

This example shows the way in which the model is generalized to ordered attributes. The measures of effect are just like those for dichotomies, and the equations for r and s are slight variations upon the dichotomous equations.

The general equations for the measures of effect, for any combination of order variables and dichotomies, are

$$a_i = \frac{1}{v} \sum_{c=1}^{v} (p_{ic} - p_c) \tag{4.7}$$

where, as before, c is a particular combination of the effects other than the one in question; and v is the total number of such combinations, i.e., the total number of comparisons possible for attribute i. In the example above, this was six for each of the dichotomous effects, and four for each of the two gradations on the ordered variable.

Weighting for a_i's in this case is carried out, when appropriate, as indicated in Section 3 above.

The most critical task in such an analysis is notation, for if the notation is set up properly, it indicates directly the presence or absence of a given effect. In the above, the notation 1, 2, 3, ... m is used to refer to the particular attribute or variable. For dichotomies, the presence of an effect in the positive direction is indicated by the presence of that subscript. For an ordered variable i, the particular gradation is indicated by the number of i's:

0	1	2	3	4 ...
—	i	ii	iii	$iiii$

In the further development below, for a variable with k categories, this is simplified by appending a subscript to i:

0	1	2	3	4 ...	$k-1$
i_0	i_1	i_2	i_3	i_4	i_{k-1}

This may not be the best system of notation, but it or another at least as good is necessàry to keep straight the various effects in a complex combination of independent variables.

The general equations for r and s with ordered variables have not been solved. Perhaps a better notation would aid this. Until then, the value of r for each type of system must be determined anew, by use of the least squares equations. These equations, however, simplify greatly. Taking the derivative with respect to r gives an equation with all the p's on one side, and a sum of r's and a_i's on the other equal to the r's and a_i's implied in the p's (and indicated by the subscripts). For example, in a case with one attribute and one ordered classification with four levels, the derivative with respect to r gives

$$p_. + p_1 + p_2 + p_{12} + p_{22} + p_{122} + p_{222} + p_{1222}$$
$$= 8r + 4a_1 + 6a_2 + 4a_{.2} + 2a_{..2} \tag{4.8}$$

This equation, together with eqs. (4.1)–(4.4), which give each a_i in terms of p's, allow immediate solution for r. In this case,

$$r = \frac{1}{8}(5p. + 3p_1 + p_2 + p_{22} + p_{222} - p_{12} - p_{122} - p_{1222}) \qquad (4.9)$$

4.2 The over-all or average effect for an ordered variable

Very often, one wants to reduce the data further than in the preceding example. That is, one is willing to forego examination of the effect of each category of an ordered variable, and merely asks, What is the over-all effect of the ordered variable? This question can be answered three ways:

(a) What is the effect of a single category change in the ordered variable on p_c?
(b) What is the effect of a change from one extreme category to the other?
(c) What is the effect of the ordered variable, standardized so that it can be compared to the measures of effect for dichotomous attributes?

These questions will be examined in turn. In the example above, the average effect for a single category change will be $\frac{1}{2}(a_3 + a_{.3})$. However, in the general case, it is not necessary to solve first for the separate values a_i, $a_{.i}$, $a_{..i}$, etc. Instead, the average value for variable i with k categories, a_{i_k}, may be obtained by considering all ordered comparisons between the k values of p.

Consider an ordered variable i with k categories, assuming a given classification c on the other attributes. Then for this classification we will have $p_{ci_0}, p_{ci_1}, \ldots, p_{ci_{k-1}}$, where the subscripts $0, 1, 2, \ldots, k - 1$ refer to the category on the ordered attribute i, with p generally increasing as the subscript value increases from zero to $k - 1$. There are a total of $k(k - 1)/2$ ordered comparisons between these p's. For example, if $k = 4$, there are six differences (deleting the subscript c):

$$p_{i_3} - p_{i_0} \qquad p_{i_2} - p_{i_1} \qquad p_{i_1} - p_{i_0}$$

$$p_{i_3} - p_{i_1} \qquad p_{i_2} - p_{i_0}$$

$$p_{i_3} - p_{i_2}$$

The number of categories which separate the two p's in each difference are indicated by the subscripts. Thus the average of these differences, reduced to a single category difference is, in this example,

$$\frac{p_{i_3} - p_{i_2} + p_{i_3} - p_{i_1} + p_{i_3} - p_{i_0} + p_{i_2} - p_{i_1} + p_{i_2} - p_{i_0} + p_{i_1} - p_{i_0}}{1 \quad + \quad 2 \quad + \quad 3 \quad + \quad 1 \quad + \quad 2 \quad + \quad 1}$$

or simplifying,

$$\frac{3(p_{i_3} - p_{i_0}) + (p_{i_2} - p_{i_1})}{10}$$

The general term for the numerator for k categories is

$$\sum_{j=0}^{h} (k - 1 - 2j)(p_{i_{k-1-j}} - p_{i_j})$$

where the limit h is

$$\frac{k - 3}{2} \qquad \text{(if k is odd)}$$

$$\frac{k - 2}{2} \qquad \text{(if k is even)}$$

The general term for the denominator is $\sum_{j=0}^{h} (k - 1 - 2j)^2$, where h is defined as above. This simplifies to $\binom{k + 1}{3}$, or $\dfrac{(k + 1)k(k - 1)}{6}$. Thus the estimate of a_i for this ordered variable, when intermixed with other classifications, is

$$a_{i_k} = \frac{1}{v} \sum_{c=1}^{v} \frac{6 \sum_{j=0}^{h} (k - 1 - 2j)(p_{i_{k-1-j'c}} - p_{i_{j,c}})}{(k + 1)k(k - 1)} \tag{4.10}$$

It should be recognized, of course, that the more categories k there are on the ordered variable, the smaller a_{i_k} will be. To put the measure a_{i_k} in the form that will answer question (b) above, that is, the total effect of variable i from one extreme category to another, it is merely necessary to multiply a_{i_k} by $k - 1$. It should be noted that in order for the sum of a's plus r and s to add to one, a_{i_k} must be in this form multiplied by $k - 1$.

To turn to question (c) above, it is often desirable to be able to compare measures of effect of different attributes and variables independent of the number of categories they have. One way to do so, of course, is to dichotomize each variable, and compare the values of a_i obtained on the dichotomous attributes. Apart from that, however, one simple way to make a_i's comparable, though they are based on different numbers of categories, is to standardize them to an equivalent dichotomous value. This may be done by assuming that the ordered variable is collapsed into a dichotomy at the middle category, and determining the average number of categories separating the collapsed segments. Then by multiplying a_{i_k} by this number, a value comparable to the dichotomous a_i is obtained. (For this calculation to give a value that would be identical to the actual dichotomous a_i, the sample would have to be distributed rectangularly over the ordered categories.) The values of this number for the first few values of k are

$k = 2$	3	4	5	6	7
$d_k = 1$	$\dfrac{4}{3}$	2	$\dfrac{12}{5}$	3	$\dfrac{24}{7}$

The general equation for d_k is given by

$$d_k = \frac{k}{2} \qquad \text{(when } k \text{ is even)} \tag{4.11}$$

$$d_k = \frac{(k+1)(k-1)}{2k} \text{ (when } k \text{ is odd)} \tag{4.12}$$

Then the standardized a_i for comparison to dichotomies is given by

$$a_i = d_k a_{i_k} \tag{4.13}$$

4.3 Unordered classes: in particular, institutional effects

In addition to ordered variables, persons may be classified into categories that have no intrinsic order. Often these are social groups or institutions, and we wish to know the effect of the group or institution on behavior.

An example of this is provided by research carried out by Stanton Wheeler (1963) on inmate cultures in Scandinavian prisons. Wheeler had fifteen prisons, and had classified the men in the prisons according to whether they were young or old at first arrest and according to whether they had many friends or few friends among the other inmates (see Table 6.4). The dependent variable was conformity to institutional norms, and the proportions listed below are proportion conformist. The number of cases is small in a number of cells, and the best procedure would be to use the weighted estimates for a_i. However, the example will be clearer if unweighted estimates are used, so they will be used below.

Just as in preceding sections, we can ask the effect of each of the two dichotomous attributes; but we can also ask the effect of the institutions. The difficulty of answering this lies in the fact that the institutions are unordered. Thus the procedure for the ordered comparisons given in Section 4.2 cannot be directly used. If some way of ordering the institutions were given, then that procedure could be used. For example, if the institutions were ordered according to "permissiveness," this would allow calculation of a measure of the effect of institutional permissiveness, using the procedure of Section 4.2.

However, this does indicate a method for examining institutional effect without the introduction of another variable to order the institutions. For the institutions can be ordered according to one of the classifications given above, and examined on each of the others. They can first be ordered according to the proportion conformist among the young with many friends, that

220   **Introduction to Mathematical Sociology**   [Ch. 6

Table 6.4

Institution	YOUNG Many friends	Few friends	OLD Many friends	Few friends
1	.60 (5)	.67 (18)	.29 (7)	.96 (22)
2	.58 (12)	.63 (56)	.74 (19)	.79 (52)
3	.14 (7)	.75 (4)	.50 (14)	.71 (24)
4	.59 (29)	.63 (40)	.48 (23)	.63 (40)
5	·13 (15)	.50 (4)	.54 (26)	.63 (19)
6	.59 (17)	.63 (19)	.74 (19)	.89 (28)
7	.46 (46)	.61 (56)	·61 (81)	.60 (84)
8	.39 (26)	.25 (8)	.57 (42)	.71 (7)
9	.67 (21)	.83 (18)	.62 (39)	.90 (30)
10	.73 (51)	.66 (29)	.91 (45)	.89 (18)
11	.43 (14)	.58 (64)	.77 (17)	.73 (33)
12	.55 (11)	.65 (79)	.90 (10)	.84 (59)
13	.60 (30)	.49 (61)	.58 (12)	.79 (69)
14	.54 (39)	.53 (17)	.56 (16)	.75 (12)
15	.67 (15)	.53 (53)	.80 (15)	.76 (63)

is, the left column. Then for each of the other classifications, eq. (4.10) for ordered variables can be used. The calculations are carried out below to illustrate the procedure. The numerators are calculated as follows:

	SUBGROUP 1(i)	2	3	4
$14(p_{i14} - p_{i0})$	14(.73 − .13)	14(.66 − .50)	14(.91 − .54)	14(.89 − .63)
$12(p_{i13} - p_{i1})$	12(.67 − .14)	12(.53 − .75)	12(.80 − .50)	12(.76 − .71)
$10(p_{i12} - p_{i2})$	10(.67 − .39)	10(.83 − .25)	10(.62 − .57)	10(.90 − .71)
$8(p_{i11} - p_{i3})$	8(.60 − .42)	8(.67 − .58)	8(.29 − .77)	8(.96 − .73)
$6(p_{i10} - p_{i4})$	6(.60 − .46)	6(.49 − .61)	6(.58 − .61)	6(.79 − .60)
$4(p_{i9} - p_{i5})$	4(.59 − .54)	4(.63 − .53)	4(.74 − .56)	4(.89 − .75)
$2(p_{i8} - p_{i6})$	2(.59 − .55)	2(.63 − .65)	2(.48 − .90)	2(.63 − .84)
$\Sigma =$	20.12	5.76	5.14	9.26

The denominator is $14^2 + 12^2 + 10^2 + 8^2 + 6^2 + 4^2 + 2^2 = 560$. Dividing the numerator by the denominator gives a_{ik} for each of the subgroups, where each in turn is considered as the dependent variable.

$$a_{i_k} = \frac{20.12}{560} = .036 \quad \text{subgroup 1 } (i)$$

$$= \frac{5.76}{560} = .010 \quad \text{subgroup 2}$$

$$= \frac{5.14}{560} = .009 \qquad \text{subgroup 3}$$

$$= \frac{9.26}{560} = .017 \qquad \text{subgroup 4}$$

These numbers show the average difference in p between adjacent institutions for each subgroup, when the institutions are initially ordered according to the first subgroup. If there were no institutional effect, the expected value of a_{i_k} for subgroups 2, 3, and 4 would be zero. That for subgroup 1 would be greater than zero, of course, since the institutions were ordered according to it. But the positive values of a_{i_k} for each of the other subgroups shows the institutional effect. Thus the measures for subgroups 2, 3, and 4 can be considered measures of effect of subgroup 1 upon the other three. The effect is greatest upon subgroup 4, the old with few friends, and least upon subgroup 3, the old with many friends.

By dividing each number through by .036, the result is the amount of change on each subgroup relative to the change for the subgroup used for ordering:

1.00	subgroup 1	.25	subgroup 3
.28	subgroup 2	.47	subgroup 4

Thus the institutional effect here is such that when the institutions are ordered on the first subgroup, subgroups 2, 3, and 4 show respectively .28, .25, and .47 as much difference between institutions, in the same direction, as does subgroup 1 itself.

We can now order the institutions successively according to subgroups 2, 3, and 4, and carry out similar calculations in each case. This will give us a matrix of absolute values for a_{i_k}, and a matrix of relative values. The matrices are given in Tables 6.5 and 6.6.

This analysis shows that subgroup 4's conformity is the best predictor of the others' conformity. This suggests that subgroup 4, the old at first

Table 6.5

			Institution Classified by Subgroup			
			1	2	3	4
			YOUNG		OLD	
			Many	*Few*	*Many*	*Few*
Absolute	Young	Many	(.036)	.008	.018	.024
measures		Few	.010	(.026)	.003	.013
a_{i_k} for	Old	Many	.009	.002	(.036)	.008
		Few	.017	.012	.007	(.024)
Average (excluding diagonal)			.012	.006	.009	.016

Table 6.6

			1	2	3	4
			YOUNG		OLD	
			Many	*Few*	*Many*	*Few*
Relative	Young	Many	1.00	.31	.50	1.00
sizes of		Few	.28	1.00	.08	.54
a_{i_k} for	Old	Many	.25	.00	1.00	.33
		Few	.47	.47	.20	1.00
	Average		.33	.26	.26	.62

arrest with few friends among inmates, is the most sensitive indicator of the conformity of other inmates. Other evidence from this research suggests that these strong relations represent the dependence of the old with few friends on the conformity of others (especially the young with many friends), while the high values for the young with many friends result from the dependence of other inmates on them.

Thus what began as an attempt to find a single institutional effect ends with a rich analysis of the relations between the behavior of different subgroups in the institution. In general, there are institutional effects (the one exception being that the conformity of the young with few friends shows no relation to the conformity of the old with many friends), and their varying sizes show something about the relations among different subgroups in the institution.

One further difference remains, however, between the ordered variable and the unordered variable. In the former, the number of categories, k, was a meaningful quantity that should be reflected in a_{ik}. Consequently, the measure a_{ik} was the difference in p due to a single category change. However, here the number of institutions should not affect the resulting measure. Here, as more institutions were added, a_{ik} would decrease; and the distance between extreme institutions, $(k-1)a_{ik}$, would increase. Instead, what is necessary is a measure that is invariant with the number of institutions. Such a measure is that given by eq. (4.13), which reduces a_{ik} to the form a_i comparable with the dichotomous case.[5] After such a standardization, the measure of the institutional effect is no longer a function of the number of categories, but is

[5] For some purposes, an alternative measure may be desirable, which shows the average difference between two institutions when the institutions are ordered according to a given subgroup. In this case, instead of using eq. (4.10) for obtaining a_{i_k}, a modified equation using the same numerator would give $a_i{}^*$ where $a_i{}^*$ signifies the average difference between institutions on the dependent variable when ordered according to the independent one, i. The numerator of eq. (4.10) is the total sum of differences between institutions, taken over $k(k-1)/2$ ordered comparisons between the institutions. Thus dividing the numerator by the number of comparisons gives the average difference for a single comparison in place of eq. (4.10):

directly comparable with the measures a_i for dichotomous attributes. Carrying out such a transformation in the above example first requires use of eq. (4.12), to give

$$d_k = \frac{16 \times 14}{2 \times 15} = 7.46$$

Multiplying each of the values of the matrix in Table 6.5 by this value gives standard measures a_i that may be compared to the dichotomous measures (see Table 6.7).

Table 6.7

			INSTITUTION CLASSIFIED BY SUBGROUP			
			1	2	3	4
			YOUNG		OLD	
			Many	*Few*	*Many*	*Few*
Standard	Young	Many	(.268)	.060	.139	.179
measures of		Few	.075	(.194)	.022	.097
a_i for	Old	Many	.067	−.002	(.266)	.060
		Few	.127	.090	.052	(.179)
	Average		.090	.049	.071	.112

Table 6.7 shows that the institutional effects on conformity of the inmates are of the same order of magnitude as most of the effects examined elsewhere in this chapter.

The results of this section allow application of this multivariate technique to unordered variables, and what is particularly important in sociological analysis, to group or institutional effects. It provides a particularly useful

---

Footnote 5—*contd.*

$$a_i^* = \frac{1}{v_c} \sum_{v_c=1}^{h} \frac{2\Sigma_{j=0}(k-1-2j)(p_{i_{k-1-j},c} - p_{i_j,c})}{k(k-1)}$$

The relation between a_i^* and a_{i_k} is

$$a_i^* = \frac{(k+1)a_{i_k}}{3}$$

and the relation between a_i^* and a_i [see eq. (4.13)] is

$$a_i^* = \frac{(2k+1)a_i}{3k} \qquad \text{(when } k \text{ is even)}$$

and

$$a_i^* = \frac{2ka_i}{3(k-1)} \qquad \text{(when } k \text{ is odd)}$$

Thus the relation between a_i^* and a_i is approximately independent of k.

tool for the study of the relation between attitudes or behavior of various subgroups within the group or institution. It constitutes an alternative to the usual examination of "structural effects," in which the institutional effect is inferred by classifying an institution according to an independent variable (proportion x) then according to a dependent variable (proportion y), holding constant the individual effects by separating the x individuals from the $\bar{x}$ (see Davis, Spaeth, and Huson, 1961, and Blau, 1960). This approach offers several advantages over that, including direct comparability of institutional effects with those of other attributes, the study of relations among different subgroups' behavior, and freedom from statistical artifact.[6]

5. MULTIPLICATIVE OR INTERACTION EFFECTS

All the models discussed above have assumed additive effects of attributes or ordered variables when they act simultaneously upon a dependent attribute. Many attributes do have additive effects, and the examples above illustrate this. Others, however, do not, and this section will illustrate two types of nonadditive effects which occur with some frequency in statistical analysis. Unfortunately, these two types do not solve the general problem of how to handle nonadditive effects in such multivariate analyses. They only make a start, leaving a large portion of the problem unsolved.

5.1 Intensifier attributes and intensified relationships

A few years ago a seminar was organized by Professor Paul Lazarsfeld at Columbia University's Bureau of Applied Social Research; it was devoted to examining several general forms of relationship which had been found over and over again in quantitative analysis of survey data. One of these forms of relationships was called the "intensifier pheno-menon."[7] The usual character of such a relationship is something like this: one attribute, such as religion, taken as the independent attribute relative to a second, such as voting, shows the usual kind of relation, for example, Catholics tend to vote Democratic, while Protestants tend to vote Republican. But then a second independent attribute is introduced, for example, in this case, attendance at church or nonattendance at church. When this second attribute is introduced into the relation, the table now shows a peculiar form: the new variable acts not independently, but rather to "intensify" the original relationship. The tabulation, holding constant church attendance, would look something like this:

---

[6] Arthur Stinchcombe has shown, in an unpublished memorandum, that an apparent structural effect of x on y may occur through a statistical artifact, due to misclassification errors plus an individual effect of x on y.

[7] The major results of the seminar's study of the intensifier phenomenon are reported in Menzel and Suchman (1955).

| | Nonattenders | | Attenders | |
	Protestant	Catholic	Protestant	Catholic
Per cent Democratic	35	60	15	80

Substantively, of course, this intensification of the relationship is entirely understandable, and not unexpected. Formally, however, it is different from the relations presented up to this point. Church attendance does not generally increase the tendency to vote Democratic, nor does it generally decrease it. By itself, it would show little or no relation to the vote. Thus a model of effects of the following sort would be grossly in error:

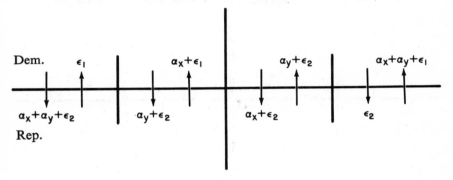

where α_x is the effect of religion on vote, and α_y is the effect of church attendance on vote.

Such a model would show that α_y is approximately zero. While this is certainly true, that church attendance *per se* does not have an independent relation to vote, it misses the important effect that church attendance does have.

There seem to be two solutions for this problem. One, which is applicable for these two attributes because of their content relation, but not in other cases, is to incorporate the two attributes into one ordered classification, ranging from "attending Protestant" to "attending Catholic," with the two other groups in the middle.

	Attending Protestant	Nonattending Protestant	Nonattending Catholic	Attending Catholic
Per cent Democratic	15	35	60	80

With such a combining of these two attributes into one variable of four levels, a single variable model is appropriate, with three effect parameters, one for each change in level.

While this solution would be appropriate for cases like this one, in other cases it would be meaningless to combine the two attributes in this way. The second solution, which is appropriate for all cases, is one in which the transition rate of the intensifier attribute is in a *multiplicative* relation to the transition rate of the other attribute, as follows:

α_x = effect of religious affiliation on vote,

α_y = effect of church attendance on relation between religious affiliation and vote.

The diagram of the transition rates of the model would be

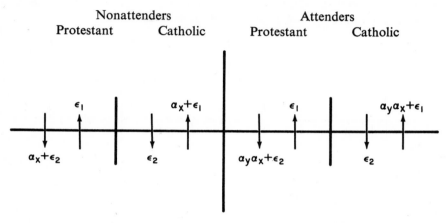

For this situation there are four independent pieces of data (the four p's) and three independent parameters to estimate, so that a least squares analysis could in theory be carried out to provide estimates of the parameters of effect and random shock. However, the least squares procedure seems extremely difficult because of the multiplicative form of the components of p^*. The simplest procedure seems to be to solve each half of the table independently, getting an estimate of α_x/ε_1 and of $\alpha_x\alpha_y/\varepsilon_1$, and two estimates of $\varepsilon_2/\varepsilon_1$. The estimate of $\alpha_x\alpha_y/\varepsilon_1$ can then be divided by that of α_x/ε_1 to give an estimate for the "intensifier" parameter, α_y. Then, if desired, all the estimates can be put in the form of the preceding section, with the denominator equal to $\alpha_x\alpha_y + \varepsilon_1 + \varepsilon_2$.

An example below will show both the incorrect analysis, assuming additive effects, and an analysis along the lines just discussed, assuming multiplicative effects.

Example: Liberalism and knowledge of issues, in voting behavior

It was found in a study of politics in the printers' union (Lipset, Trow, and Coleman, 1956) that liberalism was related to voting for the union president: liberals tended to vote for the Progressive candidate, conservatives for the Independent candidate.

	Conservatives	Liberals
Proportion voting Progressive	.59	.83
n	(123)	(139)

In this election, the Progressive candidate was generally stronger (i.e., the random shocks were predominantly in the Progressive direction), but apart from this general tendency, there is considerably greater voting for the Progressive candidate by liberals than by conservatives. The estimates of effects and random shocks are

$a = .83 - .59 = .24$ (effect of liberalism)
$r = .59$ (random shocks toward Progressive)
$s = .17$ (random shocks toward Independent)

But now if another attribute, knowledge of the issues of the campaign, is introduced, it has a considerable effect, as shown in Table 6.8.

Table 6.8

PROPORTION VOTING FOR PROGRESSIVE CANDIDATE (1952 ELECTION)

	Low in knowledge		High in knowledge	
	Conservatives	Liberals	Conservatives	Liberals
Proportion	.67	.75	.39	.89
n	(87)	(59)	(36)	(80)

The effect of knowledge is not the ordinary effect, that of increasing or decreasing the Progressive candidate's vote among all groups of voters. Instead it intensifies the already-existing relationship, by making liberals more likely to vote Progressive and Conservatives less so. If an ordinary estimation of effects were carried out, assuming an independent effect of knowledge, the above data (using eqs. (2.1), (2.5), and (2.10)) would give

$a_1 = \quad .29$ (effect of liberalism)
$a_2 = -.07$ (effect of knowledge)
$r = \quad .57$ (random shocks toward Progressive)
$s = \quad .22$ (random shocks toward Independent)

This analysis, giving a negative value near zero for the effect of knowledge, is obviously inappropriate. To be sure, it shows that the independent effect of knowledge is nearly zero, but it fails to catch the kind of intensifying effect that knowledge has. This is striking when the values of a, b, r, and s are used to generate estimates values of p:

	$p.$	p_1	p_2	p_{12}
p (actual)	.67	.75	.39	.89
p (estimated)	.57	.86	.50	.79

This is clearly a bad fit when there is only one degree of freedom (four p's, and three independent parameters).

Carrying out the analysis the other way gives the following estimates:

$$\frac{\alpha_x}{\varepsilon_1} = \frac{p_1 - p.}{p.} \tag{5.1}$$

$$= \frac{.75 - .67}{.67} = .12$$

$$\frac{\alpha_x \alpha_y}{\varepsilon_1} = \frac{p_{12} - p_2}{p_2} \tag{5.2}$$

$$= \frac{.89 - .39}{.39} = 1.28$$

$$\alpha_y = \frac{\dfrac{\alpha_x \alpha_y}{\varepsilon_1}}{\dfrac{\alpha_x}{\varepsilon_1}} \tag{5.3}$$

$$= \frac{1.28}{.12} = 10.7$$

$$\frac{\varepsilon_2}{\varepsilon_1} = \frac{1}{2}\left(\frac{1 - p_1}{p.} + \frac{1 - p_{12}}{p_2}\right) \tag{5.4}$$

$$= \frac{1}{2}\left(\frac{.25}{.67} + \frac{.11}{.39}\right) = .33$$

These estimates can now be used to regenerate the estimated p_i's:

$$p. = \frac{\varepsilon_1}{\alpha_x + \varepsilon_1 + \varepsilon_2} = \frac{1}{.12 + 1 + .33} = .69 \tag{5.5}$$

$$p_1 = \frac{\alpha_x + \varepsilon_1}{\alpha_x + \varepsilon_1 + \varepsilon_2} = \frac{1.12}{.12 + 1 + .33} = .77 \tag{5.6}$$

$$p_2 = \frac{\varepsilon_1}{\alpha_x \alpha_y + \varepsilon_1 + \varepsilon_2} = \frac{1}{1.28 + 1 + .33} = .38 \tag{5.7}$$

$$p_{12} = \frac{\alpha_x \alpha_y + \varepsilon_1}{\alpha_x \alpha_y + \varepsilon_1 + \varepsilon_2} = \frac{2.28}{1.28 + 1 + .33} = .87 \tag{5.8}$$

The regenerated data, compared with the actual data, are

	p_1	p_2	p_3	p_4
p (actual)	.67	.75	.39	.89
p (estimated)	.69	.77	.38	.87

In this example, the effect of the intensifier attribute, knowledge, was great, for it amplified the effect of the original attribute, liberalism, more than ten times. As the data show, the effect of liberalism on voting was very small *without* the intensifying effect of knowledge about the issues.

Another example of this intensification is the following general datum:[8] at a high level of income, a person's satisfaction with his job is not correlated highly with income differences (within the high income level); at a low level of income, a person's satisfaction with his job is highly correlated with income differences. That is, low income intensifies the effect of income upon job satisfaction. In this case, the intensifier attribute would be the gross classification of income, and the intensified attribute would be fine classification of income, within the gross categories.

5.2 Interaction between individual attributes and situational attributes

One type of "interaction effect" among qualitative attributes is the intensification discussed above. But there is another frequent type of multivariate relationship which appears to show a different kind of interaction. This is an interaction between individual attributes and situational ones. The situation provides a stimulus, which *acts upon* the individual attributes to produce behavior, and does not *add* to them.[9] Or to put it differently, the situation provides an opportunity, and the individuals act upon that opportunity, differentially according to their capacities.

This general fact manifests itself in survey results by a general phenomenon which may be stated as follows: The category which is initially higher also gains more under a stimulus situation. This generalization is not always true,[10] and of course is made less true by the ceiling effect, which holds down the initially high group. Nevertheless, it is a frequent occurrence. The characteristic result is illustrated by Table 6.9 which shows the effect of experimental films in the U.S. Army upon the knowledge of men at two different intelligence levels (Hovland *et al.*, 1949, p. 145).

Reading across the table shows that the film had some effect, that a subsequent review increased this effect, and that a preliminary introduction before the film was even more effective in increasing the effect of the film. But comparing the two intelligence groups shows that the increase in the proportion was slightly greater for the men with high intelligence than for those with low, even though the men with higher intelligence were closer to the upper limit of 1.0. The greatest increase for the men with low AGCT

---

[8] I am grateful to Alex Inkeles for bringing this finding to my attention.

[9] Or, as some psychologists would prefer to say, the individual attributes act upon the stimulus. In any multiplicative model, these two statements are equivalent, since multiplication is commutative. The statements differ only according to which coefficient they would term the "multiplier," and which they would term the "multiplicand."

[10] A case in which it is not true is examined in Chapter 5, Section 6.1.

scores was .092, while the greatest increase for the men with high AGCT scores was .142. The difference is shown even better by use of Hovland's "effectiveness index," which corrects for the ceiling effect.[11] This index is $(p_s - p)/(1 - p)$, where p_s refers to the stimulus condition, and p refers to the absence of the stimulus. As Table 6.10 shows, the effectiveness of each experimental variation was greater for those of high intelligence level.

Table 6.9

<small>PROPORTION OF CORRECT ANSWERS IN A POST-FILM QUIZ OF FIFTEEN TRUE-FALSE QUESTIONS</small>

| | | | SITUATION | |
Intelligence level	No film	Film only	Film with review	Film with introduction
Low (AGCT I, II)†	.338	.380	.414	.430
High (AGCT III, IV)	.462	.567	.586	.604

† AGCT: Army General Classification Test.

One can pose two alternative models for these data and for other data like them: the additive one, which has been discussed throughout preceding sections, and on which the effectiveness index is based, and an interaction model. The two models are shown in the accompanying diagrams.

The first model is nothing other than the one-way effect model of earlier chapters, with the transition rate α for the effect of intelligence, and the

Table 6.10

<small>EFFECTIVENESS INDICES FOR EXPERIMENTAL FILM</small>
(All relative to absence of the film)

Effectiveness	Film	Film with review	Film with introduction
For low AGCT level	.063	.115	.139
For high AGCT level	.195	.230	.264

transition rate β for the effect of the stimulus. The random shocks toward knowledge, ε_1, are other individual and situational factors. The second model also incorporates one-way effects, but these are multiplicative, between situation and individual, though additive within each class of factors. There is apparently one more parameter in the multiplicative than in the additive one, but η may be taken arbitrarily equal to one without loss of generality.[12]

---

[11] This index is the same as that developed in Chapter 4 for the one-way effect of a single attribute, and in terms of that model, is $\alpha/(\alpha + \varepsilon_1 + \varepsilon_2)$.

[12] Alternatively, ε_1 could be taken equal to one, or a new parameter could be set equal to $\varepsilon_1\eta$, and the other variables redefined in terms of this new parameter. This substitution would eliminate one parameter.

Additive model

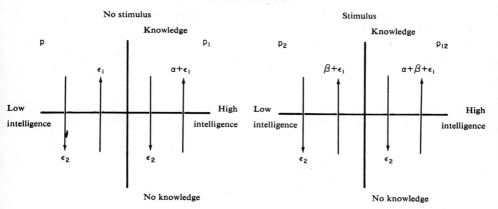

The transition rates for the first model are

ε_1 = random shocks toward knowledge in absence of stimulus or high intelligence,

α = added effects toward knowledge due to high intelligence,

β = added effects toward knowledge due to stimulus, and

ε_2 = random shocks toward lack of knowledge.

Multiplicative model

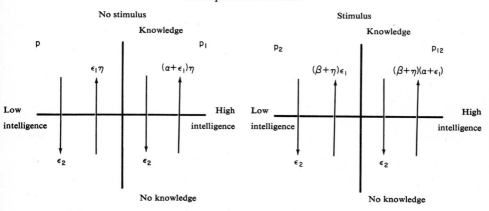

The transition rates for the second model are

η = situational effects toward knowledge in absence of stimulus,

β = added situational effects toward knowledge in presence of stimulus,

ε_1 = individual effects toward knowledge without high intelligence,

α = added individual effects toward knowledge due to high intelligence, and

ε_2 = random shocks toward lack of knowledge.

This means that both models have the same number of parameters: two "random shocks" in the absence of intelligence and stimulus, and two transition rates, one for the effect of each factor.

The question which may be asked, then, is this: In survey results of the type illustrated by Table 6.5, which model is appropriate, if either? Do either of these models account for the general result stated earlier: "The category which is initially higher also gains more under a stimulus situation"? More precisely, the question can be put: With either model, can the effect of the stimulus situation be specified by the same parameter of effect operating for both categories of people? With the interaction model, can the greater "effectiveness" of the stimulus for the initially higher group be accounted for by the interaction between the individual and situational parameters? A number of tabulations which involve a situational factor and an individual factor were located to examine this question. Using these data, we may compare the additive and multiplicative models. From the diagrams above, it can be shown that for the additive model,

$$\frac{\beta_1}{\varepsilon_2} = \frac{p_2}{1 - p_2} - \frac{p_.}{1 - p_.} \tag{5.9}$$

$$\frac{\beta_2}{\varepsilon_2} = \frac{p_{12}}{1 - p_{12}} - \frac{p_1}{1 - p_1} \tag{5.10}$$

where β_1 is the estimate of the effect of the situation for type 1 persons (low intelligence), and β_2 is the estimate of the effect of the situation for type 2 persons (high intelligence), and for the multiplicative model,

$$\beta_1 = \frac{p_2 - p_.}{p_.(1 - p_2)} \tag{5.11}$$

$$\beta_2 = \frac{p_{12} - p_1}{p_1(1 - p_{12})} \tag{5.12}$$

When there are more than two categories of persons, then the estimates are β_3, etc. When there is more than one stimulus (Table 6.5), then a β is calculated for each stimulus (all relative to the no-stimulus situation).[13]

After calculating separate β's for each category of persons, then an average β is calculated for the average effect of that stimulus situation. Then a predicted proportion may be calculated for each category of persons, by substituting the average value of β into eqs. (5.9) or (5.10) for the additive model, and (5.11) or (5.12) for the interactive model, and solving for p_2 or p_{12} (see Table 6.11).

---

[13] In the above equations, it appears that the absolute value of β is obtained in the multiplicative model. This is not so, for there is an implicit η dividing each β. As a consequence of setting η equal to one, this remains implicit.

Table 6.11

COMPARISONS OF ACTUAL EFFECTS OF STIMULUS SITUATIONS UPON DIFFERENT CATEGORIES OF PERSONS, WITH PREDICTIONS FROM INTERACTIVE AND ADDITIVE MODELS

	NO FILM	FILM ONLY			FILM WITH REVIEW			FILM WITH INTRODUCTION		
		Actual	*Inter.*	*Add.*	*Actual*	*Inter.*	*Add.*	*Actual*	*Inter.*	*Add.*
Low	.34	.38	.41	.45	.41	.44	.47	.43	.45	.49
High	.46	.57	.53	.54	.59	.57	.55	.60	.58	.56
(Average β)		(.32)	(.29)			(.52)	(.38)		(.62)	(.44)

Proportion of men at each educational level whose answers to a fact-quiz question indicated they knew the excuse the Japanese gave for invading Manchuria[a]

EDUCATION	CONTROL	FILM		
		Actual	*Inter.*	*Add.*
Grade school	.13	.35	.48	.60
High school	.18	.60	.57	.61
College	.25	.73	.67	.63
(Average β)			(5.11)	(1.35)

Average before and after levels on 31 opinion items reliably affected by four "Why We Fight" films, for men of different educational levels[b]

EDUCATION	BEFORE Control group	Actual	AFTER Inter.	Add.
Grade school	.453	.552	.56	.57
Some high school	.476	.581	.59	.59
High school graduate	.494	.603	.60	.60
College graduate	.508	.628	.62	.61
(Average β)			(.55)	(.53)

Proportion of men at different educational levels believing that "appeasement made things worse in the long run"[b]

EDUCATION	CONTROL	FILM		
		Actual	*Inter.*	*Add.*
Grade school	.53	.56	.66	.73
High school graduate	.61	.73	.73	.76
College graduate	.67	.82	.78	.78
(Average β)			(.70)	(1.27)

Proportion knowing a symptom of cancer[c]

EDUCATION	1945	1955		
		Actual	*Inter.*	*Add.*
Grade school	.30	.42	.53	.74
High school	.50	.71	.73	.77
College	.66	.88	.84	.81
(Average β)			(1.64)	(2.41)

[a] Hovland *et al.*, 1949, p. 152.

[b] *Ibid.*, p. 153.

[c] These data are based on area probability samples of the adult U.S. population, from two surveys (Nos. 136 and 367) of the National Opinion Research Center. Jacob Feldman, in an analysis of these data, discovered the added gain of the higher-educated, and made the data available to me.

The comparisons of the two models with the actual changes which occurred show the superiority of the interaction model. Clearly there does seem to be something like an interaction between individual attributes and situational ones. With the additive model, the groups get closer and closer as the higher one approaches the ceiling. This ceiling effect is counteracted in the interaction model by the impact of the individual characteristics on the situational ones.

However, in almost every case, even the interaction model understates the excess gain made by the initially high groups. What may be the case is this: the interactive effects take account of the differential impact that a given stimulus makes upon persons of different sensitivity when they are exposed to it. But it does not take account of the tendency of the more sensitive persons also to expose themselves more to stimuli: to pay more attention to the stimuli which surround them.

This hypothesis may or may not account for the deviations from the model. The important point is that without the model, no such hypotheses are possible. They require a knowledge of what one should *expect* if given processes are operating, and unless we can mirror those processes theoretically, we cannot provide the knowledge of what to expect.

Another caveat should be added here. In all the discussion above, the assumption was made that there was aggregate equilibrium, not only before the stimulus, but after it. In any detailed investigation, a series of measurements is necessary to learn just how far from aggregate equilibrium the system is.

These two types of interaction between attributes illustrate the general class of effects which are not simply additive, but are multiplicative in their relations with one another. As the examples indicate, it is important not to carry out a multivariate analysis blindly without closely inspecting the data, nor without thinking about the conceptual relation that two variables should have.

6. ONE-WAY EFFECTS vs. TWO-WAY EFFECTS

In the beginning of this chapter, mention was made of the two alternative assumptions about relations of one attribute to another: one-way effects and two-way effects. The former is consistent with thinking of the independent attribute as the absence or presence of something; the latter is consistent with thinking of it as the presence of one thing or the presence of another.

In the exposition above, the latter assumption was used, together with the assumption that the effects are equal in the two directions (an untestable assumption with cross-sectional data). This means that, for every classification by the independent attributes, the *sum* of the transition rates is the same; they are just divided up differently between state 1 and state 0 in the various classifications.

However, the alternative assumption, of one-way effects, might be more relevant for certain situations. For a situation with two independent attributes, the transition rates would look like this under such an assumption:

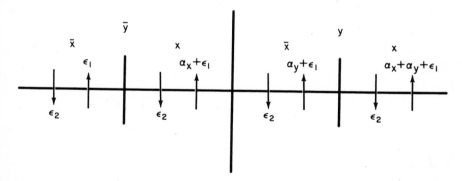

In this case, the statistic for each classification which standardizes the various parameters is $p/(1 - p)$. For the two-attribute case,

$$\frac{p_{\cdot}}{1 - p_{\cdot}} = \frac{\varepsilon_1}{\varepsilon_2} \tag{6.1}$$

$$\frac{p_1}{1 - p_1} = \frac{\alpha_x}{\varepsilon_2} + \frac{\varepsilon_1}{\varepsilon_2} \tag{6.2}$$

$$\frac{p_2}{1 - p_2} = \frac{\alpha_y}{\varepsilon_2} + \frac{\varepsilon_1}{\varepsilon_2} \tag{6.3}$$

$$\frac{p_{12}}{1 - p_{12}} = \frac{\alpha_x}{\varepsilon_2} + \frac{\alpha_y}{\varepsilon_2} + \frac{\varepsilon_1}{\varepsilon_2} \tag{6.4}$$

The terms on the right may be labelled a_1^*, a_2^*, and r^* for the two effects and random shock, respectively, and a least squares procedure carried out for their solution as before. The only difference is that this time the quantities from which the deviations are being minimized are no longer the p's but rather $p/(1-p)$.

After the analysis is carried out, the terms a_1^*, a_2^*, r^*, and $s^* (s^* = \varepsilon_2/\varepsilon_2 = 1)$ cannot be considered as a partitioning of the total variation as in the other case, for the conceptual model is somewhat different here. We are thinking of each of the effects a_1^*, a_2^*, and the random shock r^* as acting against the random shock toward state 0. Thus these measures a_1^*, a_2^*, r^*, and $s^* (s^* = 1)$ are not a partitioning of the total variation throughout the table, but are separate partitionings of the variation in each of the classifications. As such they cannot be directly compared with the measures a_1, a_2, r, and s of the other approach, but can be compared only through the p^* values they generate. The sizes of a_1^* and a_2^* relative to one another are comparable to the relative sizes of a_1 and a_2, but the sizes of r^* and s^* relative to a_1^* and a_2^* are not.

Example

It is worth while comparing for a specific example the results produced by this assumption with those produced by the earlier assumption. The first example, presented at the beginning of the chapter, will be re-examined:

$$a_1^* = \frac{1}{4}\left(\frac{p_1}{1-p_1} + \frac{p_{12}}{1-p_{12}} + \frac{p_{13}}{1-p_{13}} + \frac{p_{123}}{1-p_{123}} - \frac{p.}{1-p.} - \frac{p_2}{1-p_2} \right.$$

$$\left. - \frac{p_3}{1-p_3} - \frac{p_{23}}{1-p_{23}} \right) \quad (6.5)$$

$$= \frac{1}{4}(.79 + 1.27 + .85 + 1.38 - .47 - .82 - .59 - .67)$$

$$= .435$$

and $a_2^* = .360$, $a_3^* = .035$, $r^* = .440$, and $s^* = 1$.

To compare the relative sizes of a_1^*, a_2^*, and a_3^* to a_1, a_2, and a_3, a factor k may be used to set $ka_1^* = a_1$, and then:

$$ka_1^* = .125 \qquad .125 = a_1$$
$$ka_2^* = .103 \qquad .100 = a_2$$
$$ka_3^* = .010 \qquad .010 = a_3$$

Thus the relative sizes of the measures of effects produced by the two methods are nearly the same. The predicted values of p by the second method [using eqs. (6.1)–(6.4) and the additional third-variable equations, and substituting a_1^*, a_2^*, a_3^*, and r^* into the right side of these equations], for comparison with the actual values and with the values predicted by the first method, are given below:

	p.	p_1	p_2	p_{12}	p_3	p_{13}	p_{23}	p_{123}
Actual	.32	.44	.45	.56	.37	.46	.40	.58
First method	.33	.46	.43	.56	.34	.47	.44	.57
Second method	.30	.47	.44	.55	.32	.48	.45	.56

The second method does not reproduce the p's as well as the first in this case. This is somewhat to be expected, since the least squares solution in this second case minimized the squared deviation of $p/(1-p)$, rather than p. However, if the system were behaving more in accordance with these second assumptions than with the first, the fit of the second model should be better, even to the p's.

6.1 A relative assessment of the two approaches

For several reasons the first approach, assuming a two-way effect, seems preferable to the second, assuming a one-way effect, except where there are theoretical reasons to the contrary. The resulting measures are more intuitively appealing, consisting as they do of a partitioning of the total variation in the table. The predicted p^* will usually more closely approximate the actual p's, since it is the deviation from the p's themselves which is being minimized. Finally, under some conditions where a high interaction effect or sampling variation makes one of the p's near 1.0, this gives a very large value of $p/(1-p)$, which then has an unduly large effect on the estimation of the parameters of effect in the second method. A weighting procedure could be introduced to counteract this. However, this is an added complication which further suggests the desirability of the first method.

7. UNSOLVED PROBLEMS

Some of the most immediate further problems for solution are mentioned below.

7.1 General models for ordered variables and continuous variables

Although a method was discussed for dealing with ordered classifications rather than dichotomous attributes as independent variables, it is necessary to complete this in various ways. The general equations for r and s in a system of m ordered attributes with differing numbers of levels is a major unsolved problem.

7.2 Ordered classes as dependent variable

In all the discussion of this chapter, the dependent attribute has been restricted to a dichotomy. However, this is not necessary. A model like the one below (for a single dichotomous independent variable) is a next step.

This model has two parameters of effect, the transition rates α and β, and equations could be set up to solve for these (continuing to make the assumption of aggregate equilibrium).

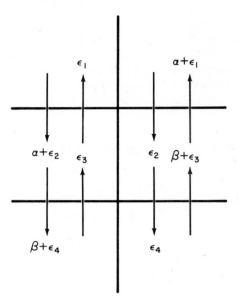

7.3 Giving a metric to ordered classes

The inclusion of ordered classes among the independent variables of a multivariate analysis suggests a further attractive strategy: attaching a metric to an ordered classification on the basis of its effect on the dependent attribute. The usual incorrectness of any metric attached to an attitude scale on the basis of population distribution has been discussed in Chapter 2. What is suggested here, however, is to attach a metric on the basis of the scale's functional relation to other attributes. To put it colloquially, we give each scale position a metric based on the amount of work it does for us.

Consider, for example, a cumulative type of attitude scale used as an independent variable for some behavior. Very often in an analysis we simply collapse such scales into two or three classes because of the complexity of the analysis involved in using the full information. Suppose, instead of this, we carried out an analysis of the sort described in this chapter, using the full set of scale positions. The result of such an analysis would be a set of effect parameters, one for each of the scale positions representing the added effect of that scale position beyond the effect of the next lower one. Now, rather than stopping with these effect parameters, the strategy would be to define a metric as follows.

Each scale position is to have a numerical value such that each unit of distance along the resulting continuum has the same amount of effect upon the dependent attribute. That is, we define a metric such that the metricized scale is linearly related to the dependent attribute. The zero position is arbitrary in such a metric, as is a multiplicative scale factor. What is introduced by such a metric is the concept of "distance" between points on the scale. This concept of distance has a definite functional significance, deriving from the way it is defined: Each unit of distance has the same increment of effect upon the dependent attribute in question.

But one might well ask, What will have been gained by the introduction of such a metric? Several things: since more than one scale may be involved in the analysis, then when a metric is associated with each of them, it is possible to *add* the two or more scale values on the two or more scales. Units on one are substitutable for units on another, because they have the same effect on the behavior which is the dependent attribute. It is possible to give each individual a total sum, and individuals with the same sum, however arrived at, are the same in terms of their predicted behavior on the dependent attribute in question.

A second use of such a metric derives from the added power this allows in further statistical analysis relative to the same dependent behavior. The scale could be treated just as any other continuous variable, with the added advantage of knowing it was linearly related to the behavior in question.

Another kind of use is perhaps even more important. It is possible to examine the same scale in its effects on other dependent attributes, and *if* nearly the same metric—that is, the same relative distances between scale positions—results from those other relationships, then this is an empirical finding of the first magnitude. This means that generally, in its relation to various dependent attributes, the units of distance on the scale have functional significance. Then if several such scales or other ordered classifications show such an invariant metric over these dependent attributes, the attitudes or other classifications are truly substitutable for one another in general, and individuals can be characterized relative to a number of dependent behaviors by the sum of values on the several independent variables.

7.4 A general model for interaction effects

In Section 5, two types of interaction effects were examined, and models were set up for them. However, the general problem remains unsolved. That these two types of interaction do not exhaust the possibilities, nor solve the general problem of interaction effects, is abundantly evident. An example will make this clear. In a study of male juvenile delinquency in Nashville, Tennessee, it was found that there was a general relation between social class and delinquency, and between race and delinquency. But this relation was not constant; the lower-class Negro boys were more delinquent than the additive model would predict. There was an apparent interaction between social class and race to produce this deviation. Such an interaction is not handled by the procedures discussed in Section 5.[14]

7.5 Machine procedures for calculations

Digital computers can easily be programmed for carrying out calculations of these measures. However, the following observations are relevant. The calculation of any effect parameter, a_i, is so simple that it seems fruitful to program the calculations only when one of these conditions is met: (a) if a very general program is written, using the general equations (4.10) and (4.13); (b) if the program is part of a basic data-processing program which calculates the p's from the basic data; in such an instance, the output of the program would be not only the p's, but the a_i's, r, and s, as well; or (c) if the program incorporates a procedure to compensate for small sample size, as discussed in Section 3.

7.6 Multivariate analysis of over-time data

Another extension is the combination of multivariate and over-time analysis. Often there are data at two time periods for the same individuals, as discussed in Chapter 5. Although the examples used there are restricted to two-variable analysis, the method is directly applicable to multivariate analysis. Since the same model underlies this chapter and that one, over-time data can be efficiently incorporated into multivariate analysis of the sort outlined in this chapter. Having solved for the q_{ij}'s by the methods discussed in Chapter 5, it is possible to use the equations of this chapter for estimating the components of q_{ij}. This strategy has been carried out in another publication (Coleman, 1964, Chapter 2).

---

[14] This example was provided by Albert J. Reiss, who attempted to use it to force me into solving this interaction problem. I would gladly have cooperated, but the problem itself has resisted.

CHAPTER 7

MULTIPLE-LEVEL SYSTEMS AND EMERGENT PROPOSITIONS

One of the special problems which is peculiar to sociology and some disciplines in natural science is the existence of multiple-level systems of relations. A variable which characterizes a group will affect some attribute of individuals within the group, and these attributes in turn will affect the attribute of the group. A good example of this may be found in a study of union politics (Lipset *et al.*, 1956, p. 167): It was found that shops with high political *consensus* also had a higher level of *average political activity* among the men (see Table 7.1). It was impossible from the data to determine whether the activity generated consensus or consensus generated activity. Nevertheless, one might suppose that both relations held: where there was political consensus, discussions were freer and a kind of "political resonance" could develop which would generate high activity. At the same time, it is likely that the existence of an initially high level of activity would tend to create consensus, for the deviants would more likely be brought into line than they would in a group which had low political activity.

Table 7.1

RELATIONSHIP BETWEEN SHOP POLITICAL CONSENSUS AND MEN IN SMALL SHOPS
(UNDER 30 ITU MEMBERS) RECENTLY ACTIVE IN UNION POLITICS

	In shops with high consensus	In shops with low consensus
Per cent active in union politics	29	7
Number	(125)	(28)

But how is such a pair of relations to be handled? Is it to be solely on the group level, so that the variables are "degrees of consensus" and "average level of activity"? Or is it to be made up of a set of relations on the individual level, where the following relations are expressed?

(a) (Resonance creates activity) The more nearly one's associates are like oneself in their beliefs on a given subject, the more strongly will one come to act in that direction;

(b) (Activity creates consensus) The more active one is on a given topic, the more he will convince his associates to believe as he does.

The individual-level propositions have a certain attractiveness, perhaps not so much because they are more "fundamental" as because, if a system is constructed properly, it becomes possible to *derive* the group-level proposition as a deduction. Yet there is difficulty inherent in the individual-level propositions, because they cannot be left to remain at the individual level; they must be joined together to mirror the functioning of a social system. At the individual level they are simple, and almost trivially true. But to take these individual propositions and join them to create an emergent group-level proposition (i.e., a proposition which is more than the sum of the individual-level propositions) is no simple task. Using continuous variables, each of the propositions above would require the simultaneous solution of as many differential equations as there are group members, an extremely difficult feat if the group is larger than two persons.

One of the virtues of the discrete-state model is its ability to treat such complexities, and to do so with relatively simple mathematics. It is possible, in the case under discussion, to derive from each of the two individual-level propositions an emergent group-level one. The two propositions are developed below.

1. ACTIVITY AS A FUNCTION OF CONSENSUS

The individual-level proposition as stated above is as follows:

Process 1: Resonance creates activity. The more nearly one's associates are like oneself in their beliefs on a given subject, the more strongly will one come to act in that direction.

Let there be two opposing states of belief, A and B, and two states of activity, active and inactive.[1] This means that at any instant of time, a given individual may be characterized as being in one of four states, labelled as indicated below:

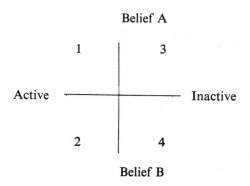

Belief A

For this proposition, we consider no transitions between the two states of belief, but only between the two states of activity.

In the absence of the processes described by the proposition, there are random shocks, η_1, in the direction of activity (states 1 and 2), and η_2 in the direction of inactivity (states 3 and 4). The proposition indicates that in addition, there is, for the persons in state 3 (belief A, inactive), a transition rate toward activity (state 1) dependent upon the number of persons in belief state A (states 1 and 3). If this dependency is assumed to be linear, then the total transition rate is[2]

$$q_{31} = \alpha(n_1 + n_3) + \eta_1 \qquad (1.1)$$

where α is the effect of each person in generating activity among his fellow-believers. Similarly, for the persons in state 4 (belief B, inactive) there is a transition rate toward activity (state 2) dependent upon the number of persons in belief state B (states 2 and 4).

$$q_{42} = \alpha(n_2 + n_4) + \eta_1 \qquad (1.2)$$

There is no explicit statement in the proposition about movement toward

---

[1] This appears to restrict the individual to all-or-none behavior, but in fact does not. The proportion in any state may be viewed as the proportion of time an individual spends in that state, as well as the usual interpretation of the proportion of persons in that state at any time. These two interpretations are entirely consistent under conditions of aggregate equilibrium.

[2] To be absolutely precise, the individual himself should be subtracted from n_3 to give $q_{31} = \alpha(n_1 + n_3 - 1) + \eta_1$. A similar correction holds for eq. (1.2) though not for eqs. (1.4) and (1.5). However, except for small group sizes, this term can be neglected; it will be neglected in the subsequent discussion.

inactivity as a function of the number of persons of opposing beliefs. Two alternative formulations will be considered, one including such "damping" pressures on the assumption that they are implied by the process, and one without them. Without the damping pressures, q_{13} and q_{24} are

$$q_{13} = q_{24} = \eta_2 \qquad\qquad (1.3)$$

With these pressures, which are a function (assumed linear) of the number holding the opposing belief, q_{12} and q_{24} are

$$q_{13} = \beta(n_2 + n_4) + \eta_2 \qquad\qquad (1.4)$$
$$q_{24} = \beta(n_1 + n_3) + \eta_2 \qquad\qquad (1.5)$$

where β is the effect of each person in damping the activity of those of the opposing belief.

The model is as diagrammed below, with the two alternative forms of q_{13} and q_{24} indicated in brackets.

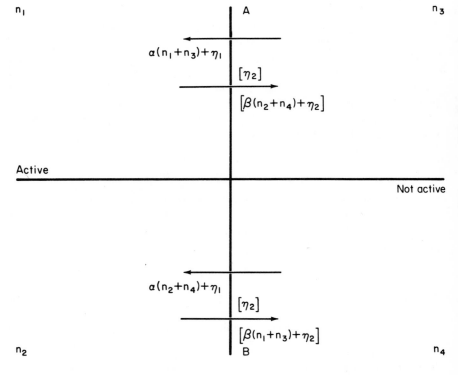

To examine the group-level proposition implies examination of the levels of activity (that is, $(n_1 + n_2)/n$) for different distributions of belief. According to the proposition, when there is high consensus (a large majority in states 1 and 3 or a large majority in states 2 and 4), then there should be more activity (more persons in states 1 and 2) than when there is a more even distribution of belief.

Such a proposition implicitly assumes a state of aggregate equilibrium, so the equilibrium equations may be used to examine the effect of the distribution of belief upon activity. Considering first the model without damping pressures, the equilibrium equations for n_1 and n_2 can be found to be

$$\frac{n_1}{n} = p \quad - \quad \frac{p\eta_2}{p\alpha n + \eta_1 + \eta_2} \tag{1.6}$$

$$\frac{n_2}{n} = 1 - p - \frac{(1-p)\eta_2}{(1-p)\alpha n + \eta_1 + \eta_2} \tag{1.7}$$

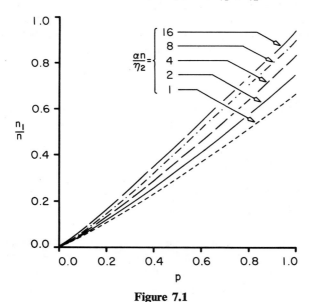

Figure 7.1

where p is the proportion holding belief A ($p = (n_1 + n_3)/n$). From these equations, it is possible to calculate, for a given distribution of beliefs (p), a given set of transition rates (α, η_1, and η_2), and a given group size, what the resulting level of activity is at aggregate equilibrium. The reason that group size enters as a parameter into eqs. (1.6) and (1.7) is that the model assumes that *each person* whose belief coincides with one's own has a given effect α in increasing one's activity. Thus the larger the group, the greater the effect of one's associates in pushing him toward activity.

The results of calculations are shown in Figure 7.1 by examining the relation between n_1/n and p, for the condition in which $\eta_1 = \eta_2$, and for varying values of $\alpha n/\eta_2$. When $\alpha n/\eta_2 = 0$ (i.e., when $\alpha = 0$) then because the random shocks toward activity equal those toward inactivity, the total number of active persons will be exactly half those in each belief category, and thus half the total group, independent of the distribution of beliefs. The graph shows what happens to the activity level within a given belief category as $\alpha n/\eta_2$ increases, successively to 1, 2, 4, 8, and 16. This increase could, of course, be due either to an increase in α, the effect of each fellow-believer, or in the group size. As $\alpha n/\eta_2$ increases, the figure shows that the level of activity within the belief category increases beyond half. The increase is especially pronounced at high levels of p, for an increase in p is an increase in the number of fellow-believers, and thus in the pull exerted toward activity.

The total activity for a given level of $\alpha n/\eta_2$ and a given distribution of beliefs may be found by adding together the two values of n_1/n corresponding to p and $1 - p$ from the appropriate $\alpha n/\eta_2$ line. The group-level proposition may be shown by examining, for some value of $\alpha n/\eta_2$ greater than zero, the total activity as a function of the distribution of beliefs. This is done in Table 7.2, with data taken from the graph, for three values of $\alpha n/\eta_2$ (including $\alpha n/\eta_2 = 0$).

Table 7.2

PROPORTION OF PERSONS IN GROUP WHO ARE ACTIVE, FOR DIFFERENT DISTRIBUTIONS OF BELIEF, AS A RESULT OF PROCESS 1 STATED ON PAGE 242 (FIRST ALTERNATIVE FORM)

Distribution of belief		$\alpha n/\eta_2 = 0$	$\alpha n/\eta_2 = 1$	$\alpha n/\eta_2 = 4$
p	$1 - p$			
.5	.5	.50	.60	.75
.4	.6	.50	.60	.75
.2	.8	.50	.62	.78
0	1.0	.50	.67	.83

As the table indicates, as long as $\alpha n/\eta_2 \neq 0$, activity increases as the group becomes more skewed. The group-level proposition emerges from the model set up at the individual level. The greater strength of the process acts mainly to increase the level of activity rather than the correlation between consensus and activity.[3] Nevertheless, the correlation exists so long as $\alpha n/\eta \neq 0$.

The alternative form of this process, including a "damping" effect of opposing believers, can be investigated in much the same way. Because it includes another parameter β, there is greater freedom in adjusting parameters than in the preceding case. This may be seen from eqs. (1.8) and (1.9), which give the equilibrium equations for the activity levels in both belief groups:

$$\frac{n_1}{n} = \frac{p(p\alpha n + \eta_1)}{p\alpha n + (1 - p)\beta n + \eta_1 + \eta_2} \tag{1.8}$$

$$\frac{n_2}{n} = \frac{(1 - p)[(1 - p)\beta n + \eta_2]}{p\alpha n + (1 - p)\beta n + \eta_1 + \eta_2} \tag{1.9}$$

[3] This is due to the ceiling effect on activity as it reaches high levels. At higher values of $\alpha n/\eta_2$, the correlation decreases, because of the ceiling effect.

Although these equations appear much more formidable than the comparable ones for the alternative form (eqs. 1.6 and 1.7), their behavior may be investigated quite as easily as the behavior of those. As before, the relation between level of activity and distribution of beliefs is calculated for a range of parameter values, and plotted in a chart, Figure 7.2. As before, the condition is that $\eta_1 = \eta_2$, and in addition, $\beta n = \alpha n$. The investigation is carried out for the same set of parameter values as before, $\alpha n/\eta_2 = 1, 2, 4, 8,$ and 16.

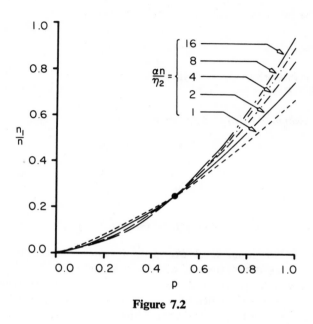

Figure 7.2

Figure 7.2. shows a quite different situation than for the alternative model; unless the proportion of people with the given belief is greater than 0.5, the activity level is *lower* than it would be without the hypothesized process.[4] The opposing believers reduce the activity level more than fellow-believers increase it.

The group-level proposition may again be examined by means of Table 7.3, which shows the total activity at different belief distributions. The pattern in this table is quite different from that of Table 7.2. There the level of activity increased not only as the distribution of belief became more skewed, but also as the process strengthened (as $\alpha n/\eta_2$ increased). Here no increase in level of activity occurs at all when the group is evenly divided;

---

[4] The dividing line of 0.5 is due to the assumed equality of β and α; if they were not equal, it would be greater than 0.5 if the damping effects (β) were greater than the activating effects, and less than 0.5 if the reverse were true.

the damping from opposition persons exactly balances the activating effects of fellow-believers.

These different deductions of the two alternative forms of the process suggest the dangers of formulating mathematical propositions at the group level, without reference to the social-psychological processes which underlie them. As long as the propositions remain qualitative, the difficulties remain obscured; but when they are to be given mathematical precision, there is no *a priori* way of knowing just what form they should take, without deriving them from the processes operative at the individual level.

Table 7.3

Proportion of Persons in Group Who are Active, for Different Distributions of Belief, as a Result of Process 1 on page 242 (second alternative form)

Distribution of belief		$\alpha n / \eta_2 = 0$	$\alpha n / \eta_2 = 1$	$\alpha n / \eta_2 = 4$
p	$1 - p$			
.5	.5	.50	.50	.50
.4	.6	.50	.51	.51
.2	.8	.50	.56	.62
0	1.0	.50	.67	.83

2. CONSENSUS AS A FUNCTION OF ACTIVITY

The second individual level proposition which may account for the correlation between consensus and activity is as follows:

Process 2: Activity creates consensus. The more active one is on a given topic, the more he will convince his associates to believe as he does.

Now, in examining this second proposition, we assume that there are no changes in activity, but only changes in belief. In the absence of the process stated above, there would be only random shocks, ε_1 in the direction of belief A, and ε_2 in the direction of belief B. According to the proposition, there is in addition, for persons with belief B (in states 2 and 4) a transition rate toward belief A (states 1 and 3) dependent upon the number of active persons with belief A (that is, the number in state 1). If this dependency is assumed to be linear, then the total transition rates for those in states 2 and 4 are

$$q_{21} = q_{43} = \gamma n_1 + \varepsilon_1 \tag{2.1}$$

where γ is the conversion effect of each person on those with opposing beliefs. Similarly, for those in states 1 and 3:

$$q_{12} = q_{34} = \gamma n_2 + \varepsilon_2 \tag{2.2}$$

The model is as indicated in the diagram opposite:

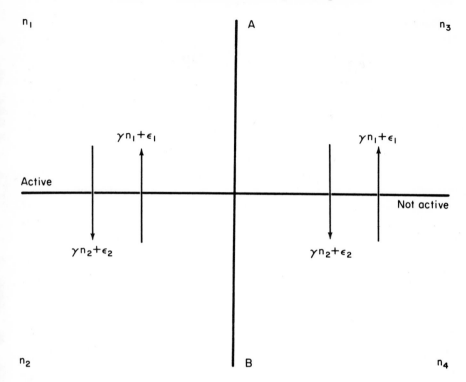

The group-level proposition implies that the higher the proportion of persons in states 1 and 2 (active), the more skewed the distribution will be toward belief A or belief B. The equilibrium equations may be used to examine this. First, we find the ratios n_1/n_2 and n_3/n_4:

$$\frac{n_1}{n_2} = \frac{\gamma n_1 + \varepsilon_1}{\gamma n_2 + \varepsilon_2} \qquad (2.3)$$

$$\frac{n_3}{n_4} = \frac{\gamma n_1 + \varepsilon_1}{\gamma n_2 + \varepsilon_2} \qquad (2.4)$$

As these equations indicate, the distribution of beliefs among the inactives is purely a slave to the distribution among the actives, for it depends solely on that distribution and on the random shocks. Thus the first task is to find the equilibrium distributions of beliefs among the actives, and to examine its dependency on the number of actives. When this is done, by means of eq. (2.3), a peculiar fact emerges. The equilibrium distribution between n_1 and n_2 depends simply upon the random shocks, as if there were no conversion effect γ:

$$\frac{n_1}{n_2} = \frac{\varepsilon_1}{\varepsilon_2} \qquad (2.5)$$

Heuristically, this "cancelling out" of the conversion effects is produced by the following: for any given A, there is a transition rate γn_2 (neglecting random shocks) tending to pull him into state 2. There are n_1 persons subject to this rate, so the expected rate of flow across the 1–2 boundary is $\gamma n_2 n_1$. For any given B, the transition rate is γn_1; but there are n_2 persons subject to this rate, so the expected rate of flow in the 2–1 direction is $\gamma n_1 n_2$. These expected flows exactly cancel one another, whatever the magnitude of γ, and whatever the distribution among n_1 and n_2. This leaves only ε_1 and ε_2 to determine the point of aggregate equilibrium. Consequently, the distribution of beliefs among the actives at aggregate equilibrium is independent of the number of actives, quite different from the group-level proposition which predicts more skewed distributions as the proportion of actives increases.

This distribution of n_1 and n_2 in terms of ε_1 and ε_2 can be substituted into eq. (2.4) to find the equilibrium distribution of beliefs among the in-actives. When this is done, the result is identical to that for the actives:

$$\frac{n_3}{n_4} = \frac{\varepsilon_1}{\varepsilon_2} \tag{2.6}$$

The over-all result, then, is that the distribution of beliefs of persons within the group is not a function of activity through the process of group influence often studied by social psychologists. There is apparently no greater tendency for groups to become skewed when there is a great deal of activity on the matter than when there is little activity.

This result, however, is misleading. It deals with the state of the group at aggregate equilibrium, and never asks the question, How much of the time will a group be at or near its position of aggregate equilibrium? Although we ordinarily speak of the system moving toward aggregate equilibrium from a nonequilibrium starting point, this considers only the mean or average movement. The very fact that the model is a statistical one means that it will fluctuate around the point of aggregate equilibrium, even after it has once reached this point. The question then is, In this fluctuation, how much of its time will a group spend at or near its equilibrium point? Often, such a question need not be asked, for there is rough comparability in this from one model to another. Here the matter is crucial, however, because there is not comparability. When large additional transition rates are added to the random shocks, as are γn_1 and γn_2, then this lowers greatly the stability of the system, even though on the average, the flows produced by these rates cancel each other out. The greater these flows are, the greater the random variability to which they are subject. And the important point for the proposition at hand is that such random variability increases the skewness of the distribution of beliefs. Thus, in accordance with the proposition, as the proportion of the group in states 1 and 2 (and consequently, the size of the transition rates γn_1 and γn_2) increases, the group will more likely be skewed toward one or the other belief.

Whether or not this discussion is a convincing one, the matter ought to be taken out of the realm of "convincing discussions" and into the realm of formal mathematics, to substantiate the discussion. This cannot be done in the present chapter; it must remain until Chapter 11, Section 6, where the examination treats not merely the mean point of the group at aggregate equilibrium, but also the total distribution. It is possible to use those results here, to show how the increase in number of actives affects the degree of skewness or consensus in the group. In Table 7.4 is shown, for groups of size 10, the way in which the variance of p in the expected distribution of beliefs increases as the proportion of actives increases. (The mean of the distribution is, as indicated by eqs. (2.5) and (2.6), independent of this, and depends only on the ratio of the random shocks in the two directions. The variance is, of course, a measure of the expected deviation of the proportion away from its mean, which is implicitly assumed here to be 0.5. The greater the variance, the greater the expected deviation.

Table 7.4

THE VARIANCE OF THE DISTRIBUTION OF BELIEFS IN A GROUP AS A FUNCTION OF THE PROPORTION OF ACTIVES, WHO CONVERT OTHERS ACCORDING TO PROCESS 2 ON PAGE 248[a]

Proportion of actives	Variance of p
0	.025
.2	.063
.4	.089
.6	.109
.8	.125
1.0	.138

[a] Eq. (6.9) of Chapter 11 is used, solving for σ^2/N^2, which is the variance of p. In this equation, $c = \gamma/(\eta_1 + \eta_2)$, taken arbitrarily to be 1.0, and N is taken as 10.

Thus the second group-level proposition is confirmed, though in a somewhat different way from the first. Each of them illustrates how individual-level processes, embedded in the context of a group of individuals, may give rise to emergent group-level propositions.

3. CONCLUSION

The general point of this chapter has been to show the way that emergent group-level propositions may be developed from individual-level ones. The propositions at the individual level may be so well known as to appear trivial, as in the present example. Yet the group-level propositions deduced from them may be far from obvious or trivial.

In general, the attempt to develop formal group-level relations directly, without recourse to individual behavior, may pose considerable difficulty. Unless precise quantitative data exist, the form of the group-level relation, and the operational meaning of the concepts, may have to be quite arbitrary. But by moving from the individual level to that of the group, the operational meaning of the concepts is well specified, and the form of the relation derives from the more easily verifiable individual-level relations.

CHAPTER 8

ONE-WAY PROCESS WITH A CONTINUOUS INDEPENDENT VARIABLE

1. INTRODUCTION

In the preceding chapter, process models were approached from the point of view of two dichotomous variables in relation. But processes of the type outlined there are very general, and not restricted to relations between dichotomous variables. Consider, for example, a model for transition from life to death:

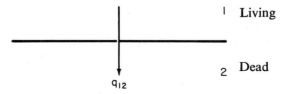

If we know the death rate, q_{12}, for a given homogeneous group, we can calculate very simply the expected proportion still alive at any time t after observing them all alive at time zero:

$$\frac{dn}{dt} = -q_{12}n \tag{1.1}$$

or, by integration,

$$\ln\frac{n_1}{n_0} = q_{12}t \tag{1.2}$$

or

$$p_t = e^{-q_{12}} \tag{1.3}$$

where p_t is the expected proportion of those living at time zero who are still alive at time t.

This example shows the basic process in its simplest form: there are only two states, and there is a shift in only one direction (from living to dead). In the preceding chapters, this simple case was elaborated (a) to include shifts in both directions; (b) to decompose the transition rate q_{12} into components which were due to dichotomous attributes x, z, w, . . ., which were causally related to the dependent attributes; and (c) to include the possibility of changes in these other attributes dependent upon this one. It is evident that numerous other kinds of elaborations could take place. For example, if to the simple death process above is added a birth process, then we have this kind of model:

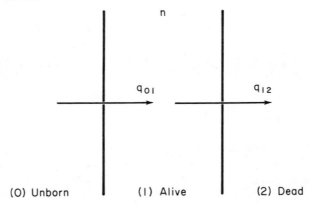

This case constitutes a departure from the preceding cases, for *both* the birth and death rates are functions of the number of persons in state 1, the number alive. The process looks like this:

$$\frac{dn}{dt} = q_{01}n - q_{12}n \tag{1.4}$$

or

$$p_t = e^{(q_{01}-q_{12})t} \tag{1.5}$$

and the population is growing or declining exponentially depending upon whether the birth rate q_{01} or the death rate q_{12} is larger.

This and other elaborations, such as the logistic model of diffusion discussed in Chapter 1, and others to be discussed in subsequent chapters, show the fundamental quality of this kind of model, and suggest how it might be modified to reflect one or another kind of social or psychological process.

The modification employed in this chapter is one in which the simple process of eq. (1.1) is modified by making the transition rate, q_{12}, a function of a continuous variable rather than a dichotomous attribute. The simplest case is that in which the change in the transition rate q_{12} per unit change in the independent variable x is constant. That is,

$$\frac{\partial q_{12}}{\partial x} = \alpha \qquad (1.6)$$

where α is the rate of change of q_{12} with respect to x .The partial derivatives (∂) are written to indicate that all other variables, z, w, v, ..., which can affect q_{12} are held constant. If eq. (1.6) is integrated, we obtain

$$q_{12} = \alpha x + \varepsilon \qquad (1.7)$$

where ε is the transition rate q_{12} evaluated when x is zero. Or to look at it a little differently, ε is the transition rate due to other variables which have an effect on the attribute in question, just as ε in the preceding chapters was the transition rate due to all other variables or attributes except those explicitly considered.

Such a notion as that expressed by eq. (1.7) is hardly foreign; for example, to use the case of death rates again, it is obvious that death rates increase with age. That is, the probability of a man of age sixty dying before he is sixty-one is much larger than that of a man of age twenty dying before he is twenty-one. If this probability of dying within a year increased linearly with age, then eqs. (1.7) and (1.1) together would represent the relation between age and dying. Actually, however, death rates increase faster than linearly with age, so that the simple linear model would not suffice. Incidentally, in ordinary life tables, the age-specific annual rates of mortality are the q_{12}'s for the process of eq. (1.1).

Although death rates do not increase linearly with age, many processes do fit this linear model. Simple though it is, the model has a surprisingly wide scope, in terms of the kinds of data which fit it. Several classes of examples, together with empirical data, will be presented below to illustrate the scope and application of the model. In this chapter only one-way processes will be treated, reserving until Chapter 9 the elaboration into two-way processes with an equilibrium state.

2. PURCHASES OF CONSUMER GOODS AS A FUNCTION OF INCOME

The purchase of consumer goods can be conceived as a process consisting, in the simplest case, of two states separated by the act of buying, that is, not owning and owning:

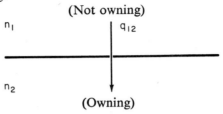

(Not owning)

n_1

q_{12}

n_2

(Owning)

If q_{12} is a linear function of income, x, then this model becomes

$$\frac{dn_1}{dt} = - (\alpha x + \varepsilon)n_1 \tag{2.1}$$

To find the proportion of persons who bought during a given time period, t, this equation may be integrated.

$$\ln\frac{n_{11}}{n_{10}} = - (\alpha x + \varepsilon)t \tag{2.2}$$

where n_{10} is the number of potential purchasers at time zero, and n_{11} is the number who had still not purchased after the time interval t.

A considerable amount of data exists on the purchase of consumer goods as a function of income. The data presented below are taken from work by economists, in one case automobile purchases within the period of a year, and in another case, purchase of any durable goods during the year. In both cases, the relation is linear only within an income band of about $850 or $1000 to $4500. Beyond $4500, income has no effect at all. Despite this restricted range of fit, the purchase process fits conceptually the model so nicely that it is worth while beginning with it.

In Tables 8.1 and 8.2 $\ln p$ is computed for the two examples, $1 - p$ being the proportion of families who have purchased within the year. By using the notation p in place of n_{11}/n_{10} in eq. (2.2), and taking t to be one year (the same for everyone), the equation reduces to

$$\ln p = - (\alpha_x + \varepsilon) \tag{2.3}$$

where $p =$ the proportion that has not purchased by time t,

    $\varepsilon =$ the rate of purchase at zero income, and

    $\alpha =$ the rate of increase of purchasing per unit increase in income.

If there is a critical point of income, c, below which no purchases of this item are made, then in place of a rate of purchase ε at zero income, ε is zero and the basic rate equation becomes

$$\frac{dn_1}{dt} = -\alpha(x - c)n_1$$

which when integrated gives

$$\ln p = -\alpha(x - c)$$

Table 8.1†

Income	Proportion buying durable goods, $1 - p$	p	$-\ln p$
0–1000	.22	.78	.248
1000–1999	.29	.71	.343
2000–2999	.45	.55	.598
3000–3999	.57	.43	.843
4000–4999	.58	.42	.867
5000–7499	.53	.47	.755
7500–9999	.54	.46	.777
10,000 plus	.59	.41	.892

† Data from Lansing and Klein, 1955.

A second set of data concerns purchases of new automobiles. The data are given in Table 8.2 and Fig. 8.1.

Table 8.2†

Income	Proportion buying new cars within year, $1 - p$	$-\ln p$
450	.02	.02
800	.008	.01
1350	.005	.00
1900	.05	.051
2300	.10	.105
3000	.15	.164
4300	.265	.308
5900	.240	.274

† Data from M. J. Farrell, 1954, approximated from the data presented on a chart.

Figure 8.1 shows that the data have a roughly linear relation within the $500–$4500 range; beyond that, income has no effect at all on rate of consumer purchases. The line for durable goods which is fitted to these points (by eye only) intercepts the axis nearly at the (0,0) point, so that one parameter value, ε, is approximately zero. The other parameter, α, equals .024/$100, that is, with each $100 increase, .024 of the families who would not have made a durable goods purchase at a $100 lower level of income make such a purchase. This parameter, and the other as well, have a rather special significance, for they are dimensionally defined, and allow one to compare

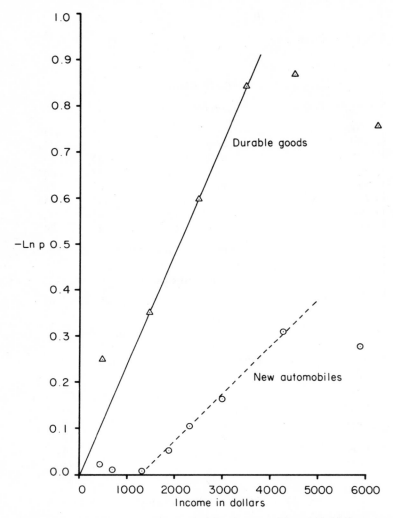

Figure 8.1. Purchase of Durable Goods as a Function of Income; Purchase of Automobiles as a Function of Income

explicitly the effect of one unit of the independent variable x on the dependent variable.

The data for automobile purchases, again, indicate that above $4400, income has no effect on rate of new-car buying; and they show further that in contrast to other durable goods of Figure 8.1, the rate of car-buying drops to zero at about \$1300. Beyond this, it is evident that these data provide a better fit for the linear model than do those in the other case. In this case, the value of α, the rate of increase per \$100 in the proportion of the remaining families[1] buying a car per year, is .01, less than half the value for all durable goods. Thus a given increase in income has less than half the effect in increasing automobile purchases than it does in increasing purchases of all durable goods taken together.

So far, this model has been extremely simple, comprising only two states, with a transition in only one direction and with only one independent variable. It would seem that a better model of consumer purchasing would be one which takes the consumer from one purchase to another, as pictured below:

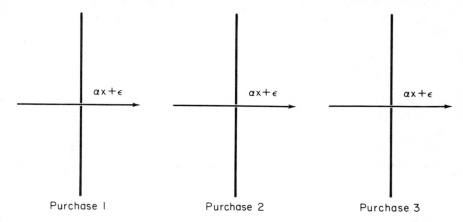

| Purchase 1 | Purchase 2 | Purchase 3 |

However, no such elaboration is possible unless observations include the *number* of purchases made within a given period. In such a case, an elaboration of this type would be fruitful.

A second kind of elaboration is the introduction of additional independent variables. For example, as a second variable, expected income is sometimes included by economists along with income *per se*, in a regression analysis.

The direction of such elaboration is similar to that for multiple dichotomous variables in the preceding chapters. The total rate of change in q_{12} with change in all variables can be written as a sum of the partial rates of change due to each variable:

$$dq_{12} = \frac{\partial q_{12}}{\partial x}\,dx + \frac{\partial q_{12}}{\partial z}\,dz + \frac{\partial q_{12}}{\partial w}\,dw + \ldots \qquad (2.4)$$

and integrating gives

$$q_{12} = \alpha x \quad\quad + \beta z \quad\quad + \gamma w \quad\quad + \ldots + \varepsilon' \qquad (2.5)$$

---

[1] That is, families which would not have bought a car had their income been \$100 lower.

Thus the equation relating purchases within a period of time to these variables x, z, and w becomes

$$\ln p = -(\alpha x + \beta z + \gamma w + \varepsilon') \qquad (2.6)$$

Standard techniques of multiple regression, with $\ln p$ as the dependent variable, can be used for fitting this multivariate model to data. The situation becomes exactly like the case in which the dependent variable is continuous.

3. CENSUS STATISTICS: ILLITERACY RATES

The life-death transition has already been mentioned as a process of this general type, but one in which death rates do not increase linearly with age. Other census data, however, do fit this linear model. Illiteracy provides a good example. Think of education as a process which, operating over the period of childhood, shifts a person from a state of illiteracy to a state of literacy:

$$q_{12} \uparrow \text{Literacy}$$
$$\overline{\phantom{q_{12}}} \quad \text{Illiteracy}$$

Consider further that educational facilities have improved through time, so that q_{12}, the shift rate from literacy to illiteracy, is a function of the date at which the person was educated. If it is assumed that the incremental improvement in educational facilities in the United States has been constant over the period from 1860 to 1930, say, then the process is as above:

$$\frac{dn}{dt} = -(\alpha x + \varepsilon)n \qquad (3.1)$$

where x = date at which education was received;

$\quad \alpha$ = rate of improvement in educational facilities per year (or more precisely, increase per year in proportion of illiterate children shifting to literacy over the educational period); and

$\quad \varepsilon$ = proportion of children shifting from illiteracy to literacy per unit time when $x = 0$ (ε is unimportant here, since the zero point on x is arbitrary).

The model is applied as in the previous case. Integrating eq. (3.1) gives

$$\ln p = -(\alpha x + \varepsilon)t$$

where $1 - p$ is as before, the proportion who did not make the transition—in this case, the proportion remaining illiterate; and the unit of time is taken to be the period of the educational process, so that $t = 1$.

Two homogeneous subgroups of the population, as different from one another as possible, were selected for examination, and age-specific rates of illiteracy were used (Statistical Abstracts, 1946). (Illiteracy rates by date were available for all ages of the population taken together, but this tends to mask any changes in the same way that a "moving average" does, by including persons who received their education at different times.) Table 8.3 gives the age-specific illiteracy rates for urban native whites and rural-farm Negroes, the two subgroups selected.

Table 8.3

ILLITERACY BY AGE (1930 CENSUS)

		(a) URBAN NATIVE WHITE		(b) RURAL-FARM NEGROES	
	Average	Proportion		Proportion	
Age	age	illiterate, p	− ln p	illiterate, p	− ln p
10–14	12	.00167	6.39	.078	2.55
15–19	17	.00272	5.91	.129	2.05
20–24	22	.00370	5.60	.195	1.64
25–34	30	.00409	5.50	.232	1.46
35–44	40	.00551	5.20	.275	1.29
45–54	50	.00759	4.89	.346	1.06
55–64	60	.01000	4.61	.441	.820
65 plus	75	.01780	4·02	.648	.435

Figure 8.2 shows that both sets of data fit well for the ages from 20 to 75, but that for both groups, the two youngest ages show sharply less illiteracy than would be expected. It may be that this has something to do with the mode of reporting children's illiteracy by parents in census interviews. If not, however, these data show that the incremental improvement per year in educational facilities increased radically about 1915 (when those persons 20 years old in 1930 were being educated).[2] The α-values for the two groups for the two periods are given in Table 8.4.

Table 8.4

YEARLY INCREASE IN PROPORTION OF CHILDREN EDUCATED TO LITERACY (VALUES OF α FROM FIGURE 8.2)

1860–1915		1915–1930	
Native urban whites	.030	Native urban whites	.090
Rural-farm Negroes	.023	Rural-farm Negroes	.090

This example is only one of numerous kinds of census data which can fruitfully be explored with this model. For example, marriage rates as a function of age are amenable to this model, though it is obvious that, as with death rates, the probability of marrying within a given year, if unmarried

[2] The question of which interpretation is valid would be solved by later censuses. However, later census reports do not include illiteracy by age for these separate population groups.

at the beginning, is neither constant for all ages nor is it a linear function of age. It is, of course, curvilinear, increasing up to some point between twenty and thirty and then decreasing again.

Similarly, other vital statistics are amenable to this model. Although most such processes do not vary linearly with age, the use of the linear assumption

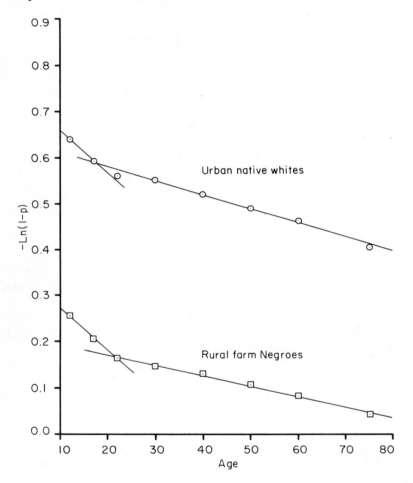

Figure 8.2. Literacy as a Function of Age (1930 census)

can show the way they depart from linearity. The important point is, it is the transition rate q_{12} that should be examined in assessing the effect of a continuous variable on a dependent action. In sum, any one-way process operating continuously through time as a function of some dependent variable like age, income, city size, or date, may be amenable to treatment by the linear model outline in this chapter, or by some modification of the linearity assumption. When there is a reverse flow as well, and the data are in the form of equilibrium states, this is quite another matter, and will be treated in the next chapter. Before that, however, it is useful to compare this model with one which has been in use among biologists for over twenty years, the model of probit analysis.

4. PROBIT ANALYSIS: A COMPARISON WITH THIS MODEL

Biologists long ago found themselves in much the same position that quantitative sociologists find themselves in, the situation which prompted the process models of these chapters. They carried out experiments in which animals were fed a drug in particular concentration, and a certain proportion of the animals were killed, the proportion increasing as the concentration went up. Ordinarily, there is a kind of "critical point" in concentration below which no animals are killed, but above which some are killed.

The problem of the biologists was somehow to assess the effectiveness of the drug in terms of the proportion of animals it killed. If the dependent variable were continuous, they could have used, or at least tried, a simple linear relation between response and concentration. Having a dichotomous dependent variable, however, they were forced to create a new model specifically for this purpose. Accordingly, they developed a model of "probit analysis," which makes the following assumptions: the animals have tolerances for the drug which are normally distributed with respect to the logarithm of the drug's concentration. As the concentration increased, it passed the tolerances of more and more animals, thus killing them. If the concentration were x_1, then the proportion killed, $p(x_1)$ would be

$$p(x_1) = \int_{-\infty}^{\ln x_1} \phi \, d(\ln x) \tag{4.1}$$

where ϕ is the normal probability function. This model has led to plotting the logarithm of the concentration vs. "probits," which is the proportion killed transformed so that the distance between p-values is proportional to their distance along the abscissa of a normal curve. Thus a p of .30 would be closer to a p of .70 than a p of .90 would be to a p of .99. Such a plot should give a straight line if the basic probit assumption (of tolerance normally distributed with respect to the log of the concentration) is met. Much data have been analyzed by this model and found to fit rather well a straight line on a probit vs. a log-concentration plot.

Some economists (see M. J. Farrell, 1954) have been led to use the probit analysis model, feeling precisely the same need that the biologists— and sociologists as well—have felt: the need for a model characterizing the "effectiveness" of a continuous independent variable in changing a dichotomous dependent variable. The economists' problem is exemplified by the first two sets of data in the chapter; variables like income are the independent variables, and purchasing or not purchasing is often the dependent variable.

What is proposed here is that for problems of this nature, whether they are in economics, sociology, or even biology, the model developed in this chapter is more appropriate than the probit analysis model.

For the biologist's problem, the hypothesized process of this model is simpler, the assumptions are more plausible, and the elaborate computations of probit analysis are almost absent, except for calculating tests of significance or confidence intervals. The model developed here assumes only that each unit of concentration of drug has an equal effect on the death rate. That is, the death rate is a linear function of the concentration (*not* the logarithm of the concentration) of the drug.

The model's assumptions are as follows:

(1) The death rate in the absence of the drug is ε. (Ordinarily, ε can be considered zero over the period of the experiment, although in some cases a natural death rate must be taken into account.)

(2) The drug has a critical point of concentration c, below which the death rate remains at ε.

(3) Above the critical point of concentration, an increase of one unit of concentration of the drug adds an amount α to the death rate. An increase of two units of concentration beyond the critical point adds an amount 2α to the death rate. When the concentration is x units, the death rate is $\alpha(x - c) + \varepsilon$; and if $\varepsilon = 0$, the death rate is $\alpha(x - c)$.

(4) The toxicity of the drug is manifested throughout a period of time t, after which the drug has been passed by the organism or has killed the organism.

With these assumptions, the model is as follows:

For $x < c$, the natural death rate is

$$\frac{dn}{dt} = -\varepsilon n \tag{4.2}$$

For $x > c$, it is

$$\frac{dn}{dt} = -[\alpha(x - c) + \varepsilon]n \tag{4.3}$$

Integrating eq. (4.3) gives

$$\ln p = -(\alpha x - \alpha c + \varepsilon)t \qquad (x > c) \tag{4.4}$$

where p = the proportion still alive.

The measures of effectiveness of the drug are, of course, α, the change in death rate per unit change in concentration, and c, the concentration at which the first effect occurs. The assumptions are simple linear assumptions, and the resulting parameters are exactly analogous to the coefficients of a linear regression equation.

Equation (4.4) is the basic equation from which these coefficients can be estimated. The parameter t can be dropped, since it is a constant and of no interest; and in the usual case, the natural death rate, ε, is zero. This gives

$$ -\ln p = \alpha x - \alpha c \qquad (x > c) \tag{4.5} $$

from which values of α and c can be determined by least squares or other estimation, since values of p and x are given in the experimental data.

It appears that conceptually this model is a simple and straightforward representation of what might be the process involved. What is equally important is that it seems to fit the biological data at least as well as does the probit analysis model. From Finney's basic text on probit analysis (1952), every set of data for which probits had been fitted by minimum χ^2 methods were

Table 8.5

TOXICITY OF ROTENONE AND PYRETHRINS ON HOUSEFLIES
($N = 1000$ for each experiment in first series; 900 for each in second)†

| | ROTENONE | | | PYRETHRINS | | 1 : 5 MIXTURE | | 1 : 15 MIXTURE | |
| | Series 1 | Series 2 | | Series 1 | Series 2 | | | | |
Conc., mg/cc	killed, $1 - p$	killed, $1 - p$	Conc., mg/cc	killed, $1 - p$	killed, $1 - p$	Conc., mg/cc	killed, $1 - p$	Conc., mg/cc	killed, $1 - p$
.10	.24	.28	.50	20	.23	.30	.27	.40	.23
.15	.44	.51	.75	35	.44	.45	.53	.60	.48
.20	.63	.72	1.00	53	.55	.60	.64	.80	.61
.25	.81	.82	1.50	80	.72	.875	.82	1.20	.76
.35	.90	.89	2.00	88	.90	1.175	.93	1.60	.93

† Finney, 1952, p. 149.

compared with this model, after fitting this model by minimizing χ^2. The resulting values of χ^2 were compared, and in four cases out of seven, this model had lower χ^2 values than did the probit model.

Perhaps the best example to illustrate the use of the model here is one in which two poisons were first tested separately, and then in two mixtures. The toxicity of rotenone and pyrethrins was tested separately on houseflies, and then a 1 : 5 mixture and a 1 : 15 mixture of rotenone and pyrethrins were tested. Thus not only can the model be fitted to the poisons separately, but also the resulting parameters can be used to predict the outcome of the two mixtures. That is, if we know the α's and c's for each poison separately and the relative concentrations in the mixture, the values of α and c and the resulting line can be found for each mixture, assuming the effects of the poisons are additive.

The data for the two poisons, separately and in mixture are presented in Table 8.5.

Figure 8.3 shows the graph of $-\ln p$ vs. concentration for the two poisons, each series being plotted separately. The linear model appears to fit quite well in both cases; for every concentration except .25 mg/cc rotenone, the straight line lies between the two points obtained in the two series. The equations for the two lines (which were fitted by eye) are

$$- \ln p = 7.75x - .45 \qquad \text{(rotenone)}$$

$$- \ln p = 1.26x - .38 \qquad \text{(pyrethrins)}$$

From these equations, the predicted equations for the two mixtures can be calculated. For the 1 : 5 mixture,

$$- \ln p = \frac{1}{6}(7.75x - .45) + \frac{5}{6}(1.26x - .38)$$

$$= 2.34x - .39$$

Similarly for the 1 : 15 mixture,

$$- \ln p = \frac{1}{16}(7.75x - .45) + \frac{15}{16}(1.26x - .38)$$

$$= 1.66x - .39$$

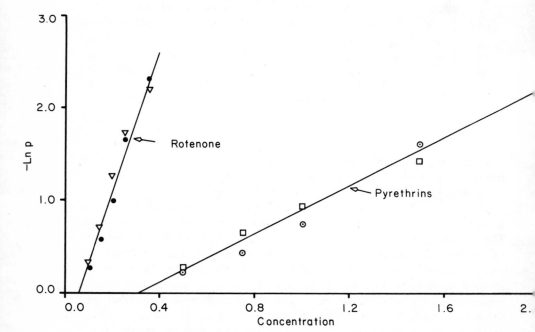

Figure 8.3. Toxicity of Rotenone and Pyrethrins on Houseflies

In Figure 8.4 are plotted the data for the two mixtures, together with the predicted lines from the above equations. The fit seems remarkably good, considering the variability of the data (as indicated by the differences between the two series carried out on the poisons separately). The fit suggests not only that the linear assumptions are met in each poison separately, but also that the effects of the two poisons are additive when they are given in mixtures. In contrast, a probit analysis carried out originally (Finney, 1952, p. 148 ff.) concluded that there was an interaction effect between the two poisons. On grounds of parsimony alone, this seems to be added evidence that the probit

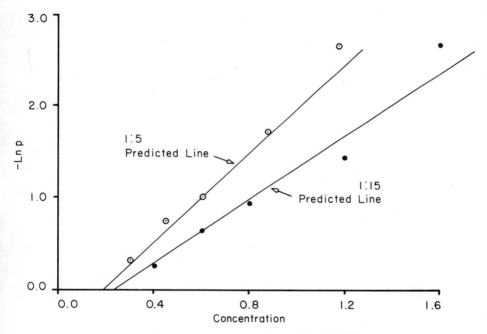

Figure 8.4. Toxicity of mixtures of Rotenone and Pyrethrins
(Actual points and predicted lines)

model does not accurately reflect the process which occurs, while the model presented here does.

This extended comparison of the model with probit analysis provides further evidence that this model may have a very wide range of applicability. True, the problems of drug toxicity are not the problems of sociology—but the formal stimulus-response framework (stimulus varies continuously, and response is dichotomous) is like that found in many sociological and social-psychological problems. The model is apparently appropriate to the problems of drug toxicity, and to social and consumer-response processes like those discussed in Sections 2 and 3 above; but whether it is appropriate to processes which are more strictly sociological or social-psychological in nature remains to be seen. The next chapter examines this question, by applying the model to a number of sets of data which are more closely linked to sociological problems, and by elaborating the model itself in sociologically relevant directions.

CHAPTER 9

SOCIAL AND PSYCHO-LOGICAL PROCESSES AND THEIR EQUILIBRIUM STATES

CONTINUOUS INDEPENDENT VARIABLES

1. TWO-DIRECTIONAL PROCESSES

The processes discussed in this chapter, at least in the first sections, are formally much like those of the preceding chapter: there is a dichotomous dependent variable, which is ordinarily a response of some sort, and a continuous independent variable modifying the rates of response. In two ways, however, these processes are different; first, the examples discussed are in content much closer to what we ordinarily think of as social-psychological processes. Secondly, they are in form all *two-directional* processes, in which the data usually reflect an equilibrium state. Later in the chapter more elaborate processes and over-time data will be discussed; for the moment the focus remains on processes which differ only in these two ways from those of Chapter 8.

The situation is something like this: there is a dependent variable, such as, say, voting Democratic, which is a function of some other variable like the size of plant a man works in (i.e., the number of fellow-workers surrounding him). But besides this effect, there are shifts in both directions, "random shocks" due to other variables. If the two states are labelled 1 (Democratic) and 2 (Republican), then we may assume that the transition rate from state 2 to state 1 is a function of an independent variable x, using the same assumption as in the preceding chapter. That is, we assume that the rate of change in q_{21} with change in x, holding all other variables constant, is constant:

$$\frac{\partial q_{21}}{\partial x} = \alpha \tag{1.1}$$

and by integration,

$$q_{21} = \alpha x + \varepsilon \tag{1.2}$$

In this case, ε is the transition from state 2 to 1 due to other variables when x is zero. As in the preceding chapters, q_{12} and q_{21} can be thought of as a lumping together of the partial effects due to all variables, as follows:

$$dq_{21} = \frac{\partial q_{21}}{\partial x} \, dx + \frac{\partial q_{21}}{\partial z} \, dz + \frac{\partial q_{21}}{\partial w} \, dw + \ldots \tag{1.3}$$

$$dq_{12} = \frac{\partial q_{12}}{\partial x} \, dx + \frac{\partial q_{12}}{\partial z} \, dz + \frac{\partial q_{12}}{\partial w} \, dw + \ldots \tag{1.4}$$

The above assumption (eq. 1.1), that the rate of change in q_{21} with change in x is constant, and the assumption that the rate of change in q_{12} with change in x is zero, result in the following integrated form of eqs. (1.3) and (1.4):

$$q_{21} = \alpha x + \beta z + \gamma w + \theta \tag{1.5}$$

$$q_{12} = 0 + \beta' z + \gamma' w + \phi \tag{1.6}$$

The effects of remaining variables other than x are lumped together as random shocks to give

$$q_{21} = \alpha x + \varepsilon_2 \tag{1.7}$$

$$q_{12} = \varepsilon_1 \tag{1.8}$$

Since the rate of change of n_2 (the number in state 2) with time is equal to the number moving in minus the number moving out, the equation for the expected change in n_2 per unit time is

$$\frac{dn_2}{dt} = \varepsilon_1 n_1 - (\alpha x + \varepsilon_2) n_2 \tag{1.9}$$

In some special cases, the assumption will be made that the effects of other variables are the same in both directions, so that ε_1 and ε_2 are equal. For many processes, however, this assumption is not warranted and will not be made.

Statistical equilibrium for this process occurs when the expected number moving into state 2 equals the expected number moving out, or $dn_2/dt = 0$. Thus at equilibrium,

$$\varepsilon_1 n_1 = (\alpha x + \varepsilon_2)n_2 \tag{1.10}$$

or

$$\frac{n_2}{n_1 + n_2} = p_2 = \frac{\varepsilon_1}{\alpha x + \varepsilon_2 + \varepsilon_1} \tag{1.11}$$

or, by inverting, we have

$$\frac{1}{p_2} = \frac{\alpha}{\varepsilon_1}x + \frac{\varepsilon_1 + \varepsilon_2}{\varepsilon_2} \tag{1.12}$$

$$\frac{1}{p_2} = ax + b \tag{1.13}$$

where p_2 is the proportion in the "residual" state, away from which the variable x acts.

Equation (1.13) is the basic equilibrium equation for this continuous independent variable, two-directional process. It corresponds to eq. (2.3) of the preceding chapter for the nonequilibrium state. Just as in that equation, the relation is linear—but instead of the logarithm of the residual proportion on the left-hand side, here it is the reciprocal. This equation, for equilibrium data in a dichotomous response situation, can be treated just like an ordinary regression equation for continuous variables.

In the succeeding sections, this process is applied to several situations for which data exist, most of them situations in which the *number of persons* (in a small group, in a city, in a worker's shop) is the independent variable. After these applications, elaborations and variations of the process will be discussed.

2. VOTING FOR IN-GROUP MEMBER IN AN ELECTION AS A FUNCTION OF SIZE OF IN-GROUP

In most political elections, candidates usually receive more votes from their "home town" or from groups with which they identify themselves (religious, ethnic, social groups) than from the electorate as a whole. V. O. Key calls this increment in votes "friends and neighbors" voting, and shows how widespread it is in local and state elections in some southern states (1949, pp. 37–52). Key shows many instances in which a candidate's primary source of electoral strength comes from his home counties, making for striking geographic patterns of votes. In rural and small-town areas, this tendency is particularly strong, as it might well be, for it is in these small communities that voters are more likely to know the candidate personally, or to know someone who knows him.

All this suggests that friends-and-neighbors voting might decrease sharply as the size of the in-group increases. That is, in a large group, mere size makes it less likely that the average voter in the group will vote on the basis of a personal relationship to the candidate. The simplest assumption as to how this vote for a group member will decrease with size is a linear one, in which the tendency to vote on the basis of group membership decreases linearly with group size.

In formalizing this process, there are two states, state 2 being "voting for a fellow group member on the basis of group membership," and state 1 being "voting for either candidate, independently of group affiliation."[1] A voter in the second state always votes for his group member; a voter in the first state votes no differently than he would if he were an outsider.

Equations for shifts between the two states are

$$q_{12} = \varepsilon_1 \tag{2.1}$$

$$q_{21} = \alpha x + \varepsilon_2 \tag{2.2}$$

The rate of change of n_2 per unit time is

$$\frac{dn_2}{dt} = \varepsilon_1 n_1 - (\alpha x + \varepsilon_2)n_2 \tag{2.3}$$

where α = the increase per added group member in the proportion of those who shift per unit time away from voting on the basis of "group membership,"

n_1 = the number of people in the group voting for the group member because he is a group member, and

n_2 = the number of people in the group voting independently of group membership.

(Neither of the latter two quantities can be directly evaluated in terms of data which could be collected; however, this problem will be treated shortly.)

Roughly the assumption of linearity says that with each new person coming into the group, there is a constant rate of increase in the tendency to vote independently of group membership.

A diagram for the process is as follows:

---

[1] These may seem more artificial states than the states of voting for or against the fellow group members. However, it is the states as defined in the text that should be directly affected by other group members.

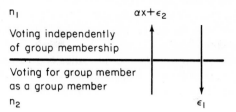

If one is in state 2, he votes for his fellow group-member on the basis of his relation to him; if he is in state 1, he is only as likely to vote for his fellow group-member as is an outsider. There is presumably an equilibrium state, with a constant interchange between favoring the group member as a group member (state 2) and disregarding group membership (state 1). At equilibrium, when the rates of exchange in the two directions are equal, the linear relation may be derived from eq. (2.3), as in eqs. (1.9)–(1.13):

$$\frac{1}{p_2} = \frac{\alpha}{\varepsilon_1}x + \frac{\varepsilon_1 + \varepsilon_2}{\varepsilon_2} \tag{2.4}$$

Now the proportion p_2 is not the proportion voting for the fellow group-member, but rather the proportion voting for him *over* and *above* those who would vote for him anyway. If r is the proportion voting for this man among the total electorate, and p is the proportion voting for him within the group, then the proportion of *excess* votes, p_2, is simply $p - r$, that is,

$$p_2 = p - r \tag{2.5}$$

where p and r are both observable in voting statistics. Substituting $p - r$ for p_2 in eq. (2.4), we obtain

$$\frac{1}{p - r} = \frac{\alpha}{\varepsilon_1}x + \frac{\varepsilon_1 + \varepsilon_2}{\varepsilon_1} \tag{2.6}$$

$$\frac{1}{p - r} = ax + b \tag{2.7}$$

Equation (2.7) gives the relation between the excess proportion of votes in the in-group, that is, $p - r$, and the size of the group.

Data which can test this model have been collected for other purposes. In a study on sources of internal political cleavage in the printers' union, data were gathered on friends-and-neighbors voting both within shops in local elections and within locals in international elections (see Coleman, 1955, p. 229). In the New York and Chicago locals, there are hundreds of small shops in which candidates for local office work. Thus in local elections, a man's "friends and neighbors" are his shopmates. In international elections, candidates are proposed from one or another local (most of which are no larger than a medium-sized shop in the New York or Chicago local); thus in these elections, it is members of a candidate's local who are his "friends and neighbors."

Since these shops and locals varied radically in size (from 3-man shops and 10-man locals to 500-man shops and 9000-man locals), they can be used to test this model. The data are shown in Table 9.1.

Table 9.1

FRIENDS-AND-NEIGHBORS VOTING IN UNION ELECTIONS BY MEMBERS OF THE PRINTERS' UNION

SIZE RANGE	AVERAGE SIZE	NUMBER OF SHOPS	AV. PER CENT EXCESS VOTE FOR CANDIDATE IN OWN SHOP OR LOCAL
New York, 1949–52			
0–20	14	(11)	51
21–30	24	(10)	43
31–100	53	(13)	40
101–200	141	(11)	33
201–400	260	(10)	29
401 plus	492	(21)	20
Chicago, 1949–1952			
0–40	18	(10)	28
41–100	65	(10)	20
101–225	197	(10)	11
226–469	393	(7)	12
International, 1948–1952			
0–140	74	(9)	42
141–225	168	(11)	37
226–400	305	(9)	24
401–452	434	(11)	19
453–600	505	(20)	22
601–1400	1019	(20)	24
1401 plus	2810	(19)	19

In Figure 9.1 are plotted, for the New York and Chicago locals and the international union, the reciprocal of the excess votes, $1/(p - r)$, by shop or local size. With some exceptions, the data fit this model quite well. Considering that each point is based on a sample of only about ten shops or locals, the fit seems quite good indeed, with one outstanding exception: the locals above 500 men in size in the international elections. As the size of locals increases beyond 500 men, the friends-and-neighbors vote does not continue to go down as expected, but remains an excess of about 20%. The value for the largest Chicago shops shows the same deviation.

The explanation for this consistent deviation probably lies in the group identification mentioned earlier. That is, if friends-and-neighbors voting was simply due to a kind of "local pride" or group identification, apart from any personal relation to the candidate, then there would be no reason to expect it to decrease with size of shop or local. Apparently among locals in the ITU, some of the friends-and-neighbors excess came from some such local pride, and was not dependent on a personal relation to the candidate. Some of the Chicago friends-and-neighbors vote seems to have come from the same source. For the New York local, this could be true as well, but since the friends-and-neighbors vote never goes below 20%, and the linear relation holds even for the largest shops, nothing can be said.[2]

Beyond providing a fit to the data, these models allow estimation of the parameters a and b. The meanings of these parameters are as follows: $1/b$ is the average excess proportion of votes that would be given to a shopmate in a shop with no one other than the candidate and voter in it (i.e., thinking of x, as defined, to be shop size minus the voter and the candidate); and

Table 9.2

	$1/b$	a
Chicago	.33	.0310
New York	.46	.0058
International	.59	.0082

$a = \alpha/\varepsilon_1$ is the rate of increase per added shop member in the tendency to vote independently of group membership, relative to the tendency to vote for the shopmate (ε_1).

For the three sets of data, the parameter values are as in Table 9.2.

These parameters show that in the Chicago local friends-and-neighbors voting is lowest on two counts. The initial tendency to vote for a shopmate ($1/b$) is smallest, and the rate of fall-off with group size (a) is largest. For New York as compared to the international, New York's zero-shop rate is smaller, but the fall-off is not so rapid as in the international.

This example has shown, perhaps better than those of the preceding chapter, just how this general model can be applied to social-psychological data. The independent variable used here, group size, is a very general one, and worthy of extended exploration with models such as these. It seems likely that a serious application of this linear-process model and modifications

---

[2] Besides the data presented here are similar data (in Coleman, 1955, p. 229) for these same shops and locals concerning votes for the *party* of the candidate, what might be called "coattail" votes. For the shops of the New York local, the linear model fits these data as well; but the Chicago and international data are more erratic.

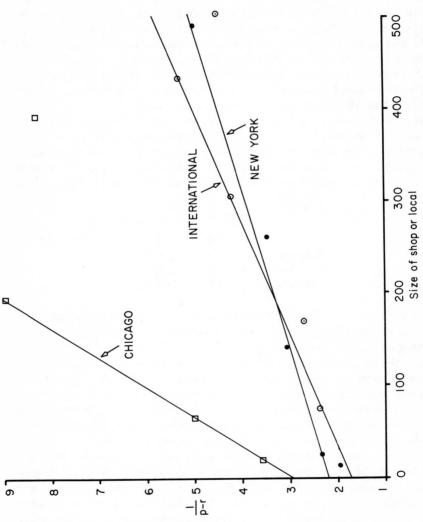

Figure 9.1. Voting for Home Candidate in Union Politics as a Function of Size of Shop or Local

of it to data in which group size is an independent variable would add considerably to our knowledge about the nature of group influence upon an individual. In the succeeding examples of this chapter, some beginnings in such a direction are made, using first a set of data on group size from this same study of printers and then one other set of data.

3. PROPINQUITY, FRIENDSHIP, AND GROUP SIZE

When persons are members of a small group within a larger one, they often choose friends disproportionately from this small group. Sometimes this tendency is due to greater contact with members of the small group; sometimes it is due to having values or experiences in common with them. Whatever the reason, we would expect this tendency to choose friends within

Table 9.3

WITHIN-SHOP ASSOCIATION AS A FUNCTION OF SHOP SIZE

Shop size	Average size	N	(a) Proportion choosing friends within shop	(b) Proportion whose opinion leader is in shop	(c) Proportion whose off-job associations are with shopmates
3–10	6	(67)	.09	.35	.22
11–20	15	(49)	.21	.43	.19
21–30	25	(50)	.31	.51	.31
31–40	35	(51)	.41	.38	.34
41–200	135	(70)	.42	.57	.51
200 plus	300	(147)	.36	.78	.60

the group to be larger if the group is a larger part of the whole. But what precisely should be the form of this relation?

Data from the above study of members of the printers' union makes it possible to study this relation between size and in-group choice in a particular context. In an interview with 434 union members in shops ranging from three to five hundred in size, several questions about friendship and association with fellow shop members were asked. The questions were

(1) A question concerning whether each of the two men he named as his best printer friends were members of his shop;
(2) A question about whether the man "whose opinions about union affairs you most respect" is a member of the same shop; and
(3) A question about whether the printers seen off the job are men he works with.

Table 9.3, columns (a), (b), and (c) show that in each of these cases, men in large shops tend to name shopmates considerably more often than do men in small shops. But does this tendency vary with size of shop in such a way that it is possible to set up a simple model of the process which will explain the data? The answer is both *yes* and *no*, as will be evident shortly.

The formal model can be set up rather simply, as follows: Let the average rate of friendship-producing contacts with each person within one's shop be denoted by α, and let the average rate of such contacts with each person outside be β. Then the total rate of contact with insiders is αx, if x is the number of persons in the shop, and the total rate of contact with outsiders is $\beta(N - x)$, where N is the total size of the union. The very simplest postulate is that the rate of establishment of friends is proportional to the rate of contact, so that the model would be characterized by the following equations:

$$q_{21} = \alpha x \tag{3.1}$$

$$q_{12} = \beta(N - x) \tag{3.2}$$

where state 1 is having one's best friend within the shop, and state 2 is having one's best friend outside the shop. Diagramatically, the process is

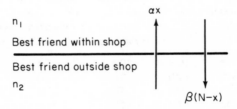

At equilibrium, the rates of exchange are equal, and eqs. (3.1) and (3.2) give, as the equilibrium state,

$$p_2 = \frac{\beta(N - x)}{\beta(N - x) + \alpha x} \tag{3.3}$$

For these data, $N - x$ can be assumed constant, since N is about 9000 and x has a maximum of 300. Thus it can be assumed without great error that the "pool" of printers outside the shop is the same for a member of a large shop as for a member of a small one. Equation (3.3) becomes

$$p_2 = \frac{\beta N}{\beta N + \alpha x} \tag{3.4}$$

and inverting gives

$$\frac{1}{p_2} = \frac{\beta N + \alpha x}{\beta N} \tag{3.5}$$

$$\frac{1}{p_2} = 1 + \frac{\alpha}{\beta N x} \tag{3.6}$$

$$\frac{1}{p_2} = 1 + ax \tag{3.7}$$

where p_2 is the proportion of persons whose best friend is outside the shop.

Equation (3.7) can now be used in conjunction with the survey data of Table 9.3(a). In that table are listed, for each size shop, values of p_1, the proportion of persons whose two best friends are within the shop. Equation (3.7), which has only a single free parameter, indicates that the quantity $1/p_2$ [or $1/(1 - p_1)$] should be linearly related to size, with the line passing through the point $x = 0$, $1/p_2 = 1$. Figure 9.2 shows that for the small groups, the data fit this linear assumption quite well; for the larger groups, it breaks down completely. As a matter of fact, it appears that for groups larger than about forty persons, there is no increase with size at all in the likelihood of choosing someone within the shop as a best friend.

Even as matters stand, however, the assumption of linearity does seem to fit fairly well for shops of thirty-five men or fewer. This fit gives one important result which should not be overlooked. It gives an estimate of the parameter a, which has an explicit dimensional meaning in terms of the assumptions of the model.

$$a = \frac{\alpha}{\beta N} \tag{3.8}$$

and α/β is the ratio of friendship-producing contacts with a given person in the shop to those with a given person outside the shop.

These values of the parameters of these models are one of the most important fruits of model-building such as this. First the fit of the model suggests that the process actually taking place is or is not the one described by the model; and then the parameter values give a quantitative statement of the rate at which the process is operating.

Figure 9.3, on which is plotted data of the other two questions, from Table 9.3, columns (b) and (c), shows very much the same result. In these two graphs, however, there seems to be a nonlinear relation even for the small groups, reaching a maximum somewhere before a size of one hundred.

When the assumptions of the model are re-examined, it becomes clear just why there is this lack of linearity, and the tapering off at large sizes. It was assumed that the rate of contact with each shopmate (and thus the rate of friendship formation) was the same for a large shop as for a small shop. Obviously, as a shop gets beyond a certain size, it passes beyond the number of men with which one can have close contact. It might be expected, then, that below such a "critical point" in size, a man's total contacts with his shopmates increase linearly with size; but beyond this, they do not increase at all. This would account for a straight-line relation up to the critical point, followed by a horizontal line beyond this point. However, it might be that the frequency of contact per shopmate (that is, α) decreases with size, though

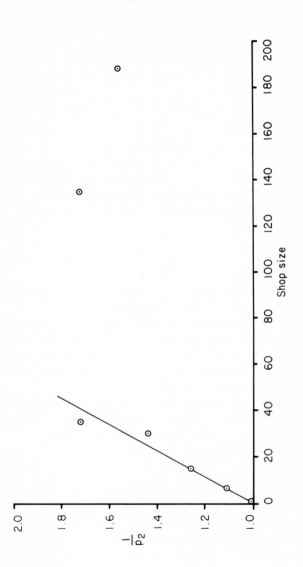

Figure 9.2. Choosing Friends within the Shop as a Function of Shop Size

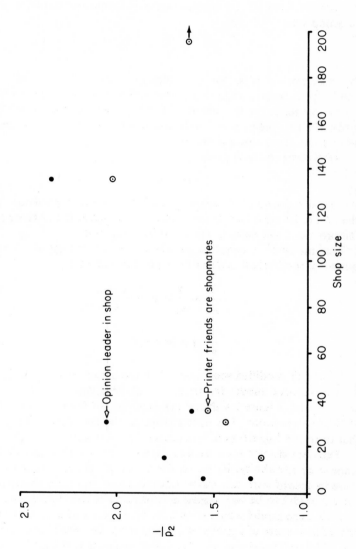

Figure 9.3. Social Relations with Shopmates as a Function of Size of Shop

the *total* amount of contacts with shopmates increases more and more slowly with size.

Perhaps the simplest variation on the linear model is the following assumption:

Rather than assuming that the change in q_{21} per added group number is constant, as in eq. (1.1), assume that it is proportional to the reciprocal of the group size:

$$\frac{\partial q_{21}}{\partial x} = \frac{\alpha}{x} \tag{3.9}$$

This assumption says, for example, that the increment in within-group friendship formation added by a new member when the group is of size 100 is only one-tenth the increment added by a new member when the group is of size 10. This seems a plausible assumption, probably more plausible than the original linear assumption.

Integrating eq. (3.9) gives

$$q_{21} = \alpha \ln x + \varepsilon_2 \tag{3.10}$$

where ε_2 is a constant of integration, which is the rate of friendship formation when there is one other person in the group beside the chooser (i.e., $x = 1$). The process is not defined when x is less than one.

This modified assumption about the rate of change of q_{21} results in the following equilibrium relation (if q_{12} is denoted by ε_1):

$$\frac{1}{p_2} = \frac{\alpha}{\varepsilon_1} \ln x + \frac{\varepsilon_2 + \varepsilon_1}{\varepsilon_1} \tag{3.11}$$

$$\frac{1}{p_2} = a \ln x + b \tag{3.12}$$

Thus this modified model based on the assumption of eq. (3.9) might be a more realistic model for friendship choices within an in-group than the linear model. Figure 9.4 shows the data plotted for this model for the three friendship questions. The only change in the coordinates of the graph is a change to the logarithm of size rather than size itself.

The data do not show an unambiguous fit, for they show a considerable amount of variability. However, for the larger groups the data are certainly more in accord with this model than with the preceding linear one. In order for the model to be well tested, considerably better data are necessary.

This same model would seem to be appropriate to a number of phenomena related to the size of a group or a community. Ordinarily the implicit mechanism which relates size to the dependent response is the added stimulation or reinforcement provided by added persons in one's environment whose response roughly parallels one's own. But everyone's environment is limited, so that a new face added to 10,000 already surrounding an individual is diluted 10,000 times in its effectiveness. Such "dilution" of effectiveness proportional to the existing stimulus is precisely equivalent to the assumption in eq. (3.9).

Note, however, that this assumption, that the effectiveness of added environmental stimuli is proportional to the amount of existing stimuli, is not like that used by the biologists in probit analysis (see Chapter 8, Section 4). Here the assumption is one of reduced effectiveness because the stimulus cannot *get to* the individual; in the biologist's case, the administration of the drug ensured that the stimulus gets to the organism. In cases in which the stimulus is known to get to the individual and is not "diluted" or "crowded out" by existing environmental stimuli, then we would expect the ordinary linear model of eq. (1.13) to hold, just as the linear model was found to hold for the biologists' data.

In the next section, a further class of responses is examined as a function of group size, and again it appears that the logarithmic model is most appropriate.

4. INVOLVEMENT IN WORKERS' ACTIVITIES AS A FUNCTION OF SIZE OF WORKPLACE

It has frequently been noted that workers in large plants are generally more radical politically than are workers in small shops. Furthermore, it has been observed that workers in large plants are more involved in their worker organizations—their unions and other occupationally linked associations—than are small-shop workers. This quite general phenomenon seems to derive from an effect like that discussed at the end of the preceding section. When men are surrounded by others whose responses are similar to their own, there is a mutual reinforcement which leads each to a stronger response. Conversely, when a man has few associates who share the same experiences and feel a common cause, his own response is not reinforced but is weakened by the many other forces acting upon it.

This general phenomenon was very much in evidence in the study of printers discussed in earlier sections. Some printers were "totally surrounded" by other printers, in their workshops, in their neighborhood associations, and in their family. Others had many nonprinter neighbors, their family backgrounds were devoid of printers, and even in their workplace they were as much in contact with employers and other nonprinters as with printers. In interviews, the sharp difference in involvement in printers' affairs between the "totally surrounded" and the "isolated" was readily apparent.

The one quantitative measure of the number of other workers surrounding a man obtained in this study (and in at least one other survey) was the size of his workplace. In accordance with the above qualitative observations, it would seem that a printer's or other worker's involvement in occupationally

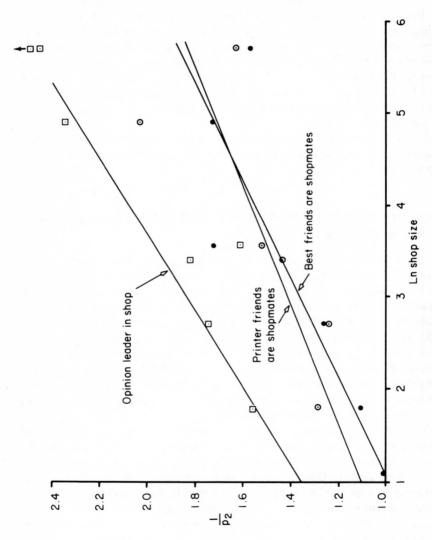

Figure 9.4. Social Relations with Shopmates as a Function of Shop Size (logarithmic model)

related interests should increase with the logarithm of his shop size, in accordance with eq. (3.12):

$$\frac{1}{p_2} = a \ln x + b$$

where p_2 = proportion who are not involved, and

x = shop size.

A question from the printers' study can be used with this equation. The data are reproduced in Table 9.4.

Table 9.4

INVOLVEMENT IN ITU AS A FUNCTION OF SIZE OF WORKPLACE

Shop size	Average size	N	Proportion saying ITU is "best union"
0–10	6	(64)	.453
11–20	15	(49)	.510
21–30	25	(49)	.633
31–40	35	(50)	.580
41–200	135	(70)	.630
200 plus	300	(147)	.653

These data are plotted and a straight line is fitted by eye in Figure 9.5, which shows that the fit is rather good. It appears that this model may be appropriate to this group size—involvement relation. Data from another study, reported in Table 9.5 and plotted in Figure 9.6 further substantiates the relation. These data concern German workers (Institut für Demoskopie, 1952, reported by Lipset aud Linz, 1956) and are responses to the following questions:

(1) Workers' position is best improved by
  (a) Struggles against employers (response 1), or
  (b) Cooperation with employers.
(2) Union policies are
  (a) Too moderate ⎫
  (b) Just right   ⎬ response 1, or
  (c) Too radical. ⎭
(3) When a newspaper says a law is good for the workers and the unions say it is bad, to which do you give most weight?
  (a) Union (response 1),
  (b) Newspaper, or
  (c) Other answer.

Figure 9.6 shows that the data do fit rather well the relation expressed by eq. (3.12). It appears that this model may fit a rather wide range of situations

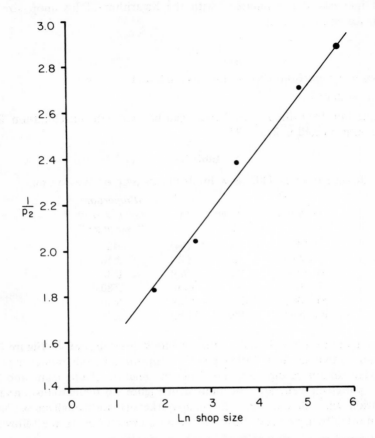

Figure 9.5. Belief that Own Union is "Best Union" as a Function of Shop Size (logarithmic model)

Table 9.5†

Shop size	Aver. size	Question 1, p_1	Question 2, p_1	Question 3, p_1
Under 5	2.6	.22	.48	.33
5–20	12.5	.29	.57	.42
20–100	60	.30	.64	.41
100–1000	550	.37	.73	.48
1000 plus	1300	.37	.81	.59

† Total $N = 2663$.

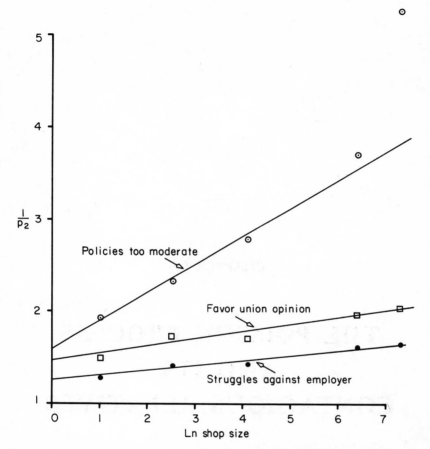

**Figure 9.6. Agreement with Workers' Values as a Function of Shop
Size (logarithmic model)**

for which the linear relation is not appropriate. In particular, many responses
which depend upon group size or community size may conform to this
relation.[3]

In this chapter, the relation between a continuous independent variable
and a dichotomous dependent variable has been extended to the consideration
of equilibrium states. Two models, one a simple linear model, and the second,
based on a slightly different assumption from the linear one, were presented.
Data which fit these two models suggest that each might have a rather wide
range of applicability.

[3] Other data on community size from various surveys have been analyzed, and the fit
is roughly the same as that of the data shown in Fig. 9.5.

CHAPTER 10

THE POISSON PROCESS AND ITS CONTAGIOUS RELATIVES

The processes under consideration in the preceding chapters have an intimate relation to a distribution which has a long and honorable history in statistics, the Poisson distribution. In this chapter the assumptions underlying the Poisson distribution will be examined, and related models with numerous social applications will be developed. This chapter will be an adventure which begins to explore the territories into which the Poisson process leads.

1. THE ASSUMPTIONS UNDERLYING THE POISSON

Suppose we consider a very slight modification of the basic model under consideration throughout this section. There are a great number of elements, to which some event can happen. The transition rate governing the occurrence of this event is, say, α. Once an event has occurred for an element, it continues to be governed by the same transition rate as before—the event may or may not occur again for that element, with the same likelihood as it initially had. A good example to give intuitive meaning to the process is one described by Feller (1957, p. 150): the occurrence of flying-bomb hits in particular small areas of .25 square kilometer in London during World War II. The elements are the areas, the events are the bomb hits. We would expect the occurrence of hits in particular areas to proceed according to this process. The states for this model are the numbers of events which have occurred to an element. The process may be diagrammed as follows:

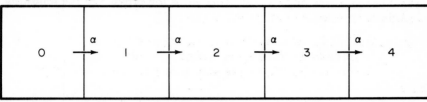

The Poisson distribution is the distribution of elements in each of these states after a given period of time. This distribution may be found as follows: First, the probability of being in state 0:

$$\frac{dp_{0t}}{dt} = -\alpha p_{0t} \tag{1.1}$$

Integrating gives

$$p_{0t} = p_{00}e^{-\alpha t} \tag{1.2}$$

where p_{0t} is the proportion of elements in state 0 at time t. Thus the proportion of elements to which the event has never occurred is simply $e^{-\alpha t}$. The proportion to which it has occurred once may be found in several ways. It is useful to consider two, for both have specific applicability to certain other problems to be considered later. First of all, following the same general procedure as in the derivation of p_{0t}, we use the identity:

rate of gain or loss in state 1 = (number entering per unit time) − (number leaving per unit time)

This gives, as the differential equations describing the system, eq. (1.1) above, for p_{0t}, plus

$$\frac{dp_{it}}{dt} = \alpha p_{i-1,t} - \alpha p_{it} \qquad (i \geqslant 1) \tag{1.3}$$

with the initial condition that p_{00} equals one. For p_{1t}, this becomes

$$\frac{dp_{1t}}{dt} = \alpha p_{0t} - \alpha p_{1t} \tag{1.3'}$$

But from eq. (1.2), $p_{0t} = p_{00}e^{-\alpha t}$, which may be substituted into eq. (1.3') giving

$$\frac{dp_{1t}}{dt} = p_{00}e^{-\alpha t} - \alpha p_{1t} \tag{1.4}$$

This is a linear differential equation of the first order, which may be integrated to give

$$p_{1t} = p_{00}\, \alpha t e^{-\alpha t} \tag{1.5}$$

and since p_{00} is 1.0,

$$p_{1t} = \alpha t e^{-\alpha t} \tag{1.5'}$$

A second way of finding p_{1t} is by considering what events must happen to an element over time to locate it in state 1 at time t, and adding up all possible ways that such events might occur. Thus p_{1t} is the product of the following probabilities summed over all points in time.

p_{1t} = (probability of no event until time τ [$= e^{-\alpha\tau}$])
    $\times$ (probability of an event at time τ [$= \alpha d\tau$])
    $\times$ (probability of no event from time τ to time t [$= e^{-\alpha(t-\tau)}$])

This is

$$p_{1t} = \int_0^t [e^{-\alpha\tau}][\alpha][e^{-\alpha(t-\tau)}]\, d\tau \tag{1.6}$$

$$= \alpha \int e^{-\alpha t}\, d\tau$$

Integrating gives

$$p_{1t} = \alpha t e^{-\alpha t} \tag{1.7}$$

Either of these two methods may be used to obtain the proportion of elements in state 2 and subsequent states. Following out the second method for p_{2t}, we begin with the probability of being in state 1 at time τ, $[\alpha\tau e^{-\alpha\tau}]$; then we consider the probability of moving to state 2 at time τ, $[\alpha d\tau]$; and finally, we consider the probability of not moving until time t, $[e^{-\alpha(t-\tau)}]$. Thus we have

$$p_{2t} = \int_0^t [\alpha\tau e^{-\alpha\tau}][\alpha][e^{-\alpha(t-\tau)}]\, d\tau \tag{1.8}$$

$$= \alpha^2 \int \tau e^{-\alpha t}\, d\tau$$

Integrating gives

$$p_{2t} = \frac{\alpha^2 t^2 e^{-\alpha t}}{2} \tag{1.9}$$

The general result for state i is

$$p_{it} = \frac{(\alpha t)^i e^{-\alpha t}}{i!} \tag{1.10}$$

This is the form of the Poisson frequency distribution. Usually the time period is taken as one for convenience, since it is seldom a variable in the usual applications of the distribution. When this is done, the ordinary form of the Poisson distribution results:

$$p_i = \frac{\alpha^i e^{-\alpha}}{i!} \tag{1.11}$$

The expected number of events to occur to any element, the mean of the distribution, is simply αt, or if t is taken as one, as above, it is α.

The appropriateness of the Poisson process for social phenomena lies not in its empirical fit to social data. It lies instead in the assumptions on which the distribution is based. In the first place, it deals with *numbers* of elements, or proportions, and with numbers of events. Therefore, continuous-variable measurements, which are extremely rare in social science, are unnecessary. Second, the Poisson process occurs continuously over time, rather than at discrete "trials," like the binomial distribution. Thus, for naturally occurring events, in contrast to controlled experiments, something akin to the Poisson process is often appropriate.

Finally, the Poisson process is appropriate to social phenomena because it constitutes a rational model whose assumptions can mirror our assumptions about actual phenomena. Thus, it need not be simply an empirical frequency distribution like the normal curve, applied because it fits the data. The normal curve provides no such rational model, though it does stand as an approximation to both the binomial and the Poisson.[1] It should be noted that this perspective upon the normal and Poisson distributions is not shared by many statisticians; usually statisticians are not concerned with uncovering substantive processes, and are thus less concerned with such a distinction as that made above.[2]

Example 1

Two examples of the application of the Poisson distribution to social data are given below.

This example is the famous first application of the Poisson distribution by Bortkewitsch (1898): The number of deaths due to kicks by a horse was recorded for 10 corps in the Prussian army over a period of 20 years.[3] This

---

[1] Although the normal curve has been derived from postulates about errors in observations by Gauss and others, an implicit assumption about size of errors or distance along a continuum is always made. This makes the normal distribution inapplicable to mirror processes such as those considered here.

[2] One valuable book which does present this view is Thornton Fry's *Probability and Its Engineering Uses*, published in 1928. This book is a delight to the scientist seeking to use probability models to mirror what goes on in his field. The reason, very likely, is that Fry was himself engaged in developing probability models for problems in telephone traffic, and, perhaps more important, he wrote the book to aid others engaged in the same task, and not for the critical plaudits of mathematicians. As a telephone engineer, Fry presents numerous models related to the Poisson which reflect various problems in telephone traffic. Feller's basic text (1957) shows the same interest in substantive problems.

[3] There were in fact fourteen corps, but four of those had abnormally large numbers of deaths due to horse-kicks, so that they were excluded. Their existence, however, illustrates the general problem of heterogeneity. If the corps included in the calculation had been very heterogeneous in their tendencies toward deaths from horse-kicks (i.e., had different transition rates, α), then the Poisson distribution would not be applicable. See Thorndike (1926) for examples in which such heterogeneity exists, and the effect it has on the distribution.

provides 200 cases or observations, where the observation is one corps over a period of a year. The average number of deaths per corps-year was 0.61, and the distribution of deaths is shown in Table 10.1.

Table 10.1

Deaths from the Kick of a Horse in the Prussian Army

(i) Number of deaths	(n_i) Number of corps with i deaths per year	(n_i, calculated) Calculated number of corps with i deaths per year†
0	109	108.7
1	65	66.3
2	22	20.2
3	3	4.1
4	1	0.6
	200	199.9

† Calculated by eq. (1.11), using $\alpha = .61$.

This example fits quite well, suggesting that the assumptions underlying the Poisson distribution were well met for horse-kicks in the Prussian army.

Example 2

The second example is the number of telephone calls in five-minute intervals made from a group of six pay telephones in a transportation terminal, observed between noon and 2 P.M. on seven days. This example is taken from Thorndike (1926). The total number of five-minute intervals observed was 138, and the average number of calls per period was 3.39. The conditions of this example suggest that it ought to fit the Poisson distribution except for one source of deviation: When a phone is used, it is unavailable for subsequent use immediately. At maximum, only a rather small number of calls could be made from the group of six telephones in five minutes. If each call lasted one minute, for example, the total possible number of calls from the six phones would be only thirty.

Neglecting this possible source of deviation, this example can be used. Table 10.2 presents the data, together with the calculated Poisson distribution. These data fit the Poisson distribution quite well, despite the difficulty posed above.

Many other applications of the Poisson have been presented in the literature (see, for example, Thorndike, 1926, and Feller, 1957, p. 149), though most of these illuminate some physical or physiological process rather than a social one. The Poisson model is seldom directly applicable to social phenomena of interest. It gains value principally through its modified versions, which may be developed to fit the particular processes which are felt to be operating. A number of these are developed below.

Table 10.2

NUMBER OF CALLS IN 5-MINUTE INTERVALS FROM A GROUP OF SIX
PAY TELEPHONES

(i) Number of calls	(n_i) Intervals with i calls	$(n_i,$ calculated) Calculated number of intervals with i calls
0	8	4.7
1	13	15.8
2	20	26.8
3	37	30.3
4	24	25.6
5	20	17.4
6	8	9.8
7	5	4.8
8	2	2.0
9	1	0.8
	138	138.0

2. THE POISSON WITH EXHAUSTION, AND THE TWO-STATE MODEL

It will be helpful to think of the basic process at hand in a slightly different way: Let the states 0, 1, 2, 3, etc., represent not numbers of events which have occurred to a given element, but rather numbers of elements (e.g., individuals) which have carried out a particular act. Suppose we ask the question, What is the probability that one person, two persons, etc., in a group have bought a car in time t? Now the transition rates become somewhat different. The model can be described as follows:

p_i = the probability that i persons have bought cars in time t,
N = the number of persons in the group, and
α = the transition rate for any one person to buy a car in time dt.

Therefore αN = the transition rate moving the system from state 0 (no persons having bought) to state 1 (one person having bought).

And because one individual is now removed after one person has bought,

$\alpha(N - 1)$ = the transition rate moving the system from state 1 to state 2.

And in general,

$$\alpha(N - i) = \text{the transition rate moving the system from state } i \text{ to state } i + 1.$$

When these changes are introduced into eqs. (1.1) and (1.3), the differential equations describing the process are

$$\frac{dp_0}{dt} = -\alpha N p_0 \tag{2.1}$$

and

$$\frac{dp_i}{dt} = \alpha(N - i + 1)p_{i-1} - \alpha(N - i)p_i \qquad (1 \leqslant i \leqslant N) \tag{2.2}$$

with the initial condition that $p_0 = 1$.

Solving these equations by either method of Section 1 gives

$$p_0 = e^{-\alpha t N}$$

$$p_1 = N(1 - e^{-\alpha t})e^{-\alpha t(N-1)}$$

and generally,

$$p_i = \binom{N}{i}(1 - e^{-\alpha t})^i e^{-\alpha t(N-i)} \tag{2.3}$$

Note the resemblance of this to the binomial distribution. In fact, if the quantity $1 - e^{-\alpha t}$ is taken as the probability of "success" on one of N trials (as it can be, since $1 - e^{-\alpha t}$ varies between zero and one), then this distribution is precisely the binomial distribution for N trials.

It is important to note what this model is, and how it differs from the Poisson. It is applicable to situations in which some event or action (such as buying a car) can occur to each of the N elements involved, and each has the same transition rate α toward carrying out the event at any instant. Then the question is asked, How many of these individuals do carry out the event in time t?

But how is this different from the basic two-state model we have examined in earlier chapters? Is the above situation any different from the situation for which the two-state model of not buying or buying with a transition rate, α, from state 1 to state 2 was used? The answer is *no*, the situations are not different. But the apparent contradiction between the models is not a real one. The calculation in previous chapters concerned a probability, p_2, for an individual, or an expected number, n_2, for a group of size n. The equation for the expected number is

$$n_2 = n(1 - e^{-\alpha t}) \tag{2.4}$$

Equation (2.3), in contrast, gives the full probability distribution, the probability of no men buying, the probability of one buying, etc. The expected value of this probability distribution is identical with eq. (2.4). That is, from eq. (2.3) can be derived the expected value, identical to (2.4):[4]

$$E(i) = N(1 - e^{-\alpha t}) \tag{2.5}$$

This indicates the important relation between these two models, and the relevance of this "Poisson with exhaustion" for the models which have been developed in other chapters. All those models have provided expected values, that is, expected numbers of persons or expected proportions of the total, for the given changes or equilibrium states, while this provides a probability distribution. Pictorially it is as represented in Figure 10.1. This figure shows the line $N(1 - e^{-\alpha t})$, which is the curve of $n_2(t)$ for the two-state model, $dn_1/dt = -\alpha n_1$, and the shaded distribution curve shows the probability

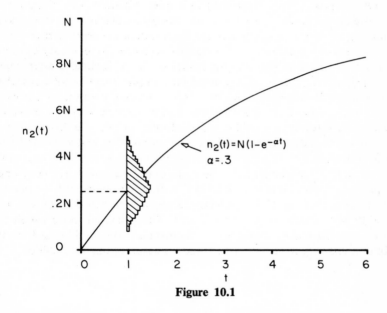

Figure 10.1

distribution vertical to the plane of the paper around the mean value $N(1 - e^{-\alpha t})$. Note that, as indicated by eq. (2.3), this is simply a binomial distribution with $p = 1 - e^{-\alpha t}$. The general result, for the two-state models discussed in previous chapters, is that the probability distribution (for one-way processes) of the proportion shifted is simply a binomial distribution with parameters $p = 1 - e^{-\alpha t}$ and N = total number of elements or individuals (where α is the transition rate for the process and t is the time over which the process has acted).

[4] The letter i in this chapter and the next corresponds to n_1 or n_2 in preceding chapters wherever the models reduce to the same form, as in eqs. (2.4) and (2.5). An upper case N is used for the size of the group, corresponding to a lower case n in preceding chapters.

One application of this Poisson-with-exhaustion model, then, is clear. It can be used to test the fit of data to the two-state models above. For example, one can ask such questions as, What is the probability that i persons bought a car between time t and $t + t_1$? when we know the number in the total group, and that x_1 of them had already bought at time t.[5] The two-state model would give the expected number of persons who shifted from not-bought to bought within this time interval, while the present model gives the probability distribution over all i. However, the model has uses beyond this. A very important one for the purposes of social science will arise later in this chapter, and in the next: The model can easily be generalized, as a binomial cannot, into one representing mutual (rather than sequential) contagion effects, which can come nearer to mirroring actual social phenomena. Or the model may be applied in a quite different way. Suppose we now let the elements which can shift from state to state be individuals, as in the application of the Poisson model. Each individual may perform 1, 2, 3, . . ., acts, up to a maximum of N acts, but no more. Suppose, for example, that the act consisted of learning the names of one's classmates after school opens. Suppose the class is a fairly small one, so that there is full association and no segregated subgroups, and that no one knew the names of any classmates to begin with. Then if each name had associated with it a transition rate and these rates were all alike, we would expect that the distribution of persons, in terms of the number of classmates' names they know, would follow eq. (2.3). Furthermore, this distribution should change over time in accordance with eq. (2.3), reaching finally the asymptote N, at which everyone knew everyone else's name. Note that so long as a distribution at only one point in time is desired, then eq. (2.3) is effectively just a binomial distribution with probability of "success" equal to $1 - e^{-\alpha t}$. The principal thing which this equation adds to the binomial is the time dimension, indicating how the distribution changes with time if the model's assumptions are fulfilled.

Example

An example which indicates the applicability of the model is similar to the name-learning mentioned above. Many experiments have been done on the learning of material (e.g., nonsense syllables) from lists of a certain length. Ordinarily, a number of subjects are tested, and the average amounts of time needed to learn different proportions of the list are recorded. If $E(i)$ is taken as the average number of words learned at a given time, and $E(i)/N$ the average proportion learned, then the model can be applied by using eq. (2.5):

$$E(i) = N(1 - e^{-\alpha t})$$

---

[5] Fry derives this probability in his discussion of models related to the Poisson (1928, pp. 220–237, especially pp. 236–237).

The model can be applied at each time period, to obtain an estimate of α, since t and $E(i)/N$ are known for each time period. If the various α's are constant, then the model fits the data. Table 10.3 shows data from an experiment in learning a list of six nonsense syllables, in which the average proportions of the list learned during successive sixths of the total learning time are tabulated. The estimates of α from eq. (2.5), made on the basis of each observation, are listed with the data. Each value of α is that which would be estimated if it were known only that the process had proceeded the indicated distance in the indicated time.

As the estimates of α indicate, the Poisson-with-exhaustion model does not fit these data. It is instructive to examine why. Note that in this model the transition rate is a constant times the number of words yet to be learned [see eq. (2.2)]. If there are six syllables yet to be learned, the rate of shifting to the state of having learned one syllable is six times the rate if there is only

Table 10.3

AVERAGE PROPORTIONS OF A LIST OF SIX NONSENSE SYLLABLES
LEARNED IN SUCCESSIVE SIXTHS OF TOTAL LEARNING TIME†

t	Proportion learned $E(i)/N$	α
1	.233	.265
2	.450	.299
3	.605	.310
4	.723	.321
5	.834	.359
6	1.000	

† From Robinson and Darrow, 1924.

one syllable to be learned. That is, there is an assumption that the probability of learning any one syllable within a given time is completely independent of the number of others being learned. It assumes, in other words, that all six syllables could be learned as fast as a single one. This is obviously an incorrect assumption; it implies infinitely expandible attention, with parallel processing of the syllables to be learned. Empirically, in fact, it is found that not only does the *total* time for learning increase as the length of the list increases, but also the time per item increases, when the number of items is large (see Thurstone, 1930).

If, in contrast, the six words to be learned in time period 1 had *altogether* the same rate of being learned as the single one remaining at the end, then only one-sixth of the words would be learned on the average during the first time period. This would be the assumption of constant transition rates from state to state, as in the ordinary Poisson distribution. Substantively, it is the assumption that attention is confined to one syllable at a time, with purely sequential processing of first one syllable and then the next. If the data are examined with this assumption in mind, they again turn out not to fit: instead of one-sixth of the words being learned in each time interval, more are learned in early intervals.

The behavior thus seems to be somewhere between these two assumptions: The transition rates per syllable are not constant, as the exhaustible model implies, but neither is the aggregate transition rate for the system constant. It decreases as the number of words to be learned decreases, though not as rapidly as the exhaustible model predicts.

Parenthetical note. The Poisson distribution is often derived as an approximation to the binomial, useful when the binomial assumptions are met, and when N is large and the binomial p ($= 1 - e^{-\alpha t}$ in the exhaustible Poisson) is small. The large N and small p give a distribution which clusters around the lower left-hand corner of Figure 10.1. Figure 10.2 shows the relation between the Poisson and the binomial or exhaustible Poisson. (Included on the graph are the data for the learning experiment discussed above.) The straight line represents the mean of the Poisson distribution, $[E(i) = \alpha t]$, while the curve represents the mean of the exhaustible Poisson, $[E(i) = N(1 - e^{-\alpha t})]$. The straight-line approximation to the curve (and thus frequency distributions of which these are the means) is very close down in the corner, when $E(i)$ is quite small relative to N, but the line diverges from

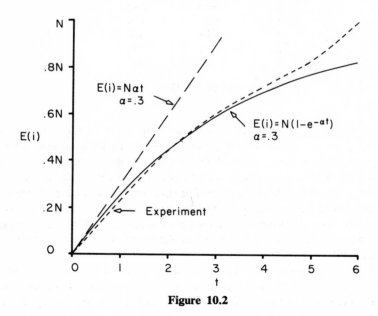

Figure 10.2

the curve when $E(i)$ is higher relative to N. The exhaustible Poisson represents the precise continuous-time analog of the binomial distribution, while the ordinary Poisson is an approximate analog when $E(i)$ is small relative to N. The advantage of using the Poisson as an approximation to either of these other two distributions is, of course, that it is much simpler computationally.

It is important not to be misled by the above paragraph and by the usual treatment of the Poisson distribution in texts on statistics into thinking of that distribution as merely an "approximation." When its assumptions are fulfilled, as they sometimes are, it is the exact distribution, and any other becomes an approximation.

3. A CONTAGIOUS POISSON

One reason that the Poisson distribution is not more applicable to much social data is the fact that when one person takes an action, then the probability of a second person's taking the action is changed. Often it is increased (a positive "contagion" of the action); sometimes it is decreased (a negative contagion, or aversion). Or when a person acts once, his probability of taking this action again is changed. Often it is greater (as in positively reinforced trials in learning, and particularly in operant conditioning); sometimes it is less (as in negatively reinforced trials in learning).

Thus much social and individual behavior takes the form of contagion or learning. Without going into the social psychological or physiological mechanisms which take place in these two phenomena, we can nevertheless develop models which follow the broad outlines of these occurrences.

Perhaps the simplest generalization of the Poisson distribution to take into account contagion or learning is to posit an increment in the transition rate in each succeeding state. That is, the transition rates q_{ij}, from state i to state j, are, for the first few states,

$$q_{01} = \alpha \qquad \text{(as in the Poisson)} \qquad (3.1)$$
$$q_{12} = \alpha + \beta$$
$$q_{23} = \alpha + 2\beta$$
$$\text{etc.}$$

Generally,

$$q_{i,i+1} = \alpha + i\beta \qquad (3.2)$$

The differential equations describing the processes are

$$\frac{dp_0}{dt} = -\alpha p_0 \qquad (3.3)$$

and

$$\frac{dp_i}{dt} = [\alpha + (i-1)\beta]p_{i-1} - (\alpha + i\beta)p_i \quad (i \geqslant 1) \qquad (3.4)$$

with the initial condition that $p_0 = 1$. According to this model, then, the transition rate increases linearly with i. A reasonable application of this would be influence processes, where β represents the influence of one person carrying out the action and influencing others in a large population to follow suit.

It is easy to see that this model would lead, at an ever-increasing rate, to greater and greater numbers of persons carrying out the act. The derivation of the distribution of p_i analogous to eq. (1.11) for the Poisson and eq. (2.3) for the exhaustible Poisson (but not so simple as those) is carried out in the Appendix to this chapter; below is the resulting equation for the frequency distribution of i:[6]

$$p_i = \frac{\alpha(\alpha + \beta) \ldots (\alpha + [i - 1]\beta)e^{-\alpha t}(1 - e^{-\beta t})^i}{i!\beta^i} \tag{3.5}$$

This is a formidable-looking distribution function, but one in which the parameters α and β can easily be estimated. To estimate α and β, we need only obtain the equations for the mean and variance of the distribution, and then use the estimates of the mean and variance to estimate α and β. The derivations of mean and variance are carried out in the Appendix to this chapter. The mean and variance of i are (letting $t = 1$ for simplicity):

$$\mu = \frac{\alpha}{\beta}(e^\beta - 1) \tag{3.6}$$

$$\sigma_i^2 = \mu e^\beta \tag{3.7}$$

and the estimates of the mean and variance are

$$\hat{\mu} = \sum_{i=0}^{\infty} i p_i' \tag{3.8}$$

$$\hat{\sigma}_i^2 = \sum_{i=0}^{\infty} (i - \mu)^2 p_i' = \sum_{i=0}^{\infty} i^2 p_i' - \mu^2 \tag{3.9}$$

where p_i' are the observed proportions in state i. By using eqs. (3.6) and (3.7), the estimates of α and β, in terms of $\hat{\mu}$ and $\hat{\sigma}_i^2$, are found to be

$$\beta = \ln\frac{\hat{\sigma}_i^2}{\hat{\mu}} \tag{3.10}$$

$$\alpha = \frac{\hat{\mu}^2\beta}{\hat{\sigma}_i^2 - \hat{\mu}} \tag{3.11}$$

[6] At first I naively assumed that this distribution had never been derived before, but there is a long history of contagion models either identical to this or nearly so; usually, as in this case, the new "discoverer" of the distribution has been unaware of its previous derivation by others. See Feller (1943) for a general discussion of these models.

Thus after estimating the mean and variance from the data, eqs. (3.10) and (3.11) may be used to estimate α and β.

It turns out that the distribution function of this model is identical to that of a contagious model developed many years ago by G. Polya, using different assumptions of contagion. Polya began with an urn model, in which there were two kinds of balls. In contrast to the usual binomial model of drawing with replacement, Polya's model involves not only replacement of the ball drawn, but also adding to the urn a new ball of the same color. In this way, numerous drawings of one color of ball would result in a greatly increased probability of that color being drawn.

The limiting form of the Polya distribution is identical to that developed above, in eq. (3.5), although the parallel is not immediately evident. As Feller presents the Polya distribution, it is (using symbols consistent with usage in this chapter):

$$p_i = \binom{\lambda p + i - 1}{i}\left(\frac{p}{1+p}\right)^{\lambda p}\left(\frac{1}{1+p}\right)^i \tag{3.12}$$

This appears to be a very different distribution from that of eq. (3.5); but if we let $\alpha/\beta = \lambda p, p = 1/(e^{-\beta t} - 1)$, then the two distributions turn out to be identical.

The Polya distribution has been used in numerous investigations of accident statistics (see O. Lundberg, 1940). It is somewhat disappointing that the present distribution is "nothing new"; however, the assumptions on which it is based provide a somewhat different heuristic than do those of Polya, one which seems particularly suited to social phenomena.

Somewhat more disturbing is the fact that still another distribution is identical to this. As Feller (1943) shows, the Polya distribution, derived from assumptions of contagion, and the Yule-Greenwood distribution, derived from assumptions of *heterogeneity* and no contagion, are identical. The Yule-Greenwood model is one which assumes that a set of Poisson processes are operative, with the Poisson parameters themselves distributed in a particular fashion.

Therefore, as Feller points out, it is impossible to choose between a contagious interpretation and a heterogeneity interpretation merely on the basis of the empirical distribution itself, no matter how well it fits a theoretical distribution. What are required in addition are over-time data, which can show the development of contagion if it exists.

This does not mean, of course, that such models are not useful, but only that we must be cautious in interpreting the deviation from a straight Poisson as being due to contagion rather than heterogeneity. The matter of inter-pretation will be discussed in more detail after an example is presented.

Example 1: Teen-age girls' purchase of phonograph records

In recent research on teen-agers (Coleman, 1961) a question was asked of all girls concerning the number of phonograph records they had bought in the past month. It seems reasonable that a process of the sort discussed here should be operative. That is, a girl has only a small likelihood of buying a record, but having bought one, she is more likely to buy a second. Having bought the second, she is even more likely to buy a third, and so on. Her initial transition rate of buying a record is α, and each record she buys increases this rate by an amount β.

The data are shown in Table 10.4. Many girls do not buy any records; but those who do, tend to buy more than one. From these data may be calculated the mean number of records bought, $\mu = 2.21$, and the variance in number bought, $\sigma^2 = 8.19$.[7] From these values, the parameters α and β may be estimated by use of eqs. (3.10) and (3.11):

$$\beta = \ln \frac{8.19}{2.21} = 1.31$$

and

$$\alpha = \frac{(2.21)^2(1.31)}{8.19 - 2.21} = 1.07$$

Using these estimates for α and β, this distribution is given in Table 10.4, along with the actual distribution. Included as well is a Poisson without contagion to show the difference in the distributions.

Table 10.4

NUMBER OF GIRLS BUYING i PHONOGRAPH RECORDS IN A ONE-MONTH
PERIOD, IN AN UPPER-MIDDLE-CLASS HIGH SCHOOL

i	n_i	Contagious Poisson $\alpha = 1.07, \beta = 1.31$	Poisson $\alpha = 2.21$
0	347	306	98
1	111	182	216
2	113	121	239
3	108	83	176
4	89	58	97
5	44	41	43
6	20	29	16
7	18	21	5
8	9	15	1
9 or more	32	35	0

This contagious Poisson distribution does not give an excellent fit by any measure; but the fitted distribution does conform to the general characteristics

[7] The category of "9 or more" records does not allow exact calculation of the mean and variance. It is assumed that there was an end effect in responding, so that the category "9 or more" drew responses that should legitimately have been in category 8, as well as responses that would legitimately have been more than 9. Considering both effects, in calculating the mean and variance, this category was arbitrarily taken to be 13.

of the actual distribution, while the Poisson does not begin to do so. The actual data and the contagious Poisson are shown graphically in Figure 10.3.

It is important to remember that a fit, however good, of this model to

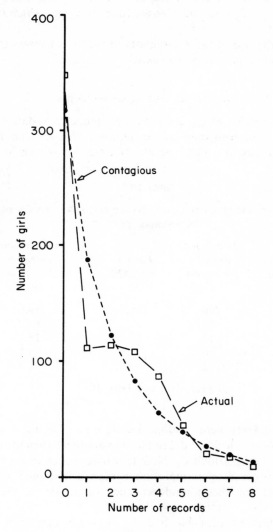

Figure 10.3

the data does not imply that a contagious process is at work. The fact that this distribution is identical to one based on heterogeneity assumptions means that any interpretation of contagion must be a very conjectural one. However, since the model gives other deductions beyond the mere distribution at a given point in time, its assumptions could be further tested by these other deductions. For example, since the parameters are specific to a given unit of time (one month in this case), these parameter values would give predicted distributions for any period of time—one week, three months, or any other. These predictions could be tested against data which used various reporting periods.

In any case, the size of the β parameter of the model shows the degree of "correlation" among purchases that exists.

Example 2: Industrial accidents

A second illustration of application of this model uses data on industrial accidents. The data, consisting of the number of men who had various numbers of accidents in a given period of time, are shown in Table 10.5.

Table 10.5

NUMBER OF MEN WITH GIVEN NUMBERS OF ACCIDENTS IN AN
INDUSTRIAL PLANT†

Number of accidents (i)	Number of men with i accidents n_i	Poisson $\alpha = .429$ n_i	Poisson with contagion $\alpha = .372, \beta = .285$ n_i
0	200	188.2	199.0
1	64	80.7	64.9
2	17	17.4	18.7
3	6	2.5	5.1
4	2	0.3	1.4

† From Hill and Trist, 1953.

Now if these accidents were random among men (that is, if no one were accident-prone, or one accident did not lead to another), then the assumptions of the Poisson would be fulfilled. (Note that here it is clearly a Poisson-type nonexhaustible process operating, rather than a binomial with a limit. Therefore, except for the nonindependence of accidents, the process is isomorphic with the Poisson.)

But an examination of Table 10.5 shows clearly that there is noninde-pendence; that more men have several accidents (three or four) than the Poisson model predicts. This suggests that the contagious model might be appropriate, even though it is fairly clear that here there is more heterogeneity (accident-proneness) than contagion (one accident leading to another). However, when the model is fitted in the way described in Example 1, the second column of Table 10.5 indicates that whatever the interpretation of β, the model does fit rather well. The size of α, .372, is a measure of the general accident rate for those who have had no accidents, while the size of β, .285, indicates that those who have had one accident have a rate for the second which is .285 higher than those who have had none, or about .657.

The relative sizes of α and β in any application such as this one provide a measure of the contagion (or, in this case, heterogeneity) in relation to the initial transition rate, α. In this case, the value of β indicates that there is a relatively high amount of contagion or heterogeneity.

Before turning to other contagion models (in particular, equilibrium models, which will be discussed in some detail in the next chapter), the same kind of relation can be drawn between this distribution (or a slight simplification of it, as indicated below) and the exponential growth curve that exists between the exhaustible Poisson and the simple two-state model discussed in earlier chapters. That is, this model provides a total frequency distribution, while the exponential growth curve provides a mean or expected value. An exponential growth curve is one in which the rate of change in the people carrying out an action is proportional to those who are *already* carrying it out:

$$\frac{dn}{dt} = \beta n \tag{3.13}$$

or, by integration,

$$n_t = n_0 e^{\beta t} \tag{3.14}$$

where n is the number of people already carrying out the action. Such a curve has explosive potentialities, as demographers observe when they point out that population growth fits the assumptions of this model if the birth rate is higher than the death rate.[8] But note one peculiar point about this model: if $n_0 = 0$, there is no way for it to get started. It has no initial transition coefficient, as in the contagion model just discussed. If it is modified in this way, then it becomes an expression for the mean value of the contagion model, just as the straight line, αt, and the negative exponential, $N(1 - e^{-\alpha t})$, were for the Poisson and exhaustible Poisson, respectively:

$$\frac{dn}{dt} = \beta n + \alpha \tag{3.15}$$

Integrating this gives

$$n_t = \frac{\alpha(e^{\beta t} - 1)}{\beta} \tag{3.16}$$

---

[8] In applications to population growth, the model is $dn/dt = k_1 n - k_2 n$, where k_1 is the birth rate of the population and k_2 is the death rate. See Pearl (1925) and Volterra (1931) for discussion of the application of this model to population growth. In the next part of this chapter there will be a more detailed discussion of population growth in relation to a modified contagion model.

This value is identical to the expected value for the contagious distribution of eq. (3.5):

$$E(i) = \mu = \frac{\alpha(e^{\beta t} - 1)}{\beta}$$

It is important to keep clear the points of correspondence of these models. In the two-state exponential growth model, the states characterize the individual dichotomously: having begun the action or not, having caught the flu or not, being born or not (in the population growth application). Or, in application to repeated actions of a single individual, the states characterize the particular act: its existence or nonexistence, and n is the expected number of actions that have been carried out.

In the multistate model, the states characterize the *system*: e.g., one person having carried out the act; two having carried it out; etc. Or, in repeated actions of an individual, having acted once, twice, three times, and so on.

Thus, as in the other cases, the contagious distribution provides the frequency distribution for a familiar exponential growth curve. However, the correspondence between these two may be made a little differently, by modifying the contagious process to give what may sometimes be a more useful model. Often we think of artificially "seeding" a growth process, by stocking a pond with a few fish to spawn, or by planting a rumor and leaving it to spread, or by plugging a song until it begins to "catch on." Even when the seeding is not artificial, as in the spontaneous occurrence of rumor, or the occurrence of a new fad among a group of teen-agers, the innovation coefficient, α, may be so low relative to the transmission or growth coefficient, β, that it can be neglected. When this can be done, a simplified contagion model can be developed in which we *start* with the system in state 1 (e.g., one person knowing a rumor, or, in the case of operant conditioning, with one action having been taken). Then we ask, What is the probability that the system will be in state i after time t? The differential equations describing this system are

$$\frac{dp_1}{dt} = -\beta p_1 \tag{3.17}$$

and

$$\frac{dp_i}{dt} = (i - 1)\beta p_{i-1} - i\beta p_i \quad (i \geqslant 2) \tag{3.18}$$

with the initial condition that $p_1 = 1$.

A diagram shows the process described by the model:

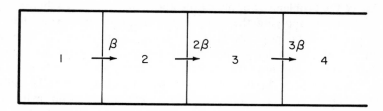

By proceeding as in the other derivations, we arrive at the frequency distribution:

$$p_i = e^{-\beta t}(1 - e^{-\beta t})^{i-1} \tag{3.19}$$

The expected value of i is nearly the exponential growth curve:

$$E(i) = e^{\beta t} - 1 \tag{3.20}$$

or, putting it differently, the expected value of $i + 1$ is identical to the exponential growth curve:

$$E(i + 1) = e^{\beta t} \tag{3.21}$$

This simplified contagious Poisson is of course not applicable where the innovation rate (α) is reasonably large relative to the contagion rate (β). A rough rule of thumb for its application is this: Whenever an empirical distribution includes p_0, then it is not applicable, and the more complicated model is required; whenever the distribution begins with p_1, the simpler model is applicable. It should be noted, however, that this model places somewhat greater restriction on the fit than does the model with an innovation parameter. Here there is only one parameter, rather than two. Closer insqection of eq. (3.19) indicates also that the relation between adjacent states is a very simple one. If we let $1 - e^{-\beta t} = x$, then

$$p_i = (1 - x)x^{i-1} \tag{3.22}$$

and

$$\frac{p_i}{p_{i-1}} = x \quad (x < 1) \tag{3.23}$$

As eq. (3.23) indicates, the ratio of sizes of adjacent states is constant, thus providing a very restricted distribution.

To apply this distribution empirically, the equation for the expected value of i can be used to estimate β, the only parameter:

$$E(i + 1) = \mu + 1 = e^{\beta}$$

$$\beta = \ln(\mu + 1)$$
$$= \ln(\Sigma i p_i + 1) \tag{3.24}$$

4. AN EXHAUSTIBLE CONTAGION MODEL

One of the problems in applying the above model is precisely the same as the problem in applying the Poisson distribution: Only when i is small relative to the total population, is the model appropriate. So long as the population which can carry out the act is limited, then there is a limiting N which the model does not take account of. In many applications, some limiting N exists. Even in population growth, which would seem to be unlimited because there is no total N (as there is in rumor transmission or in medical epidemics), there is a limitation, imposed by scarcity of food. Thus it has been found, for human populations, naturally existing animal populations, and experimental animal populations, that the population growth curve is not exponential, but roughly logistic, reaching an upper limit determined by the natural environment. Raymond Pearl (1925) carried out extensive investigations of population growth among men and animals; A. J. Lotka (1929)

Table 10.6

NUMBER OF NIGHTS IN THE WEEK THAT BOYS REPORT GOING OUT WITH OTHER BOYS (HIGH SCHOOL STUDENTS IN AN UPPER-MIDDLE-CLASS SUBURB)

Number of nights i	Number of boys n	Number of nights i	Number of boys n
0	78	4	71
1	151	5	45
2	316	6	26
3	189	7	51

studied this problem in detail also. A number of investigators have used the logistic curve for approximating physiological growth curves of single organisms. See, for example, Nathan Shock (1951).

Particularly in the study of social contagion, where we are interested not merely in the skew distributions when i is very small, but in the whole course of contagion, it is necessary to take exhaustion into account in a contagion model. Such an "exhaustible contagion" model will be more fully applicable to social phenomena than any of the three (Poisson, exhaustible Poisson, and contagious Poisson) yet discussed, for it includes two elements which are crucial in social phenomena: nonindependence of actions and limited populations. If, for example, one is concerned with the spread of an activity in small groups (i.e., the proportion of groups in which one man is doing the activity, the proportion in which two are doing it, etc., a given time after it is introduced), none of the preceding distributions are appropriate. As in the example in Chapter 1, of the spread or use of a new drug among doctors, many problems concern the spread of an innovation in limited populations. Or take still a different case: Suppose we ask teen-age boys how many nights a week they go out with the other boys, as indicated in Table 10.6. Suppose further that going out one night leads to going out a second. Then the distribution is contagious, far less clustered around the mean than we would expect (by assumption of independence between going out one night and going out the next); yet the total N is seven, so that the contagious model above could hardly be used. Whenever we are concerned with situations in which the activity has spread to a reasonably large part of the population or to a reasonably large part of the exhaustible framework (i.e., seven nights of the week), then the ordinary contagious distributions of eqs. (3.5) and (3.17) will not suffice.

The postulates of this model of exhaustible contagion are laid out below. First, each individual is characterized by a transition rate, which is composed of an "independent" part and a "contagion" part: $\alpha + \beta i$. But the transition rate for the system as a whole is the sum of the transition rates for each individual. When the system is in state i, this means that i persons have already shifted, so that the number left to shift is $N - i$. Therefore, the total transition rate for the system from state i to $i + 1$ is

$$\text{total transition rate} = (N - i)(\alpha + \beta i) \tag{4.1}$$

The equations that describe this model are

$$\frac{dp_0}{dt} = -N\alpha p_0 \tag{4.2}$$

and

$$\frac{dp_i}{dt} = (N - i + 1)[\alpha + (i - 1)\beta]p_{i-1} - (N - i)(\alpha + i\beta)p_i \quad (1 \leqslant i \leqslant N) \tag{4.3}$$

with the initial condition, $p_0 = 1$. A diagram shows the states of the model:

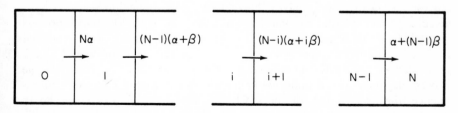

A simplified modification of this model assumes "seeding" and has no independent initiation parameter α. The general transition rate for this model is

$$\text{transition rate} = (N - i)i\beta \tag{4.4}$$

The equations that describe this simplified process are

$$\frac{dp_1}{dt} = -(N-1)\beta p_1 \qquad (4.5)$$

and

$$\frac{dp_i}{dt} = (N-i+1)(i-1)\beta p_{i-1} - (N-i)i\beta p_i \quad (1 < i \leqslant N) \qquad (4.6)$$

with the initial condition that $p_1 = 1$.

It is this modified model which is the stochastic counterpart of the logistic curve, for the logistic assumes seeding and contains only the contagion parameter. Note the interesting fact that the transition rates in this simplified model are symmetrical around $N/2$; the transition rate from 1 to 2, where there are yet $N-1$ persons to be influenced but only one influencer, is the same as that from $N-1$ to N, where there are $N-1$ persons to do the influencing, but only one person left to influence. This does not assume, of course, that the influence of one man on the other members of the group is the same as the influence of the group on the man. Quite to the contrary: the influence of any man on any other is assumed to be β, so that the total influence on any *one* man when the group is in state 1 will be β, while the group's influence upon the remaining holdout when the group is in state $N-1$ will be $(N-1)\beta$.

Unfortunately, even the simpler of these two models is extremely difficult to solve analytically to obtain the distribution function. The derivation is carried out in Bailey (1957, pp. 39–41), but it is so involved that it will not be reproduced here.[9]

One point may be noted in the correspondence between this model and its deterministic analog, resulting in the logistic curve. In the previous models of this chapter, the expected value of the distribution was equal to the deterministic equation. Here, however, this is not the case. The deterministic model, $dn_2/dt = kn_2(N-n_2)$, where n_2 is the number who have acted, corresponding to i here, makes the rate depend on the number who have acted, n_2, times the number who have not, $N-n_2$. If the stochastic process depended, as this equation implies, on the *expected* number who have acted times the expected number who have not, then this equation would give a result corresponding to the mean value for the stochastic process. But the process depends instead upon the *actual* number in each group. As a consequence, the mean value for the stochastic model will be different, and in general less, than the logistic curve. The expression for the mean of the simpler process (without an innovation rate α) has been found in explicit

---

[9] For any reader who wishes to use Bailey's solution, it is important to note that his $p_r(\tau)$ are the probabilities of there being r nonactors (or "susceptibles," in his medical interpretation). For use of his equations, set his $n = N - 1$, $r = N - i$, and $\tau = \beta t$.

form by Haskey (1954), and is reproduced here from Bailey (1957, p. 43). It is[10]

$$\mu = \sum_i \frac{(N-1)!}{i!(N-i-1)!}\left[(2i-N)^2\beta t + 2 - (2i-N)\sum_{j=N-i}^{i-1}\frac{1}{j}\right]e^{-i(N-i)\beta t} \qquad (4.7)$$

The complications produced by even this simple process suggest the difficulties involved in more involved models of this sort. It is likely that much of the future work will have to by-pass explicit solutions and turn to computer simulations which mirror the desired process.

5. WHEN TO USE FREQUENCY DISTRIBUTIONS AND WHEN EXPECTED-VALUE EQUATIONS

When does one need to use the frequency distributions? The answer to this lies in part in the kind of data one has. If there are data on one system (e.g., a group in which a rumor is spreading, or one song gaining in popularity, or one person having accidents), then only the curves representing expected values can be used. Examples of such uses are in Tables 5.8 and 10.3. Sometimes, however, only cross-sectional data, or data at two times, exist on a single system. Examples of this sort make up the body of Chapters 4–9. There, we cannot even test whether changes do occur, on the average, in accordance with the differential equations. Such cases require an assumption about the processes in operation, in order even to estimate the transition rates from the differential equations.

However, sometimes we have cross-sectional data on many systems. Such are the data in most of the examples of this chapter. In the accident-frequency example, the "system" was an individual, who could have 0, 1, 2, or more accidents; in the record-purchasing example, the "system" was again an individual, with 0, 1, 2, or more purchases of records. In the death-by-horsekick example, each "system" was an army corps having 1, 2, 3, or more deaths within the year. In the example of boys going out at night, each system is a boy.

When the data are of this sort, they are of a rather peculiar form. They consist of the number of "systems" in which i is 0, the number in which i is 1, and so on. Often they are highly skewed, pushed up against the low-frequency end.

When such is the form of the data, the mean-value equations will not be helpful; since the data are cross-sectional, they cannot be used to describe a curve over time. It is in such cases that the models of this chapter and the next are useful. The models can be thought of as frequency distributions for the corresponding two-state models, or alternatively as expected-value models for a multistate, rather than a two-state, model.

---

[10] The lower limit for i in the summation is $N/2$ if N is even; it is $N/2 - 1/2$ if N is odd. The upper limit is $N - 1$.

APPENDIX—DERIVATION OF THE DISTRIBUTION OF p_i FOR
THE CONTAGIOUS POISSON

The transition rates are

$$q_{01} = \alpha \tag{A.1}$$

$$q_{i,i+1} = \alpha + i\beta \tag{A.2}$$

The rate of decrease of p_0 is described by eq. (A.3), just as with the Poisson:

$$\frac{dp_0}{dt} = -\alpha p_0 \tag{A.3}$$

$$p_0 = e^{-\alpha t} \tag{A.4}$$

The equation for p_1 can be found as in the second method used in deriving p_1 for the Poisson distribution, that is, by considering the way in which the system can be in state 1: If there is a jump from state 0 to 1 at time τ, then $q_{1\tau}$ is the probability of being in state 0 until τ, times the probability of an event at time τ, times the probability of no event until time t. These probabilities are $e^{-\alpha\tau}$, $\alpha d\tau$, and $e^{-(\alpha+\beta)(t-\tau)}$. The probability p_1 is then the integral of $q_{1\tau}$ over all $d\tau$ between zero and t.

$$p_1 = \int_0^t q_{1\tau} d\tau = \int_0^t e^{-\alpha\tau} \alpha e^{-(\alpha+\beta)(t-\tau)} \, d\tau \tag{A.5}$$

$$= e^{-(\alpha+\beta)t} \frac{\alpha(e^{\beta t}-1)}{\beta}$$

Similarly, $q_{2\tau}$ is the probability of being in state 1 until τ, times the probability of an event at time τ, times the probability of no event until time t. These probabilities are $e^{-(\alpha+\beta)\tau}\alpha(e^{\beta\tau}-1)/\beta$, $(\alpha+\beta)d\tau$,

and $e^{-(\alpha+2\beta)(t-\tau)}$.

$$p_2 = \int_0^t q_{2\tau} \, d\tau = \int_0^t \frac{e^{-(\alpha+\beta)\tau}\alpha(e^{\beta\tau}-1)}{\beta}(\alpha+\beta)e^{-(\alpha+2\beta)(t-\tau)} \, d\tau \tag{A.6}$$

$$= \frac{e^{-(\alpha+2\beta)t}\,\alpha(\alpha+\beta)}{\beta}\int_0^t (e^{2\beta\tau}-e^{\beta\tau}) d\tau$$

$$= \frac{e^{-(\alpha+2\beta)t}\alpha(\alpha+\beta)(e^{\beta t}-1)^2}{2\beta^2}$$

Now this equation takes the form

$$p_i = \frac{e^{-(\alpha+i\beta)t}\alpha(\alpha+\beta)\ldots[\alpha+(i-1)\beta](e^{\beta t}-1)^i}{i!\beta^i} \tag{A.7}$$

If we assume that eq. (A.7) holds for p_i, and find that p_{i+1} is of this form, then this completes the derivation. (Since the equation does take this form for $i = 2$, then by showing that it holds for $i + 1$, whatever the value of i, this means that we could move up in steps from two to any value of i desired.) If p_i is given by eq. (A.7), then p_{i+1} is

$$p_{i+1} = \int_0^t \frac{e^{-(\alpha+i\beta)\tau}\alpha(\alpha+\beta)\ldots[\alpha+(i-1)\beta](e^{\beta\tau}-1)}{i!\beta^i}$$
$$(\alpha + i\beta)e^{-[\alpha+(i+1)\beta](t-\tau)}\,d\tau \qquad (A.8)$$

$$= \frac{e^{-[\alpha+(i+1)\beta]t}\alpha(\alpha+\beta)\ldots(\alpha+i\beta)}{i!\beta^i}\int_0^t (e^{\beta\tau}-1)^i e^{\beta\tau}\,d\tau \qquad (A.9)$$

The quantity under the integral is of the form $x^n\,dx$, with the exception of a factor β, where $(e^{\beta\tau}-1) = x$. Thus it can be integrated to give

$$\frac{(e^{\beta\tau}-1)^{i+1}}{\beta^{(i+1)}}\Big|_0^t$$

or

$$\frac{(e^{\beta\tau}-1)^{i+1}}{\beta^{(i+1)}}$$

Replacing this for the quantity under the integral in eq. (A.9) gives

$$p_{i+1} = \frac{e^{-[\alpha+(i+1)\beta]t}\alpha(\alpha+\beta)\ldots(\alpha+i\beta)(e^{\beta t}-1)^{i+1}}{(i+1)!\beta!} \qquad (A.10)$$

This equation is identical, for $i + 1$, to eq. (A.7) for i, so the derivation is complete. The first and last expressions in the numerator can be expressed more simply as $e^{-\alpha t}(1 - e^{-\beta t})^{i+1}$, thus putting the equation in the form of eq. (3.5).

The expected value, or mean, of i, is found as follows:

$$E(i) = \mu = \sum_{i=0}^{\infty} ip_i \qquad (A.11)$$

But, using the relation between p_i and p_{i-1} obtained by means of eq. (A.7), we obtain

$$\Sigma ip_i = \sum_{i=0}^{\infty} p_{i-1}\frac{e^{-\beta t}[\alpha+(i-1)\beta](e^{\beta t}-1)}{\beta}$$

$$= \sum_{i=0}^{\infty}(i-1)p_{i-1}(1-e^{-\beta t}) + \Sigma p_{i-1}\frac{\alpha}{\beta}(1-e^{-\beta t})$$

However, $\sum_{i=0}^{\infty}(i-1)p_{i-1}$ is equal to μ, by eq. (A.11), and $\sum_{i=0}^{\infty} p_{i-1} = 1$, since this is a summation over all values of i, so that

$$\mu = \mu(1-e^{-\beta t}) + \frac{\alpha}{\beta}(1-e^{-\beta t})$$

and solving for μ gives

$$\mu = \frac{\alpha}{\beta}(e^{\beta t} - 1) \qquad (A.12)$$

The variance is found in a similar fashion:

$$\sigma_i^2 = \Sigma(i - \mu)^2 p_i \qquad (A.13)$$

$$= \Sigma i^2 p_i - 2\mu\Sigma i p_i + \mu^2\Sigma p_i$$

$$= \Sigma i^2 p_i - \mu^2$$

But, using eq. (A.7) as in the derivation of μ, we obtain

$$\sigma_i^2 = \sum_{i=0}^{\infty} i p_{i-1}\frac{e^{-\beta t}[\alpha + (i-1)\beta](e^{\beta t} - 1)}{\beta} - \mu^2$$

Subtracting and adding to the right-hand side gives

$$\sigma_i^2 = \sum_{i=0}^{\infty} (i-1) p_{i-1}\frac{e^{-\beta t}[\alpha + (i-1)\beta](e^{\beta t} - 1)}{\beta}$$

$$+ \sum_{i=0}^{\infty} p_{i-1}\frac{e^{-\beta t}[\alpha + (i-1)](e^{\beta t} - 1)}{\beta} - \mu^2$$

$$= \sum_{i=0}^{\infty} (i-1)^2 p_{i-1}(1 - e^{-\beta t}) + \sum_{i=0}^{\infty} (i-1) p_{i-1}\frac{(\alpha + \beta)(1 - e^{-\beta t})}{\beta}$$

$$+ \sum_{i=0}^{\infty} p_i\frac{\alpha}{\beta}(1 - e^{-\beta t}) - \mu^2$$

$$= \sigma_i^2(1 - e^{-\beta t}) + \mu\frac{(\alpha + \beta)}{\beta}(1 - e^{-\beta t})^\beta + \frac{\alpha}{\beta}(1 + e^{-\beta t}) - \mu^2$$

Solving for σ_i^2 gives

$$\sigma_i^2 = \mu e^{\beta t} \qquad (A.14)$$

CHAPTER 11

THE POISSON PROCESS AND ITS CONTAGIOUS RELATIVES

EQUILIBRIUM MODELS

Often, social data come in the form of equilibrium distributions. The example of boys going out at night in the last chapter illustrates this well: We treated the data as a one-way nonequilibrium process which we intercepted at some point t; but in reality the ebb and flow of evening social activities is just that—an ebb and flow, a two-way process. In some cases, the form of the data determines whether the appropriate model is an equilibrium one or a one-way process. If data exist on the number of cars a man *has purchased* in the last six months, the model is a one-way process like those above; if data exist on the number of cars a man *owns*, we have a two-way process, and equilibrium models are appropriate.

A two-way process of course is not limited to the investigation of equilibrium states. The kinetics of such a process may be studied as well. However, *if* we want to examine equilibrium states, only such two-way processes are appropriate. Since much social data are of a static cross-sectional nature, the assumption of equilibrium and the development of models or theories to aid such investigations occupy an important place in social theory.

The strategy, then, in this chapter will be to extend the models of the preceding chapter to two-way processes, but solely for the examination of equilibrium states. This will allow the study of somewhat more complex substantive problems without getting into overburdening mathematics.

1. A POISSON WITH A BACKWARD FLOW

Consider the case of a model to account adequately for the number of friends a person has. There is a certain rate of acquisition of new friends and a certain rate of losing old ones. If there were only an acquisition process, and not a loss as well, then people would add more and more and more friends as time went on. If that were the case, the process would be an ordinary one-way flow, a Poisson or some similar distribution. Or we could arbitrarily consider only the one-way process by asking a sample of persons how many friends they *acquired* over a given period of time. But suppose instead we simply observed the number of friends each one had at a given point in time; and suppose further we found or assumed that the distribution remained constant over time (although of course particular individuals might move up or down). What would be the appropriate model?

Let us assume, as we did with the one-way flow models, that people are *alike* in their tendency to acquire and lose friends. Assume also that there is no contagion, no aversion, and no exhaustion of available people (that is, acquiring one friend does not affect one's likelihood of acquiring another). Then let the acquisition coefficient for each person be

$$\alpha = \frac{\text{(number adding a friend)}}{\text{(persons available as friends) (number in this state) (time)}}$$

and the loss coefficient,

$$\beta = \frac{\text{(number losing a friend)}}{\text{(friends held) (number in this state) (time)}}$$

This means that the transition rate from state i (having i friends) to state $i + 1$ is $N\alpha'$, where N is the total pool of potential friends. Since N is assumed $>>i$, and thus constant over all states i, $N\alpha'$ may be collapsed to give $N\alpha' = \alpha$. The transition rate down from state $i + 1$ to i, however, is dependent not only on β but also upon $i + 1$ itself, since β is a coefficient of loss per friend held: $(i + 1)\beta$.

The differential equations describing this process are

$$\frac{dp_0}{dt} = -\alpha p_0 + \beta p_1 \tag{1.1}$$

and

$$\frac{dp_i}{dt} = -(\alpha + i\beta)p_i + \alpha p_{i-1} + (i+1)\beta p_{i+1} \quad (i \geqslant 1) \tag{1.2}$$

In the derivations below, and in all subsequent work in this chapter, the differential equations themselves will not be used, since we are investigating only equilibrium states, that is, the condition when $dp_i/dt = 0$ for all i.

Diagrammatically, the transition rates look like this:

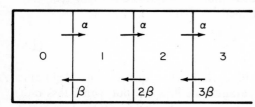 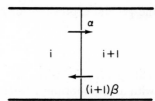

The condition of statistical equilibrium tells only that the proportion of persons in each state remains the same; but the added knowledge that there is only one way out of state 0 tells that the number crossing from state 0 to state 1 per unit time equals the number crossing from state 1 back to state 0. Or (if p_0 and p_1 are used to represent the proportions of persons in states 0 and 1, rather than n_0 and n_1 to represent absolute numbers):

$$p_0 \alpha = p_1 \beta$$

This relation forces a similar equilibrium flow between state 1 and state 2:

$$p_1 \alpha = p_2 2\beta$$

And so on, the general term being

$$p_i \alpha = p_{i+1}(i+1)\beta \tag{1.3}$$

If the general term is expressed as a function of p_0, it becomes

$$p_i = \frac{p_0}{i!} \left(\frac{\alpha}{\beta}\right)^i \tag{1.4}$$

The sum of the proportions in each state is an infinite series, which must equal one if there is to be a proper distribution function, and thereby equilibrium. The series is

$$p_0 + p_0\frac{\alpha}{\beta} + p_1\frac{\alpha}{2\beta} + \ldots + p_i\frac{\alpha}{(i+1)\beta} + \ldots \tag{1.5}$$

If each term is expressed as a function of p_0, as in eq. (1.4), the series becomes (letting $\alpha/\beta = a$):

$$p_0\left(1 + a + \frac{a^2}{2!} + \frac{a^3}{3!} + \frac{a^4}{4!} + \ldots + \frac{a^i}{i!} + \ldots\right) \tag{1.6}$$

This is the familiar exponential series, which is equal to e^a, and convergent for all values of a. Since the distribution must equal one,

$$1 = p_0 e^a \tag{1.7}$$

or

$$p_0 = e^{-a}$$

When this value for p_0 is substituted into the expression for p_i (eq. 1.4), the general expression for p_i is obtained:

$$p_i = \frac{e^{-a}a^i}{i!} \tag{1.8}$$

This expression turns out to be simply a Poisson distribution. Beginning with an equilibrium model which parallels the Poisson, but with a loss rate, the same distribution results, this time as an equilibrium state. This result has important implications for practice, for it means that in mirroring social distributions, the Poisson may be used just as legitimately for equilibrium situations as for data which interrupt some one-way process. When such equilibrium data fit the Poisson distribution, it means that the parameters of acquisition and loss have the general form of those presented above (i.e., the acquisition parameter is independent of the state and the loss parameter from state i is a constant multiplied by i).

Applying this model to two distributions of friendship choices in a high school, one of boys and the other of girls, shows that the model does not at all fit. Obviously, in both cases, something other than the simple non-contagious acquisition and loss processes are operative among these boys and girls (see Table 11.1).

There are numerous other applications of this model, some of them including the examination of nonequilibrium states as well as equilibrium. A good example might be certain kinds of learning experiments, in which a number of units, such as nonsense syllables, are learned, but there is a process of forgetting going on at the same time. In such a case, the acquisition parameter α is a parameter of acquisition per unit time (again assuming that the available pool from which new syllables are acquired is large enough to be considered inexhaustible).[1] The loss parameter, β, is a parameter of loss per word already known (i.e., the assumption is that each syllable has the same probability of fading out of memory per unit time, independently

---

[1] If the size of the pool is exhaustible, the resulting model is one which reduces, at equilibrium, to a binomial distribution rather than a Poisson.

Table 11.1

DISTRIBUTION OF FRIENDSHIP CHOICES IN A LARGE SUBURBAN
HIGH SCHOOL

Number of choices	GIRLS		BOYS	
	Actual	Expected	Actual	Expected
0	49	49	99	99
1	86	143	150	224
2	109	210	174	254
3	149	204	144	192
4	137	149	118	109
5	111	87	90	49
6	78	43	66	18.6
7	67	18	53	6.1
8	40	6.5	20	1.7
9	34	2.1	19	.4
10	22	.6	8	.1
11	12	.2	4	
12	7	.1	5	
13	1		0	
14	4		1	
15	2		1	
16	3		1	
	911		953	

of the number of other symbols presently known). With such a model, and data from experiments of continuous learning of nonsense syllables, it would be possible to examine both the dynamics (i.e., learning) and the equilibrium distributions (i.e., the number of nonsense syllables learned at equilibrium).

2. A MODIFICATION OF THE MODEL, AND APPLICATION TO CONSUMER BEHAVIOR

The preceding model, as a two-way analog of the one-way Poisson distribution developed in Chapter 10, embodies a particular assumption about dropping back from state i to $i - 1$: an assumption that the farther out one is, and the more items he possesses, the harder it is to maintain his position. That is, we assumed a constant loss rate *per friend* that one possesses. Then if the loss rate per friend is β, the transition rate from state 1 to 0 is β, that from 2 to 1 is 2β, and that from state i to $i - 1$ is $i\beta$. For most applications of an "equilibrium Poisson" model of this sort, this is reasonable. The rate of loss should be constant *per item possessed*, and consequently proportional to the state the system is in. However, there are some exceptions. In applications where only the most recent acquisition is subject to loss (like the monkey scrambling up the side of the well, who slips back a foot for every two feet he gains), then an assumption of constant loss rate, independent of i, is appropriate.

The transition rates in this model are for acquisition identical to the preceding model, α; but for loss, a constant, independent of i, β.

The differential equations describing this process are

$$\frac{dp_0}{dt} = -\alpha p_0 + \beta p_1 \tag{2.1}$$

and

$$\frac{dp_i}{dt} = -(\alpha + \beta)p_i + \alpha p_{i-1} + \beta p_{i+1} \quad (i \geqslant 1) \tag{2.2}$$

Again, only the condition in which $dp_i/dt = 0$ for all i is relevant here. Diagrammatically, the model is

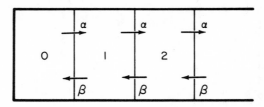

In this modified model, then, the equilibrium condition states that

$$p_0 \alpha = p_1 \beta \tag{2.3}$$

which implies that

$$p_1 \alpha = p_2 \beta \tag{2.4}$$

which implies that

$$p_2 \alpha = p_3 \beta \tag{2.5}$$

and so on. Expressed as a function of p_0, the proportion in state i is

$$p_i = p_0 \left(\frac{\alpha}{\beta}\right)^i \tag{2.6}$$

In this case, another infinite series is generated, as follows (again letting $\alpha/\beta = a$):

$$p_0 + p_0 a + p_0 a^2 p_0 a^3 + \ldots + p_0 a^n + \ldots \tag{2.7}$$

Now what happens if the acquisition rate is greater than the loss rate, that is, $\alpha > \beta$? This would mean that $a > 1$, and each state would have more people in it than the preceding one, all the way out to infinity. In other words, in such a system, there would be no equilibrium after all. Like a one-way

Poisson process operating over a long time, and like the monkey who loses less each time than he gains, it would simply go out to infinity.

However, if the acquisition rate is *smaller* than the loss rate, what happens? The terms representing the probability of being in each state form the series, $p_0 + p_0 a^2 + p_0 a^3 + \ldots$. The question becomes one of the convergence or divergence of this series—a geometric series—as a is greater or less than one. It turns out, as we might intuitively suppose, that when $a < 1$, the series converges. The sum, s, of a geometric series is

$$s = \frac{p_0}{1 - a} \tag{2.8}$$

This sum must be equal to the sum of the probabilities, that is, 1. Therefore, substituting 1 for s and solving for p_0 gives

$$p_0 = 1 - a = 1 - \frac{\alpha}{\beta} \tag{2.9}$$

Thus by substituting this into eq. (2.6), we have the expression for the general term p_i:

$$p_i = \left(1 - \frac{\alpha}{\beta}\right)\left(\frac{\alpha}{\beta}\right)^i \tag{2.10}$$

or

$$p_i = (1 - a)a^i \tag{2.11}$$

This model appears at first to be of little use in social and psychological applications. However, a slight modification of the assumptions may show the model in a more useful light. Suppose we think of purchases of various brands of some frequently bought item, say, coffee. Thinking of the purchases of this item over time, it is possible to set up the following model: an individual has a transition rate toward buying brand A, and a transition rate toward buying any other brand. Suppose we ask the question: Just how many people are going to make one purchase, two purchases, three purchases, etc., of brand A before shifting to another brand? This is another way of stating the perennial problem of brand loyalty for a product. This question, in conjunction with the above assumptions, gives rise to a model which can be diagrammed as follows:[2]

---

[2] The differential equations for the process are

$$\frac{dp_0}{dt} = -\alpha p_0 + \sum_{i=1}^{\infty} \beta p_i$$

and

$$\frac{dp_i}{dt} = -(\alpha + \beta)p_i + \alpha p_{i-1}$$

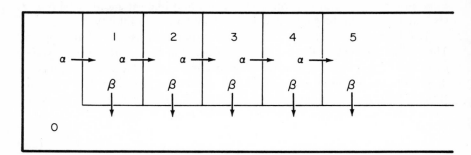

The states labelled 1, 2, 3, . . . are the states of having bought brand A one, two, three, etc., times in succession without having switched to another brand. The state 0 is the state of having bought another brand at the last purchase.

If this model agrees with the data, then there is no brand loyalty operative at all.[3] For the probability of buying the brand next time if one has bought it four times in a row is no greater than the probability of buying it if something else was bought last time. If, on the other hand, the data are not consistent with the model, by showing more people in high-numbered states than the model would predict, this is evidence of brand loyalty—of greater and greater loyalty to the brand one has been buying.

This model, as described above, results in an equilibrium distribution identical to the geometric series of eq. (2.11). The equilibrium between states is expressed by

number crossing into state i per unit time = number going out

that is,

$$p_{i-1}\alpha = p_i(\alpha + \beta) \qquad (2.12)$$

or

$$\frac{p_i}{p_{i-1}} = \frac{\alpha}{\alpha + \beta} \qquad (2.13)$$

or

$$p_i = \left(\frac{\alpha}{\alpha + \beta}\right)^i p_0 \qquad (2.14)$$

This may be solved as above to give an equation identical to (2.11):

$$p_i = (1 - x)x^i \qquad (2.15)$$

where $x = \alpha/(\alpha + \beta)$ and p_i is the proportion of all consumers who, at the time of the measurement, have made exactly i purchases of brand A since buying a different brand.

Note that although the distribution is the same here as in eq. (2.11), the

_____

[3] Or, if we are examining data on associative learning, with rewards for the correct response (= brand A), this model would be one of no learning at all.

parameter x is a different function of the transition rates. As the definition of x shows, x must always be between zero and one, since both α and β are greater than zero by definition. Thus the series must always converge. The slowness of convergence (and thus the apparent—but spurious—brand loyalty) which different brands would show depends upon the relative sizes of α and β, that is, the popularity of the brand. The more popular the brand—and x [or $\alpha/(\alpha + \beta)$] is also the proportion of the market which brand A has—the more likely that successive purchases of it will be made before shifting to another.

It should be recognized that the quantities p_i are not the proportions of persons who made exactly i purchases and then shifted to another brand. They are the proportions of persons who, at any particular time, have made exactly i purchases of the brand—whether they will shift to another purchase on the next brand or not. If the data are in this other form—the proportion who made i successive purchases before they defected, counting only the first such sequence for each person—then these latter proportions are the states of a nonequilibrium model. If, however, the data are the total number of sequences of exactly i purchases (that is, letting each person count more than once if he was involved in more than one sequence of brand A purchases in the time segment examined), then we once again have this same equilibrium model, since we are measuring the total flow into state 0 for the system as a whole, and we assume the system to be in equilibrium. In that case, the proportion of sequences of exactly i purchases turns out to be proportional to the p_i of eq. (2.13). This follows from the fact that the numbers who defect per unit time from state i are proportional to p_i, through the transition rate β. Thus the distribution of eq. (2.15) can be used in either case—whether the data are numbers of persons who have bought brand A exactly i times, regardless of their subsequent purchase, or numbers of sequences of exactly i purchases before defection to another brand.

Fortunately, consumption data are available for use with this model. There are several market research agencies which maintain continuing panels of households which record their daily purchases of items. These data offer remarkable possibilities for analyses of buying patterns, but until now have been only very little analyzed.[4]

To illustrate the present model, only one set of data will be utilized: the number of sequences of purchases of brand A coffee which are 1, 2, 3, 4, . . . purchases in length. The data, as tabulated below, constitute the total number of shifts out of state 1, 2, 3, 4, . . . where state i is defined as the state of

---

[4] The first analysis of such data in terms of stochastic processes was by Alfred Kuehn (1958). A detailed analysis of purchase patterns in coffee from this point of view has been carried out by Ronald Frank (1962). The sequences used for illustration in the example below were taken from Frank's data. I have also applied a quite different stochastic process, described in Chapter 13, to separate out inter-individual and intra-individual variability in behavior.

having made i consecutive purchases of brand A since the first purchase of this brand.

These data can be tested against the distribution of eq. (2.15) as a way of seeing whether this purchase behavior is consistent with the model of this section. However, the data of Table 11.2 are not directly convertible into p_i's; as explained earlier, they are proportional to the p_i's, being the "precipitate" into state 0 from each state 1, 2, ... Thus a modification of eq. (2.15) must be used. If we let the proportion of the total precipitate (or

Table 11.2

NUMBER OF SEQUENCES OF PURCHASES OF BRAND A
COFFEE OF LENGTH i IN A 12-MONTH PANEL OF
524 FAMILIES†

i Number of consecutive purchases	n_i Number of sequences of i consecutive purchases	Proportion of sequences of length greater than i
0	—	1.000
1	261	.294
2	61	.130
3	18	.081
4	9	.057
5	5	.043
6	5	.030
7	4	.019
8 plus	7	

† A few families which never shifted away from brand A are excluded, and all sequences which were uncompleted at the end of the period are excluded.

total sequences) which comes from state 1 be called y, then the proportion coming from state 2 is yx, the proportion coming from state 3 is yx^2, and in general the proportion coming from state $i - 1$ is yx^i. Thus

$$\frac{n_i}{n} = yx^{i-1} \tag{2.16}$$

or

$$p_i' = yx^{i-1} \tag{2.17}$$

where n_i is the number of sequences of length i, n is the total number of sequences (of length one or greater), and p_i' is the proportion of such sequences that are of length i. Since the sum of the series is 1.0, and the sum of an infinite series of the form yx^i is $y/(1 - x)$, then $y/(1 - x) = 1$, or $y = 1 - x$. Therefore,

$$p_i' = (1 - x)x^{i-1} \qquad (2.18)$$

Since the data are in the form of n_1, n_2, . . ., that is, the total number of sequences of total length 1, 2, . . ., it is eq. (2.18) that can be used in conjunction with the data, rather than eq. (2.15), which gives the proportion of all

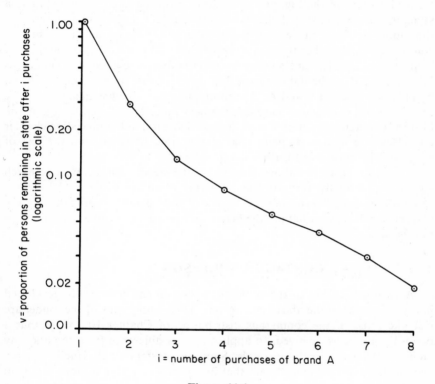

Figure 11.1

persons at any time who are in state i, $i = 0, 1, 2, . . .$.[5] However, a slight variation on eq. (2.18) will be used, to reduce the irregularities due to small numbers of cases at the tail. Let us define a quantity v_i to be the proportion of sequences greater than i in length. That is,

$$v_i = 1 - (\text{sum of } i \text{ terms})$$

[5] If p_i, the proportion in state i, in eq. (2.15) were based on only those in states 1, 2, . . ., excluding those in state 0, it would be identical to the proportion of precipitates from state i. This is seen by multiplying eq. (2.15) by $1/(1 - p_0)$, and since $p_0 = 1 - x$, this means multiplying eq. (2.15) by $1/x$.

Since the sum of the first i terms is $1 - x^i$, we have

$$v_i = 1 - (1 - x^i) \qquad (2.19)$$

or

$$\ln v_i = i \ln x \qquad (2.20)$$
$$= ik$$

By use of semilogarithmic paper eq. (2.20) can be used to test the model, for a plot of v_i on the logarithmic scale vs. i on the linear scale will give a straight line with $v_0 = 1$ if the model fits the data. Figure 11.1 shows that the model does *not* fit very well—that the points lie on a curve which is concave upward, rather than on a straight line. This means that the dropoff tends to get smaller and smaller as the number of consecutive purchases increases. That is, the data suggest that there is some brand loyalty induced by past purchases of brand A: The more purchases one has made, the more likely one will continue to purchase the next time. This directly suggests use of some contagious assumption of the sort discussed in the preceding chapter and elsewhere in this chapter. That elaboration, however, and the test of such models, must await further development.[6]

It is clear, from the above analysis, that here is a direction of research which is potentially very fruitful, in terms of the possible models which can be developed, in terms of the existence of good data for testing the models, and for deciding just what are the behavioral processes involved in consumption behavior.[7]

3. A TWO-WAY CONTAGIOUS POISSON

A two-way analog to the contagious Poisson can be usefully developed in a way similar to the above derivations. The assumptions of the model are just like those of the contagious distribution of Chapter 10, except that a two-way process is involved. In application, its difference from the one-way model is illustrated by this example: Suppose a system is behaving in accordance with the principle of "them that has, gets"—songs in a large part gain popularity because they are already popular, or social movements which have many followers are likely to gain more followers, or artists who have followers are likely to gain more. Given this situation, we have both acquisition and loss: The song or social movement may acquire and lose followers. It acquires them through the influence of its present followers; it loses them through

---

[6] An extensive analysis of these data, examining each household separately, has been carried out by Frank (1962). The analysis shows that the apparent contagion vanishes when each household's behavior is considered separately. That is, there is heterogeneity rather than contagion.

[7] Models of this sort, together with a contagion parameter, were originally intended to be included in a general discussion of learning processes, which has been omitted. It should be evident that there is no substantive difference between what I have called "brand loyalty" above and general processes of associative learning under conditions of reward.

erosion due to various influences. Thinking of the example of an artist or popular entertainer, suppose we set up the following model:

(a) Each person has a given transition rate (α') of becoming a fan, owing to influences independent of the existing fans (e.g., from a television program);

(b) Each person has a given transition rate (β) toward dropping away and becoming no longer a fan;

(c) Every person in the group who is a fan has an effect on each of those who is not, adding an increment (γ') in the direction of becoming a fan to the transition rate of each who is not;

(d) All individuals are alike in their transition rates, and the rates are constant over time. Although this is an unrealistic assumption, it can be relaxed in a more complicated model. (See Section 9, at the end of the chapter, on unsolved problems.)

Given these assumptions, the transition rates for each individual when there are i fans already are

Toward being a fan: $\alpha' + i\gamma'$, and

Away from being a fan: β.

Diagrammatically:

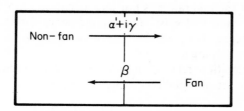

Just as in the section on one-way processes, the total group can be considered finite or infinite in size. That is, we can develop an exhaustible contagion process or a nonexhaustible one, where N is assumed infinite.

The nonexhaustible process which is appropriate to the present example when the total population is very great, relative to the number of fans, will be treated first. The transition rates for the system are

$$N(\alpha' + i\gamma') \text{ or } \alpha + i\gamma \qquad \text{and} \qquad i\beta$$

where N—assumed very large—is the number of potential fans. The simplifying assumption here is that i is negligible relative to N, so that N may be used in the transition rate above rather than $N - i$.

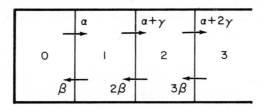

The differential equations describing the process are

$$\frac{dp_0}{dt} = -\alpha p_0 + \beta p_1 \tag{3.1}$$

and

$$\frac{dp_i}{dt} = -(\alpha + i\gamma + i\beta)p_i + [\alpha + (i-1)\gamma]p_{i-1} + (i+1)\beta p_{i+1} \quad (i \geqslant 1) \tag{3.2}$$

As before, the general behavior of these equations is not investigated, but only the stationary state (if one exists), where $dp_i/dt = 0$ for all i.

As in the preceding examples, if there is to be a stationary state, there must be an equilibrium between each pair of adjacent states, allowing us to write

$$p_0\alpha = p_1\beta$$
$$p_1(\alpha + \gamma) = p_2 2\beta$$

and in general

$$p_i(\alpha + i\gamma) = p_{i+1}(i+1)\beta \tag{3.3}$$

An examination of these equations suggests what can also be proved mathematically: If the loss rate β is not larger than the contagion parameter γ, then no equilibrium will exist. The infinite series formed by adding all the terms will diverge. Thus we shall consider only the case in which β is larger than γ in developing an equilibrium model.

The general equation relating p_0 and p_i may be found by successive substitution in the set of equations expressed by eqs. (3.1–3.3). This gives

$$p_i = p_0 \frac{\alpha(\alpha + \gamma) \ldots [\alpha + (i-1)\gamma]}{i!\beta^i} \tag{3.4}$$

If we substitute a for α/β and c for γ/β, to simplify the equation, it becomes

$$p_i = p_0 \frac{a(a+c) \ldots [a + (i-1)c]}{i!} \tag{3.5}$$

The infinite series formed by the sum of p_i, which must equal one if there is to be equilibrium, is [by use of eq. (3.5)]

$$\sum_{i=0}^{\infty} p_i = 1 = p_0 \left\{ 1 + \frac{a}{1} + \frac{a(a+c)}{2!} \ldots \frac{a(a+c) \ldots [a + (i-1)c]}{i!} + \ldots \right\} \tag{3.6}$$

As this series stands, it is not identical to any familiar infinite series. However, if ck is substituted for a, the series becomes a negative binomial:

$$1 = p_0 \left[1 + \frac{ck}{1} + \frac{c^2 k(k-1)}{2!} + \ldots + \binom{k+i-1}{i}c^i + \ldots \right] \tag{3.7}$$

which is the expansion

$$1 = p_0(1-c)^{-k} \tag{3.8}$$

or

$$p_0 = (1 - c)^k \tag{3.9}$$

Substituting back into eq. (3.7) gives the value of p_i in terms of k and c:[8]

$$p_i = \binom{k + i - 1}{i}(1 - c)^k c^i \tag{3.10}$$

By using the relations

$$\hat{\mu} = \sum_{i=0}^{\infty} i p_i \quad \text{and} \quad \hat{\sigma}^2 = \sum_{i=0}^{\infty} i^2 p_i - \hat{\mu}^2$$

it is possible to find k and c in terms of μ and γ^2 very much as was done in the Appendix of the preceding chapter. This gives

$$c = 1 - \frac{\hat{\mu}}{\hat{\sigma}^2} \left(= \frac{\gamma}{\beta} \right) \tag{3.11}$$

and

$$k = \frac{\hat{\mu}^2}{\hat{\sigma}^2 - \hat{\mu}} \left(= \frac{\alpha}{\gamma} \right) \tag{3.12}$$

The distribution given in eq. (3.10) is identical, though expressed in a different form, to the distribution of Section 3 in the preceding chapter, given in eq. (3.5) of that chapter. However, the transition parameters α and β of that chapter (which will be labelled α^* and β^* here, to prevent confusion with the symbols of the present chapter) are quite different from those in the present chapter. Here, α and β are the parameters for forward and reverse transition, respectively, and γ is the contagion parameter. The exact relation between α^* and β^* on the one hand, and α, β, and γ on the other, is

$$c = \frac{\gamma}{\beta} = 1 - e^{-\beta^* t} \tag{3.13}$$

$$k = \frac{\alpha}{\gamma} = \frac{\alpha^*}{\beta^*} \tag{3.14}$$

Thus if the data under consideration are generated by some two-way process at equilibrium, the ratios of transition rates to be estimated will be γ/β and α/β, using eqs. (3.11) and (3.12), while if the data are from a one-way process which has not gone to completion, the transition coefficients will be α^* and β^*, using eqs. (3.10) and (3.11) of Chapter 10. In either case, the distribution is the same, and it is identical to the negative binomial distribution and the

---

[8] For nonintegral values of k, it is perhaps better to express $\binom{k + i - 1}{i}$ in terms of its equivalent, $\dfrac{\Gamma(k + i)}{i!\Gamma(k)}$.

limiting form of the Polya distribution, as discussed in the preceding chapter. The latter, as given by Feller (1957, p. 131), is

$$p_i = \binom{\lambda p + i - 1}{i} \left(\frac{p}{1+p}\right)^{\lambda p} \left(\frac{1}{1+p}\right)^i \tag{3.15}$$

and this equation is identical to (3.10) if $1/(1 + p)$ is taken as c, and λp is taken as k. The fact that all these distributions—the one-way contagious Poisson, the equilibrium contagious Poisson, the negative exponential, and the Polya—all take the same form, though the underlying assumptions differ widely, illustrates again, as Feller has emphasized (1943, p. 398), that one cannot infer the existence of a particular type of process solely from the distribution found. Most important is the fact that the negative binomial is based on assumptions of heterogeneity, rather than contagion, as are the other three. Thus not even assumptions about contagion can be strongly confirmed on the basis of the distribution alone.

Example 1. Distribution of Sociometric Choices[9]

Suppose a group of girls was formed, and some time afterward each of the girls was asked to name the person she would most like to have as a roommate. Now suppose that initially all the girls were alike in their likelihood of generating this feeling among the others; but once one girl was chosen by someone, then this increased her chances of being chosen by the others. These assumptions would roughly correspond to those on which the contagion model is based.[10] It is obvious empirically that these are not wholly realistic assumptions; that there is both heterogeneity and contagion, not contagion alone. We will attempt to apply the present model to the data; if it does give a reasonable fit and allows estimation of the parameter c, we must be careful to interpret the size of c as being due not to contagion alone, but to contagion or heterogeneity or both.

A set of sociometric data which is appropriate, subject to the above caveats, to the assumptions of this model was gathered by Moreno and Jennings (1945) for seven 26-member cottages of girls, in which each girl chose three others from within her cottage. These are the same data used in an example in Chapter 14, Section 1. The greater appropriateness of these data than other sociometric data lies in the fact that there were seven cottages (which will be lumped together, as replications) of the same size, and in the

[9] Rapoport and Horvath (1961) have independently applied the Polya distribution to the distribution of sociometric choices.

[10] There is one way in which this situation does not correspond to the contagious Poisson: This example has a limit at 25 choices received, while this model does not provide for exhaustion. However, as long as the contagion is not so great as to approach this limit, this model may serve as an approximation in exactly the way that the Poisson can serve as an approximation to the exhaustible Poisson or binomial.

fact that in addition, random "choices" were carried out with independent trials, numbered balls drawn from a box. There resulted two distributions: one for the randomly generated data, in which each ball had a probability of 1/26 of being picked on each trial, and there was no contagion; and one for the actual groups of girls.[11] Thus we would expect the random data to be close to a binomial distribution (or, since the average proportion of choices received was only 1/26, to a Poisson used as an approximation), while actual data may not. Table 11.3 shows the distribution of the random data, the distribution of the actual data, the Poisson, and the binomial distributions.[12] It is clear that the random data are close to the binomial and Poisson, while the actual data are not. There is clearly a greater number of choices for a few people, and more girls are left out altogether than would be expected by chance. The question is, now, can this nonchance distribution be accounted for by the model proposed here? In order to test this, the model can be fitted by estimating the mean and variance, then using eqs. (3.11) and (3.12) to estimate c and k, and finally using these estimates in eq. (3.10) to generate values of p_i. The mean, of course, is 3, since every girl gave three choices, and there were as many recipients as choosers. The variance is estimated as 7.14. By eqs. (3.11) and (3.12),

$$c = 1 - \frac{\hat{\mu}}{\hat{\sigma}^2} = .58$$

and

$$k = \frac{\hat{\mu}^2}{\hat{\sigma}^2 - \hat{\mu}} = 2.17$$

or

$$a = ck = 1.26$$

Thus a $(= \alpha/\beta)$, the initiation rate for choices relative to the loss rate, is 1.26, while there is a contagion effect of c $(= \gamma/\beta)$ (or its equivalent, in a heterogeneity interpretation) of .58 for every choice a girl receives. The fit of the model is shown by Table 11.3. The fit of the contagious Poisson looks reasonably good. With these skew distributions, the important part of the distribution is the tail—the hypothetical distribution may tail off too fast, as does the Poisson relative to these data, or too slowly. The slowness with which the distribution tails off may be roughly thought of as the size of the contagion effect.

[11] The chance is not exactly a binomial with $p = 1/26$, since each girl cannot choose herself, and since she made three choices without replacement. However, these modifications have little effect upon the chance frequencies.

[12] Both the actual data and random data are presented in tabular form in Table 14.1, Chapter 14; the aggregate data, together with the fitted distribution, are presented in Table 11.3.

One caution in interpreting this fit as a good one is of course the fact that there are two parameters here, an initiation parameter a and a contagion parameter c, whereas the binomial and Poisson have only one. Therefore, the model has more freedom to fit the data.

A word should be added about the contagion interpretation vs. the heterogeneity interpretation. For some situations there is a sharp distinction between the two interpretations, both in terms of the inferred process, and

Table 11.3

SOCIOMETRIC CHOICES RECEIVED, TOGETHER WITH POISSON, BINOMIAL, AND CONTAGIOUS POISSON DISTRIBUTION

(i) Number of choices received	n_i Number of balls drawn i times†	Binomial $p = 1/26$ $n = 78$	Poisson $\alpha = 3$	Number of girls receiving i choices (7 cottages)	Contagious Poisson $k = 2.17$ $c = .58$
0	9	8.5	9.1	35	27.7
1	19	26.6	27.2	29	34.9
2	50	40.9	40.8	30	32.1
3	35	41.4	40.8	26	25.9
4	37	31.1	30.6	16	19.4
5	19	18.4	18.4	14	13.9
6	11	9.0	9.2	8	9.7
7	2	3.7	3.9	10	6.6
8	0	1.3	1.5	6	4.4
9	0	.4	.5	4	2.9
10	0	0	.1	1	1.9
11	0	0	0	3	1.2
12	0	0	0	0	0.8
	182	181.3	182.1	182	181.4

† Only six of the seven experiments were reported, giving a total of 156 rather than 182, so the data were multiplied by 182/156 and recorded, to facilitate comparison.

in terms of practical implications. However, in this case, the two interpretations may not be so sharply different. What is heterogeneity among the girls from one point of view may be contagion from another. At one point in time, the girls may appear to one another very different in their degrees of attractiveness, but this difference—this heterogeneity—may have developed from a process of social contagion in attitudes toward each girl, which might have easily gone one way as another, early in the formation of the groups.

4. AN EQUILIBRIUM CONTAGIOUS POISSON WITH EXHAUSTION

The model of the preceding section is appropriate to problems in which the increase can continue without end—problems where the number of states is very large, and can be considered infinite. In contrast, however, the number of states is strictly limited for many sociological problems, particularly those in which a state represents the number of individuals engaged in some action, out of a group limited in size. In such problems, the infinite-state model is quite inappropriate.

A good example of such a process is some normatively prescribed behavior or attitude in groups. There is a certain "individualistic" tendency to carry out the behavior or hold the attitude, and in addition, a tendency to stop carrying out the behavior or holding the attitude. In addition to these individual tendencies, there is a normative pressure, from the other members of the group.[13] Such a process is a very general one in sociology and undoubtedly takes several forms (depending, for example, on whether the behavior is carried out in the presence of other group members, whether the attitude is overtly expressed, and if so, whether it is expressed in the presence of all other members, or only some of them). Despite this possible multiplicity of forms that the process might take, it is worth while setting down one possibility, that which is most closely related to the other models of this section.

Before doing so, however, it should be noted that the model is applicable also to *intrapersonal contagion* or operant conditioning, for repetitive actions which have some restricted upper limit. An example is that mentioned in the preceding chapter: high school boys going out at night. It may be that going out one night of the week leads to going out another night. Yet the week has only seven nights, so that there are only eight possible states in the model: going out 0, 1, 2, 3, 4, 5, 6, or 7 nights. It might be that for certain learning experiments, where there is a limited number of actions to be learned, but each action learned facilitates the learning of others, a model of this sort would be appropriate. In the exposition of the model, below, an interpersonal process in a group is assumed to facilitate exposition; however, the model can be reinterpreted in this other way.

The postulates of the present model are identical to those in Section 3, and the model differs only in that the simplifying assumption of that section (that the number of group members is very large) is absent. Instead, the number of persons, i, carrying out the action, is not negligible relative to N, requiring us to use $N - i$ in place of N in the transition rate. The individual

---

[13] A model for the opposite (and perhaps more frequent) case in which the group norm acts to constrain a behavior or attitude toward which each member has a positive tendency is identical to the one considered here, except that the states are labelled differently: state i in this model is $N - i$ in the other.

transition rates are as in Section 3, and the transition rates for the group are

$$\text{from state } i \text{ to } i + 1 = (N - i)\,(\alpha + i\gamma)$$

(from i persons carrying out the action to $i + 1$), and

$$\text{from state } i \text{ to } i - 1 = i\beta$$

(from i persons carrying out the action to $i - 1$).

The differential equations describing the process are

$$\frac{dp_0}{dt} = -N\alpha p_0 + \beta p_1 \tag{4.1}$$

$$\frac{dp_i}{dt} = -\left[(N - i)(\alpha + i\gamma) + i\beta\right]p_i + (N - i + 1)\left[\alpha + (i - 1)\gamma\right]p_{i-1}$$
$$+ (i + 1)\beta p_{i+1} \qquad (0 < i < N) \tag{4.2}$$

and

$$\frac{dp_N}{dt} = -N\beta p_N + \left[\alpha + (N - 1)\gamma\right]p_{N-1} \tag{4.3}$$

The behavior of the system is investigated only at equilibrium, where $dp_i/dt = 0$ for all i. Investigation of the dynamics of the system would be interesting in the study of the behavior of a single group over time; however, that is not considered here, and is in fact probably too involved for analytical solution, but must be investigated by numerical analysis.

The distribution of p_i (the probability of the group being in state i) at equilibrium may be found as in the preceding section. The distribution (substituting k for α/γ and c for γ/β), is[14]

$$p_i = \frac{\dbinom{N}{i}\ a[a + c]\ldots[a + (i - 1)c]}{\sum\limits_{j=0}^{N}\dbinom{N}{j}a[a + c]\ldots[a + (j - 1)c]} \tag{4.4}$$

This reduces further, upon substitution of k for a/c, to

$$p_i = \frac{\dbinom{N}{i}c^i(k + i - 1)!}{\sum\limits_{j=0}^{N}\dbinom{N}{j}c^j(k + j - 1)!} \tag{4.5}$$

For the (usual) case in which k is not a positive integer, this equation can be expressed as:

---

[14] The numerator is meant to be interpreted as one when $i = 0$, and the first term in the denominator is meant to be interpreted as one.

$$p_i = \frac{\binom{N}{i} c^i \Gamma(k+i)}{\sum\limits_{j=0}^{N} \binom{N}{j} c^j \Gamma(k+j)} \tag{4.6}$$

This distribution function is somewhat more complicated than the others in this chapter, and I have not been able to reduce it to a simple function of the form of eq. (3.10), nor to obtain expressions for the first and second moments in terms of the distribution which would allow estimation of k (or a) and c from data. However, it is possible to obtain an estimate of a from the relation between the observed p_0 and p_1, and an estimate of $a + c$ from the relation between p_1 and p_2. In some cases where N is small, this may allow good enough estimation to apply the model to data.

Using eq. (4.1) for the condition of equilibrium, dp_0/dt equals zero, and solving for α/β gives

$$\frac{\alpha}{\beta} = \frac{p_1}{Np_0} = a \tag{4.7}$$

Using the fact that the equilibrium across the 0–1 boundary forces one across the 0–2 boundary, then we have

$$(N-1)(\alpha+\gamma)p_1 = 2\beta p_2 \tag{4.8}$$

or

$$\frac{2p_2}{(N-1)p_1} = \frac{\alpha+\gamma}{\beta} \tag{4.9}$$
$$= a + c$$

It would be possible to set up a general equation of the form of eq. (4.7) to give

$$\frac{(i+1)p_{i+1}}{(N-i)p_i} = a + ic \qquad (0 \leqslant i < N) \tag{4.10}$$

and then to solve for a and c by regression methods, or by plotting $(i+1)p_{i+1}/(N-i)p_i$ vs. i, and reading off the slope and intercept as c and a, respectively. However, difficult problems of weighting are involved, since some p_i will be based on many cases, and others on few cases. In addition, there is the inconvenience that an abnormally low value of p_i depresses the plot at $i-1$ and greatly increases it at i, thus making any plot of fallible data behave erratically. It would be useful to have a procedure which would give about as good fit as the data were capable of, in the sense of least squares or (as in estimators using the first two moments) in the sense that the fitted distribution would have the same mean and variance as the actual one.

This model, along with minor variations of it, seems particularly interesting in mirroring behavior that is controlled by norms. This model itself seems appropriate for behavior that is constrained or encouraged (in one direction only) by others in the group; a modification seems appropriate for behavior that is constrained by an external norm. If the behavior is constrained by a fixed norm exerting an effect on each person carrying out the action, and if each person carrying out the action has a tendency α to carry it out, the transitions between states would look like this:

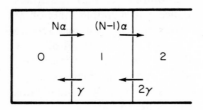 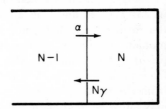

This model, and modifications of it, will be dealt with in the next section, with a somewhat different substantive application. It is useful to note here, however, that even when a model cannot be completely solved, it is often possible to examine whether the data appear to conform to it or not, by carrying out a transformation upon the p_i's. In the example above, this transformation was $(i + 1)p_{i+1}/(N - i)p_i$, and plotting this vs. i would give some idea whether the data did or did not fit. Similarly in other cases, even when the distribution function cannot be found, a transformation of this sort, relating p_i and p_{i+1}, can often be useful.

5. A MODEL FOR VOTING IN SMALL GROUPS: AN EQUILIBRIUM EXHAUSTIBLE POISSON

One of the most plentiful supplies of quantitative data available to the sociologist is voting data. The necessity in society of periodically taking a vote provides a quantitative reflection of social processes which helped shape the vote. Many of these processes have to do with the particular content of the election; these are of no concern to us here. Some, however, are "contentless," general social processes which operate without regard for the particular issues at stake. Perhaps the most interesting of these are the processes, in a democracy, which establish a rough balance of support between the parties. The question of what keeps the vote for each party in a two-party system near the fifty per cent line, and what forces tend to push it back there when it does deviate—these are central problems in describing the operation of a political system.[15]

Unfortunately, these problems of a political system are too large for us to make much headway on them at this point. For the present, we will

[15] See Stokes and Iversen (1962) for an interesting Markov model which is directed at testing whether there are re-equilibrating forces.

consider a much more simple process which vote distributions reflect: the interdependence between the votes of men in the same sociological unit— precinct, ward, town, district, state, etc. Such interdependence may, of course, rise through mutual influence; or, on the other hand, it may arise from a common history or common problems facing the electorate in that district, leading them to cast their votes alike, and differently from the votes of another district.

To give an indication of the type of data to which the model will be applied, Figures 11.2, 11.3, and 11.4 show, for 2-, 3-, and 4-man shops respectively (in the International Typographical Union in New York City, 1949–1952), the distributions of votes in union-wide elections. With each of these figures is a corresponding binomial distribution (taking as p the average proportion of votes case for the winner among the shops of that size in these elections—the vote in every election being between 50% and 60%), showing (as a solid line) what the vote would be like if each man cast his ballot independently, with probability p that it would be for candidate A, who finally became the winner. Obviously, men in the same shops tend to vote more alike than would be expected from chance. But the question is, what kind of model can represent the processes which led them to vote alike?

To begin with, let us think of a group with N members, with each member voting for one of two candidates. The stochastic equilibrium model will then have $N + 1$ states, each state i ($i = 0, 1, 2, \ldots, N$) representing i votes for candidate A. Now think of the process through which these votes come to be cast. Men "made up their minds" over the course of the campaign, switching from one candidate to the other, and finally casting their vote at election time for whichever candidate they happened to favor at that time. Thus men were engaged in a back-and-forth process before the election, suggestive of a two-way flow model between each state.

To start out, let us make four simplifying assumptions, which we know are not true, but which can later be modified.

(a) Assume that individuals are alike, *each* having a transition rate α toward candidate A and β toward candidate B.

(b) These transition rates are independent of time; men are as likely to change at one time in the campaign as another.

(c) The transition rates are independent of the existing positions of other persons in the group; that is, there is no influence of individuals upon one another. This is, of course, the exact antithesis of the interdependence in voting which is actually found; however, this assumption of noninterdependence will be modified shortly in a contagious version of the model.

(d) The system is in equilibrium when the vote is taken. Empirically, this is often not true, of course. For example, there is evidence that through the course of the campaign, the out-party continues to gain and, if the campaign were continued longer, would win more elections (see

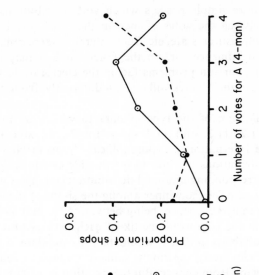

Figure 11.4

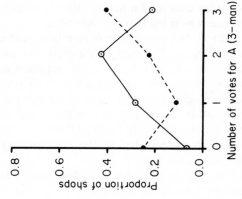

Figure 11.3

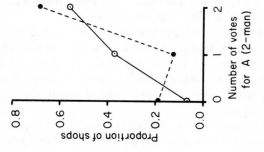

Figure 11.2

Lipset, Trow, and Coleman, 1956, pp. 348–351). There is also evidence that in recent U.S. elections, the Democrats gained through the course of the campaign, and would have won more elections if the campaigns had been longer (Berelson, Lazarsfeld, and McPhee, 1954). However, without the assumption of equilibrium, the model would be much more difficult to solve, and for some purposes (such as the examination of interpersonal influence, in which we are interested here) would tell little more than the equilibrium model, so long as only data on the votes themselves—and not on intentions leading up to the vote—were gathered.

Given assumptions (a), (b), and (c), what are the transition rates for a group between each pair of states i and $i + 1$? By assumptions (a) and (c), each individual is characterized by two coefficients: β, shifting him from candidate A to B and α, shifting him from candidate B to A. Thus the *individual* stochastic model upon which this group is based would be a familiar two-state two-directional model, where state A is "favoring candidate A," and state B is "favoring candidate B."

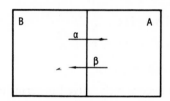

When the group is in state i, this means that i persons are in favor of A; therefore, the total transition rate from state i to state $i - 1$ will be the sum of all the individual transition rates from A to B. Since this number of persons is i, the rate from state i to $i - 1$ becomes $i\beta$.

The total transition rate toward candidate A is simply the sum of all the individual transition rates. Since there are $N - i$ individuals favoring B when the group is in state i, this means that the transition rate from i to $i + 1$ is $(N - i)\alpha$. Diagrammatically, the model looks like this:

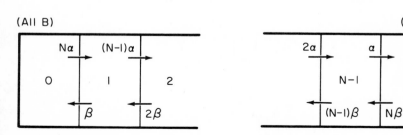

The differential equations describing the process are

$$\frac{dp_0}{dt} = -N\alpha p_0 + \beta p_1 \tag{5.1}$$

$$\frac{dp_i}{dt} = -[(N-i)\alpha + i\beta]p_i + (N-i+1)\alpha p_{i-1} + (i+1)\beta p_{i+1}$$
$$(0 < i < N) \tag{5.2}$$

and

$$\frac{dp_N}{dt} = -N\beta p_N + \alpha p_{i-1} \tag{5.3}$$

The behavior of the system at equilibrium may be studied through finding the proportion in each state at equilibrium, assuming that α and β are given. At equilibrium, the same procedure used in the models above is possible: Since there is a barrier on one side of state 0, there must be balancing shifts across the 0–1 boundary. Since this is true, and p_1 remains constant at equilibrium, there must also be balancing shifts across the 1–2 boundary. And so on. This gives the following simultaneous equations:

$$p_0 N\alpha = p_1 \beta \tag{5.4}$$

$$p_1(N-1)\alpha = p_2 2\beta$$

$$p_2(N-2)\alpha = p_3 3\beta$$

$$p_{N-1}\alpha = p_N N\beta$$

As before, these can be successively solved in terms of p_0 to give

$$p_1 = p_0 N\frac{\alpha}{\beta} \tag{5.5}$$

$$p_2 = p_0 \frac{N(N-1)}{2}\left(\frac{\alpha}{\beta}\right)^2$$

$$p_3 = p_0 \frac{N(N-1)(N-2)}{2 \times 3}\left(\frac{\alpha}{\beta}\right)^3$$

$$\vdots$$

$$p_i = p_0 \binom{N}{i}\left(\frac{\alpha}{\beta}\right)^i$$

$$\vdots$$

$$p_N = p_0 \left(\frac{\alpha}{\beta}\right)^N$$

Now we sum the terms and set them equal to one, in order to find p_0. This time the sum goes from zero to N rather than from zero to infinity, since the model has only $N + 1$ states. But even before summing the terms (i.e., the right sides of these equations), they begin to look familiar, something like the terms of a binomial expansion. In fact, factoring out p_0 gives

$$1 = p_0\left[1 + N\frac{\alpha}{\beta} + \frac{N(N-1)}{1\times 2}\left(\frac{\alpha}{\beta}\right)^2 + \ldots + \binom{N}{i}\left(\frac{\alpha}{\beta}\right)^i + \ldots + \left(\frac{\alpha}{\beta}\right)^N\right] \qquad (5.6)$$

and the quantity in brackets is simply the binomial expansion: $\left(\frac{\alpha}{\beta} + 1\right)^N$. Substituting this for the expansion gives

$$1 = p_0\left(\frac{\alpha}{\beta} + 1\right)^N \qquad (5.7)$$

Then solving for p_0 gives

$$p_0 = \frac{1}{\left(\frac{\alpha}{\beta} + 1\right)^N}$$

$$= \left(\frac{\beta}{\alpha + \beta}\right)^N \qquad (5.8)$$

Thus the number of groups, p_0, in which no persons vote for candidate A, is given by eq. (5.8). In previous chapters, it was shown that in a two-state model with parameters α and β, the quantities $\beta/(\alpha + \beta)$ and $\alpha/(\alpha + \beta)$ have the usual properties of probabilities. If we substitute ρ for $\alpha/(\alpha + \beta)$, and $1 - \rho$ for $\beta/(\alpha + \beta)$, giving $\rho/(1 - \rho)$ for α/β, eq. (5.8) becomes

$$p_0 = (1 -)\rho^N \qquad (5.9)$$

and in general,

$$p_i = \binom{N}{i}(1 - \rho)^N\left(\frac{\rho}{1 - \rho}\right)^i \qquad (5.10)$$

Thus eq. (5.5) becomes simply the terms of a binomial distribution:

$$p_1 = N(1 - \rho)^{N-1} \qquad (5.11)$$

$$p_2 = \frac{N(N-1)}{2}(1 - \rho)^{N-2}\rho^2$$

$$\cdot$$
$$\cdot$$
$$\cdot$$

$$p_i = \binom{N}{i}(1 - \rho)^{N-i}\rho^i$$

$$\cdot$$
$$\cdot$$
$$\cdot$$

$$p_N = \rho^N$$

In other words, the stochastic model proposed on p. 337 results, at equilibrium, in nothing other than a binomial distribution. This seems at first both surprising and a little disappointing. But the surprise should fade when we reflect upon the assumptions of the model, and the fact that intuitively they correspond, for a process continuous in time, to the "independent trial" assumptions of the binomial.

The disappointment that we have "nothing more" than a binomial distribution requires a little closer scrutiny. To be sure, the resulting distribution is simply a binomial. But to cast the model aside, observing this only, and disregard the fact that the distribution was derived from a continuous-time, double-flow model, is to discard too much. Note that this model allows what an ordinary binomial does not. First of all, and most important for our purposes, the process of sequential trials which underlies the binomial distribution is incompatible with a notion of *mutual* influence or mutual contagion. Here, however, we can reflect such mutual influence by introducing a contagion transition rate, γ, along with the independent transition rates α and β.

But the "contagious binomial" is not the only new possibility opened up by this model. In assumption (b) of the model, a socially and psychologically unrealistic assumption was made: that the transition rates α and β are independent of time. The model may be modified by replacing this assumption with a more realistic one. One might propose, for example, that the transition rates decrease from the start of the campaign to the finish; that as the time of decision approaches, α and β get smaller. The assumption might be

$$\frac{\partial \alpha}{\partial t} = -k\alpha \qquad \text{and} \qquad \frac{\partial \beta}{\partial t} = -k\beta$$

On the other hand, the transition rates may *increase* as the voting time approaches. Psychological evidence is not clear on this point,[16] although there is some evidence on how the rate changes at different points in the U.S. presidential campaigns.[17]

Another way this model can be of use while the ordinary binomial distribution cannot is in the examination of changes in the distribution over time. The equations for p_i at a given time before the process has reached

---

[16] On the one hand, there is evidence that as an issue becomes more salient, it becomes more tightly consistent with other elements in the individual's psychological structure and social environment, and more difficult to dislodge; on the other hand, in this very process of becoming tightly consistent with other elements, it must sometimes change. The problem is an important one in psychological theory, one which I had hoped to discuss in this book. However, the formulations are not well enough specified to include at this time. Other discussions related to this may be found in Chapters 12 and 13.

[17] See Anderson (1954), pp. 49–51. Anderson develops a quite different kind of stochastic process from the ones described here (a discrete-time Markov chain), and using panel data on changes throughout in the campaign. These transition probabilities were less toward the end of the campaign than in the middle of the campaign.

equilibrium are not derived here. However, once they are derived, and once panel data are available on many groups through time, then the model could be applied to these groups.

It is clear, then, that there is more to this model than the binomial distribution, which is just one of its deductions. The next section, where we return to notions of contagion, will discuss in detail one of the important additions which arises.

6. VOTING MODELS: CONTAGION WITHIN THE GROUP

The preceding section has laid the groundwork for a contagious model. Retaining assumptions (a), (b), and (d)—see p. 337—we now change (c) to make an individual's transition rates contingent upon the states that his fellow group-members are in. Keeping in mind precisely the kind of contagion effect desired, we set down the following assumption, which parallels the ones made in previous contagion models.

(c′) The transition rates for each individual are increased by an amount γ for each of the persons in the group who hold the opposing position.

This contagion assumption says, in effect, that the influence of other group members is additive—that the contagion or persuasion effect is γ times the number of persons who are on the other side.

It will be best to set down first what the two-state model would be for the individual when in a group of size N in which i members favor A.

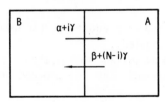

Transition rates for the individual are

Shifting to A $= \alpha + i\gamma$ (if he is one of the $N - i$ persons in B)
Shifting to B $= \beta + (N - i)\gamma$ (if he is one of the i persons in A)

Note that here, in contrast to the preceding model diagrammed on page 339, the corresponding individual two-state model is dependent on the state the group is in. Before, the individual's shifts were independent of the group; now they depend upon it through their dependence on γ.

The compound transition rates for the group model of $N + i$ states are

$$q_{i,i+1} = \text{(individual transition rate from B to A)}$$
$$\times \text{(no. of individuals in state B)}$$
$$= [\alpha + i\gamma](N - i)$$

$$q_{i,i-1} = \text{(individual transition rate from A to B)}$$
$$\times \text{(no. of individuals in state A)}$$
$$= [\beta + (N - i)\gamma]i$$

Diagrammatically,

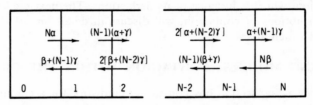

The differential equations describing the process are

$$\frac{dp_0}{dt} = -N\alpha p_0 + [\beta + (N - 1)\gamma]p_1 \tag{6.1}$$

$$\frac{dp_i}{dt} = -\{(N - i)(\alpha + i\gamma) + i[\beta + (N - i)\gamma]\}p_i$$
$$+ (N - i + 1)[\alpha + (i - 1)\gamma]p_{i-1}$$
$$+ (i + 1)[\beta + (N - i - 1)\gamma]p_{i+1} \qquad (0 < i < N) \tag{6.2}$$

and

$$\frac{dp_N}{dt} = -N\beta p_N + [\alpha + (N - 1)\gamma]p_{N-1} \tag{6.3}$$

Although this is a complicated set of equations, it simplifies greatly when only equilibrium states are investigated.

To solve for the values p_0, p_1, etc., that is, the proportion of groups that we would expect to find in each state, we proceed just as before, with N simultaneous equations.

$$p_0 N\alpha = p_1[\beta + (N - 1)\gamma] \tag{6.4}$$

$$p_1(N - 1)(\alpha + \gamma) = p_2 2[\beta + (N - 2)\gamma]$$

.
.
.

$$p_i(N - i)(\alpha + i\gamma) = p_{i+1}(i + 1)[\beta + (N - i - 1)\gamma]$$

.
.
.

$$p_{N-1}[\alpha + (N - 1)\gamma] = p_N N\beta$$

By setting up the whole set of such equations, then expressing all p_i in terms of p_0, and finally solving for p_0, it is possible to obtain the distribution function for p_i. To simplify the expression, first let $a = \alpha/(\alpha + \beta)$ and $c = \gamma/(\alpha + \beta)$. Then, in terms of a and c, the distribution function is[18]

$$p_i = \binom{N}{i} \frac{\prod\limits_{j=0}^{i-1} (a + jc) \prod\limits_{j=0}^{N-i-1} (1 - a + jc)}{\prod\limits_{j=0}^{N-1} (1 + jc)} \tag{6.5}$$

(The first product term in the numerator is taken as one for p_0, while for p_N, the second product term is taken as one.) As with earlier models, we may simplify by substituting $kc = a$, factoring out c^N, and replacing products by the equivalent gamma function. We get

$$p_i = \frac{\binom{N}{i} \Gamma(k + i)\Gamma\left(N + \dfrac{1}{c} - k - i\right)\Gamma\left(\dfrac{1}{c}\right)}{\Gamma(k)\Gamma\left(N + \dfrac{1}{c}\right)\Gamma\left(\dfrac{1}{c} - k\right)} \tag{6.6}$$

or in terms of factorials:

$$p_i = \frac{\binom{N}{i}(k + i - 1)!\left(N + \dfrac{1}{c} - k - i - 1\right)!\left(\dfrac{1}{c} - 1\right)!}{(k - 1)!\left(N + \dfrac{1}{c} - 1\right)!\left(\dfrac{1}{c} - k - 1\right)!} \tag{6.6'}$$

The parameters a and c may be estimated by

$$a = \frac{\Sigma i p_i}{N} \tag{6.7}$$

$$c = \frac{\sigma^2 - Na(1 - a)}{N^2 a(1 - a) - \sigma^2} \tag{6.8}$$

where σ^2 is the estimate of the variance of i:

$$\sigma^2 = \Sigma i^2 p_i - (\Sigma i p_i)^2 \tag{6.9}$$

Thus a, which is simply the average proportion of persons in position A, and c, which is an estimate of the size of the contagion parameter γ, relative to α and β, can be estimated from the mean and variance, respectively, of the distribution of the groups.

How, given the distribution of eq. (6.5), it is possible to go back to the data on voting in small shops, presented in Figures 11.2, 11.3, and 11.4, and ask: Is this model at all consistent with these data?

The data from these shops can be treated separately for shops from size 2

---

[18] Just as an earlier model (eq. 3.10) was identical to the limiting form of the Polya distribution, this is identical to the Polya distribution after N draws from the urn (see Feller, 1957, p. 131).

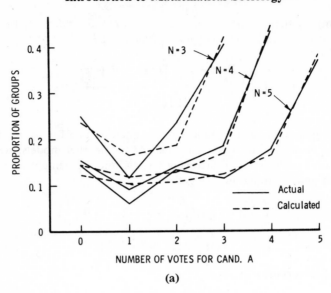

(a)

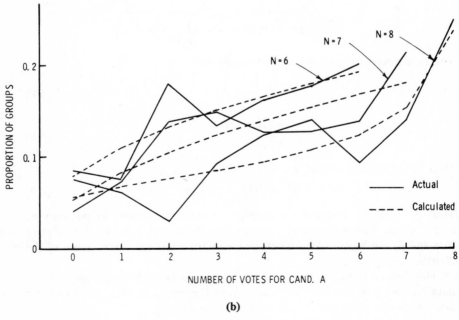

(b)

Figure 11.5

**Distribution of Small Shops in Printers' Union, Voting in Union
Elections: Actual (solid) and Calculated (broken line):
(a) 3-, 4-, and 5-man groups; (b) 6-, 7-, and 8-man groups.**

to 12, for there are sufficient numbers of shops of each size. Thus the model can be fitted to the data separately for each of these sizes of shops. Using eqs. (6.7) and (6.8) to estimate a and c from the data shown in Table 11.4, the values of Table 11.5 were estimated. The values of a and c listed in

Table 11.4

NUMBER OF SHOPS OF SIZE N IN NEW YORK TYPOGRAPHICAL UNION ELECTIONS IN WHICH i MEN VOTED FOR THE CANDIDATE WHO WON (4 ELECTIONS, 1949–1952)

N	i												
	0	1	2	3	4	5	6	7	8	9	10	11	12
2	3	2	11										
3	32	15	30	52									
4	22	13	20	26	62								
5	16	7	15	13	20	24							
6	9	8	19	14	17	18	21						
7	4	7	13	14	12	12	13	20					
8	5	4	2	6	8	9	6	9	16				
9	8	3	1	7	4	5	6	9	8	8			
10	1	3	4	3	8	5	2	5	3	6	6		
11	2	3	1	0	2	2	6	2	2	1	3	7	
12	0	0	3	4	2	1	4	3	1	2	6	4	3

Table 11.5 were used to fit the empirical curves for these sizes of groups. The empirical and theoretical curves are plotted in Figure 11.5 for groups from size 3 to 8. (The size 2 groups are not included, for they have only two degrees of freedom, and the model has two parameters, thus not allowing a test of the fit.)

Table 11.5

VALUES OF a AND c

N	a	c	N	a	c
2	.75	2.00			
3	.60	1.09	8	.63	0.56
4	.66	0.95	9	.57	0.65
5	.58	0.66	10	.55	0.65
6	.58	0.41	11	.60	0.66
7	.60	0.40	12	.61	0.36

The theoretical curves fit rather well for the smaller groups, where the total number of groups is large, but not so well for the larger groups, where the smaller number of cases apparently reduces the regularity of the data. On the whole, the model does fit the data with fair adequacy, indicating that these groups do in fact behave as if there were contagion or social influence of the sort expressed by assumption (c'). This is not to say that this "proves" social influence or contagion effects were occurring to the degree indicated by the data; again the problem of heterogeneity vs. contagion exists, for again a model can be developed which gives a distribution identical to that found here, yet is based on assumptions of heterogeneity rather than contagion. The heterogeneity assumption is equivalent to saying that there was not social influence, but instead selectivity of new group members on the basis of their political preferences. Again the problem is identical to the problem of using cross-sectional correlations to infer causal relations between two variables. These models are no better off and no poorer off than correlation coefficients in their ability to establish causation from cross-sectional data. If over-time data existed, then it would be easy to distinguish between heterogeneity and contagion, by examining groups immediately after they formed, and then at intervals until a statistical equilibrium was reached.

Perhaps just as interesting as the fact that the model fits the data rather well is the value of the contagion parameter c for different-sized groups. Note that c systematically decreases as the size of the group increases, up to size 7, beyond which it remains roughly constant. Since c is proportional to the influence each member exerts upon each other, this suggests that each person's influence per other person in the group decreases as the group increases from size 2 to 7. Perhaps, however, the *total* influence exerted by each person remains the same as the group size goes up from 2 to 7, even though his influence is less on each group member. If this is so, then the quantity $c(N-1)$ should remain constant, for $c(N-1)$ is proportional to his total influence over all other members of the group. This quantity, $c(N-1)$, is listed in Table 11.6 for these groups.

Table 11.6

N	$c(N-1)$	N	$c(N-1)$
2	2.00	8	3.92
3	2.18	9	5.20
4	2.85	10	5.85
5	2.64	11	6.60
6	2.05	12	3.96
7	2.40		

This quantity appears to be rather constant for groups up to size 7, beyond which there is a tendency to increase. There is too much variability of the data to tell conclusively. The need for precise and extensive experimentation with different-sized groups is indicated. Such experimentation, in which there was initial random selection of members, issues were unrelated to past experience and only to the ongoing group activity, and in which data were gathered over time, would give definite answers to matters which can now only be conjectured upon: Does the mechanism of influence in undifferentiated small groups behave in the way described by assumption (c')? Is social influence under such circumstances linear (i.e., additive) as the model implies? How does an individual's influence upon any other in the group diminish as the group size increases? All these questions could be directly answered if there were good experimental data.

It seems rather peculiar that each member's influence per other members should decrease up to groups of size 7, and then remain constant. Such a possibility seems quite unlikely. It is more reasonable to suspect that at size 7 there begins to be some kind of differentiation of the group, or structuring into subgroups, so that a different kind of process occurs.

One alternative hypothesis may be examined, however. Consider as a random variable the proportion voting for candidate A in each shop (which we will call r). The estimate of the mean of this random variable is a, as defined by eq. (6.7), and the estimate of the variance is σ^2/N^2 [because σ^2, as defined by eq. (6.9), is the variance of i]. The variance of r can be partitioned into two variances: the variance between groups of a random variable, r', which is the probability of voting for candidate A in a particular group, and the binomial variance within groups due to the fact that there are N independent trials, each with probability r' of being for candidate A. This last variance is $\dfrac{r'(1-r')}{N}$, where r' is the probability of voting for candidate A within a particular group. Let the average of this variance be designated by av. $\left[\dfrac{r'(1-r')}{N}\right]$. Then the partitioning into between-group and within-group variance is

$$\sigma_r^2 = \sigma_{r'}^2 + \text{av.} \left[\frac{r'(1-r')}{N}\right] \qquad (6.10)$$

The hypothesis, then, is this: It is a fact that as group size increases, σ_r^2 decreases. Perhaps this can be explained completely by the necessary decrease in the second term on the right of eq. (6.10) as the group size increases. The between-group variance, $\sigma_{r'}^2$, is independent of the group size.

This hypothesis of course does not provide an explanatory mechanism or model to account for the constancy of $\sigma_{r'}^2$. It simply proposes that $\sigma_{r'}^2$, the between-group variance, is constant, independent of group size.

This hypothesis may be tested with the existing data. We have no estimate of the average within-group variance of the underlying random variable r', but this variance may be roughly approximated by $a(1-a)/N$.[19] The variance of r' may then be estimated by

$$\sigma_{r'}^2 = \sigma_r^2 - \frac{a(1-a)}{N} \qquad (6.11)$$

---

[19] This will give an approximation which is too high, since a is an estimate of the mean of r'; but it will be too high by a constant factor for all sizes of groups, and thus will not affect the test of this hypothesis.

The quantity on the right is simply the numerator of the equation for estimating c [eq. (6.8)], divided by N^2. This quantity is listed in Table 11.7 for the groups from size 2 to 12.

Table 11.7

ESTIMATES OF TOTAL AND BETWEEN-GROUP VARIANCE FOR VOTING IN GROUPS FROM SIZE 2 TO 12

N	$\sigma_{\tilde{p}}^2$ (total)	$\sigma_{\tilde{p}'}^2$ (between-group) (see eq. 6.11)	N	$\sigma_{\tilde{p}}^2$ (total)	$\sigma_{\tilde{p}'}^2$ (between-group) (see eq. 6.11)
2	.156	.063	8	.102	.073
3	.163	.083	9	.113	.086
4	.138	.082	10	.113	.088
5	.126	.077	11	.108	.086
6	.100	.059	12	.077	.057
7	.093	.059			

Although the data are irregular, there seems no definite trend one way or the other as group size increases, and it appears that perhaps this hypothesis is correct, and the between-group variance is constant.

However, there are other data which can be brought to bear on this general question. From these same elections, means and variances of the proportions voting for the winning candidate have been calculated for larger shops, in size intervals 8–15, 16–30, 31–50, 51–99, and 100 plus. Also for Typographical Union locals throughout the country, means and variances have been calculated for locals of 100–499, 500–999, and 1000 plus, in the seven international elections between 1940 and 1954.[20] The total variances, between-group variances, c, and $c(N-1)$, for all these sizes are given in Table 11.8. The last three of these have been calculated for the average-sized group within the indicated interval.

It is evident from these data that none of the quantities examined is constant as the group size changes. Clearly, for large groups, the least constant is $c(N-1)$. Both $\sigma_{\tilde{p}'}^2$ and c decrease by about the same amount as size increases.

A still further set of data to which my attention was called by James March (see March, 1956), are relevant at this point. In 1909 in England, an empirical regularity in election statistics was reported, though its origins may have been before that. (See Kendall and Stuart, 1950, for a quotation of this verbal report.) The regularity goes something like this: If, in single-member constituency elections with two parties, the ratio of the total votes received by the two parties in all constituencies is *cubed*, this gives the ratio of the

[20] See Coleman (1955) for references to *Typographical Journal*.

seats won by the two parties. For example, if the total votes for the two parties throughout the country were in the ratio of 60 : 40, the ratio of seats won by the two parties would be in the ratio of $60^3 : 40^3$, or 216 : 64. That is, if the majority party won 60% of the votes, they would win 77% of the seats.

If each constituency gave the majority party the same vote, 60% in this case, then such a regularity could not hold. In fact, the minority party would not win *any* seats. Thus it is evident that such a regularity depends on the fact that there is some variability between constituencies, some giving a majority to the minority party. Such variability could not be accounted for by the binomial variance within each district, since the districts are not small enough for binomial variance to have any appreciable effect on the district's vote.

Table 11.8

OVERALL VARIANCES, BETWEEN-GROUP VARIANCE, c, AND $c(N - 1)$ FOR VARIOUS-SIZED SHOPS AND LOCALS IN THE TYPOGRAPHICAL UNION

N	N(aver.)	σ^2	σ_r^2,	c	$c(N - 1)$	Number of shops or locals
Shops						
8–15	11	.078	.056	.35	3.5	228
16–30	22	.053	.042	.23	4.8	195
31–50	38	.053	.047	.25	9.3	74
51–99	65	.014	.010	.04	2.6	37
100 plus	260	.023	.022	.10	26.0	44
Locals						
100–499	195	.034	.032	.15	29	587
500–999	630	.028	.028	.13	82	89
1000 plus	2200	.019	.019	.08	176	57

The interesting fact is that such a regularity has been found to hold fairly well in various British elections and one New Zealand election by a number of authors (*Economist*, 1950, pp. 5–7; Kendall and Stuart, 1950, 1952; Butler, 1951, pp. 306–333, 1952; Cadart, 1955) and in Russian elections as well (March, 1956). It has never, to my knowledge, been found to be grossly inaccurate in prediction. What this means is that the variability between constituencies is roughly the same in all these elections. Kendall and Stuart show that the variability predicted by the cube law is almost identical to that which would be produced if r (the proportion for candidate A in a district) were distributed normally with variance $\sigma_r^2 = .0187$.

In other words, election statistics in the United States and England show that r has a variance of roughly .0187, independent of the constituency size and other factors. This value is lower than those in column 3, Table 11.8

(or in column 4) for the Typographical Union elections, though they are decreasing, and the largest is approximately this value. It may be that those would level off at about .0187, if the sizes were larger, in the size range of the constituencies studied in general elections.

This constant value of .0187 for σ^2, independent of the average size of the districts, means that the quantity c is constant. For if we divide the numerator and denominator of eq. (6.8) by N^2, to get the variance of r, σ_r^2, in place of σ_i^2 (that is, $\sigma_r^2 = \sigma_i^2/N^2$), this gives

$$c = \frac{\sigma_r^2 - [a(1-a)/N]}{a(1-a) - \sigma_r^2}$$

Then, in this equation the term $a(1-a)/N$ in the numerator is negligible, and the denominator is independent of changes in N. The value of c in this case can be roughly estimated:

$$\frac{.0187}{.24 - .0187} = .085$$

Here the matter must stand. Kendall and Stuart suggest that some sort of Markov process with sequential dependencies would account for the data as found. This is essentially what the present model is, except that it has the conceptual advantage of allowing mutual dependence among voters, rather than sequential dependence. The amount of dependence, however, is far too large to be accounted for by an interpersonal influence mechanism such as that proposed in the model. It says that in a constituency of thousands of members, each member has an average effect on the vote intention of each other member who favors the opposition such that he shifts his basic tendency to vote by .085, relative to the existing "independent" tendency of about .50, which is the value of a. This is clearly unrealistic and suggests that, instead, the political processes themselves in these districts generates in some fashion this diversity between districts.

It should be mentioned, in closing our examination of this general problem of voting in groups or constituencies, that this diversity or variance is extremely important in the maintenance of a democratic political system. If it were the case that a 51% majority in the nation as a whole would give the winning party a 51% majority in every district—as it would, if there were not diversity among the districts beyond what would be expected from chance (if voters in different districts were drawn randomly from the same population)—then democratic politics would be impossible, unless something like proportional representation were instituted. Democratic politics depends upon such local diversity to maintain the opposition while it is out of power,[21]

[21] For a general discussion of this problem of diversity in political systems, see Lipset, Trow, and Coleman (1956), Chapter 5.

and to generate the ideas and leaders by which the opposition can unseat the majority party.

Consequently, it is of a great deal of importance to learn about the mechanism by which the variation among election districts is maintained. The model presented here does not contain this mechanism, for it is appropriate to small groups, where there is interpersonal contact; what is needed is some theory which is appropriate to a differentiated group within which a two-party system exists. Perhaps the present model will serve as a stimulus to investigation of the general problem.

At the level of small, undifferentiated groups, such as the small union shops first examined, the present model can be taken much more seriously. It appears that the quantity $c(N - 1)$, that is, the total influence exerted by a group member, may be constant up to groups of about size 7; and it further appears that the assumption of additive influence may be accurate, because the model fits the empirical distributions rather well. Both these tentative conclusions are based on weak evidence, however, and much more investigation is required to test them. It is clear, for example, from Asch's experiments (1951), that in a group situation where each member is required to make a public announcement of his vote, the existence of a minority of *one* has an important effect on a subsequent voter in allowing him to deviate from the majority, while a second person in the minority group has much less effect. If this had been the case with the groups examined here (in which there was a secret ballot) the present model would not have fit nearly so well. There would have been many more groups with votes of 0 or N, many fewer with 1 or $N - 1$. Because this was not the case, and the data fit the model as well at 1 and $N - 1$ as at any other point, it is clear that a single-person minority, without a cohort, was not unstable as in the Asch experiments. Nevertheless, much work in testing the proposed mechanism, or developing models with others which could be tested, remains to be done. In the last pages of this chapter, some suggestions of alternative models will be made.

7. REWARD STRUCTURES AND THE ALLOCATION OF EFFORT

The model of the previous section was applied to situations of voting in groups. But the process, and variations upon it, is a much more generally applicable one for social situations. In particular, groups often act to encourage certain activities among their members, and to discourage others. Furthermore, since this encouragement or constraint comes from within the group, it is not fixed, but varies as the group members' activities vary. For example, groups appear to act both in a *conservative* direction and in a *radical* one: in the early stages of any social change, they exert constraints upon the tendencies of those members who want to change; but if the change is strong enough to cause a large proportion of the group to change, then the constraints act in the *other* direction, pushing the laggard members to change. That is, groups first act to hold a person back, and then act to pull him along, pressing first for a conservative unanimity, and then for a radical one. The model discussed above is appropriate for such a situation, when treated dynamically.

More generally, groups constitute reward structures, and the model examined above is an example of one. Another reward structure is one almost diametrically opposed to this: the structure in which each person punishes others who are engaging in the same activity. This would be expected when all are competing for some limited reward, and another person's engaging in the activity reduces the expected reward of the first person.

In particular, there are two kinds of reward structures of particular interest:

(1) Situations in which one person's achievement contributes to another's goals, and in turn the other encourages the efforts leading to such achievement. An example is an athletic contest between two high schools: the achievements of one school's athletes contribute to the goals of all members of that school, who in turn cheer their team on, accord the athletes high status, and give them numerous other rewards.

(2) Situations in which one person's achievement takes away from another's success, and in turn the other discourages efforts leading to such achievement. For example, in scholastic activity in a high school, one person's extra efforts force others to work harder, simply to maintain the same relative position, and as a consequence they discourage such unlimited efforts.

There is a special case of each of these two structures, of particular interest because of its frequent occurrence: the case when the activities are *alike* among performers and rewarders, so that each performer is a rewarder (or punisher), and each rewarder is a performer.

The problem, then, is to examine the allocation of group members' effort among two or more activities under these two different reward structures: when one member's efforts help bring success to others who are engaging in that activity, and when his efforts subtract from their success. Suppose first that the activities are interrelated so that a member's efforts can help those engaged in the same activity, and he is consequently encouraged into this activity by those engaging in it. One way this effect may occur is through an added transition rate, γ, toward an activity from every person engaging in the activity.[22] If there are i persons in activity A, and he is in B, then his transition rate to A will be $\alpha + i\gamma$; the remainder of the $N - 1$ persons,

---

[22] This is not the only way such effects may occur. Part of the difficulty in deciding between alternative forms of effect resides in the very concept of reward. This problem is discussed briefly toward the end of the section.

$N - 1 - i$, are in activity B, so that if he finds himself in A, the transition rate to B will be $\beta + (N - 1 - i\gamma)$:

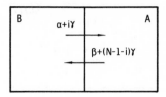

If all other members of the group were fixed in their choice of A or B (as in the Asch experiments, where all members of the group but one were accomplices of the experimenter), then the variable individual, governed by the process pictured above, would be found in A and B with probabilities as follows, at equilibrium:

$$p_A = \frac{\alpha + i\gamma}{\alpha + \beta + (N - 1)\gamma} \qquad (7.1)$$

$$p_B = \frac{\beta + (N - 1 - i)\gamma}{\alpha + \beta + (N - 1)\gamma} \qquad (7.2)$$

However, the systemic problem arises when we let all N group members be variable. What division of activities would we then expect to find among the N members, and what distribution would we expect to find around this number, if we observed the group a number of times? The answer to this will tell something different from eqs. (7.1) and (7.2). Those tell how the individual's behavior is influenced by others in his group under a particular assumption about individuals' effects on one another. These latter questions ask how the *group's* behavior is affected by this reward structure.

Once we shift to a study of the group's behavior, the model should be recognizable as precisely the model of the preceding section; though the substance is more general than voting, the structure is identical. We can ask, then, about the parallel model under conditions of punishment for engaging in the same activity.

7.1 Structures with mutual punishments

In structures of activity where each member's achievements reduce the success of others in that activity, the interdependence is of a very different sort (e.g., if several boys are competing for the attention of two girls, each boy will attempt to discourage the others from trying for the same girl he is trying for). If $N - 1$ of the group members are fixed, and i are in A, while $N - 1 - i$ are in B, then the one variable member might be characterized by the following process (where θ is the transition rate brought about by each member's punishment):

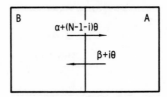

In this model, the i other persons carrying out activity A act to force this variable member *out* of A if he is there, while previously they acted to induce him *into* A, if he was in B. In this case, the individual's equilibrium probability of being found in A or B, respectively, is

$$p_A = \frac{\alpha + (N - 1 - i)\theta}{\alpha + \beta + (N - 1)\theta} \tag{7.3}$$

$$p_B = \frac{\beta + i\theta}{\alpha + \beta + (N - 1)\theta} \tag{7.4}$$

But as in the previous case, our interest is not in the behavior of the individual, but rather in the behavior of the *group*, under this structure of punishments. A diagram for the group stochastic process is given below:

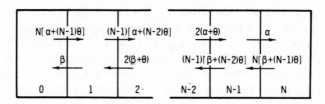

By a similar procedure to that carried out for the reward model, it is possible to find the expected distribution of groups that would be found at equilibrium. This is in form very similar to eq. (6.5), the distribution function for the reward model:

$$p_i = \frac{\binom{N}{i} \prod_{j=N-i}^{N-1} (a + js) \prod_{j=i}^{N-1} (1 - a + js)}{\prod_{j=N-1}^{2N-2} (1 + js)} \tag{7.5}$$

where $s = \theta/(\alpha + \beta)$.

The mean and variance of i are related to the parameters a and s as follows:

$$\mu = \frac{N[a + (N - 1)s]}{1 + 2(N - 1)s} \tag{7.6}$$

$$\sigma^2 = \mu \left\{ 1 + \frac{(N - 1)[a + (N - 2)s]}{1 + (2N - 3)s\beta} \right\} - \mu^2 \tag{7.7}$$

and the two parameters of the distribution, a and s, may be estimated by first estimating the mean and variance of i, then

$$s = \frac{\mu(N - \mu) - \sigma^2 N}{\sigma^2 N(2N - 3) - \mu(N - 2)(N - \mu)} \tag{7.8}$$

and

$$a = \frac{\mu}{N} + \left(\frac{2\mu - N}{N} \right)(N - 1)s \tag{7.9}$$

It is interesting to compare the parameters of this "punishment" distribution to those of the "reward" distribution as given in eqs. (6.7) and (6.8). In that case, the individualistic tendency toward activity A—that is, a—was directly reflected by the mean number of people carrying out activity A, as is true also for the binomial. In this case, the individualistic tendencies described by a are not directly reflected by the mean. The punishment distorts the mean in the direction of $N/2$, as eq. (7.9) and Figure 11.7 indicate. The mean mirrors a only under special circumstances: if the mean of p_i is equal to $N/2$ [so that $2\mu - N = 0$ in eq. (7.9)], or if the variance equals the binomial variance [so that $s = 0$ in eq. (7.9)]. In the latter case, since the punishment parameter, s, is zero, the process reduces to a binomial. The reward parameter, c, and the punishment parameter, s, are completely dependent on the amount that the estimated variance departs from the binomial variance, being larger for the reward process [see eq. (6.8)] and smaller for the punishment process. The denominators in eqs. (6.8) and (7.8) are positive so long as the estimated variance does not exceed, for the reward process, or fall below, for the punishment process, the maximum or minimum variances consistent with the model (i.e., when γ approaches infinity or θ approaches infinity).

The relation of the reward and punishment distributions to the independent binomial distribution is shown in Figures 11.6 and 11.7 by the set of distributions having $N = 5$ and $a = .6$, with varying values of s. The effect of the reward structure is as indicated in previous examination. The effect of the punishment structure is to hold the group far closer to an equal number of persons engaging in each activity than would be found if people were behaving independently.

Example. Teen-agers spending evenings out

In the preceding chapter, an example of teen-age boys spending 0, 1, ... 7 evenings out per week was mentioned, without a model being applied to it. It might be that either the reward process or the punishment process was

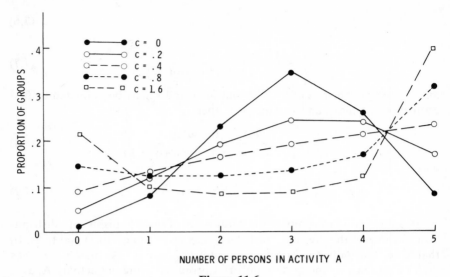

Figure 11.6

Distribution of groups under varying conditions of mutual reinforcement, according to eq. (6.5).

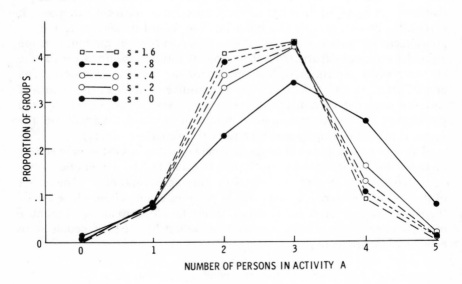

Figure 11.7

Distribution of groups under varying conditions of mutual punishment,
according to eq. (7.5).

operative to generate these data. In this case, the application of course is to intrapersonal processes, rather than interpersonal ones, so that i and N refer to nights rather than to individuals. The application here would be as follows:

(a) *Reward process:* Each teen-ager has for each night that he presently stays home a tendency α to go out; added to that α is an increment γ for each night that he presently goes out, due to the pleasure or gratification gained from going out.

Each teen-ager has for each night of the week that he presently goes out a tendency β to stay home; added to this is an increment γ for each night that he presently stays home, due to the pleasure or gratification gained from staying home.

(b) *Punishment process:* Each teen-ager has for each night that he presently stays home a tendency α to go out; added to that is an increment γ for each *other* night that he stays home, due to an uncomfortableness that builds up from staying home.

Each teen-ager for each night that he presently goes out a tendency β to stay home; added to this is an increment γ for each other night that he goes out, due to an uncomfortableness that builds up about going out too often.

If the reward process is operative, we could think of this as spontaneous or operant behavior, α, in which both activities are enjoyable; if the punishment process is operative, we could think of this either as a vacillation between two unpleasant activities, or as behavior in response to a double norm of "not to go out too much," and "not to stay home too much." *A priori*, it would seem that either process might be operative here.

Table 11.9 shows the frequency of going out i nights each week among boys and girls in a large suburban high school. For each group, the mean and variance were calculated. The mean number of nights was 2.56 nights for boys, and 2.05 for girls. The variance in number of nights out is 2.95 for boys, compared to a binomial variance of 1.63. Thus the boys' behavior is more dispersed than a pure binomial model would indicate, in the direction of the reward model. The variance in number of nights out for the girls is 1.37, compared to a binomial variance of 1.45. Thus the variance for the girls is *less* than that of a binomial, their behavior more concentrated around the mean number of nights out than a binomial model would predict. Their behavior is in the direction of the punishment model. The values of the parameters were calculated, and fitted distributions were calculated. They are presented in Table 11.9 with the actual data.

The fits of the models to the data are not very good. It is probable that the processes are not those that the models suggest, for in both cases, the concentration at $i = 2$ nights out is much greater than the model predicts. Undoubtedly, the constraints differ for different nights of the week, with higher tendencies to go out on Friday and Saturday nights than on other ones. However, the data are interesting in that they show the possibility that a reward process may dominate in one group (e.g., the boys), and a punishment or constraint process dominate in another, for the same behavior. This result, incidentally, is consistent with a number of other differences in boys' behavior: they seem to be more spontaneous, with higher variances in such diverse activities as time spent studying, time spent watching television, and number of phonograph records bought (see Coleman, 1961, p. 22).

The most desirable data for use with these models is, as implied earlier, data on group behavior, to allow identification of the structures of rewards and punishments operative in the group.

Table 11.9

NUMBER OF TEEN-AGERS GOING OUT WITH OTHER TEEN-AGERS
i NIGHTS OF THE WEEK

	Boys		*Girls*	
i	*Actual*	*Fitted* $a = .366,$ $c = .158$	*Actual*	*Fitted* $a = .268,$ $s = .0102$
0	78	109	54	72
1	151	177	228	224
2	316	196	353	289
3	189	175	164	198
4	71	133	50	78
5	45	84	22	18
6	26	41	6	2
7	51	12	5	1
	927	927	882	882

7.2 A note about the effect of rewards and punishments

In Thorndike's early discussion of the "law of effect," he defined a satisfying state of affairs (that resulting from reward) and an annoying state of affairs (that resulting from punishment) as follows:

By satisfying state of affairs is meant one which the animal does nothing to avoid, often doing such things as attain and preserve it. By a discomforting or annoying state of affairs is meant one which the animal commonly avoids and abandons. (Thorndike, 1911, p. 241.)

This statement of the effect of rewards and punishments implies that each has *two* effects. Reward induces the subject to both *attain* and *preserve* the state which brings rewards. Punishment leads him to *avoid* and *abandon* the state which brings punishment. The effects "attain" and "avoid" occur when the individual is in another state; the effects "preserve" and "abandon" occur when the individual is already in the state where he is rewarded or punished.

With the models presented above, only one effect occurs for reward, and one for punishment. The transition rate γ, induced by reward, occurs when the individual is in another state, and leads him to attain this state. There is no parameter to lead him to preserve this state as a consequence of reward. Conversely, in the punishment model, the transition rate θ is one leading him to abandon the punished activity; there is no parameter corresponding to avoidance.

It is not impossible, of course, to incorporate both effects into the model (though it is impossible to make them additive effects). However, it seems to me that such effects should derive simultaneously from a single concept. What is needed is a kind of probabilistic counterpart of pressure or voltage: when the pressure in a vessel is low relative to surrounding pressure, there are two effects: the gas already in does not leave; and the gas nearby is drawn in. What is required here is a similar concept such that a change in a single parameter would simultaneously affect both the incoming and the outgoing transition rates.

8. THE EQUILIBRIUM SIZE DISTRIBUTION OF FREELY FORM-ING GROUPS[23]

A few years ago (1953), John James published a paper reporting a number of observations of the size distribution of "freely forming" small groups in various public situations. These data, some of which are reproduced in Table 11.10, are intriguing to the quantitatively oriented sociologist, for they seem to show the outcome of some "natural processes" by which groups acquire and lose members.

Table 11.10

GROUPS OBSERVED ON A SPRING MORNING IN EUGENE, OREGON

Size of group	Number of groups
1	1486
2	694
3	195
4	37
5	10
6	1

Total 2423

---

[23] This section is a modification and elaboration of Coleman and James (1961).

Yet the data seem impermeable to explanation until one approaches them as statistical equilibria of a stochastic process such as these continuous-time processes examined in the present chapter. Even so, there is always the possibility that there are certain particular factors which complicate matters—as would be the case if, for example, the groups were observed on the sidewalk walking to a dance. There would, of course, be a predominance of couples, and any model based on general rates of acquisition and loss of group members would be doomed to failure.

However, these data of James's do not appear at first glance to have been disturbed by dances and the like. Each size appears less frequently than the next smaller size. Since this is so, can we construct a model, of the general type developed elsewhere in this chapter, to account for the phenomena? Perhaps the simplest model which might explain why the distributions take the form they do is a model of acquisition and loss, with the following assumptions (which include no "contagious" assumption):

(1) The states of the model represent the number of persons in the group. Thus a group may be in state 1, 2, 3, 4, ...

(2) From each state, there is a constant probability of loss of a member into the pool of single persons, proportional to the number of members in the group. This is another way of saying that each person has the same probability per unit time of dropping out of a group, independent of the size of the group. Taken in the limit, the process is a continuous-time process, and the transition rate for a group from state i to $i - 1$ is $i\beta'$, where β' is independent of the size of the group.

(3) Each group has a constant probability per unit time of gaining a member, proportional to the number of single persons available. This is a process of random encounter, independent of the size of the group, and dependent only upon the number of independent persons available for an encounter. [This assumes that encounters of a group ($n \geqslant 2$) with other groups of two or more members would not result in consolidation. Under some conditions, one might want to assume that these encounters resulted in the consolidation of the two groups, as is assumed here for the case of encounters with single individuals.] In the limit, this is a continuous-time process in which a group has a transition rate from state i to state $i + 1$ of $n_1\alpha$, where n_1 is the number of single individuals, and α is independent of the size of the group.

Note that these assumptions do not necessarily imply a constant flux, a constant acquisition and loss among, say, groups of pedestrians walking down the street. Less restrictively, one can assume that the acquisition-and-loss process went on at the time of formation of the groups, after which every group maintained its initial size. The assumptions do imply, however, a closed set of persons with no gains or losses from the total set.

8.1 The stochastic process and its deterministic approximation[24]

The basic differential equation of the process which incorporates these assumptions is at the level of the single group: The probability of moving down to i from state $i + 1$ in time dt, plus the probability of moving up from state $i - 1$, minus the probability of moving down from i to $i - 1$ or up from i to $i + 1$:

$$dp_i = \Pr [i + 1, i; dt] + \Pr [i - 1, i; dt] - \Pr [i, i - 1; dt] - \Pr [i, i + 1; dt] \tag{8.1}$$

This equation expresses the rate of change in the probability that a given group will be in state i. The first term on the right-hand side of the equation is the probability that a group will move from state $i + 1$ to i in a small increment of time, dt. In accordance with postulate (2) above, this is $(i + 1)\beta$ $p_{i+1} \, dt$, where p_{i+1} is the probability of the group being in state $i + 1$ (with $i + 1$ members). The third term is similar, being the probability that the group of size i will lose a member and move to $i - 1$: $i\beta p_i \, dt$. The second and fourth terms involve the acquisition of a member, and according to postulate (3) above, depend upon the number of single individuals, n_1 times an interaction coefficient α, times the probability that the group is in state $i - 1$ or i. These terms are, respectively, $n_1 \alpha p_{i-1} \, dt$, and $n_1 \alpha p_i \, dt$. Thus for all groups of size 2 or greater, the equation becomes (after dividing through by dt)

$$\frac{dp_i}{dt} = (i + 1)\beta p_{i+1} + n_1 \alpha p_{i-1} - i\beta p_i - n_1 \alpha p_i \tag{8.2}$$

The equation for change in the probability that the group is in state 1 includes only the first and the fourth terms:

$$\frac{dp_i}{dt} = 2\beta p_2 - n_1 \alpha p_1 \tag{8.3}$$

However, these equations describe the behavior of *a single group*, assuming that the environment, consisting of other groups in various states, is held constant. But, we are interested in describing the behavior of *a system of groups*.[25] New groups (of size 1) are formed when a group loses a member,

[24] See also Chapter 18, as well as several discussions in Bailey (1957), for discussion of the relation between stochastic and deterministic models for the same process.

[25] This was pointed out by Harrison White (1962), who noticed an error in the Coleman-James (1961) original formulation, which attempted to describe the behavior of the system of groups by equations that described the behavior of the single group. White points to the correct approach for the system of groups, but his techniques do not allow their solution, and he takes an approach similar to this one (though with different substantive postulates), which constitutes an approximation for the behavior of the system of groups. Goodman (1963a) shows more clearly the inherent difficulties in both White's and Coleman-James's approaches, and carries the development of these models further, by use of more powerful mathematical tools.

and groups (of size 1) vanish when a group adds a member. Consequently, to describe the behavior of the system of groups stochastically requires a much more complex approach, in which the state of the system is defined, not as the group being of a given size, but as the number of groups of size 1, 2, ... Thus one particular state would be described by a vector, $(n_1, n_2, \ldots, n_i \ldots)$. Because such an approach is beyond the limits of present techniques for solution, we will employ the process for a single group as a deterministic approximation for the stochastic process that describes the system. The approximation is much like that of deterministic population-growth models, and deterministic epidemic models. (See White, 1962, Coleman, 1962, and Goodman, 1963a, for further discussion of this problem.)

In making this shift, eq. (8.2) is reinterpreted as the rate of change of the *proportion* of groups in size i, p_i is defined as the proportion of groups of size i, and the proportion of groups of size 1 is $p_1 = n_1/n$ (where n is the total number of groups). This identification of p_1 and n_1/n makes n_1 a dependent variable in the system, since there is an equation for the rate of change of p_1 —which will, however, be different from eq. (8.3). Precisely these terms, where n_1 appears in eq. (8.2), make this deterministic equation give different results than the expected value of the stochastic process for the system, because they make the acquisition rate dependent on the product of two "average" proportions, while it is stochastically dependent upon the exact numbers of groups of size 1 and i, which fluctuate around these proportions. This fluctuation means that the average of the product of $n_1 n_i$ is somewhat less than the product of the averages. However, as n_1 and n_i become large, the average of the product approaches the product of the averages, and the deterministic model approaches the mean value of the stochastic model.

For describing the system of groups, the value of p_1 is increased by the loss rate from all groups of size 2 or greater, times the proportion of groups of each of these sizes:

$$(2\beta p_2 + 3\beta p_3 + \ldots + i\beta p_i + \ldots)\, dt = \beta \sum_{i=2}^{\infty} i p_i\, dt$$

In addition, there is an increment due to the breakup of the groups of size 2, yielding two groups of size 1. Consequently the total increment to p_1 in time dt is

$$\beta \sum_{i=2}^{\infty} i p_i\, dt + 2\beta p_2\, dt$$

The decrease for groups of size 1, in turn, comes about by the acquisition of a new member by all groups of size 1 on up, times the proportion of groups of each size:

$$(\alpha n_1 p_1 + \alpha n_1 p_2 + \ldots + \alpha n_1 p_i + \ldots)\, dt = \alpha n_1 \sum_{i=1}^{\infty} p_i\, dt$$

In addition there is an extra loss whenever a group of size 2 forms, because two single individuals are subtracted from the pool. Thus the total decrement to p_1 in time dt is

$$\alpha n_1 \sum_{i=1}^{\infty} p_i \, dt + \alpha n_1 p_1 \, dt$$

The rate of change in p_1 is thus:

$$\frac{dp_1}{dt} = \beta \sum_{i=2}^{\infty} i p_i + 2\beta p_2 - \alpha n_1 \sum_{i=1}^{\infty} p_i - \alpha n_1 p_1 \qquad (8.4)$$

8.2 Derivation of the equilibrium distribution

There will be no attempt to examine the dynamic properties of this process, but only the distribution of groups at equilibrium. For this purpose, it is convenient to think in terms of a "rate of flow" of groups across the boundary between state i and $i-1$. This "rate of flow," deriving from postulates (2) and (3), is

$$w_{i-1,i} = n_1 \alpha p_{i-1} - i\beta p_i \qquad (i \geqslant 2) \qquad (8.5)$$

where $n w_{i-1,i}$ is the number of groups gained by state i from state $i-1$ per unit time and n_1 is the number of groups of size 1. Dividing through by n (the total number of groups) puts the equation completely in terms of proportions:

$$\frac{w_{i-1,i}}{n} = p_1 \alpha p_{i-1} - \frac{i\beta}{n} p_i \qquad (8.6)$$

If we consider only the situation in which statistical equilibrium exists, then the proportion in each state i $(i = 1, 2, \ldots)$ is constant. This does not imply directly that the flow across each boundary is in equilibrium, with $w_{i,i-1}/n$ equal to zero, for state i might gain from state $i-1$ what it loses to state $i+1$. However, it can easily be shown that such an assumption of compensating disequilibrium at each boundary produces a contradiction. Thus, there must be equilibrium across the boundary between states 1 and 2, and, as a consequence, across every other boundary between states. Equation (8.6) becomes

$$p_{i-1} p_1 \alpha = p_i \frac{i\beta}{n} \qquad (i \geqslant 2) \qquad (8.7)$$

$$p_i = p_{i-1} \frac{n\alpha p_1}{i\beta} \qquad (i \geqslant 2) \qquad (8.8)$$

Or, writing p_i in terms of p_1 through successive substitutions, we have

$$p_i = \frac{p_1}{i!} \left(\frac{n\alpha p_1}{\beta} \right)^{i-1} \qquad (8.9)$$

and summing over all groups of size 2 or greater gives

$$\sum_{i=2}^{\infty} p_i = \sum_{i=2}^{\infty} \frac{p_1}{i!}\left(\frac{n\alpha p_1}{\beta}\right)^{i-1} \tag{8.10}$$

Substituting for the left-hand size its equivalent, assuming that the series converges, we obtain

$$1 - p_1 = \sum_{i=2}^{\infty} \frac{p_1}{i!}\left(\frac{n\alpha p_1}{\beta}\right)^{i-1} \tag{8.11}$$

or transposing p_1 results in

$$1 = p_1 + \sum_{i=2}^{\infty} \frac{p_1}{i!}\left(\frac{n\alpha p_1}{\beta}\right)^{i-1} \tag{8.12}$$

The right-hand side may be made equal to an exponential series (minus the first term), showing that the sum of p_i does in fact converge, and therefore, that there will in fact be an equilibrium distribution with $\Sigma p_i = 1$.

$$1 = \frac{\beta}{n\alpha} \sum_{i=1}^{\infty} \frac{1}{i!}\left(\frac{n\alpha p_1}{\beta}\right)^{i} \tag{8.13}$$

$$1 = \frac{\beta}{n\alpha}(e^{n\alpha p_1/\beta} - 1) \tag{8.14}$$

Solving for p_1 gives

$$p_1 = \frac{\beta}{n\alpha} \ln\left(\frac{n\alpha}{\beta} + 1\right) \tag{8.15}$$

and substituting the value of p_1 from eq. (8.15) into eq. (8.9) gives the value for p_i in terms of $n\alpha/\beta$:

$$p_i = \frac{\beta}{n\alpha\, i!}\left[\ln\left(\frac{n\alpha}{\beta} + 1\right)\right]^{i} \tag{8.16}$$

Or, if we let $\ln\left(\frac{n\alpha}{\beta} + 1\right) = k$, eq. (8.16) becomes

$$p_i = \frac{k^i}{i!(e^k - 1)} \tag{8.17}$$

It turns out that eq. (8.17) is nothing more than a Poisson distribution without the zero observation (called a truncated Poisson). However, if the model *fits* the data, then more has been done than simply "fit a truncated Poisson" to the data, since there is a rational model of acquisition and loss to explain the data. Furthermore, the parameter k provides a measure with explicit meaning which can be used to characterize the situation which was observed. Thus, situations can be compared by means of such a measure, telling something about the situation.[26]

Beyond this, the model could be carried in at least two directions: first, toward examining nonequilibrium situations, in which people were coming together, and groups were forming, reforming, losing and gaining members. Secondly, if the data do not fit the model as laid out above, it is not difficult to incorporate a contagion assumption—that is, an assumption that a person is more likely to join a large group than a small one—or perhaps other modifications of the simple acquisition-and-loss assumptions.

Going back to the present model, it is possible to see just how closely it does fit James's data, gathered in various situations.

The equation for p_i, eq. (8.17), cannot easily be used directly for estimating k, but a simple transformation will help. Using the expression for the mean of the distribution, we obtain

$$\mu = \sum_{i=1}^{\infty} ip_i = p_1 + \sum_{i=2}^{\infty} ip_i \qquad (8.18)$$

and substituting from eq. (8.8) for p_i gives

$$\mu = p_1 + \sum_{i=2}^{\infty} ip_{i-1}\frac{n\alpha p_1}{i\beta} \qquad (8.19)$$

$$= p_1 + \frac{n\alpha p_1}{\beta} \sum_{i=1}^{\infty} p_i$$

or

$$\mu = p_1 + \frac{n\alpha p_1}{\beta} \qquad (8.20)$$

Substituting from eq. (8.15) for the second p_1 results in[27]

$$\mu = p_1 + \ln\left(\frac{n\alpha}{\beta} + 1\right)$$

---

[26] Goodman shows, however, that unless systems of groups are fairly large in numbers, the data cannot be expected to fit a truncated Poisson, due to the stochastic disturbances discussed in Section 8.1.

[27] Alternatively, p_i could be directly factored out of the right-hand side of eq. (8.20) to give a different estimator for k. If this were done, then the estimator for $n\alpha/\beta$ would be:

$$\frac{n\alpha}{\beta} = \frac{\mu}{p_1} - 1 \quad \text{or} \quad k = \ln\frac{\mu}{p_1}$$

This would give slightly different estimates of the parameter than those obtained by eq. (8.21); but it appears that this estimation method gives all the weight to the p_1 observation, thus producing somewhat less good fits than the method used here. However, the two methods do not give very different results unless the model fails to fit the data well.

or

$$\mu = p_1 + k$$

or

$$k = \mu - p_1 \tag{8.21}$$

Rather than solving in terms of k, it is desirable to solve in terms of the ratio of acquisition to loss rates, α/β. However, k equals $\ln[(n\alpha/\beta) + 1]$, and this quantity includes n, the total number of groups, which is a dependent phenomenon. By using the fact that $N = \mu n$, $\mu = k + p_1$, and $p_1 = k/e^k - 1$, it is possible to establish a relation between $N\alpha/\beta$ and k. Making the necessary substitutions, we have

$$\frac{N\alpha}{\beta} = ke^k \tag{8.22}$$

Thus having the observed distributions, it is possible to estimate k by eq. (8.21), and then to use this value of k to estimate $N\alpha/\beta$.

For twenty-one sets of data collected by John James (see James, 1953), the model was fitted, and values of k (and from them, values of $N\alpha/\beta$) were calculated. The actual distributions, fitted distributions, and values of $N\alpha/\beta$ are given in Table 11.11.

The model in most of these instances shows a remarkably good fit to the data. Only in groups 4, 11, and 16 is χ^2 large enough to indicate that the difference between actual and calculated values could hardly have happened by chance.[28]

What is surprising is that these data may be fitted by a model that employs no assumption of contagion or heterogeneity, which would tend to elongate the tail of the distribution. As a consequence, these distributions of group size can be explained quite parsimoniously by the single parameter, a ratio of acquisition to loss (the components of which will be examined shortly).

Table 11.11

FREE-FORMING SMALL GROUP SIZE[a]

Group size	Frequency		$\dfrac{N\alpha}{\beta}$	k
	Actual	Calculated		
1. Pedestrians—Eugene, Spring, Morning				
1	1486	1495.0		
2	694	671.0		
3	195	201.0	2.22	.900
4	37	45.0		
5	10	8.0		
6	1	1.0		
Total	2423			

[28] Horvath and Foster (1963) have applied this model to size distributions of groups of allies in war alliances, with reasonably good fit.

Group size	Frequency		$\dfrac{N\alpha}{\beta}$	k
	Actual	*Calculated*		

2. Pedestrians—Eugene, Spring, Afternoon

1	1151	1153.0		
2	509	503.0		
3	147	146.0	2.08	.871
4	23	31.8		
5	7	5.5		
6	3	0.8		
	Total 1840			

3. Pedestrians—Eugene, Winter, Morning

1	424	423.0		
2	136	134.0		
3	24	28.4	1.17	.626
4	5	4.5		
5	1	0.6		
6	1	0.1		
	Total 591			

4. Pedestrians—Portland, Spring, Morning

1	1677	1666.0		
2	331	357.0		
3	59	51.0	0.67	.431
4	12	5.5		
5	1	.5		
	Total 2080			

5. Pedestrians—Portland, Spring, Afternoon

1	1218	1218.0		
2	251	246.0		
3	25	33.1	0.61	.406
4	6	3.3		
5	1	0.3		
	Total 1501			

6. Shopping Groups—Eugene, Spring, Department Store and Public Market

1	316	316.0		
2	141	141.0		
3	44	41.8	2.18	.892
4	5	9.3		
5	4	1.7		
	Total 510			

Group size	Frequency		$\dfrac{N\alpha}{\beta}$	k
	Actual	*Calculated*		

7. Shopping Groups—Eugene, Winter, Department Store

Group size	Actual	Calculated	$\dfrac{N\alpha}{\beta}$	k
1	124	119.0		
2	52	60.1		
3	21	20.3	2.78	1.01
4	5	5.1		
5	3	1.0		
6	1	0.2		
Total	206			

8. Shopping Groups—Portland, Spring, Two Department Stores

Group size	Actual	Calculated	$\dfrac{N\alpha}{\beta}$	k
1	955	964.0		
2	340	312.0		
3	50	67.0	1.24	.647
4	10	10.8		
5	1	1.4		
Total	1356			

9. Play Groups—Eugene, Spring, Public Playground A

Group size	Actual	Calculated	$\dfrac{N\alpha}{\beta}$	k
1	306	304.0		
2	132	139.0		
3	47	42.4	2.30	.916
4	10	9.7		
5	2	1.8		
Total	497			

10. Play Groups—Eugene, Spring, Public Playground B

Group size	Actual	Calculated	$\dfrac{N\alpha}{\beta}$	k
1	177	176.0		
2	63	63.0		
3	15	15.1	1.47	.719
4	1	2.7		
5	2	0.4		
Total	258			

11. Play Groups—Eugene, Spring, Public Playground C

Group size	Actual	Calculated	$\dfrac{N\alpha}{\beta}$	k
1	316	309.0		
2	106	113.0		
3	19	27.5	1.52	.733
4	10	5.1		
5	1	0.7		
6	3	0.1		
Total	455			

| Group size | Frequency | | $\dfrac{N\alpha}{\beta}$ | k |
	Actual	Calculated		

12. Play Groups—Eugene, Spring, Public Playground D

Group size	Actual	Calculated	$\dfrac{N\alpha}{\beta}$	k
1	305	306.0		
2	144	143.0		
3	50	44.8	2.39	.936
4	5	10.5		
5	2	2.0		
6	1	0.3		
Total	507			

13. Play Groups—Eugene, Spring, Playgrounds of 14 Elementary Schools[b]

Group size	Actual	Calculated	$\dfrac{N\alpha}{\beta}$	k
1	570	590.0		
2	435	410.0		
3	203	190.0	5.56	1.39
4	57	66.0		
5	11	18.4		
6	1	4.3		
Total	1277			

14. Play Groups—Eugene, Spring, Nursery School, Ages 2–5

Group size	Actual	Calculated	$\dfrac{N\alpha}{\beta}$	k
1	383	377.0		
2	93	104.0		
3	19	19.2	0.96	.554
4	6	2.7		
5	1	0.3		
6	1	0.0		
Total	503			

15. Play Groups—Eugene, Spring, Nursery School, Ages 4–5

Group size	Actual	Calculated	$\dfrac{N\alpha}{\beta}$	k
1	84	82.0		
2	33	36.8		
3	11	11.0	2.22	.900
4	4	2.5		
5	1	0.4		
Total	133			

16. Public Gatherings—Portland, Spring, Public Beach Swimming Pool

Group size	Actual	Calculated	$\dfrac{N\alpha}{\beta}$	k
1	276	299.0		
2	229	181.0		
3	61	73.0	4.07	1.21
4	12	22.2		
5	3	5.4		
Total	581			

Group size	Frequency		$\dfrac{N\alpha}{\beta}$	k
	Actual	Calculated		

17. Public Gatherings—Portland, Spring, Public Beach Picnic Area

Group size	Actual	Calculated	$\dfrac{N\alpha}{\beta}$	k
1	115	126.0		
2	138	115.0		
3	66	69.6	11.3	1.82
4	24	31.7		
5	13	11.5		
6	3	3.5		

Total　359

18. Public Gatherings—Portland, Spring, Railroad Depot

Group size	Actual	Calculated	$\dfrac{N\alpha}{\beta}$	k
1	265	269.0		
2	118	106.0		
3	19	27.6	1.74	.789
4	6	5.4		
5	1	0.8		

Total　409

Observations Made in Seoul, Korea, March, 1955

Situation A. Observations carried out on March 5, 1955, in a semi-residential area of Seoul, Korea. The spot chosen was on a side street about one mile from the center of the city. Small shops of all varieties are the typical establishments in the area. Time of day when the observations were made: 4 P.M. to 5:30 P.M. The groups counted were those passing a designated spot, moving in one direction only.

19.

Group size	Actual	Calculated	$\dfrac{N\alpha}{\beta}$	k
1	818	813.0		
2	194	205.0		
3	38	34.4	.841	.506
4	6	4.3		
5	1	0.4		

Total　1057

Situation B. Observations carried out on March 12, 1955, in the business district of Seoul, Korea. The spot chosen was on a main avenue about three blocks from the center of the city. Banks, hotels, department stores, and office buildings are the typical establishments in the area. Time of day when the observations were made: 3 P.M. to 4 P.M. The groups counted were those passing a designated spot moving in both directions.

20.

Group size	Actual	Calculated	$\dfrac{N\alpha}{\beta}$	k
1	897	899.0		
2	252	245.0		
3	38	44.6	0.95	.549
4	7	6.1		
5	1	0.7		

Total　1195

Group size	Frequency		$\dfrac{N\alpha}{\beta}$	k
	Actual	Calculated		
21. Nikolski Community Sweeps[c]				
1	166	161.0		
2	60	69.6		
3	26	20.0	2.04	.863
4	2	4.3		
5	3	0.7		
Total	257			

[a] Data from John James (personal communication). See John James (1953).

[b] Directed or organized play not included in observations.

[c] The sweeps were an attempt to get an approximate instantaneous picture of the small-group structure of the whole community; in other words, an attempt to determine what everyone was doing at a given time. With the assistance of the other members of the expedition, two daily sweeps over a five-day period were made. Since making the observation included going into houses, places of work, etc., the chances of making errors were large. Observations were made in the summer of 1952.

Looking at the values of $N\alpha/\beta$ in Table 11.11, we may note several generalizations:

(a) Groups in Eugene (a small city of 35,000) show a much higher acquisition-to-loss ratio than those in Portland (a city of 370,000) under similar conditions.

	Eugene, $N\alpha/\beta$	Portland, $N\alpha/\beta$
Spring morning	2.22	0.67
Spring afternoon	2.08	0.61
Department stores	2.78, 2.18	1.24

(b) Based on one comparison (Eugene, morning, group 1 vs. 3), it appears that the acquisition-to-loss ratio is higher in spring than in winter, outdoors; but indoors it appears to be higher in *winter* (based on shopping groups in Eugene, 6 vs. 7).

(c) Largest groups (i.e., largest acquisition-to-loss ratios) were found on a public beach (groups 16, 17) and in school playgrounds (13).

A word should be added about the meaning of the acquisition-and-loss coefficients, and the role of N in the parameter $N\alpha/\beta$. Given two differing values of $N\alpha/\beta$, just how are they to be interpreted? The interpretation is this: first, it is necessary to standardize the sample of observations in time or space, so that N refers to the number of individuals per unit of time or space.[29]

[29] Some of James's observations ("community sweeps") are observations over the total area at a fixed time point. These must be standardized by area covered. Others (e.g., side-

If the area covered in one community sweep is twice that of a second, then $N\alpha/\beta$ for the first must be divided by two to give N the same dimensions, in the two cases—that is, the number of persons in a standard unit area. Thus according to this model, for a given density of persons, a given α will produce, on the average, a certain number of joinings in a small period of time Δt; if the density is tripled, an α only one-third as large will produce the same number of joinings.[30]

The empirical hypothesis here is that the basic parameter of the system is α/β, and that as the density increases or decreases, but the situation and the affinities of the persons remain the same, the coalescence into groups will increase or decrease in such a way that α/β remains constant.

An example will indicate how values of α/β may be compared for different situations. In Seoul, Korea, two sets of observations were carried out, resulting in the distributions of Table 11.11, groups 19 and 20. The first (situation A) covered 1.5 hours, persons moving past a designated line (a sidewalk width), in one direction in a semi-residential area. There were 1349 persons, or 900 per hour. The second (situation B) covered 1 hour, the same length line, but persons moving in two directions in a business district. The number of persons was 1548, or 774 per hour in one direction. In the first case, k is .506, resulting in an $N\alpha/\beta$ of .84. The ratio α/β is .84/900, or .00093. In the second case, k is .549, resulting in an $N\alpha/\beta$ of .950. The ratio α/β is .00123. Thus the conclusion of this comparison is that the ratio of affiliation to de-affiliation is less in the semi-residential area than in the business district, in the proportion .00093 : .00123.

Harrison White (1962) has modified this model with a number of alternative possible assumptions. Most of White's models, though they appear to be similar to this one, are fundamentally different in their assumptions about behavior. Whereas the rate at which isolates join groups in this model is proportional to the *product* of the number of isolates and the number of groups in a given area, his rate at which isolates join groups is proportional to *either* the number of isolates alone *or* the number of groups alone. The existence of these alternative assumptions leads to interesting possibilities of testing. For example, experiments in which the density of persons in an area was systematically varied would show whether in fact k varies in such a way that α/β remains constant, as this model predicts, or stays the same, as several of White's models predict.

The outcome of controlled experiments varying population density and

---

walk observations) sampled at multiple points in time a fixed area through which groups were passing. In these cases, the total area (area of observation multiplied by number of observations; or if observations are continuous in time, area multiplied by time, assuming that the speed of movement is the same) must be standardized.

[30] This is, of course, on the average, and assuming for simplicity of exposition that β is the same in the two cases.

kind of activity would first of all test whether the mechanism is that proposed here, and secondly would show the effect of different activities upon the relative sizes of the coefficients of acquisition and loss. As with the experiments suggested for the contagion model of the preceding section, the potential fruits are great: uncovering the specific form of very general processes in social psychology, processes which have long ago been identified, but which have never been specified as to their precise form. Once the form of such a process is fixed, then the process can be used as a building block whose precise mathematical form is known, in models which link together a set of interdependent processes.

9. UNSOLVED PROBLEMS AND FUTURE DIRECTIONS FOR POISSON-TYPE MODELS

I would like to end this chapter by mentioning some of the problems which are to be solved, and what are the most obvious paths along the course this chapter and the preceding one have begun to lay out.

Perhaps the most important point to note is that future developments depend completely upon the conjunction of systematic quantitative data and a general framework of theoretic orientation. Some of the contagious models discussed here, in particular the voting distributions in groups, illustrate this well. Without an orientation to problems of small-group process, and theoretical ideas about how to describe such processes, development of the model would have been impossible. At the same time, without data on voting in large numbers of small groups, I probably would not have been led to develop the model. Or if John James had not collected the data on sizes of "freely forming" small groups, there would have been no pressure to develop the model to account for these group sizes. Once such data are collected, they force the development of models to account for them, and once such a model is developed, it in turn proves the usefulness of the data; giving, for example, parameters of acquisition and loss which can be interpreted as the "coalescing potential" of particular public situations.

What, then, are the immediate problems which are most pressing to be solved in the development and application of these models? Some are listed below.

9.1 Empirical work

(1) One of the general values of models like these is in allowing a kind of work which has until now been almost absent in sociology and social psychology: discovery of the particular form which certain well-known processes take. Consider, for example, the processes of interpersonal influence in small groups, giving rise to homogeneity of opinion and behavior, to group norms, and other things. Many experiments have been performed with

the aim of testing *whether* such processes actually occur under various conditions. But almost no experiments have been carried out to examine the precise *form* which such processes take. This absence of experimentation is in some part due to the lack of quantitative measurement in behavioral matters; but this reason is far from being the only one, for the present models, working with all-or-none responses at the individual level, and numbers of individuals, require no such measurement.

It appears to be largely the lack of quantitative models, of the sort presented here, which has made it seem impossible—or at least unfruitful—to experiment with the precise form which various group and individual processes take. However, if such experiments are carried out, and the form of the processes is established, then this can have important consequences. It begins the establishment of quantitative laws in a science which is too often seen as inherently qualitative. Such laws can serve in two ways: as phenomena to be explained, by underlying psychological or physiological processes, or as building blocks to be used in synthesizing larger systems of behavior.

For example, suppose the precise forms of the process of interpersonal contagion in a group context and the process of intrapersonal contagion of a repeated and rewarded activity were well established. Then, putting two persons together, each carrying out this repetitive activity, would link together the interpersonal and the intrapersonal processes to constitute a system of behavior, one whose outcome would be predictable by linking together in a single mathematical model the two separate models for these processes.

(2) All the models in these chapters which embody contagious assumptions (and most of the sociologically interesting ones do) constantly run up against the difficulty of interpretation: heterogeneity or contagion. This problem has been discussed throughout the chapter, and it is clear that the problem is essentially no different from the problem of using cross-sectional correlations to infer causal relations in ordinary statistical analysis. Here, as in that problem, it is imperative that over-time data be used to test for contagion vs. heterogeneity. Feller says (after showing that the Polya distribution, with contagious assumptions, is identical to a distribution of Yule, based on assumptions of heterogeneity):

> It is seen, therefore, that contrary to a wide-spread opinion, an excellent fit of Polya's distribution is not necessarily indicative of any phenomenon of contagion in the mechanism behind the observed distribution. In order to decide whether or not there is contagion, it is not sufficient to consider the distribution of events, but a detailed study of the correlation between different time-intervals is necessary. (1943, p. 398.)

The problem, then, is twofold: on the one hand, to collect data through time, which will show changes due to contagion, insofar as contagion does exist, and on the other hand, to develop techniques for using such over-time data in conjunction with the models. As the models of the present chapter stand now, nothing beyond equilibrium states has been studied—the dynamic properties of these models remain uninvestigated. The models of the preceding chapter are a little better off in this respect, for the resulting distributions all contain an explicit or implicit time parameter, allowing the comparison of distributions at different points in the process. However, such a comparison of distributions is a very inefficient way to use over-time analysis, when it is possible to trace the time path of specific individuals or groups. Much work needs to be done in developing procedures which do use efficiently such over-time information on individuals. Such work would be parallel, for these more complicated models, to Chapter 5 which examines over-time analysis for the simple two-state models.

(3) In small-group influence processes, how does the contagion parameter vary with the state the group is in? Is it constant, as assumed here, or is the influence per person greater when all but one or two in the group hold one opinion? Certain psychological experiments (Asch, 1951) suggest a great discontinuity between the group's influence in the case of *two* dissenters and in the case of a *single* dissenter. And how does the contagion parameter change with change in group size? The data reported in Section 6 above are interesting but inconclusive.

(4) Are processes by which group norms become adopted more in accordance with the model described in Section 4 of contagion from not-doing (e.g., not being a baseball fan) to doing (being a fan), or with the competitive contagion model of Section 6? That is, empirically, do group norms develop in competition with the opposing norm, or in the absence of competition? Of importance here might be the difference between values which are privately held (e.g., beliefs favoring chastity held in a college fraternity) and opposing ones which are publicly expressed (beliefs favoring nonchastity). But even this public expression or lack of it is to a large part dictated by the prevailing state of the group. These are difficult questions, and systematic quantitative data are badly needed.

(5) One of the most fertile fields for application of models like these is market behavior and mass media audience behavior, of the sort used in the example of Section 2. Probably the best over-time data by which these models can be tested are those gathered from consumer panels by several market research organizations. Not only would the application of these models to these data be of value in analysis of the data; it would serve as a strong stimulus to further development of the models themselves. These data are usually applicable, of course, to intrapersonal, rather than interpersonal processes.

9.2 Mathematical problems

(1) Two models not completed in this chapter and the last are the two exhaustible contagion models (Section 4 of the preceding chapter, and Section

4 of this chapter). For the two-way model, the equilibrium distribution was developed (eq. 4.4), but methods for estimating the two parameters and fitting the model to data were not. For the one-way model of the preceding chapter, statisticians working with epidemic models have made progress, but have not had complete success. The distribution function is exceedingly involved (see Bailey, 1957, pp. 39–41), and is not easily applied to data. For these models, as for the freely-forming group size model, where an approximation was used, there is need for more powerful mathematical methods (e.g., see Goodman, 1963a).

The importance of developing these particular stochastic models lies in the relevance of their assumptions for many social-psychological processes. For example, if we collected data through time on the acceptance of a value or norm in small groups, we would want to use this model to test against the results, to see the degree of contagion or influence, and to see whether it proceeded according to the additive assumptions of these models.

(2) In the competitive-contagion voting model of Section 6, there were three parameters, which collapse to two independent ones with cross-section data. The individual innovation parameters α and β were assumed different for the two competing actions, while the contagion parameter γ was assumed the same for both sides. Another similar model is one in which the contagion parameters differ for the two sides, as would be the case when one of the competing actions is easily visible or easily expressed (e.g., an opinion which is reinforced by general social norms) while the other is not (e.g., an opinion which goes against general social norms). The density function for such a model would look like this:

$$p_i = \frac{\binom{N}{i}\alpha(\alpha + \gamma)\ldots(\alpha + [i - 1]\gamma)\beta(\beta + \lambda)\ldots(\beta + [N - i - 1]\lambda)}{\sum\limits_{j=0}^{N}\binom{N}{j}\alpha(\alpha + \gamma)\ldots(\alpha + [j - 1]\gamma)\beta(\beta + \lambda)\ldots(\beta + [N - j - 1]\lambda)} \qquad (9.1)$$

However, this is a formidable equation, and the means of making it amenable to empirical test is not evident. If such a way is found, it may turn out that this model more accurately describes many situations of influence in a group than does the model tested here.

(3) The contagious-binomial model of Section 6 treats only *two* alternative actions. What about analogous models which treat several alternatives, just as the multinomial distribution generalizes the binomial? Models of this kind would be important whenever there are several activities competing for the attention of group members, or several activities competing for an individual's time. Such models would be of extreme interest in examining the effects of reward structures on the distribution of time among a number of activities.

(4) One trouble with allowing heterogeneity in a model is the problem:

Once we start such a model, how or where do we stop? By assuming enough heterogeneity among people or groups, any phenomenon can be explained trivially. It is, in fact, *accounting for* heterogeneity which is one problem of scientific analysis.

One technique is not to invoke heterogeneity simply as a means of accounting for unexplained variations, but to introduce it explicitly by characterizing persons according to independent variables. The suggestion here is, in a sense, to combine some of the approaches developed in Chapters 4–9, where simple models were used with independent variables, with the approach of this chapter, where more complicated ones were used without such differentiating variables. One example will indicate the possibilities. Consider a regular Poisson distribution:

$$p_i = \frac{e^{-\alpha}\alpha^i}{i!}$$

Now rather than regarding α as fixed and immutable for everyone, as we do in the Poisson, or as varying with the state of the system, as we did in some of the elaborations upon the Poisson, or being randomly distributed, as in a heterogeneity model, let it vary according to some independent variable or attribute in the manner of Chapter 4–9. For example, suppose in examining the popularity of boys in high school via a Poisson distribution (i.e., distribution of the number of choices received), we characterized boys according to whether they were out for a sport and according to whether they made a **B** average or better in school. Then we would have *four* Poisson distributions, with the following transition rates:

$$
\begin{aligned}
\alpha_1 &= \beta + \gamma + \varepsilon && \text{(out for a sport and good grades)} \\
\alpha_2 &= \beta \phantom{{}+\gamma} + \varepsilon && \text{(out for a sport)} \\
\alpha_3 &= \phantom{\beta + {}}\gamma + \varepsilon && \text{(out for good grades)} \\
\alpha_4 &= \phantom{\beta + \gamma + {}}\varepsilon && \text{(neither)}
\end{aligned}
$$

By dividing people into these four groups and fitting the four distributions, we would have (a) estimates of the effect of sports and grades on popularity; and (b) the degree to which the Poisson assumptions fit when sports and grades are held constant, and, conversely, the degree to which further heterogeneity or contagion exists.

But this is a very simple example; in general the problem is a serious one and should be studied in a comprehensive way.

(5) To what extent can the very complicated distribution functions for some of the models be simplified by going to the limit and shifting to continuous space, letting $N \to \infty$, and α, β, $\gamma \to 0$ appropriately? To be sure we would not want to do this when the number of states is small, and thus "far apart" relative to the distribution, but when N is quite large, this might be very useful. It is important that the limit be approached in such a way as to preserve the form of the distribution; otherwise, the limiting case is likely

to end up a normal distribution. Some aid may be obtained here from work in stochastic processes in biology, which appear to have a similar structure (e.g., see Bharucha-Reid, 1960, p. 215).

(6) There is a great need for models of *competition* among several attributes for the "votes" or the "attention" of a populace or an audience. A great deal of social and individual behavior is built around competition— consumer behavior, competition between candidates in politics, competition among teen-agers for the spotlight of attention, competition for friends within groups, competition among television programs for the viewers' attention, competition among popular songs, among fads and fashions, and so on. Some of these phenomena can be approximately treated with contagion models alone, of the sort developed above. But these are not at all the same as competition models, as the difference between eq. (4.4) and eq. (6.5) indicates. The first model is pure contagion in a group, with no opposing norm or behavior to compete against it. The second is competiton where there are two actions, attributes, candidates, conflicting norms, or whatever, and the group's influence on its members can be in the direction of either (or both, if the group is nearly divided between them).

However, this is a very simple situation. To consider the other extreme of complexity (but a case for which excellent data are available), there is the competitive-contagious system of popular songs. Each song rises and falls, goes through a growth and decay cycle, all the time in competition with other songs which are eroding away its present followers and capturing the attention of its potential followers.

Some of the work in this direction with deterministic models for competitive and predator-prey relations (e.g., Davis, 1960) appears useful. Needless to say, the development of adequate models of competition-contagion for studying "free choice" behavior in society is a long and arduous task. It is, however, an extremely important one.

(7) All the skew distributions examined here are those where the number of "systems"—groups, populations, individuals—is large, and the number of states is small. Many skew distributions are of the opposite sort, showing the number of votes received by the top contender, the number received by the second contender, and so on down. For example, the twenty most popular songs are ranked every week in *Billboard*, with an indication of how many sales each had.[31] Such distributions are certainly contagious: one sale leads to another. But how can the contagious models above, or similar ones, be fitted to them? One method would seem to be through examining the cumulative distribution function, rather than the density functions developed here. However, this requires added mathematical efforts.

---

[31] There is some problem in this particular case about how the data can be interpreted in terms of number of sales, since they are not given that way directly; but this is another matter.

CHAPTER 12

SOCIAL AND
PSYCHOLOGICAL
ORGANIZATION OF
ATTITUDES[1]

1. TRANSITION OF ELEMENTS WITHIN THE INDIVIDUAL

In Chapters 4–11, it has been assumed that at any given time an individual is in a particular state which corresponds to the manifest response he makes. This, of course, is an oversimplification, because some individuals are in

---

[1] I am not sure just how much my ideas in this chapter have directly derived from those of Paul Lazarsfeld (1954, 1959), in his work with latent structure analysis, and Lee Wiggins (1955), in his work with response reliability and latent structure analysis by use of panel data. I have been familiar with their work so long that I am certain many of these ideas derive directly from theirs. However, my intent is somewhat different here, for it is concerned with the social and psychological organization of attitudes, while theirs is concerned with individual attitude measurement. The formal model, of course, is different as well.

intermediate states, as likely to give one response as the other. More generally, any model which directly identifies an underlying state with a manifest response is likely to fail when applied to the microstructure of behavior.

An elaboration of the above model is one that posits a number of *elements* in the individual, which lead, when conditioned to a particular response, to that response. That is, rather than the individual being in a particular response state, hypothetical cognitive elements within him are in the response state.[2] These elements are subject to a continuous-time stochastic process similar to that dicussed in previous chapters at the level of the individual. That is, if there are two responses, then elements may be in a state conditioned to one of these responses, or in an unconditioned state. There are continuous transitions, depending upon external and internal stimuli, between the unconditioned state and each of the response states. (The detailed nature of this process is the core of a formal learning theory, and a theory of attitude change, which is not well enough developed to be treated here.) The *number* of these elements in each response state determines the probability of this response. Thus if there are m_1 elements in state 1 and m_2 in state 2, the probability of response 1 (given that response 1 or 2 is made) is $m_1/(m_1 + m_2)$.

This model has several implications for situations in which people are asked a number of attitude questions, or in situations where the same question is asked more than once (as, for example, in testing item "reliability").   This usefulness of multiple-question situations in relation to the present model may first be seen intuitively. Consider an attitude question with two possible responses, positive and negative. If the positive response is labelled 1, then the expected proportion responding positively will be given by eq. (1.1) in terms of the model's underlying parameters:

$$p_1^* = \frac{m_1}{m_1 + m_2} \tag{1.1}$$

where m_1 and m_2 are the number of elements in the stimulus (i.e., question) conditioned to responses 1 and 2. However, if the proportion p_1^* were obtained in response to a question, two opposite interpretations (and any intermediate ones) would be equally tenable:

(a) Each person is identical, being characterized by m_1 and m_2.

(b) There are two extreme types of persons, who may be labelled 1's and 2's, which exist in the population in the proportion $m_1 : m_2$. The 1's have an effectively zero probability of response 2, while the 2's have an effectively zero probability of response 1.[3]

---

[2] Such a conception has frequently been set forth in the psychological literature. Their incorporation into mathematical learning models has been carried out by Estes and Burke (1955). The development of this chapter, however, includes no learning mechanism. Chapter 13 includes a mechanism of change which can be considered a learning mechanism.

[3] If we were thinking of this response in terms of the two-state models of earlier chapters,

These two interpretations differ in where they locate the variability of the system: interpretation (a) locates all the variability *within* individuals, postulating that all individuals are alike. Interpretation (b) locates all the variability between individuals, postulating that each individual is totally organized in the direction of one of the two responses. In this case, the cleavage is wholly social, with individuals not internally divided at all.

If such organization has come about through rewards or punishments to response 1 or 2, then the difference between these two extreme situations results from very different social distributions of rewards and punishments to these responses: In the first case, all persons have received exactly the same distribution of rewards and punishments relative to these responses. In the second case, some persons have been rewarded only for response 1, while others have been rewarded only for response 2, and no one has been rewarded for both. In a society with distinct subcultures, such a distribution is frequent, while in a society with a single homogeneous subculture, the previous distribution, with everyone rewarded for the same responses, is frequent.

Obviously, in the study of the social and psychological organization of attitudes, it becomes crucial to decide between these two interpretations. In the study of public opinion, for example, differences such as these could have vastly different social consequences, as well as vastly different social sources.[4] The question becomes, then, how to separate the social variability from the psychological variability.

2. SUCCESSIVE RESPONSES TO ONE ITEM

The easiest way to begin to separate out these two components of variability is to look at successive responses of the same individuals to a single two-response item. Suppose the proportion giving a positive response at time 1 was p_1 and the proportion remained identical at time 2, p_1. Then what proportion would we expect to find giving a positive response both times? What would p_{11} be? The first interpretation (all individuals alike, all characterized by the same values of m_1 and m_2) would predict that each individual's probability of giving response 1 is alike, and estimated by p_1. Thus each has the same ratio $m_1/(m_1 + m_2)$, and each has a probability of giving response 1 twice equal to

---

with transition rates between, similar contrasting interpretations would be possible. (a) the transition rates α (proportional to m_1) and β (proportional to m_2) are extremely fast, so that each person has, independently of previously recorded position, probability $\alpha/\alpha(+\beta)$ of responding positively; or (b) the transition rates are extremely slow, so that each person is in either state 1 or 2, remaining there over any reasonable period of over investigation.

[4] Herbert Hyman (1957), in a statement about the present state of the theory of public opinion, suggests that the most important next steps lie in directions "which characterize and capture relevant features of the social distribution of opinions" (p. 59).

$$\left(\frac{m_1}{m_1 + m_2}\right)\left(\frac{m_1}{m_1 + m_2}\right), \quad \text{or} \quad p_1^2.$$

This means that we would predict p_{11} to be simply

$$p_{11} = p_1^2 \tag{2.1}$$

The contingency table between the two questions would show no relation between times 1 and 2: the cells would simply be the product of the marginals (assuming a large enough sample for the sample value to equal the expected value), as follows:

$p_1{}^2$	$p_1(1 - p_1)$	p_1
$p_1(1 - p_1)$	$(1 - p_1)^2$	$1 - p_1$
p_1	$1 - p_1$	

The second interpretation would predict a very different result for the value of p_{11}. For the type 1 individuals, $m_2 = 0$, and

$$p_{11}^{(1)} = \left(\frac{m_1}{m_1 + 0}\right)\left(\frac{m_1}{m_1 + 0}\right)$$

$$= 1 \tag{2.2}$$

For the type 2 individuals, $m_1 = 0$, and

$$p_{11}^{(2)} = \left(\frac{0}{0 + m_2}\right)\left(\frac{0}{0 + m_2}\right)$$

$$= 0 \tag{2.3}$$

Then, for the total sample, there are an estimated np_1 individuals of type 1, and $n(1 - p_1)$ of type 2, so that we would predict

$$p_{11} = (p_1)(p_{11}^{(1)}) + (1 - p_1)(p_{11}^{(2)})$$

$$= (p_1)(1) + (1 - p_1)(0)$$

$$= p_1 \tag{2.4}$$

The contingency table would show a complete relation between the first and second questions, as follows:

p_1	0	p_1
0	$1 - p_1$	$1 - p_1$
p_1	$1 - p_1$	

Thus repetition of the same item would allow us to decide between these two interpretations, while the one response would not. However, it would only be in extreme situations that either of these interpretations would be completely true. Ordinarily, there is some variability within individuals (that is, neither m_1 nor m_2 is zero), and some variability among individuals (that is, some variation in m_1 and m_2 among different persons). The question then is, how to provide a meaningful measure of this variability?

Suppose we consider the distribution of persons over the range of values of m_1 and m_2. Let the number of people at the point (m_1,m_2) be represented by $n(m_1,m_2)$. Then if the total number of persons in the sample is n,

$$n = \sum_{m_1} \sum_{m_2} n(m_1,m_2) \tag{2.5}$$

Since the probability of response 1 does not depend on the absolute sizes of m_1 and m_2, but only on $m_1/(m_1 + m_2)$, we can call this proportion v, and reduce the bivariate distribution, $n(m_1,m_2)$ to a univariate distribution $n(v)$.

Now the probability of a person at v giving response 1 is v, by definition, so the expected number of people at v giving response 1 is $v\,n(v)$. The total expected number giving response 1 is

$$n_1 = \int_{v=0}^{1} v\,n(v)\,dv \tag{2.6}$$

The expected number giving response 1 both times is

$$n_{11} = \int_{v=0}^{1} v^2\,n(v)\,dv \tag{2.7}$$

In order to locate the variability within and between individuals, it is necessary to discover something about the dispersion of $n(v)$. Let us suppose first that the proportion of persons giving response 1 is p_1'. If the distribution has zero dispersion, and is concentrated at one point, then that point is $v \approx p_1'$, and everyone is characterized by the same probability p_1, where the observed p_1' differs from p_1 only through sampling fluctuations. If the dispersion is maximum, then there are np_1' persons at $v = 1$, and $n(1 - p_1')$ persons at $v = 0$.

In order to study this dispersion, it is useful to assume a form for the distribution. Because the parameter v can vary vetween zero and 1, it is natural to think of a binomial distribution, governed by parameter p_1. However, the variance of a binomial is fixed by the number of trials N. Since the variance is for us the variable of interest, the number of trials in this binomial distribution cannot be fixed, but must be a variable which reflects the variance shown by the data. If the number of trials is one, then the only possible outcomes are zero and one, so that all persons are located at one of these two extremes. It is convenient at this point to think of N as the number of independently conditioned elements which determine the transition

rates toward responses 1 and 2. Later, other interpretations of this hypothetical number N will be introduced. With such a distribution, eq. (2.5)
becomes

$$n = n \sum_{Nv=0}^{N} \binom{N}{Nv} p_1^{Nv}(1 - p_1)^{N-Nv} \tag{2.8}$$

(where Nv takes on only integral values). Equation (2.6) for the expected
number giving response 1 becomes

$$n_1 = \frac{n}{N} \sum_{Nv=0}^{N} Nv\binom{N}{Nv} p_1^{Nv}(1 - p_1)^{N-Nv} \tag{2.9}$$

The quantity inside the summation is such as to give, when summed as
indicated, the expected value of Nv:

$$\frac{n_1}{n} = \frac{1}{N} \sum_{Nv=0}^{N} Nv\binom{N}{Nv} p_1^{Nv}(1 - p_1)^{N-Nv} \tag{2.10}$$

$$\frac{n_1}{n} = \frac{1}{N} \sum_{Nv=0}^{N} Np_1\binom{N-1}{Nv-1} p_1^{Nv-1}(1 - p_1)^{N-Nv} \tag{2.11}$$

and the summation equals Np_1, so that

$$\frac{n_1}{n} = \frac{Np_1}{N} = p_1 \tag{2.12}$$

Thus the expected proportion giving response 1, n_1/n, is equal to the probability p_1. This of course tells nothing new. But when we turn to the expected
proportion responding positively both times,

$$\frac{n_{11}}{n} = \frac{1}{N^2} \sum_{Nv=0}^{N} (Nv)^2\binom{N}{Nv} p_1^{Nv}(1 - p_1)^{N-Nv} \tag{2.13}$$

The summation gives the expected value of $(Nv)^2$ in much the same way as
above, finally giving

$$p_{11} = \frac{1}{N^2} [Np_1(1 - p_1) + N^2 p_1^2] \tag{2.14}$$

$$p_{11} = \frac{p_1(1 - p_1)}{N} + p_1^2 \tag{2.15}$$

Consequently,

$$p_{11} - p_1^2 = \frac{p_1(1 - p_1)}{N} \tag{2.16}$$

or

$$\frac{1}{N} = \frac{p_{11} - p_1^2}{p_1(1 - p_1)} \tag{2.17}$$

Thus the observed values corresponding to p_1 and p_{11} in response to the same item twice can be used to solve for a hypothetical quantity $1/N$.

In terms of an urn scheme, the character of the model, and the role of N or $1/N$, can be seen easily. Suppose there are n urns, one for each person in the sample. There are altogether nNv white balls, and $nN(1 - v)$ black balls. The balls are distributed with N balls in each urn, but randomly with respect to their color. A question and response corresponds to withdrawing a ball from an urn, looking at the color, and replacing it. A white ball is a positive response, and a black ball a negative one.

Now if there is only one ball in each urn, every draw from that urn will produce the same response. In such a case, there are only two kinds of urns, those with a white ball, and those with a black ball.

If $N = 2$, then there are three kinds of urns: white, black-white, and black. As a consequence, two white responses and two black responses are still quite likely, because it is only from the black-white urns that different responses are possible, and even there only half the time.

If, in contrast, $N \to \infty$, then all urns have the same proportion of white and black balls, and the probability of drawing a white ball on the second draw is the same for all urns, independent of the outcome of the first draw.

Since N is the number of balls in each urn, $1/N$ is the probability that a second draw (the question asked a second time) will produce exactly the same ball as the first (i.e., the second question will evoke the same element which determined the first response). Thus $1/N$ is a measure of the probability that the same element will be evoked on the second response.

Another, more provocative interpretation of N, from the perspective of public opinion, is in terms of the number of independent *stimuli* inherent in an item. If we think of an individual's response to a single unitary stimulus as always being alike, then if an item consists of nothing beyond this stimulus, the population would be totally split into two camps, those always responding positively to the stimulus, and those always responding negatively. If an item consists of many independent stimuli, then $1/N$ is very small, indicating that an individual is very unlikely to respond to the same stimulus in the item both times. Thus he is hardly more likely to respond alike in successive responses than are two different persons.

What this means practically in public opinion is that we can judge the degree to which an item (or, after the developments of the next sections, a set of different items on the same topic) is consistently viewed in the same frame of reference, or consistently interpreted as the same identical stimulus. In times when a given area of interest is not subject to public discussion or debate, an item or a set of items related to it will be seen by a person in a variety of ways, and related to a variety of independent matters. But when attention is concentrated on this area, then a person will see in this item only the one stimulus, the matter on which attention is focussed. If, for example, we had measures of the degree to which attention is focussed on a topic at different times or in different subpopulations, this focus of attention should systematically relate to the value of $1/N$ for questions related to this topic: the greater the focus, the closer $1/N$ should be to one; the lesser the focus, the closer $1/N$ should be to zero.

Rather than solving for $1/N$, as in eq. (2.17), it is possible to look at the matter in a slightly different way. From eqs. (2.6) and (2.7), the right-hand sides are the expected values of v and v^2 respectively, so that

$$p_{11} - p_1^2 = E(v^2) - [E(v)]^2 \qquad (2.18)$$

$$= E[v - E(v)]^2 \qquad (2.19)$$

$$p_{11} - p_1^2 = \sigma_v^2 \qquad (2.20)$$

Thus the variance, or squared deviation of v from its mean value, is $p_{11} - p_1{}^2$, or the standard deviation of v is

$$\sigma_v = \sqrt{p_{11} - p_1{}^2} \qquad (2.21)$$

The standard deviation of individuals from the sample mean of v—i.e., the mean of $m_1/(m_1 + m_2)$—is $\sqrt{p_{11} - p_1{}^2}$. Alternatively, the variance can be interpreted as the average squared distance between the values of v for two persons in the sample.[5] This means that σ can be roughly interpreted as the average distance between people in their v's. This holds, incidentally, independent of the form assumed for the distribution of v, since eq. (2.18) is derived from eqs. (2.6) and (2.7), in which no form of the distribution is assumed.

Consider the following hypothetical example of a repeated item, showing some, but not a perfect, relation between first and second response.

Table 12.1

II

		1	2	
	1	.48	.12	.6
I				
	2	.12	.28	.4
		.6	.4	1.0

$$\frac{1}{N} = \frac{p_{11} - p_1^2}{p_1(1 - p_1)} = \frac{.48 - .36}{.6 \times .4} = \frac{.12}{.24} = .5$$

[5] This is true because the variance can be written as the sum of squared differences between all possible pairs of values of v.

Thus $1/N = .5$, which says that individuals respond as if the response of each was based on only two elements. Using the binomial distribution, we find the proportion of persons of each type:

Group 22: $\binom{2}{0}$ $.6^0 \times .4^2 = .16$ $(v = 0)$

Group 12: $\binom{2}{1}$ $.6^1 \times .4^1 = .48$ $(v = .5)$

Group 11: $\binom{2}{2}$ $.6^2 \times .4^0 = .36$ $(v = 1)$

In group 22 (constituting .16 of the sample), there would never be a positive response; in group 12 (constituting .48 of the sample), there would be a positive response half the time; and in group 11 (constituting .36 of the sample), the response would always be positive. If we look at the standard deviation of v, we see that it is

$$\sigma_v = \sqrt{p_{11} - p_1^2}$$
$$= \sqrt{.48 - .36}$$
$$= .35$$

Thus the square root of the average squared difference (or roughly the average distance) between people in their v's is, in this example, .35.

This example indicates that it is possible to think of this situation as one in which the individual's responses derive from two independently conditioned elements (or two independently conditioned sets of elements), each conditioned with probability .6 to response 1, probability .4 to response 2. This, of course, divides the sample into three homogeneous groups, as indicated above. It is not likely that such is in fact the case; the distribution is one in which the variance among and within individuals is *as if* there were this distribution. The distribution according to the model is as indicated in Figure 12.1(a); however, the actual distribution is probably more nearly one that looks like Figure 12.1(b), with a variance equal to that of Figure 12.1, that is, a standard deviation of .35, as indicated above. There is, however, no simple continuous distribution function ranging between zero and one which is like that of Figure 12.1(b). For this reason, and because the imagery of the binomial is useful, we will continue to act *as if* the distribution were discontinuous, in $N + 1$ classes.

3. RELATION BETWEEN THIS MODEL AND THAT OF PREVIOUS CHAPTERS

It is important to keep clear the relation between the present model and the one which occupied the attention of Chapters 4–11. The data of Table 12.1 would have been analyzed quite differently in Chapter 5, for there the assumption was made that the response directly reflected the state of the respondent. If response 1 was made, then he was in state 1; if response 2, he was in state 2. Consequently, the data of Table 12.1 would have been interpreted to mean transitions between states, and transition rates between these two states would have been calculated via eq. (2.10), of Chapter 5. In the present view, however, there are more possible states of the respondent (i.e., all possible values of v), but each of these states is not characterized by a determinate response. Instead, it is characterized by a probability of giving each of the responses. Only in the extreme, when the probability of one response is zero, is the present model consistent with that one.

Undoubtedly, these are both only partly correct. In most empirical cases, there is undoubtedly change between states, and in most cases, the latent state probably is not determinately related to the response. In some cases, however, it can be assumed that one or the other case dominates. For example, when the same item is repeated within a questionnaire, the lack of complete correlation is probably not due to change. In other cases, the content

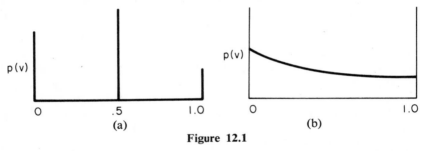

Figure 12.1

of the item suggests that the latent state corresponds almost directly to the response, and variations in response are almost certainly due to change.

In some cases, however, when one neglects the time dimension, the interpretation of the present chapter may be appropriate even though there have been changes of state. If, in one community, there is a high degree of turnover on a question of political preference, while in another there is little turnover, we may collapse the time dimension, and consider the data as if the within-individual variability existed at a point in time. This would provide a valid measure of the within- and between-individual variability in the two communities. As this example indicates, the absolute size of the transition rates between states in the model of Chapters 4–11 is closely related conceptually to the number of independent elements, N, discussed here.

4. SUCCESSIVE RESPONSES TO ONE ITEM WITH A TREND

Few social situations are like the pure case in the preceding section, in which there is no difference in the marginals between the successive responses. Particularly when there is some lapse of time, so that changes may have occurred for some individuals in the probabilities of responses 1 and 2, there will ordinarily be a change in the marginals. For example, the problem which first suggested to me the ideas presented in this chapter was a problem posed by Professor George Katona, concerned with changes over time in expectations about national business conditions. Katona's hypothesis was that there was decreased unreliability of response with increase in unanimity of expectations about national business conditions. His tabulations included the data shown in Table 12.2.

It turned out that I misunderstood the hypothesis, which was in fact concerned not with unreliability of response, but with unidirectionality of change. The models of Chapter 5 were appropriate for it, and in particular, the hypothesis could be tested (and confirmed) by examining the relative sizes of the transition rates in the two directions at each of the two periods.

However, despite this, it is possible to examine these tables from the

Table 12.2

			II (a) JUNE 1955 Better	Worse					II (b) MAR. 1957 Better	Worse	
			1	2					1	2	
I June 1954	Better	1	.468	.075	.543	Dec. 1955	Better	1	.590	.226	.816
	Worse	2	.335	.122	.457		Worse	2	.095	.089	.184
			.803	.197	1.000				.685	.315	1.000
			Toward unanimity						Away from unanimity		

viewpoint of the present model, in which the latent state is only probabilistically connected to the response. But to do so involves additional problems beyond those of the no-change case. If the proportion of positive responses at time I is characterized by $p_{1.}$, and that at time II by $p_{.1}$, then eq. (2.9) governs the response at both times, with $p_{1.}$ substituted for p_1 at time I, and $p_{.1}$ substituted at time II. However, when we turn to the equation governing p_{11}, a difficulty arises. For since some persons now have a different value of v, the distribution $n(v)$ has become a bivariate distribution $n(v,v')$, where v is his value of $m_1/(m_1 + m_2)$ at time I, and v' is his value of $m_1'/(m_1' + m_2')$ at time II. Furthermore, in this bivariate distribution, the value of v' is dependent on the value of v, even though it is not identical as it was in Section 2.

The simplest way of making the problem tractable is to go back to the quantities m_1 and m_2. If there is a total number of elements $m_1 + m_2$, and, at time 1, m_1 are conditioned to response 1 and m_2 are conditioned to response 2, then we postulate the following change between these two times [assuming the change has been toward response 1, as in Table 12.2(a)]:

For all persons, there has been a certain proportion, k, of the elements conditioned to 2 that are now conditioned to 1, so that $m_1' = m_1 + km_2$ and $m_2' = m_2 - km_2$. Consequently,

$$v' = \frac{m_1 + km_2}{m_1 + m_2} \tag{4.1}$$

$$v' = v + k(1 - v) \tag{4.2}$$

Through eq. (4.2), v' is determinately related to v, even though it is not identical. Thus, for the second time period, eq. (2.9) becomes (4.3) below, which sums the probability of giving a positive response at time II $[v + k(1 - v)]$ times the proportion of the population who had this value of v:

$$p_{.1} = \frac{1}{N} \sum_{Nv=0}^{N} N[v + k(1 - v)] \binom{N}{Nv} p_{1.}^{Nv}(1 - p_{1.})^{N-Nv} \qquad (p_{.1} \geqslant p_{1.}) \tag{4.3}$$

$$p_{.1} = \frac{1}{N}[(1 - k)Np_{1.} + Nk]$$

$$p_{.1} = p_{1.} + k(1 - p_{1.}) \tag{4.4}$$

or

$$k = \frac{p_{.1} - p_{1.}}{1 - p_{1.}} \tag{4.5}$$

For p_{11}, the probability of responding positively both times is $v[v + k(1 - v)]$, or $v^2 + k(v - v^2)$. Consequently the equation relating p_{11} to v is

$$p_{11} = \frac{1}{N^2} \sum_{Nv=0}^{N} N^2 v[v + k(1 - v)] \binom{N}{Nv} p_{1.}^{Nv}(1 - p_{1.})^{N-Nv} \tag{4.6}$$

This reduces to

$$p_{11} = \frac{(1 - k)[Np_{1.}(1 - p_{1.}) + N^2 p_{1.}^2] + kN^2 p_{1.}}{N^2} \tag{4.7}$$

Using eqs. (4.4) and (4.5) in eq. (4.7) and simplifying gives

$$p_{11} - p_{1.}p_{.1} = \frac{(1 - p_{.1})p_{1.}}{N} \tag{4.8}$$

or

$$\frac{1}{N} = \frac{p_{11} - p_{1.}p_{.1}}{(1 - p_{.1})p_{1.}} \qquad (p_{.1} \geqslant p_{1.}) \tag{4.9}$$

These equations hold for the case in which the change in over-all responses has been toward response 1 ($v' \geqslant v$, or $p_{.1} \geqslant p_{1.}$). When the opposite is true, as in Table 12.2b, the positions of $p_{1.}$ and $p_{.1}$ in eq. (4.9) must be reversed.

To look at the matter from the point of view of the variance of v, the right-hand sides of eqs. (2.10), (4.3), and (4.6) are the expected values of v, v', and vv', respectively, which allows us to write, as in the case of no change [see eq. (2.19)]:

$$p_{11} - p_{1.}p_{.1} = E(vv') - E(v)E(v') \tag{4.10}$$

$$p_{11} - p_{1.}p_{.1} = \sigma_{vv'}^2 \tag{4.11}$$

or

$$\sigma_{vv'} = \sqrt{p_{11} - p_{1.}p_{.1}} \tag{4.12}$$

Thus the covariance of v and v' for this item at two times is given by eq. (4.11) and the square root of the covariance is given by eq. (4.12). The covariance can be interpreted as the average over all pairs of individuals i and j of the product $(v_i - v_j)(v_i' - v_j')$. In the case of unchanged marginals, this reduces as indicated earlier to the average of the squared differences in v between persons.

Thus in the case of a shift in the marginals, the use of the assumption of eq. (4.2) allows again a calculation of the hypothetical quantity N, the number of independently conditioned elements that govern the relation between successive responses, or of the covariance $\sigma_{vv'}^2$.

For Table 12.2a, the calculation is

$$\frac{1}{N} = \frac{.468 - .543 \times .803}{.197 \times .543} = .30$$

Similarly for Table 12.2b, except that the subscripts must be reversed, since $p_{1.} > p_{.1}$.

$$\frac{1}{N} = \frac{.590 - .816 \times .685}{.184 \times .685} = .26$$

Thus during the periods covered by Table 12.2a and Table 12.2b, there was about the same homogeneity among people, or variability within people (each in effect with a probability of .30 or .26 of the same stimulus element being elicited the second time as the first).

The calculation of the square root of the average squared difference between persons in the two periods is made as follows:

For Table 12.2a:

$$\sigma_{vv'} = \sqrt{.468 - .543 \times .803} = .18$$

For Table 12.2b:

$$\sigma_{vv'} = \sqrt{.590 - .816 \times .685} = .18$$

Thus this measure of distance between people in their response tendencies is about the same for the two periods covered by these tables, at .18.

Another example can show as well the use of this approach to study the social and psychological organization of attitudes. In a recent research project which studied the student bodies of high schools, I found that in one school (No. 1, Table 12.3), athletes and scholars seemed to receive roughly equal status, but independently, while in other schools (Nos. 2 and 3), they were interlocked, so that the boy who was *both* athlete and scholar had extremely high status, and in another (No. 4), only the athlete had status. One hypothesis which I entertained to explain this was that in the first school, there were two distinct systems of status, with some boys striving for rewards (and giving rewards) in one, while in the other schools (Nos. 2 and 3), these two systems were merged, so that the *same* boys were striving to be both athlete and scholar, and giving status to others for achievements in both.

Table 12.3

		II SCHOOL 1				II SCHOOL 2		
		Student	*Athlete*			*Student*	*Athlete*	
I	*Student*	30	15	45	*Student*	46	11	57
	Athlete	12	43	55	*Athlete*	10	92	102
		42	58	100		56	103	159

		SCHOOL 3				SCHOOL 4		
		Student	*Athlete*			*Student*	*Athlete*	
I	*Student*	40	12	52	*Student*	54	22	76
	Athlete	14	48	62	*Athlete*	13	84	97
		54	60	114		67	106	173

The ideas of this section seem admirably suited to such a problem, for if all boys are alike, $1/N$ will near zero; if they are separated into two camps, $1/N$ will near 1.0. Boys were asked, at two times during the school year:

How would you most like to be remembered at school?

> Brilliant student
> Athletic star
> Most popular

The turnover tables in the four schools (of roughly comparable size) are shown in Table 12.3. Data for the school with the separate rewards is on the extreme left. Only the athlete-student responses are given.

The calculation of $1/N$ and $\sigma_{vv'}$ for each school according to eqs. (4.9) and (4.12) gives

$$\frac{1}{N_1} = .48 \qquad \sigma_1 = .33$$

$$\frac{1}{N_2} = .72 \qquad \sigma_2 = .40$$

$$\frac{1}{N_3} = .56 \qquad \sigma_3 = .37$$

$$\frac{1}{N_4} = .65 \qquad \sigma_4 = .38$$

Clearly the hypothesis is not confirmed. There is even *less* tight organization of attitudes (i.e., each boy's second response is less rigidly related to his first one) in school 1 than in the other schools, and less distance σ between persons. In all the schools, the values of $1/N$ and σ are high; there seems to be a rather high tendency to respond alike at both times, and consequently a high between-individual dispersion in response.

These examples show the way in which this model, in conjunction with successive responses to the same items, can provide useful measures of the between-individual variability of attitudes, allowing comparisons of different social groups, or as in the example of business expectations, the same society during two different periods of time.

5. RESPONSES TO DIFFERENT ITEMS AT ONE TIME

The next step in this examination is an obvious one, with far more practical implications than those discussed in the preceding sections. It is the step to *different* stimuli, or different attitude questions. After examining the variability within individuals in their responses to the *same* stimulus at different times, it is most natural to look at the variability in their responses to *different* questions which may evoke some of the same, and some different response elements.

For example, attitude scales are composed of questions which are intended to evoke the same attitude, so that persons can be located along a scale of that attitude. Suppose, however, we ask, for a given object toward which people's attitudes may be "scaled," just how internally organized they are toward this attitudinal object. If they are highly internally organized, then most individuals will be located at extreme points in the distribution of v, while if they are not highly internally organized, different persons will be alike in their values of v, and there will be little relation between responses to any two items.

If we look at two items whose interrelation shows a given $1/N$, this can be interpreted in terms of the urn scheme suggested earlier: each urn has N balls, placed there independently, and the probability is $1/N$ that the second draw will bring the same ball as the first. Or if we think of each question as consisting of a set of stimuli that evoke response elements, the probability is $1/N$ that the second stimulus will evoke those elements evoked by the first. This does not mean, of course, that the second stimulus will evoke the same response as the first only $1/N$ of the time; the remaining $1 - 1/N$ of the time, it evokes independent elements, that have probability v [or $v + k(1 - v)$] of leading to response 1.

Or by solving for the covariance of v and $v + k(1 - v)$, we find a measure of difference between people in their tendencies of response with respect to the items in question. If this difference is large, then people are highly internally organized (and highly socially polarized) with respect to the object or the content area covered by these items. If the difference is small, then there is little variability among persons.

The interpretation of items used with this model is different from that of the models of earlier chapters, where the items were assumed to have *effects* on one another. The interpretation here is that the items are "indicators" of underlying states, and the problem is to see just how much they are indicators of the *same* states—or stimuli that elicit common elements. To be sure, for many attributes, both this model and the model of interdependent attributes affecting one another are appropriate to some degree.[6] When used merely to provide measures (i.e., the transition rates of earlier chapters, or $1/N$ and σ here), they provide complementary information about the items. In the example below, this complementarity is evident, for the items are those used in Chapter 5 for examining the effects of each on the other.

Example

In Tables 5.10 and 5.12 are given responses to the questions (asked of high school students in the fall and the spring of a school year) of being in the leading crowd and of whether being in the crowd makes one go against his principles. It is possible with the present model to examine just how much psychological organization and how much social polarization there was around the leading crowd topic, in the fall and in the spring. For boys, the cross-tabulations between the two items in the fall and spring were as follows:

Table 12.4

		(a) FALL					(b) SPRING		
		GO AGAINST PRINCIPLES?					GO AGAINST PRINCIPLES?		
		No	*Yes*				*No*	*Yes*	
In leading crowd?	*Yes*	757	496	1253	In leading crowd?	*Yes*	898	494	1392
	No	1071	1074	2145		*No*	1035	971	2006
		1828	1570	3398			1933	1465	3398

[6] In fact, a combination of the two models, in which elements associated with a positive response to one item "convert" elements associated with a negative response to another, bringing two attitudes into greater consistency, may be appropriate for many attributes. See the next chapter for initial development of such a model.

Using eq. (4.9) (and multiplying numerator and denominator by n^2 to get rid of proportions) to solve for $1/N$ gives

$$\frac{1}{N} = \frac{3398 \times 757 - 1828 \times 1253}{1570 \times 1253}$$

$$= .14 \quad \text{(fall)}$$

$$\sigma = \frac{\sqrt{(3398 \times 757 - 1828 \times 1253)}}{3398^2}$$

$$= .16 \quad \text{(fall)}$$

$$\frac{1}{N} = \frac{3398 \times 898 - 1933 \times 1392}{1465 \times 1392}$$

$$= .18 \quad \text{(spring)}$$

$$\sigma = \frac{\sqrt{(3398 \times 858 - 1933 \times 1392)}}{3398^2}$$

$$= .18 \quad \text{(spring)}$$

The values of $1/N$ and σ are rather low both in the fall and in the spring. But they show an increase from fall to spring, indicating that the attitudes have become a little more tightly organized, and that there has come to be a little more social polarization over the school year.[7]

A comparison with the girls on the same items will show something about the relative degree of organization of attitudes concerning the leading crowd in each sex group. The relevant tables, taken from the marginals of Table 5.12, are given in Table 12.5 and calculations are carried out below:

$$\frac{1}{N} = \frac{3260 \times 716 - 1014 \times 1974}{1286 \times 1014}$$

$$= .25 \quad \text{(fall)}$$

$$\sigma = \sqrt{(3260 \times 716 - 1014 \times 1974)/3260^2}$$

$$= .18 \quad \text{(fall)}$$

[7] It is of incidental interest to note that with measures of two attitudes x and y at two points in time, it is possible to get a measure for v corresponding directly to the correlation coefficient ρ for explicitly measured continuous variables, by neglecting the effects of time. $\rho = \sigma_{xy}^2/\sigma_x \sigma_y$ where σ_x is the standard deviation of v for attribute x, σ_y is analogous for attribute y, and σ_{xy}^2 is the covariance of v and v' for attributes x and y, one taken at time 1 and the other at time 2 (to correspond to the case for σ_x and σ_y). Since there are two such σ_{xy}^2 values, we can use (in place of σ_{xy}^2, $\sigma_{x_1 y_2}$, $\sigma_{x_2 y_1}$. The equation for ρ becomes

$$\hat{\rho}_{vv'} = \frac{.16 \times 18}{.36 \times 27} = .30,$$

where the subscripts 1 and 2 indicate the times at which x and y are measured. With the data from Table 5.12, Chapter 5, this is $\hat{\rho}_{vv'} = \sigma_{x_1 y_2} \sigma_{x_2 y_1}/\sigma_{x_1 x_2} \sigma_{y_1 y_2}$.

$$\frac{1}{N} = \frac{3260 \times 799 - 2007 \times 1117}{1253 \times 1117}$$

$$= .26 \quad \text{(spring)}$$

$$\sigma = \sqrt{(3260 \times 799 - 2007 \times 1117)/3260^2}$$

$$= .18 \quad \text{(spring)}$$

Table 12.5

		(a) FALL GO AGAINST PRINCIPLES?					(b) SPRING GO AGAINST PRINCIPLES?		
		No	*Yes*				*No*	*Yes*	
In leading crowd?	*Yes*	716	298	1014	In leading crowd?	*Yes*	799	318	1117
	No	1258	988	2246		*No*	1208	935	2143
		1974	1286	3260			2007	1253	3260

The comparison of $1/N$ for boys and girls shows that in both the fall and the spring, girls' attitudes were more highly organized around this topic. The probability was about .25 in both fall and spring that the same element would be evoked, while for boys it was .14 in the fall and .18 in the spring. However, there was not an increase in $1/N$ for girls as for boys; the psychological organization stayed about the same over the school year for girls.

The comparison between σ for boys and girls is a little more puzzling, for the values for boys and girls are nearly the same, in contrast to the values of $1/N$. This requires a somewhat closer examination of the difference in meaning between $1/N$ and σ.

6. $1/N$ AS PSYCHOLOGICAL UNIDIMENSIONALITY, AND σ AS SOCIAL POLARIZATION

In examining responses to two items such as those in the example above, it is clear that the variation in marginals is an important aspect of the social distribution of attitudes. For example, 1974 girls said that the leading crowd did not impair one's principles, while only 1014 said they were in the leading crowd. For boys, a smaller proportion said the crowd did not impair one's principles, but a larger proportion said they were in the crowd. Or consider two populations in which two attitude questions were asked, with the results shown in Table 12.6. In both these populations, the value of $1/N$ would be 1.0, indicating that the second item elicited the same element as did the first with probability 1.0. But in population 2, many elements that were associated with a positive response on item 1 were associated with a negative one on item 2. In contrast, in population 1, every element that was associated with a positive response to item 1 was associated with a positive response to item 2, and similarly for those associated with a negative response. Clearly, population 1 is more polarized on the attitude dimension reflected in these two items, for no one is mixed in his response to the two items.

Table 12.6

		(a) Population 1 Attitude 2					(b) Population 2 Attitude 2		
		+	−				+	−	
	+	500	0	500		+	250	500	750
Attitude 1					Attitude 1				
	−	0	500	500		−	0	250	250
		500	500	1000			250	750	1000

As this example indicates, $1/N$ is more nearly a measure of the degree of psychological organization of the attitudes than of the social polarization. Its meaning, in fact, is in terms of psychological organization (the probability that both items will elicit the same response element). However, the covariance, $\sigma_{vv'}^2$, is a measure of social polarization. When the marginals are identical for the two items, it gives the average squared difference in v between all pairs of individuals. When the marginals differ, it gives the average product of the difference between two individuals in their value of v and the difference in their value of v', that is, av. $(v_i - v_j)(v'_i - v'_j)$. This average can be reduced either by a low average difference between v_i and v_j for pairs of individuals (due to a low value of $1/N$, that is, a low probability that the items elicit the same element, or due to most people giving the same response) or by a high discrepancy between v_i and v'_i, which means that high values of $v_i - v_j$ will seldom coincide with high values of $v'_i - v'_j$. In either case, the population is not polarized around this attitude, in the one case because most people have a mixture of potential responses to each item, and in the other because many people give mixed responses to the two items.[8]

In the above hypothetical example, the values of $\sigma_{vv'}$ reflect the difference in polarization between the two populations due to the second cause.

Population 1: $\sigma_{vv'} = \sqrt{.5 - .25} = .5$

Population 2: $\sigma_{vv'} = \sqrt{.25 - .1875} = .25$

[8] One other possibility, which can lead to a high value of $1/N$ but a low value of σ, is that nearly all persons give the same response to items 1 and nearly all give the same response to item 2. In this case social polarization is low because everyone is on the same side.

Thus despite the fact that individuals' attitudes are equally highly internally organized on these items in both populations, population 1 is much more polarized on the attitude expressed by these items.

The two measures $1/N$ and $\sigma_{vv'}$ offer, respectively, a psychological and a social measure of organization of attitudes. The measure $1/N$ constitutes a "frame of reference" measure, for it indicates the degree to which attention is focussed on a common dimension in responding to the items. The measure $\sigma_{vv'}$ constitutes a social polarization measure, for it indicates approximately the average distance between persons along this attitude dimension.[9] In order that there be high social polarization, it is necessary but not sufficient that there be high internal organization of attitudes, that is, that attention be focussed upon the attitude dimension in question. In the measures, this is reflected by the fact that in order for $\sigma_{vv'}$ to be high, it is necessary both that $1/N$ be high and that the marginals on all items not differ greatly nor be highly skewed toward one response.

With this difference in meaning made explicit, the puzzling differences in $1/N$ and σ for boys and girls in the preceding example become explicable. For the girls, the values of $1/N$ are higher, showing a higher psychological organization of attitudes on this dimension—i.e., what we ordinarily mean when we talk about a higher "correlation" of attitudes.[10] Yet they are no more socially polarized around this leading crowd dimension than are the boys because a higher proportion of girls who are *not* in the leading crowd are tolerant of its principles. Looking again at Tables 12.4a and 12.5a, it is evident on inspection that the girls' table, 12.5a, more nearly fulfills the criterion of a unidimensional scale (i.e., only 298 cases in the smallest cell, compared to 496 for the boys, with marginals not greatly different). This is reflected in the higher value of $1/N$ for girls. But it is also true that no higher a proportion of girls is at the extremes $(716 + 988)/3260 = 52\%$, than is the case for the boys $(757 + 1074)/3398 = 54\%$. This is reflected in the nearly equal values of σ for the two sex groups.

This difference between social and psychological organization is quite meaningful in the present context. There is much evidence to show that for girls in high school, the leading crowd is more salient, more nearly a focus of attention, than it is for boys. At the same time, more girls who are not in the leading crowd are motivated to get into it, and thus have positive attitudes toward it. As a consequence, although their attitudes are highly organized around this topic, they are no more split into a group which feels a part of the leading crowd and a group which is against it than are the boys. It is evident that the same variation could exist among societies: a society may be very conscious of status yet not polarized into camps with opposing attitudes toward the

---

[9] More precisely, it is the average of the square root of the product of the distance between a pair of persons on item 1 and the distance on item 2.

[10] This measure $1/N$ constitutes a useful measure of correlation between attributes. It is identical to a measure of correlation sometimes used in data analysis: ϕ/ϕ_{max}.

higher status groups. American society, for example, has often been characterized in this way.

A further example, concerning the organization of attitudes toward athletics among the same boys examined above, will show further how the differences between $1/N$ and σ manifest themselves.

Example

Boys in several high schools were asked the question about how they would like to be remembered, as an athletic star or as a brilliant student (see example, Section 4 of this chapter). They were also asked whether or not they were out for football that fall. The responses in four small schools (350–550, both sexes) and two large ones (1800 both sexes) are shown in Table 12.7.[11]

Table 12.7

OUT FOR FOOTBALL VS. WANTING TO BE REMEMBERED AS AN ATHLETE OR STUDENT

	SCHOOL 1			SCHOOL 2			SCHOOL 3			SCHOOL 4		
	Out	*Not*		*Out*	*Not*		*Out*	*Not*		*Out*	*Not*	
Athlete	39	38	77	52	77	129	43	33	76	68	50	118
Student	16	53	69	9	65	74	27	43	70	28	61	89
	55	91	146	61	142	203	70	76	146	96	111	207

	SCHOOL 8			SCHOOL 9		
	Out	*Not*		*Out*	*Not*	
Athlete	94	262	365	105	252	357
Student	26	257	283	14	176	190
	120	519	639	119	428	547

The values of $1/N$, which show the psychological unidimensionality of these items, are as follows:

	Small schools				Large schools	
	1	2	3	4	8	9
Value of $1/N$	.39	.60	.19	.33	.51	.66

[11] Some boys' responses are not tabulated because they answered in the third category of the question about how they want to be remembered. Thus the totals are smaller than half the indicated school sizes.

With the one exception of school 2, the boys in the small schools show considerably lower psychological consistency with respect to athletics than do the boys in the large schools. In the large schools and in school 2, the items are close to forming a perfect scale: almost no one who is out for football wants to be remembered as a brilliant student. In the three other small schools, there is much lower psychological consistency.

Turning to the question of social polarization, the values of σ in these schools are given below:

	Small schools				Large schools	
	1	2	3	4	8	9
Value of σ	.26	.26	.21	.25	.21	.22

In this case, the tables are turned completely: except for school 3 (which shows both lowest psychological consistency and lowest social polarization), the small schools show *more* polarization than do the large ones, despite their lower psychological consistency. The reason has again to do with the proportions giving the pro-athletic response. In both sets of schools, more students say "athletic star" than "brilliant student" in response to the attitude question, in roughly the same proportion in large and small schools. But in the large schools, much smaller proportions of boys are out for football. This leaves many boys in the anomalous position of wanting to be remembered as an athletic star, but not being out for football. Thus the schools are less polarized along these lines than the smaller schools, where the proportion out for football more nearly corresponds to the proportion wanting to be remembered as an athletic star.

7. ADDITIONAL USES AND FURTHER DEVELOPMENTS

7.1 Multiple items or stimuli

A next step beyond simultaneous consideration of two questions that may evoke related responses is consideration of a number of items together. Ordinarily, this is done for several purposes: to construct a scale, to locate various factors via factor anlysis, or latent classes via latent structure analysis, etc. Whatever the purpose, it is often of practical value merely to use a number of questions or stimuli focussed around one topic, in order to treat the responses as indicators of an individual's orientation to that topic.

A direct extension of the ideas in the above section will allow calculation of values of $1/N_{ij}$ or σ_{ij} for all pairs of items. These values can then be averaged for the set of items as a whole, or for some subset of them, to provide for a measure of the degree to which attitudes are organized toward the topic at hand, or a factor analysis may be carried out on the matrix of $1/N_{ij}$ or σ_{ij} values. For example, if the value of $1/N$ is 1.0 (its maximum) for all pairs of items, then the items show a perfect relationship (subject to the translation of v by the parameter k), and attitudes are totally organized relative to the content they cover. This, incidentally, is the condition of a perfect cumulative scale. As the average value of $1/N$ for a set of items decreases from one to zero, attitudes are less organized toward the content covered by the items.

7.2 Subpopulations

It is sometimes valuable to examine the degree of organization of attitudes among subsets of a population. One general hypothesis about social movements, for example, suggests that in the early stages, the attitudes of the adherents are almost totally organized around this activity, while the attitudes of the opponents are not organized in this direction, since they devote little attention to it. Then, as the movement gains a broader base, the psychological organization of adherents lessens. Concurrently, that of the opponents increase, as they are forced to devote attention to it.

It is for testing such hypotheses as this that the measures provided by this model can be valuable. An example below shows such a use.

Example

Following the same pair of items treated in the last example in Section 6, above, we can ask, What is the *change* over the years of high school, in the social and psychological organization of the student body around the topic of athletics? Although the same students were not followed over a four-year period, our answer to this question can be approximated (for the two largest schools) by examining each grade in school separately. Table 12.8 shows the cross tabulations in each grade.

The values of $1/N$ and σ computed from these tables are given below:

	FRESHMEN	SOPHOMORES	JUNIORS	SENIORS
		SCHOOL 9		
$1/N$	.77	.75	.71	.30
σ	.28	.22	.20	.16
		SCHOOL 8		
$1/N$		.47	.54	.55
σ		.19	.22	.23

These values show that the psychological and social organization around this topic of athletics *decreases* from freshman to senior in school 9, while it *increases* over the three years of school 8. It appears that different processes are operating in the two schools, for the changes are in just the opposite direction. Whatever the differences are due to (and there is some evidence that they are due to the very different social composition of the two communities, which present the schools with very different populations of freshmen), this example shows how these measures may be used to examine subgroups in a population, and even to infer changes in the organization of attitudes.

Table 12.8

OUT FOR FOOTBALL VS. WANTING TO BE REMEMBERED AS AN ATHLETE OR STUDENT: EACH GRADE SEPARATELY

	FRESHMEN Out	Not		SOPHOMORES Out	Not		JUNIORS Out	Not		SENIORS Out	Not	
					SCHOOL 9							
Athlete	28	48	76	36	87	123	21	65	86	20	52	72
Student	3	54	57	3	49	52	2	35	37	6	38	44
	31	102		39	136	175	23	100	123	26	90	116
					SCHOOL 8							
Athlete				40	130	170	32	79	111	22	53	75
Student				12	117	129	8	78	86	6	62	68
				52	247	299	40	157	197	28	115	143

7.3 The use of free-response or projective stimuli

The use of vague or ambiguous stimuli allows for a wide range of possible responses. Suppose the responses to several items are coded according to different objects of attention, or frames of reference. Then it is possible to obtain a measure of the degree to which these stimuli focus attention on these particular objects. Such measures, of course, are simply provided by the average p_i over all items for object i. But beyond this, it is possible to learn the degree to which this focussing of attention is evenly distributed through the population, or highly concentrated. If, for a given object of attention, the average $1/N_{ij}$ over pairs of items (i,j) is near 1.0, the focussing is highly concentrated in a subsegment of the population; if it is near zero, this focussing is evenly distributed throughout the population. The amount of such concentration can tell much about the similarities and differences in the way attention is distributed in different social systems. If, as many psychological results would suggest, the action-potential of an individual in a given direction depends upon such concentration, then such measures give an indication of the action-potential of a given (unorganized) population, in the direction of mass action on a given topic.

7.4 Interdependence of attitudes among related persons

A simple shift will allow examining the degree of organization of an attitude among socially connected persons. Instead of asking the same person two different items, and looking at their relation, we ask one question of two persons who are socially related in some way, and examine the interrelation of responses. Measures of such a relationship are developed elsewhere (see Chapter 14 for a discussion of the problem), but it is useful to note that the present measures can examine the organization of attitudes across a social relationship, just as they can the psychological organization of attitudes. In such a case, a value of $1/N$ close to its maximum of one means that the pairs of persons under study (e.g., sociometric choices, husband-wife) are highly organized relative to the matter covered by the item, and different pairs are widely different from each other. If, on the other hand, the value of $1/N$ is near zero, the attitude is no more highly consistent within this pair than in the population as a whole.

7.5 Further developments

Only the beginnings have been made here to a comprehensive model based on the ideas discussed in the introductory section. The essential new element brought in by this chapter is the notion of a nondirect correspondence between the individual's state and his response. Whereas, in previous chapters, his response was assumed to reflect directly his state, here it is assumed to derive probabilistically from a much more variable state of the individual, characterized by m_i "elements" associated with each response i.

The most promising direction of work is coordination of the present model with the model of preceding chapters by positing the basic stochastic process at the level of the elements, rather than at the level of the individuals. Such a coordination would not be useful for the kind of cross-sectional or two-wave panel data often collected, but might prove extremely useful—as well as testable—with multiwave panels. The beginning of such coordination is carried out in the next chapter.

Another potential development lies in the direction of multiple-category items. It seems likely that the basic ideas of this chapter could be extended to cover such items, although no attempts have been made in that direction.

Finally, in dealing with more than two items or more than one repetition of the same item, it seems useful to examine the relation of p_{111} and higher-order terms to the underlying parameters of the model.[12]

---

[12] In relation to this, it is useful to examine recent work by Lazarsfeld (1961) treating algebraic relations for systems of dichotomous attributes.

CHAPTER 13

CHANGE AND RESPONSE UNCERTAINTY

1. INTRODUCTION TO THE PROBLEM

The model of the preceding chapter conceived of a behavioral response as an indirect manifestation of the individual's underlying state. In contrast to the previous chapters, in which his state was taken to be identical to the response, the state was taken instead to be defined by the number of underlying "elements," m_i, leading to each response i. These numbers of elements gave rise to a probability of response i, through the relation $v_i = m_i/\Sigma m_i$ [in the two-response case considered there, the probability of positive response, $v = m_1/(m_1 + m_2)$].

This model is appealing, for it opens up the possibility of a whole set of types of persons, ranging all the way from those with a probability of zero of making response i to those with a probability of 1.0. In contrast, the earlier models allowed for only two types at any point in time, those with probability zero and those with probability 1.0, and furthermore assumed them to be homogeneous in their transition rates from each state i to each other state j.

The advantage of the models of earlier chapters, of course, lies in their ability to reflect change, and effects of certain variables and attributes in changing an individual's state on others. Furthermore, by multivariate analysis, it becomes possible to subclassify persons so that the assumption of homogeneity of transition rates for all those in a classification type is quite good.

But certain kinds of data demand an analysis that takes into account both the indirect relationship between underlying state and response and change between underlying states. In particular, whenever there are panel data of three or more waves on the same persons, it should be possible to separate out these two components. Furthermore, it becomes important to do so, for the substantive implications of the two models are quite different. For example, in consumer purchases of consumable household items like groceries (where several purchase-diary panels exist), the calculation of transition rates between brands from sequential pairs of purchases would lead to the conclusion that many people are changing their brands, while in fact they are merely manifesting fairly stable probabilities of purchasing each of several brands. This has been shown in several studies of consumer diary panels. See Alfred Kuehn (1958) and Ronald Frank (1962). Yet application of the previous chapter's model of underlying elements would not allow the identification of actual change when it does occur.

A hypothetical example will illustrate the way a three-wave panel exposes these two components. Suppose a large sample of persons gave a response to a dichotomous item with a proportion of .6 giving response A and .4 giving response B. Then, the item was repeated immediately, and a turnover table like that of Table 13.1 resulted.

Table 13.1

		Time I		
		A	B	
Time I	A	.48	.12	.6
	B	.12	.28	.4
		.6	.4	1.0

Viewing these data from the perspective of the preceding chapter, we can solve for the number of independent elements that would have produced such results, and the number of elements turns out to be 2.0. (See the preceding chapter, Section 2, for the same example.) A further implication of this result, however, is that if the same item is repeated at any later time, the turnover table will remain the same. The model is completely static, and has no mechanism of change. Suppose, however, that the item is repeated a month later, again two months later, and still again ten months later, giving cross-tabulations between time I and II, I and III, and I and IV as shown in Table 13.2.

Parts (a), (b), and (c) of this table show that something further is going on. As the time period between responses increases, the correlation between the responses declines. Some actual change seems to be occurring, to reduce this correlation as time passes. Yet a model that calculated transition rates from the I-II turnover table would grossly overstate the changes when used to predict the I-III table. Since .126 out of the original .6 that were in state A at time I were no longer there a month later, the calculations would lead us

Table 13.2

	(a) TIME II (I + ONE MONTH)				(b) TIME III (I + TWO MONTHS)		
	A	B			A	B	
Time I A	.474	.126	.6	Time I A	.468	.132	.6
B	.126	.274	.4	B	.132	.268	.4
	.6	.4	1.0		.6	.4	1.0

	(c) TIME IV (I + TEN MONTHS)		
	A	B	
Time I A	.432	.168	.6
B	.168	.232	.4
	.6	.4	1.0

to expect that two months later, .186 out of the original .6 would no longer be there [using eq. (9.1) of Chapter 5], while in fact the proportion is .132, as Table 13.2b indicates. Obviously, what is required is a model that reflects both sources of the variability in response.

Suppose we turn back to the models of earlier chapters, with transitions between states, introducing only one modification: the states of the model are not identical to the response, but rather are related to it as in the last chapter. In this case, where we have already found that there are two independent elements, the model would be a two-state one at the level of the elements, producing a three-state model at the level of the individual. It is diagrammed in Figure 13.1.

As outlined in the last chapter, when an individual is in state 0, his probability of giving response A is 0; when he is in state 1, it is .5; and when he is in state 2, it is 1.0. Although the actual states of individuals may vary in more minute degrees, the data from times I and I′ show that individuals respond *as if* there were only two independent elements (each with a probability of .6 of being associated with response A).

This model now combines both sources of the changes in response, for there are actual changes due to transition rates α and β, but besides, there is the indirect relation between the state the individual is in and his responses.

The hypothetical data in Table 13.2 were constructed by assuming that the system of Fig. 13.1 was in operation, and that the process is in aggregate

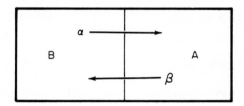

Figure 13.1(a). Two-State Model for Transitions of Elements between States of Being Associated with Responses A and B

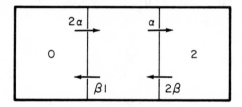

Figure 13.1(b). Three-State Model for Transitions of Individuals between States of Having 0, 1, or 2 Elements Associated with Response A

equilibrium, which first means that the following proportions of individuals are in states 0, 1, and 2:

$$
\begin{aligned}
\text{State 0:} \qquad & .4 \times .4 = .16 \\
\text{State 1:} \qquad & 2(.6 \times .4) = .48 \\
\text{State 2:} \qquad & .6 \times .6 = .36
\end{aligned}
$$

Then transition rates $\alpha = .03$/month and $\beta = .02$/month were assumed. These are transition rates of the elements, which means that the transition rates at the individual level are

$$
\begin{aligned}
\text{State 0 to 1} &= .06 \text{ per month} \\
\text{State 1 to 0} &= .02 \text{ per month} \\
\text{State 1 to 2} &= .03 \text{ per month} \\
\text{State 2 to 1} &= .04 \text{ per month}
\end{aligned}
$$

Had we been able to assess directly the individual's states at interviews I, II, III, and IV, we would have found the results shown in Table 13.3, generated by the transition rates above. Conversely, had such data been available, they would have allowed solving for the transition rates. However, such data do not exist, for the probabilistic connection between states and response means that the data such as those in Table 13.2 show only a hazy reflection of the processes of change.

Thus the data in Tables 13.1 and 13.2 result from the combined model shown in Figure 13.1, with three parameters: N (the number of independent

Table 13.3

		(a) II					(b) III			
		0	1	2			0	1	2	
	0	.151	.009	.000	.16	0	.142	.017	.001	.16
I	1	.009	.457	.014	.48	1	.017	.436	.027	.48
	2	.000	.014	.346	.36	2	.001	.027	.332	.36
		.16	.48	.36	1.0		.16	.48	.36	1.0

		(c) IV			
		0	1	2	
	0	.093	.058	.009	.16
I	1	.058	.326	.096	.48
	2	.009	.096	.255	.36
		.16	.48	.36	1.0

elements); and α and β (the transition rates of elements from B to A and A to B, respectively). The problem, however, is not so easily solved. In this case, the data were constructed, given the parameters, whereas ordinarily the data are given, and the problem is to find the parameters. In addition, only the fact that the value of N was 2 made it possible to construct the simple three-state model shown in Figure 13.1. If N had been 1.5 or 3.6 or some other nonintegral value, the approach above could not have been used. It is necessary, then, to pass on to a somewhat more general way of conceiving the problem.

2. THE CONTAGIOUS BINOMIAL AND ITS APPROPRIATENESS HERE

One way of looking at the above problem is to suppose that the actual number of elements which comprise a response is quite large, though the number of *independent* elements may be small. This was the conception of the last chapter, where the total number of elements $m_1 + m_2$ was not conceived to be related in any way to the number of *independent* elements. If the number of total elements is large, but the number of independent elements is small, this suggests the same model developed earlier in connection with voting in groups (see p. 343). There the system whose states were described by the model was a group, with individuals as elements whose transitions moved it from one state to another. Here, the system is the individual, and the elements whose transitions shift him from one underlying state to another are hypothetical internal elements, associated with one or another response. There the number of individuals was known, but there was a transition rate γ representing the influence applied to each individual by each other, in the direction of his own vote. Here, the transition rate γ would represent the effective "influence" of each element on each other one, or the effective "connectedness" of the elements. Whether there was in fact such a connectedness, or the elements are affected by the same stimulus, need not concern us here, for this model can be interpreted in either fashion.

In the model for groups in Chapter 11, the effect of γ was to increase the variance of i (where i is the number of persons in a group giving response A) beyond what it would have been had the individuals been acting independently. This increased variance was used to calculate the effective amount of influence c, where $c = \gamma/(\alpha + \beta)$, and α, β are the independent transition rates toward A and B, respectively, and $a = \alpha/(\alpha + \beta)$, by eq. (6.8) of Chapter 11. Using this same equation, but substituting $v = i/N$, we obtain:[1]

$$c = \frac{\sigma_v^2 - a(1 - a)/N}{a(1 - a) - \sigma_v^2} \tag{2.1}$$

(where N is the total number of—possibly interdependent—elements). Alternatively, σ_v^2 could have been used to calculate the number of effectively independent individuals, N^*, in the group by means of

$$\sigma_v^2 = \frac{a(1 - a)}{N^*} \tag{2.2}$$

It turns out that the variance of v, σ_v^2, calculated in the last chapter from a turnover table, may be interpreted equally well as the variance of v (or i/N) in this model from Chapter 11. For just as i/N in that chapter is the

---

[1] The variance of v, used here, is $1/N^2$ times the variance of i, used in eq. (6.8) of Chapter 11.

proportion of people in the group giving response A, v in the model of Chapter 12 is the proportion of elements within the individual conditioned to response A.

From Table 13.1, for example, $\sigma_v^2 = p_{11} - p_1^2 = .48 - .6^2 = .12$. As shown in the last chapter, and as can be verified with eq. (2.2), this is equivalent to two independent elements. When this value of σ^2 is substituted in eq. (2.1) above, and N is set equal to 2, then c should be zero, since the number of actual elements, N, equals the number of independent elements N^*:

$$c = \frac{.12 - .6 \times .4/2}{.6 \times .4 - .12} = 0$$

But when $N = 4$, then

$$c = \frac{.12 - .6 \times .4/4}{.6 \times .4 - .12} = \frac{.06}{.12} = .5$$

and if N becomes very large, the term $a(1 - a)/N$ becomes vanishingly small, so that

$$c = \frac{.12 - 0}{.6 \times .4 - .12} = 1.0$$

That is, when the total number of elements is very large, but the effective number of *independent* elements is 2, then the size of c (that is, the size of γ relative to $\alpha + \beta$) is 1.0. More generally, the right-hand side of eq. (2.2) can be substituted in eq. (2.1) to give a general relation between c and the number of independent elements, N^*:

$$c = \frac{\dfrac{a(1 - a)}{N^*} - \dfrac{a(1 - a)}{N}}{a(1 - a) - \dfrac{a(1 - a)}{N^*}} \tag{2.3}$$

$$c = \frac{\dfrac{1}{N^*} - \dfrac{1}{N}}{1 - \dfrac{1}{N^*}} \tag{2.4}$$

and if N becomes quite large, while N^* remains small, then

$$c \approx \frac{1}{N^* - 1} \tag{2.5}$$

But to return to the problem presented by data of the form of Table 13.2; that is, data from a three-or-more-wave panel. We cannot directly calculate σ_v^2 or c or N^*, for these data include changes over time, and not only the manifestation of a distribution over the v-continuum from zero to one. The problem, then, is to somehow extract from such data an estimate of σ_v^2, or c, or N^*, along with estimates of the rates of movement of individuals along the v-continuum. With such estimates, the problem of using multiwave panels (or sequences of consumer choices) to characterize a combined model of uncertainty and change would be solved—that is, it would be solved subject to the assumption that the form of the distribution is that of the contagious binomial, given by eq. (6.5) of Chapter 11. This distribution is

$$p_i = \frac{\binom{N}{i} \prod\limits_{j=0}^{i-1} (a + jc) \prod\limits_{j=0}^{N-i-1} (1 - a + jc)}{\prod\limits_{j=0}^{N-1} (1 + jc)} \tag{2.6}$$

and it is the equilibrium distribution for a continuous-time stochastic process with $N + 1$ states where the transition rates between state i and $i + 1$ depend on γ, α, and β, in the following way:

$$q_{i,i+1} = (N - i)(\alpha + i\gamma) \tag{2.7}$$

$$q_{i+1,i} = (i + 1)[\beta + (N - i - 1)\gamma] \tag{2.8}$$

and $c = \gamma/(\alpha + \beta)$, $a = \alpha/(\alpha + \beta)$. For very large N, such as we are considering here (i.e., a very large number of elements), this distribution can range from one in which $\gamma/(\alpha + \beta) = 0$, and the variance approaches zero, with all persons concentrated at one point on the continuum, to one in which $\gamma/(\alpha + \beta)$ approaches infinity, and the variance is maximum, with all persons located at either zero or one on the continuum (i.e., having either zero or one probability of giving response A). Several forms of the distribution (for $N = 100$) are given in Figure 13.2, to show how the distribution varies for different values of $\gamma/(\alpha + \beta)$, when $a [= \alpha/(\alpha + \beta)]$ is equal to .4.

It would be useful to pass to the continuous case with eq. (2.6), as N approaches infinity to obtain a continuous density function that is analogous to eq. (2.6). Lacking that [for I have been unable to let eq. (2.6) pass to the limit to obtain such a distribution; however, for aids in such an enterprise, see references cited by Bharucha-Reid, 1960, p. 215], we will continue to assume that the underlying distribution for such data as those presented in Table 13.1 is given by eq. (2.6) with N quite large, with a estimated by p_1 (the proportion giving response A) and c estimated by the estimate of N^* from the equations of the preceding chapter, and with the relation between c and N^* given in eq. (2.5), that is, $c = 1/(N^* - 1)$. But this leaves to be solved the essential problem, and that is to estimate the rates of movement α, β, and γ from three-or-more-wave turnover data, such as that of Table 13.2.

3. A CONTINUOUS-SPACE PROCESS INCORPORATING UNCERTAINTY AND CHANGE

Let us suppose for a moment that we had turnover data like those of Table 13.1, based on a repeated response with no intervening period of time for change to take place. This brings us back to eqs. (2.6) and (2.7) of the

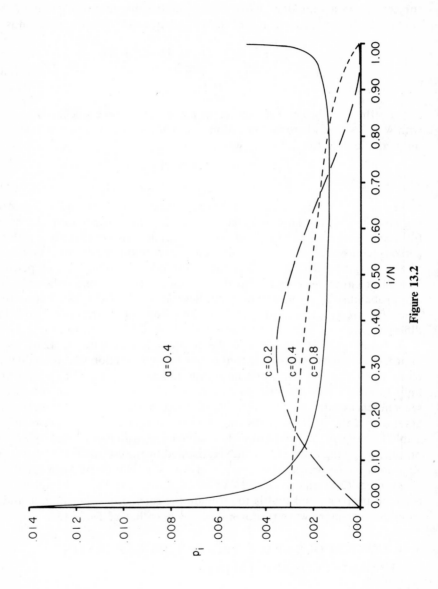

Figure 13.2

preceding chapter for relating p_{11} and p_1 to the underlying distribution, $f(v)$, (where $f(v) = n(v)/n$ of the preceding chapter), and v is the proportion of elements in the individual conditioned to response 1. Since change is to be introduced, a subscript to represent time must be added to v, p_1, and p_{11}, giving in this case v_0, $p_{1,0}$, and $p_{11,0}$. The change process, of course, is a change in the individual's underlying v, resulting in changed probability of response, and in the aggregate possible changes in p_1 and p_{11}. Using integrals rather than sums to represent the continuous case, eqs. (2.6) and (2.7) of the preceding chapter become

$$p_{1,0} = \int_0^1 v_0 \, f(v_0) \, dv_0 \tag{3.1}$$

and

$$p_{11,0} = \int_0^1 v_0^2 \, f(v_0) \, dv_0 \tag{3.2}$$

At time t (a later response), these equations become

$$p_{1,t} = \int_0^1 v_t \, f(v_0) \, dv_0 \tag{3.3}$$

and

$$p_{11,t} = \int_0^1 v_t v_0 \, f(v_0) \, dv_0 \tag{3.4}$$

Intuitively, it can be seen from eq. (3.4) that if the average v_t is identical to the average v_0 (as it is in the example of Table 13.2, remaining at .6), the value of $p_{11,t}$ will be lower than that of $p_{11,0}$, since the weighted sum of cross-products, $v_t v_0$ will be lower than the weighted sum of squares, v_0^2, assuming that there has been some movement. Furthermore, as the time between responses increases, this sum of cross-products will decrease, and $p_{11,t}$ will decrease. This corresponds to the situation shown in Table 13.2, where $p_{11,1} = .474$, and $p_{11,2} = .468$. Thus if it is possible to develop a mechanism for change in v, then it may be possible to use $p_{11,1}$ and $p_{11,2}$ to estimate the parameters of such change.

Such a mechanism is provided if we consider the process governing each element in the contagious binomial. Each element can be in state 1 or in state 2, and the differential equation expressing the rate of change in its probability of being in state 1 is, if there are m_1 others in state 1:

$$\frac{dp}{dt} = (\alpha + m_1 \gamma)(1 - p) - [\beta + (m - m_1)\gamma]p \tag{3.5}$$

where p is the probability that the element is in state 1, α and β are the transition rates into states 1 and 2 independent of other elements, and γ is the increment to the transition rate provided by each element already in the target state. (There is a discrepancy of one element in the above equation, since each element is affected by only $m - 1$ others. However, since m is very large, this can be neglected.)

Each element is identical, so that there are m processes described by eq. (3.5). Thus multiplication of eq. (3.5) by m will give the rate of change in the expected number of elements in state 1:

$$\frac{dmp}{dt} = m(1 - p)\alpha - mp\beta + mm_1\gamma - mmp\gamma \qquad (3.6)$$

When the number of elements m is very large, as assumed by the model, the expected number in state 1, mp, approaches the actual number, m_1. Thus the equation simplifies further:

$$\frac{dm_1}{dt} = (m - m_1)\alpha - m_1\beta$$

Letting $k = \alpha + \beta$, $v = m_1/m$, $a = \alpha/(\alpha + \beta)$, dividing through by m and rearranging gives

$$\frac{dv}{dt} = k(a - v) \qquad (3.7)$$

This equation provides the mechanism for change in v, consistent with the model of a contagious binomial process at the level of the elements.

For those persons for whom $v > a$, the average movement is down, and for those for whom $v < a$, the average movement is up.[2] This means that for those persons whose *present* probability (v) of giving response 1 is greater than the mean probability (a), the average movement is down, and for those whose present position is less than the mean, the average movement is up.

If equation eq. (3.7) is integrated between the limits of t and τ (where $\tau > t$), and solved for v_τ, the result is

$$v_\tau = v_t e^{-k(\tau - t)} + a(1 - e^{-k(\tau - t)}) \qquad (3.8)$$

For the case of t_1 and t_2 (the second and third interviews, respectively),

$$v_2 = v_1 e^{-k(t_2 - t_1)} + a(1 - e^{-k(t_2 - t_1)}) \qquad (3.9)$$

This relation between an individual's v's at two time periods can be used in

---

[2] This would appear to contradict the contagious assumption of this model, by producing a regression toward the mean from all positions away from it. However, it is just as in a stationary normal distribution, where a particle found to the right of the mean will have an expected movement back to the mean. Yet the random fluctuations maintain the stationary distribution, because the number to the left of this particle (toward the mean) is enough greater than the number to the right to thrust out just as many particles as are moving back. Although the expected movement is back toward the mean, the random component maintains a distribution with a stable variance.

conjunction with eq. (3.4) to give a relation between the response proportions at the two time periods. For time t_2, eq. (3.4) becomes

$$p_{11,2} = \int_0^1 v_2 v_0 \, f(v_0) \, dv_0 \tag{3.10}$$

Using eq. (3.9) to substitute for the value of v_2 in eq. (3.10) gives

$$p_{11,2} = \int_0^1 v_1 v_0 \, f(v_0) e^{-k(t_2-t_1)} \, dv_0 + \int_0^1 v_0 \, f(v_0) a(1 - e^{-k(t_2-t_1)}) \, dv_0 \tag{3.11}$$

$$p_{11,2} = e^{-k(t_2-t_1)} \int_0^1 v_1 v_0 \, f(v_0) \, dv_0 + a(1 - e^{-k(t_2-t_1)}) \int_0^1 v_0 \, f(v_0) \, dv_0 \tag{3.12}$$

But by eq. (3.4), the left-hand integral equals $p_{11,1}$, and by eq. (3.1), the right-hand integral equals $p_{1,0}$. Consequently, eq. (3.12) becomes

$$p_{11,2} = p_{11,1} e^{-k(t_2-t_1)} + p_{1,0} a(1 - e^{-k(t_2-t_1)}) \tag{3.13}$$

Furthermore, by eq. (3.3),

$$p_{1,2} = \int_0^1 v_2 \, f(v_0) \, dv_0 \tag{3.14}$$

and using eq. (3.9) to substitute for the value of v_2 in eq. (3.14) gives

$$p_{1,2} = e^{-k(t_2-t_1)} \int_0^1 v_1 \, f(v_0) \, dv_0 + a(1 - e^{-k(t_2-t_1)}) \int_0^1 f(v_0) \, dv_0 \tag{3.15}$$

By eq. (3.3), the left-hand integral equals $p_{1,1}$ and the right-hand integral equals 1, so that by rearranging terms, we can get an equation to help simplify eq. (3.13):

$$p_{1,2} - p_{1,1} e^{-k(t_2-t_1)} = a(1 - e^{-k(t_2-t_1)}) \tag{3.16}$$

Substituting the left-hand side of eq. (3.16) for its equivalent in eq. (3.13) gives

$$p_{11,2} = p_{11,1} e^{-k(t_2-t_1)} + p_{1,0} p_{1,2} - p_{1,0} p_{1,1} e^{-k(t_2-t_1)} \tag{3.17}$$

Solving for $e^{-k(t_2-t_1)}$ gives

$$e^{-k(t_2-t_1)} = \frac{p_{11,2} - p_{1,0} p_{1,2}}{p_{11,1} - p_{1,0} p_{1,1}} \tag{3.18}$$

We can solve for k by taking logarithms, changing signs, and dividing by $t_2 - t_1$:

$$k = \frac{1}{t_2 - t_1} \ln \left(\frac{p_{11,1} - p_{1,0} p_{1,1}}{p_{11,2} - p_{1,0} p_{1,2}} \right) \tag{3.19}$$

Equation (3.19) now provides an important result: it allows estimation of the total amount of movement, k, since we know the time difference, $t_2 - t_1$, and the response proportions, $p_{1,0}$, $p_{1,1}$, $p_{1,2}$, $p_{11,1}$, and $p_{11,2}$. This estimate of k in turn allows estimation of a, by use of eq. (3.16) in slightly different form:

$$a = \frac{p_{1,2} - p_{1,1}e^{-k(t_2-t_1)}}{1 - e^{-k(t_2-t_1)}} \qquad (3.20)$$

This equation provides an estimate of a, which is the equilibrium value that p_1 approaches. This can be verified by letting t_2 approach infinity in eq. (3.16) or eq. (3.20). [Two other estimates of a may be obtained by use of eq. (3.20) but applied to time periods 1 and 0 in one case, and 2 and 0 in the other. Averaging of all these estimates will reduce the influence of sampling variation in $p_{i,t}$ upon the estimate of a.]

Having estimates of k and a, we can go ahead to project $p_{1,t}$ and $p_{11,t}$ forward to any point in time, and more striking, to project $p_{11,t}$ *backward* to $t = 0$, to show what the uncertainty of response would have been if we had been able to obtain two responses from each person at zero time separation (as assumed, for example, in the hypothetical data of Table 13.1, and in the preceding chapter). The equations for projecting $p_{1,t}$ and $p_{11,t}$ forward or backward from time 0 are found from eq. (3.16) and eq. (3.17) respectively. In the first case, eq. (3.16) is used three times (once with times t and 0 replacing 2 and 1, once with times t and 1 replacing 2 and 1, and once with times t and 2 replacing 2 and 1), in order to average out the sampling variations in $p_{1,0}$, $p_{1,1}$, and $p_{1,2}$.

$$p_{1,t} = a + \frac{1}{3}e^{-kt}[(p_{1,0} - a) + (p_{1,1} - a)e^{kt_1} + (p_{1,2} - a)e^{kt_2}] \qquad (3.21)$$

The value of $p_{11,t}$ is found similarly from eq. (3.17).

$$p_{11,t} = p_{1,t}p_{1,0} + \frac{1}{2}e^{-kt}[(p_{11,1} - p_{1,1}p_{1,0})e^{kt_1} + (p_{11,2} - p_{1,2}p_{1,0})e^{kt_2}] \qquad (3.22)$$

Besides projecting forward $p_{11,t}$ to any point in time, eq. (3.22) may be used for finding $p_{11,0}$, which will show the unreliability of the response if it had been made twice at time 0 with no intervening time. Then, having that value, $p_{11,0}$, the methods of the preceding chapter may be used to solve for N^*, and that in turn may be used to solve for c, by eq. (2.5). These equations can be combined to give c directly in terms of $p_{11,0}$ and $p_{1,0}$:

$$c = \frac{p_{11,0} - p_{1,0}^2}{p_{1,0} - p_{11,0}} \qquad (3.23)$$

This value of c, together with the value of a, can then be used with eq. (2.6) to give the equilibrium distribution of persons along the continuum from zero to one [assuming that eq. (2.6) gives the correct form of that distribution, and using a large value for N].

The result, then, is that from three-wave-panel data, or consumer choice data including three sequences of choice for each person, we are able to obtain the parameters that describe the distribution of persons along the v-continuum, and the average rates of movement in each direction. A continuation of the above hypothetical example will illustrate how this is done. The data needed for the model are as follows:

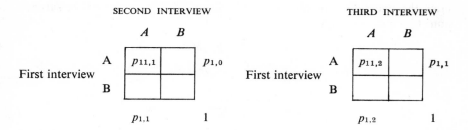

	SECOND INTERVIEW			THIRD INTERVIEW	
	A	B		A	B
First interview A	$p_{11,1}$		$p_{1,0}$	First interview A	$p_{11,2}$		$p_{1,1}$

For the example using generated data, from interviews I, II, and IV:[3]

		III (I + TWO MONTHS)			IV (I + TEN MONTHS)		
		A	B		A	B	
I	A	.468	.132	.6	.432	.168	.6
	B	.132	.268	.4	.168	.232	.4
		.6	.4	1.0	.6	.4	1.0

Using eq. (3.18), we have

$$e^{-k(10-2)} = \frac{.432 - .6 \times .6}{.468 - .6 \times .6} = \frac{.072}{.108} = .667$$

$$k = -1/8 \ln .667 = .0505$$

This value of k is equal (except for rounding error) to the sum of the transition rates characterizing each element in the discrete-space model that generated these data (see Figure 13.1a), $\alpha = .03$, $\beta = .02$. Having this value, eq. (3.20) may be used to estimate a:

$$a = \frac{.6 - .6 \times .667}{1 - .667} = 0.6$$

and using the value of k above, .0505, together with the fact that $a = \alpha/(\alpha+\beta)$, and $k = \alpha + \beta$, we estimate α to be .03, and β to be .02. These values are

---

[3] Any three interviews might have been used, but so little change occurred over the one-month period that separated I, II, and III that more reliable estimates occur by use of I, III, and IV in the estimates. (In this case of generated data, the unreliability would be due to rounding error; in the case of actual data, to sampling error.)

equal to the values of $\alpha\ (= .03)$ and $\beta\ (= .02)$, used to generate the data. From these parameters can be estimated $p_{1,t}$ and $p_{11,t}$ at any time t, by use of eqs. (3.16) and (3.13), respectively. Since there is aggregate equilibrium, $p_{1,t}$ is always .6 with these data, as substitution in eq. (3.16) would show. The value of $p_{11,t}$ will vary, however, and we can first solve for $p_{11,0}$, to show the uncertainty of response when stimuli follow in immediate succession. Using eq. (3.16), we obtain

$$p_{11,2} = p_{11,0}e^{-k(t_2-0)} + p_{1,0}a(1 - e^{-k(t_2-0)})$$

$$.468 = p_{11,0}e^{-.05(2)} + .6(.6)(1 - e^{-.05(2)})$$

$$p_{11,0} = \frac{.468 - .36 \times .095}{.905} = .48$$

Similarly, we could have obtained the same value of $p_{11,0}$ by using the data from interview IV. By using the same procedure as above, we may calculate the value of $p_{11,1}$ by replacing $p_{11,0}$ by $p_{11,1}$, and $t_2 - 0\ (= 2)$ in the exponent with $t_2 - t_1\ (= 1)$, to give .474 after solving the equation for $p_{11,1}$.

Having the value of $p_{11,0}$ allows solving for N^* by eq. (2.18) of the preceding chapter, or directly for c by eq. (3.21):

$$N^* = \frac{.6 \times .4}{.48 - .36} = 2.0$$

or

$$c = \frac{.48 - .36}{.6 - .48} = 1.0$$

This value of c may then be substituted in eq. (2.6), using any large value of N, to get the form of the distribution along the v-continuum, following the contagious binomial. For these hypothetical data, values of p_i were computed, setting $N = 100$. The line joining these values gives the approximate distribution curve for the continuous distribution. Its shape is similar to that of the distribution of Figure 13.2 in which a = .4 and c = .8.

4. INTERDEPENDENT ATTRIBUTES AND MULTICATEGORY ITEMS WITH BOTH UNCERTAINTY AND CHANGE

The model discussed above is appropriate for responses to one item over time. However, this does nothing for the situation in which two or more attributes are examined together, and one is interested in studying the interdependence of these items over time. Suppose these attributes, when examined by themselves in a three-wave panel, show both uncertainty of response and change. Yet when they are examined together, to estimate their effects on one another, using the models of Chapter 5, there is no allowance for the uncertainty. All manifest changes are treated as actual changes.

Nevertheless just as in the case of a single item, an examination of changes in the cross-tabulations between distant panel waves will ordinarily show less change than would be predicted by the transition rates estimated from waves close together in time.

It is obvious that such a situation can lead to incorrect inferences. Consider a situation in which two attributes showed a stable relationship, but no one was changing on either attribute, and consequently neither was affecting the other. Suppose further that one of these attributes showed a great deal of response unreliability. The 16-fold table produced by a panel (e.g., Chapter 5) would necessarily show that the unreliable attribute was being affected by the other. Consider, for example, the hypothetical table below. Attribute A is perfectly reliable, and does not change; attribute B has high response unreliability, but also does not change.

			II				
A	B	+ +	+ −	− +	− −	
+	+	340	60	0	0	400
+	−	60	40	0	0	100
−	+	0	0	40	60	100
−	−	0	0	60	340	400
		400	100	100	400	1000

(I is labeled at the left of the table rows)

The transition rates estimated from these data would show strong effects of attribute A on attribute B. But then suppose two waves much more widely separated showed exactly this same number of apparent changes. This would not be consistent with the assumption of a Markov process, nor with the inference of effects of attribute A on attribute B. In this example, we would be fortunate, because we could separate the sample into two, according to their responses on attribute A. But in the general case, both attributes will show change, or response uncertainty, or both.

Obviously, a generalization of the approach treated in the present chapter is needed. This generalization will be outlined here. Detailed treatment, including examination of data, will be carried out in subsequent publications (see Coleman, 1964), but the mathematical basis for the model will be given here.

As before, we assume that an individual has m elements, and that on attribute A, m_{a1} are conditioned to response A_1, and m_{a2} are conditioned to response A_2, with $m_{a1} + m_{a2} = m$. On attribute B, m_{b1} are conditioned to response B_1, and m_{b2} are conditioned to response B_2, with $m_{b1} + m_{b2} = m$.

The elements are related to the individual's response by definition as follows:

$$p_{a1} = \frac{m_{a1}}{m} \tag{4.1}$$

$$p_{a2} = \frac{m_{a2}}{m} \tag{4.2}$$

etc.

The probability of giving response a_1 and b_1 would be, if the attributes were unrelated,

$$p_{a1b1} = \left(\frac{m_{a1}}{m}\right)\left(\frac{m_{b1}}{m}\right) \tag{4.3}$$

However, the attributes are related, so that

$$p_{a1b1} = \frac{m_{a1b1}}{m} \tag{4.4}$$

where m_{a1b1} is the proportion of this individual's elements that are conditioned to response 1 on attribute A and response 1 on attribute B.[4] If the attributes are positively related, this implies that when an element is conditioned to A_1, it will tend to become conditioned to B_1, if A affects B, and when it is conditioned to B_1, it will tend to become conditioned to A_1, if B affects A. It is natural, then, to posit, at the level of these internal elements, the same stochastic model that was posited at the level of the individual in Chapter 5. This is diagrammed in Figure 13.3. If the element is in state 1, it is conditioned to A_1 and B_1; if it is in state 2, it is conditioned to A_1 and B_2, and so on for states 3 and 4. Thus if there is a positive effect of A on B, elements will tend to move from state 2 to 1 and from 3 to 4. The transition rates will show inequalities $q_{21} > q_{43}$, and $q_{34} > q_{12}$. If there is a positive effect of B on A, similar inequalities will exist in the horizontal direction: $q_{31} > q_{42}$, and $q_{24} > q_{13}$.

It may also be that the number of elements conditioned to A_1 will increase the transition rate of other elements toward A_1 (that is, increase q_{31} and q_{43}), as in the model set forth earlier in this chapter. However, for the present, this will be neglected, as it will make the model non-Markovian.[5]

If we call the expected proportion of elements in states 1, 2, 3, and 4,

---

[4] It should be evident that this relationship between attributes is within the individual, and not across individuals, since we are treating a single individual. The relationship is expressed by a correlation of his responses to the two items over time.

[5] In the dichotomous case treated earlier, it was possible to include this "contagion" effect since the contagion term dropped out of the differential equation for rate of change in v [see eq. (3.6)]. Thus that model is fully compatible with this, and the derivations below for this model reduce to that one for the case of a single dichotomy.

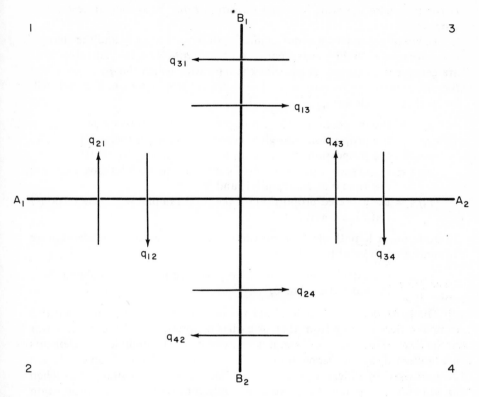

Figure 13.3

respectively, v_1, v_2, v_3, and v_4, then the differential equations defining the process are

$$\frac{dv_1}{dt} = q_{11}v_1 + q_{21}v_2 + q_{31}v_3 + q_{41}v_4 \qquad (4.5)$$

$$\frac{dv_2}{dt} = q_{12}v_1 + q_{22}v_2 + q_{32}v_3 + q_{42}v_4$$

$$\frac{dv_3}{dt} = q_{13}v_1 + q_{23}v_2 + q_{33}v_3 + q_{43}v_4$$

$$\frac{dv_4}{dt} = q_{14}v_1 + q_{24}v_2 + q_{34}v_4 + q_{44}v_4$$

In this, as before, q_{ii} is defined as being equal to $-\Sigma q_{ij}$. The terms for the zero q_{ij}'s, q_{14}, q_{23}, q_{32}, and q_{41} will be included below, so that the derivations will be applicable to the general case, say the case of a single four-category attribute, where there are nonzero transition rates from each state to each other.

The data necessary, in order to infer both the uncertainty and the change, are responses in a three-wave panel, on two items. The 16-fold tables that are generated by the panel will give the data with which the q_{ij}'s above and the uncertainty can be estimated. The expected proportions in each cell will be labelled as follows:

$p_{i,0}$ = the proportion who give response i at time 0 (wave I),

$p_{i,1}$ = the proportion who give response i at time t_1 (wave II),

$p_{i,2}$ = the proportion who give response i at time t_2 (wave III),

$p_{ij,1}$ = the expected proportion (of the total sample) who gave response i at time 0 and j at time 1, and

$p_{ij,2}$ = the expected proportion (of the total sample) who gave response i at time 0 and j at time 2.

In addition, a hypothetical proportion that would exist if the items were administered twice at time 0:

$p_{ij,0}$ = the expected proportion who gave response i at time 0 and j in a second test at time 0.

The panel covers a sample of individuals, but our assumption about this sample differs sharply from that of earlier chapters, where the process was at the level of individuals. Here, it is assumed that each individual's elements are governed by the same transition rates; but different individuals are characterized by different proportions of elements in each state. Thus when an individual responds A_1B_1, we know only that some nonzero proportion of his elements are in state 1 (the state of elements conditioned to those two responses). Thus individuals who give responses A_1B_1 are not seen as all alike, but as differing in the proportions of elements they have conditioned to responses A_1 and B_1. At time 0, each person is characterized by four numbers, v_1, v_2, v_3, and v_4, the proportion of elements in each state. (These add to 1.0, and thus consist of only three independent numbers. Thus the frequency distribution of persons over this space is a function of v_1, v_2, v_3, and time.)

The expected proportion of persons who give response 1 at time 0, $p_{1,0}$, is given as in the earlier section, by the probability of giving response 1 at time 0 if at v_1, times the proportion of individuals at v_1 at time 0, integrated over all values of v_1, from 0 to 1. The probability of giving response 1 at v_1 is merely v_1, and the proportion of individuals at v_1 at time 0 is $f(v_1,v_2,v_3,t_0)$.

$$p_{i,0} = \int_0 v_{10} \, f(v_1,v_2,v_3,t_0) \, dv_1 \qquad (4.6)$$

The expected proportion who give response 1 at time t is the probability of giving response 1 at time t_1 times the proportion of people at v_1 at time t_1.

But if we want to relate $p_{1,t}$ to the response frequencies at time 0, then it is necessary to specify $p_{1,t}$ in terms of the frequency distribution at time 0. Thus, in these terms, the expected proportion who give response 1 at time t is the probability of giving response 1 at time t, v_{1t}, if at (v_1,v_2,v_3) at time 0, times the proportion of people at (v_1, v_2, v_3) at time 0, integrated over all values of v_1, v_2, v_3, from 0 to 1.

$$p_{1,t} = \iiint_0^1 v_{1t} \, f(v_1,v_2,v_3,t_0) \, dv_1 dv_2 dv_3 \tag{4.7}$$

In this case, it is necessary to look at the probability of giving response 1 at time t as a function of the *total* position of the individual at time 0, since there may have been some movement of elements over the period of time. That is, consider two individuals with $v_1 = 0$ at time 0. For one, $v_4 = 1$, while for the other, $v_4 = 0$, $v_2 = .5$, and $v_3 = .5$. Obviously, so long as there is some movement of elements into state 1, the latter individual will have a higher v_{1t} than will the former. Thus it is necessary to specify the total position at time 0, and it is necessary to specify v_{1t} as a function of (v_1,v_2,v_3) at time 0.

To return to the system of equations (4.5), it is possible to specify v_{1t} as a function of the vector (v_1, v_2,v_3,v_4), the matrix of q_{ij}'s, and t [see Section 8 of Chapter 5]. The vector of v_i's at time t is

$$V'(t) = V'(0)e^{Qt} \tag{4.8}$$

where

$$V(t) = \begin{pmatrix} v_{1t} \\ v_{2t} \\ v_{3t} \\ v_{4t} \end{pmatrix}$$

$$e^{Qt} = R_t = \begin{pmatrix} r_{11t} & r_{12t} & r_{13t} & r_{14t} \\ r_{21t} & r_{22t} & r_{23t} & r_{24t} \\ r_{31t} & r_{32t} & r_{33t} & r_{34t} \\ r_{41t} & r_{42t} & r_{43t} & r_{44t} \end{pmatrix}$$

and each element r_{ijt}, is an exponential series formed from powers of the Qt matrix:

$$r_{ijt} = \delta_{ij} + tq_{ij} + t^2 \sum_k \frac{q_{ik}q_{kj}}{2} + t^3 \sum_k \sum_h \frac{q_{ik}q_{kh}q_{hj}}{3!} + \dots \tag{4.9}$$

and $\delta_{ij} = 1$ if $i = j$, zero otherwise. Thus, by use of eq. (4.8),

$$v_{1t} = v_{10}r_{11t} + v_{20}r_{21t} + v_{30}r_{31t} + v_{40}r_{41t} \tag{4.10}$$

The terms r_{ijt} have the properties of transition probabilities in a Markov process, so that eq. (4.10) can be seen as showing the sources of contributions to v_{1t} from the four states at time 0. As time increases, r_{iit} will decrease, while r_{ijt} $(j \neq i)$ will increase. Then eq. (4.7) becomes

$$p_{1,t} = \iiint [v_{10}r_{11t} + v_{20}r_{21t} + v_{30}r_{31t} + v_{40}r_{41t}] f(v_1,v_2,v_3,t_0) \, dv_1 dv_2 dv_3$$

$$\text{(4.11)}$$

Since r_{ijt} is a constant, each of the four terms reduces to the form of eq. (4.6) and give as a result

$$p_{1,t} = p_{1,0}r_{11t} + p_{2,0}r_{21t} + p_{3,0}r_{31t} + p_{4,0}r_{41t} \qquad \text{(4.12)}$$

Equation (4.12) gives the expected proportion of A_1B_1 responses at any time t as a function of the proportion of responses of each type at time 0 and the q_{ij}'s. It does not, however, directly aid in the solution of the q_{ij}'s, for there are twelve q_{ij}'s, and only six independent $p_{i,0}$'s and $p_{i,t}$'s, or with three waves, nine independent p_i's. For that, more data, the internal cell values of the panel tables, are necessary.

Analogous to eq. (4.6), the expected proportion responding A_1B_1 twice at time 0 is given by

$$p_{11,0} = \int_0^{'} v_{10}^2 \, f(v_1,v_2,v_3,t_0) \, dv_1 \qquad \text{(4.13)}$$

and more generally,

$$p_{ij,0} = \iint v_{i0}v_{j0} \, f(v_1,v_2,v_3,t_0) \, dv_i dv_j \qquad \text{(4.14)}$$

The expected proportion responding this way at times 0 and t is

$$p_{ij,t} = \iiint v_{i0}v_{jt} \, f(v_1,v_2,v_3,t_0) \, dv_1 dv_2 dv_3 \qquad \text{(4.15)}$$

and by a procedure similar to that used in eqs. (4.7) to (4.12), we obtain

$$p_{ij,t} = \iiint [v_{i0}v_{10}r_{1jt} + v_{i0}v_{20}r_{2jt} + v_{i0}v_{30}r_{3jt} + v_{i0}v_{40}r_{4jt}]$$
$$\times f(v_1,v_2,v_3,t_0) \, dv_1 dv_2 dv_3 \qquad \text{(4.16)}$$

$$p_{ij,t} = p_{i1,0}r_{1jt} + p_{i2,0}r_{2jt} + p_{i3,0}r_{3jt} + p_{i4,0}r_{4jt} \qquad \text{(4.17)}$$

Equation (4.17) relates $p_{ij,t}$ to $p_{ij,0}$, and if $p_{ij,t}$ and $p_{ij,0}$ were known, it might then be possible to solve for r_{ijt}, and thus q_{ij}. However, the values of $p_{ij,0}$ are not observed. Instead, values $p_{ij,1}$ and $p_{ij,2}$ are observed. This can then aid in estimation of values of r_{ijt}, and then q_{ij}.

What is necessary, in place of eqs. (4.15) to (4.17), is to translate v_{j2} back, not to v_{j0}, but to v_{j1}. Expressing v_{j2} in terms of v_{i1} gives, analogously to eq. (4.10),

$$v_{j2} = v_{11}r_{1j\tau} + v_{21}r_{2j\tau} + v_{31}r_{3j\tau} + v_{41}r_{4j\tau} \qquad (4.18)$$

where $\tau = t_2 - t_1$,

$v_{j2} =$ the proportion of elements in state j at time 2, and

$v_{i1} =$ the proportion of elements in state i at time 1.

Using eq. (4.15), and substituting for v_{j2} its equivalent in eq. (4.18), we obtain

$$p_{ij,2} = \iiint [v_{i0}v_{11}r_{1j\tau} + v_{i0}v_{21}r_{2j\tau} + v_{i0}v_{31}r_{3j\tau} + v_{i0}v_{31}r_{4j\tau}]$$
$$\times f(v_1,v_2,v_3,t_0)\, dv_1 dv_2 dv_3 \qquad (4.19)$$

This reduces to

$$p_{ij,2} = p_{i1,1}r_{1j\tau} + p_{i2,1}r_{2j\tau} + p_{i3,1}r_{3j\tau} + p_{i4,1}r_{4j\tau} \qquad (4.20)$$

A set of four equations may be set down, for $p_{1j,2}$, $p_{2j,2}$, $p_{3j,2}$, and $p_{4j,2}$. These equations contain the same coefficients $r_{1j\tau}$, $r_{2j\tau}$, $r_{3j\tau}$, and $r_{4j\tau}$. Since the values of $p_{ij,2}$ and $p_{ij,1}$ are observed, it is thus possible to solve the four simultaneous equations for the r's. The simplest method for doing so is probably that of Gauss, in which the first equation is used for eliminating the first unknown in the other three, the second equation used for eliminating the second unknown in the other two, and then the third equation used for eliminating the third unknown in the last equation. This then allows solution of the last equation for the fourth unknown, $r_{ij\tau}$. The technique is explained by Hald (1952, pp. 642–649).

The procedure is shown in abbreviated form below. For simplicity, redundant subscripts will be dropped and the symbols changed, so that $r_{ij\tau}$ becomes x_i, $p_{ij,1}$ becomes a_{ij}, and $p_{ij,2}$ becomes w_i.

(1) $\qquad\qquad w_1 = a_{11}x_1 + a_{21}x_2 + a_{31}x_3 + a_{41}x_4$

(2) $\qquad\qquad w_2 = a_{12}x_1 + a_{22}x_2 + a_{32}x_3 + a_{42}x_4$

(3) $\qquad\qquad w_3 = a_{13}x_1 + a_{23}x_2 + a_{33}x_3 + a_{43}x_4$ $\qquad$ (4.20)

(4) $\qquad\qquad w_4 = a_{14}x_1 + a_{24}x_2 + a_{34}x_3 + a_{44}x_4$

Multiplying eq. (1) by $-a_{12}/a_{11}$ and adding to eq. (2) eliminates x_1 from eq. (2) and after multiplying through by a_{11} gives

(2a) $\quad w_2 a_{11} - w_1 a_{12} = (a_{22}a_{11} - a_{12}a_{21})x_2 + (a_{32}a_{11} - a_{12}a_{31})x_3$
$$+ (a_{42}a_{11} - a_{12}a_{41})x_4$$

A similar elimination of x_1 by use of eq. (1) is made for eq. (3) and eq. (4). Then eq. (2a) is used to eliminate x_2 from the resulting equations, (3a) and (4a), to give (3b) and (4b). Eq. (3b) is shown below.

$$(w_3 a_{11} - w_1 a_{13})(a_{22} a_{11} - a_{12} a_{21}) - (w_2 a_{11} - w_1 a_{12})(a_{23} a_{11} - a_{13} a_{21})$$
$$= [(a_{33} a_{11} - a_{13} a_{31})(a_{22} a_{11} - a_{12} a_{21})$$
$$- (a_{23} a_{11} - a_{13} a_{21})(a_{32} a_{11} - a_{12} a_{31})]x_3$$
$$+ [(a_{43} a_{11} - a_{13} a_{41})(a_{22} a_{11} - a_{12} a_{21})$$
$$- (a_{23} a_{11} - a_{13} a_{21})(a_{42} a_{11} - a_{12} a_{41})]x_4$$

When x_3 is eliminated from this and the similar eq. (4b), the resulting equation may be solved for x_4. If we simplify by letting

$$c_{ijk} = w_i a_{jk} - w_j a_{ik}$$

and

$$b_{ijk1} = a_{ij} a_{k1} - a_{kj} a_{i1}$$

then

$$x_4 = \frac{(c_{411} b_{2211} - c_{211} b_{2411})(b_{3311} b_{2211} - b_{2311} b_{3211})}{(b_{4411} b_{2211} - b_{2411} b_{4211})(b_{3311} b_{2211} - b_{2311} b_{3211})}$$
$$\frac{- (c_{311} b_{2211} - c_{211} b_{2311})(b_{3411} b_{2211} - b_{2411} b_{3211})}{- (b_{3411} b_{2211} - b_{2411} b_{3211})(b_{4311} b_{2211} - b_{2311} b_{4211})} \quad (4.21)$$

This equation may be used to solve for x_4, which can then be substituted back in (3b) above to solve for x_3, then in (2a), and finally in (1), to solve for x_1.

This procedure solves one column, $r_{1j\tau}, r_{2j\tau}, r_{3j\tau}, r_{4j\tau}$, of the R_τ matrix, and the same procedure for each value of j is used to solve for the other columns. The fourth column provides a computational check, since the sum of each row is 1.0.

Having this transition matrix, it is then possible by the iterative procedure of Chapter 5, Section 8, to solve for the values of q_{ij}. These values then show the effects of attribute A upon B and B upon A.

5. CONCLUSION

In conclusion, this chapter opens up possibilities for handling multiwave panels, or long sequences of responses, taking into account both the distinction between the latent state and the manifest response, and changes in the latent state. It seems particularly valuable for opening up new directions of research in public opinion, with closely spaced interviews or diary records of opinions, data of a sort that are not now gathered; and in analysis of consumer behavior via consumer diary panels, using data that are presently gathered. Much remains to be done, however, in the further development of this model. In particular, three problems seem particularly interesting: (a) its application to long sequences of one individual's responses; (b) of even more interest, its development as discussed in Section 4, in the direction of models of earlier chapters, in which *relations* between dichotomous attributes were examined. Using further elaborations of this model, it may be possible to examine the same data from the point of view of relations between underlying variables (varying between zero and one, as v did in this chapter) that give rise to dichotomous responses. Finally, (c) there is the basis for a psychological theory of cognitive structure in this model, and from the point of view of the development of psychological theory, this is perhaps the most interesting direction of all.

CHAPTER 14

MEASURES OF STRUCTURAL CHARACTERISTICS

INTRODUCTION

The extraordinary complexity of structures of relations between people makes the task of developing measures for them a difficult one. Perhaps because of this complexity, there are continuing disputes in the literature about how to measure various structural concepts. Measures for the concept of segregation, for example, mentioned in Chapter 1, have been so abundant that one pair of authors has developed an accounting scheme simply to examine how these measures relate to one another (Duncan and Duncan, 1955). To take another example, measurement of the "social stratification" of a community has provoked several controversies in the literature, controversies about whether patterns of association or status rankings are the most appropriate data, controversies about whose rankings should be taken, controversies about how to combine various data into a final measure. (See Kornhauser, 1953, and Lipset and Bendix, 1951, for one such controversy;

and Tumin, 1953, Davis and Moore, 1953, for another.) Many alternative approaches are possible simply because the social structure is so complex and because it is possible to "see into" this complexity in a way that is not possible, for example, when measuring some personality characteristic.

The approach to be taken here will not be so ambitious as to attempt to redefine and provide measures for such classic concepts as "stratification," "social class," "group," and so on. The much more modest aim will be to examine how particular kinds of data abstracted from concrete structures can be "digested" or combined to provide measures of various tendencies which the structure exhibits. But first some more basic questions about measurement should be considered.

In Chapter 2, the conclusion was reached that quantitative measurement, to prove theoretically fruitful, had better be carried out in direct conjunction with the theory within which it is intended to be used. On an intuitive level, it comes down to the simple fact that there is no use developing a concept of "segregation" or "stratification" unless there are some definite causal relations in which the concept plays a part; and once such causal relations are made explicit, they dictate many of the decisions about how to construct a measure of the concept.

In view of such a conclusion, what value can there be in an enterprise such as the intended one of this chapter? Perhaps only this: that in the absence of formal theories within which to embed concepts, some provisional measures must be developed. Science is a kind of bootstrap operation, and provisional concepts are necessary simply in order to sort out the complexity of events and obtain some insights into what is happening.

However, if this were the only justification for the development of structural measures, then it would probably be better to continue to develop *ad hoc* indices to fit the particular study, abandoning any attempt to develop general formal and quantitative measures. The measures developed here, in contrast, find an additional justification, for they are explicitly based on "models" or theories about behavior. Some of the measures are based on models concerning what *causes* a particular structural configuration, while others are designed to fit theories about *consequences* of a particular structure when one or another process is operating within the structure. When one is faced with a particular sociometric structure, for example, then either of two kinds of questions might arise: *Why* is the structure like this (for example, why are so many choices focussed on individual A)? Or, *what will happen* to a community which has this structure when certain events arise (for example, what would happen if individuals A and B took opposite stands in a local political issue)? To give an idea of how measures are oriented toward one of these two questions, each will be discussed briefly below.

Source-Oriented Measures. There are a few rather generally applicable models which are explicitly related to the source of particular configurations. One of these concerns interdependence (or common dependence on a single factor) of choice, and one type of interdependence concerns who is chosen. Suppose there is no interdependence of choice with respect to who is chosen; then the choices will be randomly distributed among the different persons in the group. At the other extreme, suppose choices were fully interdependent; then everyone would choose the *same* person.[1]

Such a notion of interdependence of choice can serve as the basis for a measure of the average interdependence of decisions regarding whom to choose. This measure, built around statistical independence or interdependence of the choices, will be the first one developed below. Obviously, this will be a "source-oriented" measure, for the notion of interdependence, on which it is based, concerns how the choices were made, not what will happen given the structure as it stands. Similarly, other kinds of interdependence of choice can serve as the basis for other measures, some of which will be developed below.

Consequence-Oriented Measures. Suppose we examine for a moment the process of diffusion mentioned in Chapter 1 and discussed in more detail in Chapter 17. Would we expect that diffusion should occur alike in structures which differ radically in the way a closely knit community differs from a large city? Hardly so. Yet the logistic law of diffusion has no explicit element in it which takes account of such structural variations.

A closer examination, however, will reveal just where and how structural assumptions enter into this process. The rate of diffusion in that law is assumed proportional to the number of persons who have already taken on the attribute being diffused (n_1 in the notation of Chapter 17) and the number of persons who have yet to take it on (n_2, or $n - n_1$ in the notation of Chapter 17). Dimensionally, the process is as follows (labelling as "A's" those who have the attribute, and as "B's" those who do not):

$$\frac{\text{increase in A's}}{\text{time}} = (\text{number of A's}) \left(\frac{\text{number of persons contacted}}{\text{A} \times \text{time}} \right)$$

$$\times \left(\frac{\text{number of B's contacted}}{\text{person contacted}} \right) \times \left(\frac{\text{number of B's converted}}{\text{B contacted}} \right)$$

In the logistic law of diffusion, these dimensions are replaced by the following variable and constants:

$$\frac{dn_1}{dt} = (n_1)(k_1)\left(\frac{n_2}{n}\right)(k_3)$$

The constancy of k_1 through time expresses the assumption that the over-all rate of contact of each A does not change over time and does not differ among different A's, an assumption which is very often a reasonable one. Similarly,

---

[1] This assumes, of course, interdependence in a quite narrow sense, that is, actions which are *alike* with respect to the choice made.

the constant k_3 expresses the assumption that the probability of conversion of a B upon contact with an A is constant over time, and is independent of which B's and A's are in contact. But the replacement of "number of B's contacted per person contacted" with the fraction n_2/n implies a very definite structural assumption. It implies that every A, who has been converted, has the same number of contacts with the average nonconvert as with the average convert. This is a very strong structural assumption, as assumption of complete intermixing of the group. For if there were not complete intermixing, then the new convert almost certainly would have more contacts with other converts (i.e., those who converted him) than with nonconverts. If the structure were split up into small, inwardly focussed "pockets" or "cliques" which had little association with the outside, then either they would remain isolated, if the diffusing attribute did not originate with them, or they would never diffuse it outward, if it did originate with them. In other words, if the structure can be separated into cliques within which there is high association but between which there is little or none, then diffusion is restricted to the confines of these cliques. Now these considerations make it apparent that for a study of the *consequences* of a given structure in which a process of diffusion was in operation, a crucial measure is that of the "connectedness" of the structure, telling the degree to which such isolated cliques exist. Later in the chapter, some steps toward the development of measures of connectedness will be made; at the moment it is enough to see the conjunction between process theories such as diffusion, and the consequence-oriented measures to be developed here.

As in this example of the diffusion law, many models of social process imply complete intermixing of the population or complete "disorder" of the relations between them (in much the same way that certain laws of thermodynamics imply complete intermixing and consequent spatial homogeneity of the composition and temperature of a gas). Such an assumption allows many theories to remain quite simple, without building an elaborate mathematical appendage to take care of variations in structure from one group to another.

Thus the consequence-oriented measures of structure for use in conjunction with many process models will be those which characterize the degree of *deviation* from such complete intermixing. Since there are numerous directions in which structures can deviate from complete intermixing, each direction having its own consequences for one or another process, then numerous such measures are useful.

The strategy employed here, then, will be to use as a base line a structure in which all choices or contacts show complete intermixing, that is, complete "disorder" among the relations, and then to measure particular structures in terms of the distance they deviate from such complete intermixing. But what are some of the different ways that a structure can deviate from complete intermixing? Figure 14.1 gives some indication. In (a), there is order in the structure in the direction of choosing a person who is already highly chosen; in (b), there is order in the direction of not choosing a person who chooses you; in (c), there is again this tendency not to choose "down," but it proceeds in levels, rather than continuous chain; in (d), there is a tendency to reciprocate a choice made to you, or not to choose out of a restricted subgroup.

Each of these tendencies, or properties, of a structure can be measured separately—and most structures exhibit more than one such tendency. Thus the task to be begun below is the separate measurement of tendencies like those exhibited by Figure 14.1. Both a "source-oriented" and a "consequence-

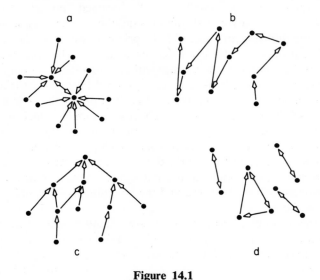

Figure 14.1

oriented" measure can be developed for some of these tendencies, as the first case will illustrate.

1. A SOURCE-ORIENTED MEASURE OF HIERARCHIZATION

The structure in Figure 14.1(a) can be considered either as an hierarchized structure, or as a structure in which all decisions about whom to choose are interdependent. Thus such interdependence concerning whom to choose will be called a tendency to hierarchization. This is one of the simplest measures of structural tendencies, for it is a measure which depends only on the distribution among people of choices received, and not upon where these choices come from. For example, if in a group of a hundred people each of whom has one choice to make, everyone chooses individual i, then there is complete hierarchization, as in Figure 14.1(a). The degree of hierarchization, then, is a measure which depends on the distribution of choices received among these hundred—the more skewed this distribution (i.e., the more people receiving either no choices or many), the more hierarchized the group.

Suppose we look at it this way: characterize each individual j in terms of the number of choices he receives, say n_j. Now suppose each person made three choices, and the choices were distributed completely at random, so that each choice is just as likely to go to one person as to another. What would be the distribution of n_j? Obviously the mean number of choices received would be three; the question is, how closely grouped around three would the n_j's be? Figure 14.2 shows, for a group of 26, what the distribution was for the average of six random experiments carried out for this purpose (Moreno and Jennings, 1945).[2] Accompanying this graph of a chance

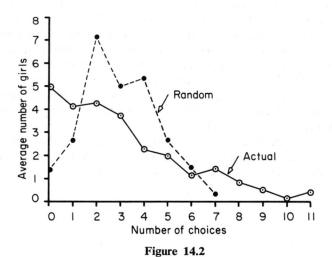

Figure 14.2

experiment is a line representing the average choice distribution in seven *actual* groups of 26 girls living together in cottages, when the girls were asked what three girls in the group they would most like to live in the same cottage with.

It seems evident that in this actual choice situation, the choices were far from random; some girls received many more choices than the random-choice experiment would predict; many more received no choices at all. The problem is then to *measure* the degree to which these choices focus on one or a few persons. Any single measure will of course sacrifice information, for it will substitute a single number for each distribution curve. But by sacrificing

---

[2] A seventh chance experiment is not included because the tabulation of results gave an incorrect total.

complexity, it will bring about comparability, so that a numerical comparison may be made between different curves.

The measure to be proposed here is based on a model of choice behavior in which choices are either made independently if no tendency toward hierarchization exists, or interdependently, with everyone tending to choose the same persons. If choices are made *independently* to the group members, then the distribution of choices will approximate that which would be expected from chance. But if there is some degree of interdependence between the choices made, so that one choice is likely to be made to the same person that other choices have gone to, some persons will get many choices, while others will get none, and the distribution will look more like the broken line of Figure 14.2. The measure, then, will be a measure of the degree of interdependence between choices which would give a distribution curve like that found (or more precisely, a distribution curve with the same variance as the actual curve). If the measure is .6, for example, this means that if every choice were .6 dependent upon the others, and .4 independent of others, such a distribution would have resulted. Or to look at it a little differently, we could say that .4 of the people made their choices independently, and then the other .6 just followed in their footsteps, choosing the same people the first .4 of the choices were directed to. If the measure is 1.0, this means that everyone chose the same person, following in the first chooser's footsteps.

The measure is derived as follows:

By use of the multivariate normal approximation to the multinomial distribution, it can be shown (see Mood, 1950, p. 272) that given a set of n choices distributed among k equally likely alternatives, the quantity

$$u = \frac{\Sigma\left(n_i - \dfrac{n}{k}\right)^2}{\dfrac{n}{k}} \tag{1.1}$$

is distributed approximately according to χ^2 with $k - 1$ degrees of freedom, with an expected value of $k - 1$. Equation (1.1) can be expressed in terms of p_i $(= n_i/n)$, the proportion of choices received by individual i:

$$u = nk\Sigma\left(p_i - \frac{1}{k}\right)^2 \tag{1.2}$$

Now if we actually had n independent choices, it would be possible to compare the quantity u to its expected value, $k - 1$. This is the basis for the usual χ^2 goodness-of-fit test which tells whether in fact the n choices *are* independent (or, alternatively, whether the p_i are equally likely). But in this case, we would already be reasonably certain, just by inspection, that the choices were not independent. Instead, we go on to ask the question, Just how interdependent are they? The question is then answered in terms of a value, n^*, which is the number of independent choices equivalent to the n interdependent ones. By *equating* the quantity u and its expected value, while substituting n^* for n, we can solve the equation for n^*, the hypothetical number of independent choices whose distribution has the same variance as the distribution of the n interdependent choices.

$$k - 1 = n^* k \Sigma \left(p_i - \frac{1}{k} \right)^2 \tag{1.3}$$

$$n^* = \frac{k - 1}{k \Sigma \left(p_i - \frac{1}{k} \right)^2} \tag{1.4}$$

This equation, however, should be corrected to take account of the fact that each man is excluded in the choices he himself makes. This was neglected for simplicity above, but when it is taken into account, eq. (1.4) becomes

$$n^* = \frac{k - 2}{k \Sigma \left(p_i - \frac{1}{k} \right)^2} \tag{1.5}$$

The ratio n^*/n can be thought of as the proportion of independence in each choice, and the measure of the degree of interdependence or common dependence of each choice is simply[3]

$$h_1 = 1 - \frac{n^*}{n} \tag{1.6}$$

$$h_1 = 1 - \frac{k - 2}{nk \Sigma \left(p_i - \frac{1}{k} \right)^2} \tag{1.7}$$

This measure of hierarchization of choice in the group, based on a model

[3] Confidence intervals for h may be computed by using in eq. (1.5), instead of the expected value of χ^2_{k-2}, the .025 and .975 values. Thus

$$h_a = 1 - \frac{\chi^2_{k-2}(.975)}{nk \Sigma \left(p_i - \frac{1}{k} \right)^2}$$

$$h_b = 1 - \frac{\chi^2_{k-2}(.025)}{nk \Sigma \left(p_i - \frac{1}{k} \right)^2}$$

where h_a and h_b are the limits of the 95% confidence interval. A statement like the following could then be made: "Ninety-five per cent of the times that such a distribution as this occurred, the actual degree of interdependence or common dependence of choices which would produce this distribution would be between h_a and h_b." A similar test would be used to determine the significance of the difference between h for one group and that for another.

about interdependence of choice behavior, constitutes the first measure to be introduced here. It can be ordinarily thought of as varying between zero and one, although more correctly it varies between zero and $n - 1/n$ (assuming

Table 14.1

DISTRIBUTION OF SOCIOMETRIC CHOICES IN SEVEN GROUPS OF GIRLS, AND DISTRIBUTION OF DRAWS OF BALLS IN CHANCE EXPERIMENTS

NUMBER OF CHOICES RECEIVED, x	NUMBER OF GIRLS RECEIVING x CHOICES *Cottage*						
	1	2	3	4	5	6	7
0	4	6	5	3	7	3	7
1	7	3	4	5	3	2	5
2	4	4	3	4	5	5	5
3	3	3	4	6	1	8	1
4	0	2	4	3	2	3	2
5	2	4	1	1	4	2	0
6	2	1	2	0	0	2	1
7	2	1	1	3	2	0	1
8	1	1	2	0	0	1	1
9	0	1	0	1	1	0	1
10	1	0	0	0	0	0	0
11	0	0	0	0	1	0	2
Total girls	26	26	26	26	26	26	26

NUMBER OF TIMES DRAWN, x	NUMBER OF BALLS DRAWN x TIMES *Experiment*					
	1	2	3	4	5	6
0	2	2	1	0	1	2
1	4	3	1	3	3	2
2	4	6	10	10	8	5
3	4	3	5	5	5	8
4	8	8	4	2	5	5
5	2	3	4	4	1	2
6	2	0	1	2	2	2
7	0	1	0	0	1	0
Total balls	26	26	26	26	26	26

positive or zero interdependence). This slight deviation from 1.0 as the upper limit is due to the fact that even at the maximum interdependence of choice, one choice is independent, determining *which* person will receive all the choices. If desired, a slight modification of h_1 can be used, one which adjusts for this so that zero and one are the limits for the measure:

$$h'_1 = \frac{nh_1}{n-1} \tag{1.8}$$

$$h'_1 = \frac{n}{n-1} - \frac{n(k-2)}{(n-1)k\Sigma\left(p_i - \frac{1}{k}\right)^2} \tag{1.9}$$

Example 1

Figure 14.2 was taken from data which Moreno and Jennings published in 1945, showing the distribution of sociometric choices within each of seven cottages of 26 girls each, as well as the distributions resulting from six random-choice experiments, in which balls were drawn from an urn. As was evident in this graph, the girls chose markedly differently from chance, focussing on a few of their fellows, and failing to choose others. In Table 14.1 are presented the choice data for each of the seven cottages and each of the six experiments.

A sample calculation, using cottage 1, is reproduced below:

$$n^* = \frac{k-2}{k\Sigma\left(p_i - \frac{1}{k}\right)^2} \tag{1.5}$$

$$= \frac{24}{26\left(\begin{matrix}.0059 + .0046 + .0007 + 0 + 0 + .0013 \\ + 0030 + .0053 + .0041 + 0 + .0081 + 0\end{matrix}\right)}$$

$$= 28.0$$

$$h_1 = 1 - \frac{n^*}{n} = 1 - \frac{28.0}{78} = .64$$

Table 14.2, giving the results of similar calculations for each cottage and each experiment, is presented below:

Table 14.2

MEASURES OF HIERARCHIZATION (h_1) AND EQUIVALENT NUMBER OF INDEPENDENT CHOICES (n^*) FOR 7 COTTAGES AND 6 CHANCE EXPERIMENTS

	n^*		h_1	
	Cottages	*Experiments*	*Cottages*	*Experiments*
1	28.0	78	.64	0
2	32.3	78	.59	0
3	36.0	104	.54	−.38
4	39.6	93	.49	−.24
5	24.5	78	.69	0
6	59.7	87	.23	−.16
7	18.5		.76	

The values for h_1 show that the experiments are all at or below zero hierarchization, while the cottages average around .4. The most hierarchized is cottage 7, and the least is cottage 6. The values of n^* show the number of independent choices for each cottage and experiment which would be equivalent to the interdependent ones actually made. As expected, the experiments all show around 78 equivalent choices[4] while the actual cottages behave *as if* there were only around 30 independent choices, or dividing by the three choices made by each girl, they behave as if there were only about ten independently choosing girls, all the others following in their footsteps.

It should be kept in mind, with this measure and others to follow, that the construction of the measure from data like those in Table 14.2 is the *second* stage of abstraction, following upon the abstraction of one particular kind of relation from the totality of actual relations between the people. In this case, a question about who the girl would most want as a cottage mate constituted the first stage of abstraction. If another question had been asked, a quite different set of relations would have been abstracted, and the final values of h_1 would have been quite different. Thus the problem of exactly what this measure actually measures is a problem both of the formal nature of the measure *and* the content of the question which elicited the choices.

Example 2

The example below illustrates quite well this possibility of abstracting different aspects of the structure. Three kinds of relations were abstracted from the social structure among the physicians in four communities (Coleman, Katz, and Menzel, 1957):

(A) When you need information or advice about questions of therapy, where do you usually turn?

(B) Who are the three or four physicians with whom you most often find yourself discussing cases or therapy in the course of an ordinary week—last week, for instance?

(C) Would you tell me who are your three friends whom you see most often socially?

Each doctor named three other doctors in response to each of these questions. Each of the three questions abstracts from the total structure a particular kind of relation; they may be conveniently summarized as relations of "therapeutic advice," "case discussion," and "friendship." Thus for each of these, a second abstraction can be carried out, obtaining a measure of the degree of hierarchization of each community with respect to each kind of relation. These are listed in Table 14.3.

---

[4] In three of the chance experiments, n^* is greater than n. Because n^* increases rapidly when the variance is less than expected (for example, n^* approaches infinity as the denominator of eq. (1.5) approaches zero) the measure should be used only when $n^* < n$.

Except in community C, structure of therapeutic advice is most hier-archized, as might be expected. The case discussion structure is less hier-archized than this, but considerably more so than the friendship structure. The differences between communities are also interesting: Communities B and D, for example, have *lower* hierarchization in case discussion, *higher* in friendship, than do communities A and C.

This table illustrates another property of the *h*-measure. It allows com-parison of groups of different sizes, as these communities are. Since it is a measure of the average degree of interdependence of each choice, the number of choices and the number of persons among whom the choices are distributed do not affect the measure. It is like a measure of the "average height" of a group in this respect.

In another respect, the similarity of the measures in Table 14.3 for communities of different sizes is of considerable interest, for it suggests that the causes of this hierarchization tendency are not affected by the number of

Table 14.3

HIERARCHIZATION OF DOCTORS IN FOUR COMMUNITIES, FOR THREE KINDS OF SOCIAL RELATIONS. ENTRIES IN TABLE ARE VALUES OF h_1 FROM EQ. (1.9)

Community	No. of doctors	Therapeutic advice	Case discussion	Friendship
Community A	106	.76	.63	.34
Community B	44	.77	.58	.59
Community C	34	.65	.67	.34
Community D	32	.75	.56	.53

doctors available for choice. The distribution of choices is flattened out in the larger communities to just the degree necessary to maintain constancy of h_1.

2. A CONSEQUENCE-ORIENTED CONCEPT OF HIERARCHIZA-TION: THE "DISORDER" OF THE CHOICES

A statistical concept which has recently received much attention through the development of information theory is the notion of "disorder," "entropy," or "information," as it is variously known, in the distribution of some quantity among a set of unordered alternatives. The intuitive conception is this: Suppose there exist k alternative cells in which an element might be located; if there is an equal probability of its being located in each, then there is a maximum amount of "entropy" or "uncertainty" in the system about where the particle is located; or to say it differently, there is a maximum amount of *disorder* in the system. If, on the other hand, the probability of its being in cell i is 1.0, and the probability of its being in any of the other cells is zero, then there is *no* uncertainty about its location, and there is complete order in the system. The statistical measure of disorder is[5]

$$H = -\Sigma p_i \ln p_i \qquad (2.1)$$

It is evident that such a conception is applicable to the structure of socio-metric relations, where the question concerns the distribution of choices among persons. As before, p_i is the proportion of all the choices received by individual i. The maximum disorder (that is, complete lack of hierarchization) among k cells is the base in which each individual gets exactly the same number of choices, so that each p_i equals $1/k$:

$$H_{max} = -\Sigma \frac{1}{k} \ln \frac{1}{k}$$

$$= \ln k \qquad (2.2)$$

Note here that the "base line" of maximum disorder (i.e., zero hierarchiza-tion) is complete equality of the p_i, where everyone receives exactly the same number of choices. In the previous measure, the base line is random distribu-tion of n choices, which would not be expected to result in exactly the same number of choices, but rather in a distribution like that of the solid line in Figure 14.2. When concerned with *sources* which generate a structure, the random-choice base line is what one would expect in the absence of tendencies of one sort or another. But when concerned with *consequences*, then the base line which matches the assumptions of the process models is that of perfect disorder, though such perfect disorder would almost never arise from chance.

The minimum disorder for this structure (in which all choices are directed to one person) is

$$H_{min} = -1 \ln 1 - \sum_{i=1}^{k-1} 0 \ln 0 \qquad (2.3)$$

$$= 0$$

A measure of hierarchization is a measure of the degree to which H deviates from H_{max}, standardized by the degree to which H_{max}, deviates from H_{min}, or

$$h_2 = \frac{H_{max} - H}{H_{max} - H_{min}} \qquad (2.4)$$

$$h_2 = \frac{\ln k + \Sigma p_i \ln p_i}{\ln k} \qquad (2.5)$$

[5] This measure was developed by Shannon (1949) by setting down the mathematical properties which a measure of "information" should have. It can also be derived from the combinatorial formula for the ratio of the number of ways n particles can be divided into k parts, each containing $n_1, n_2, \ldots n_k$, to the number of ways the n particles can be arranged, the formula on which Boltzmann, the physical chemist, based the notion of entropy: $n_1! \, n_2! \cdots n_k!/n!$. Using Stirling's approximation and letting n approach infinity, the right-hand side of eq. (2.1) follows.

$$h_2 = \frac{\Sigma p_i \ln k p_i}{\ln k} \tag{2.6}$$

Thus h_2 is the consequence-oriented measure of hierarchization based upon the notion of the degree of orderedness of the system.

It is interesting to note that the source-oriented measure, h_1, is logically related to h_2, though they of course are not identical. An alternative formula to that of eq. (1.2) for estimating u is $2n\Sigma p_i \ln k p_i$, making h_1 equal to $1 - (k - 2)/2n\Sigma p_i \ln k p_i$, as an alternative to eq. (1.7). As a result, the relation between h_1 and h_2 is

$$h_2 = \left(\frac{k - 2}{2n \ln k}\right)\left(\frac{1}{1 - h_1}\right)$$

This relationship between the two measures reflects three major conceptual differences between them. One difference is in their "base line" for zero hierarchization, as discussed above. Since h_2 takes the *random* distribution of choices as its base line, while h_2 takes the *completely equal* distribution as its base line, then if the distribution is more equal than would be expected from chance, h_1 would have a very high negative value, while h_2 would still be positive, though close to zero.

The second difference is related to the first: the conceptualization behind h_1 implies that as n increases, then if the distribution of p_i remains the same, hierarchization should increase, for this means that the interdependence of each choice is greater. The conceptualization behind h_2 assumes that it should remain the same, for the amount of "order" among the p_i's is the same.[6]

Finally, there is a difference in the metricization of these measures. Since h_2 is a direct function of the variance, and the variance increases greatly with extreme values of p_i, then h_2 is "suppressed" toward zero relative to h_1, only approaching one as the extreme values are reached. Since h_1 is a function of one minus the reciprocal of the variance, it is less sensitive to very high values of the variance, and more sensitive to low values. Table 14.4, comparing h_1 and h_2 for the seven groups of example 1 above, reflects this difference.

The first and third of these differences affect only the metrical relation of these measures, while the second affects the order relation as well. That is, for a given n and k (in which case the second difference is not applicable), h_2 and h_1 will *order* groups alike, as in Table 14.4; however, as n and k vary, h_2 and h_1 may order groups differently.

The two conceptions behind these two measurements of hierarchization, that is, the conception of "interdependence" of choice, and the conception of the "orderedness" of the choices in this system, are very general conceptions, which will underlie other measures of structural tendencies. For the study of

---

[6] Both these measures fail to take into account the problem resulting from the fact that as more choices are made by each person, the choices are no longer independent. Succeeding choices exclude the previous persons this chooser has chosen.

sources of particular configurations, measures like h_1 are appropriate; for the study of consequences of a structure when a particular process is in operation, then measures like h_2 are appropriate.

Table 14.4

COMPARISON OF TWO MEASURES OF HIERARCHIZATION FOR SEVEN COTTAGES OF GIRLS AND SIX CHANCE EXPERIMENTS

	COTTAGES		EXPERIMENTS	
	h_1	h_2	h_1	h_2
1	.64	.14	0	.06
2	.59	.13	0	.06
3	.54	.12	−.38	.04
4	.49	.10	−.24	.04
5	.69	.16	0	.05
6	.23	.08	−.16	.05
7	.76	.19		

3. "CONNECTEDNESS" OF THE STRUCTURE

The measures discussed above only hover on the edge of a characterization of the structure itself. The hierarchization measures consider only the distribution of choices received, and do not investigate where they came from. Consequently, they fail to characterize those aspects of the structure which may be of most importance for theoretical concerns.

Many of the processes with which structural measures might be used have to do with the *transmission* of something: the diffusion of some behavioral fad, the communication of information, the transmission of a rumor, and so on. If mathematical models characterizing such processes are to be constructed, then they must somehow take into account the varying degrees and kinds of connectedness in the social structures they are meant to characterize. A second group of social theories (not formal models in this case) is concerned with problems of consensus and cleavage between different segments of the population. For these theories too, the strength of social relations between various segments is a crucial determinant of consensus or cleavage. In general, the less the social connectedness between such segments, the greater will political cleavages be, and the more they will tend to diverge rather than converge as the issue grows more important.

Realizing the importance of structural variations for such theories, a number of authors have made some beginnings toward an analysis of this connectedness.[7] Rapoport (1949), Landau (1952), Shimbel (1948, 1951), and Solomonoff (1952), have investigated the characteristics of "random nets,"

---

[7] An extended expository review of this work is carried out elsewhere (Coleman, 1960).

that is, structures in which each individual establishes a (directed) connection with a given number of other persons, selecting these persons randomly from the total group. For the case in which each person makes only one connection, these authors have determined the expected number of 2-cycles, 3-cycles, 4-cycles, and so on in these random structures. (An example of a 3-cycle

is: This:

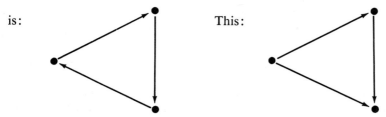

is not a cycle.) For the more general case, in which each person makes *a* connections, these expected values have not been found, though an approximate equation has been given for the expected number or cycles of *any* size that the individual is a member of (Landau, 1952). Along with this work on expected numbers of cycles, these authors (Solomonoff and Rapoport, 1951, Solomonoff, 1952) have given equations for finding the "connectivity" in a randomly connected group, where connectivity is the probability that any one member of the group is connected (taking into account direction of each link) to a randomly selected other.

As an extension of this work in the direction of a mathematical model to characterize actual structures, Rapoport (1951, 1953) has introduced the notion of distance bias, keeping the same assumption of random connections, except that the probability of choosing or contacting a person is a function of distance from the chooser along a one-dimensional continuum. An attempt has been made to use this work in the analysis of some data on diffusion of information (Rapoport, 1954).

Another direction of work, begun by Luce and Perry (1949) and followed by others (Luce, 1950, Festinger, 1949), has been to trace out the connectedness of a structure through matrix multiplication. A structure of relations such as those pictured in Figure 14.1 can be represented by a matrix in which each cell has a 0 or 1 entry, depending upon whether there is or is not a relation from the person represented by the column to the person represented by the row. For example, consider the following sociogram:

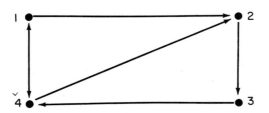

These relations can be represented by the following matrix:

To:

$$
\begin{array}{c c}
 & \begin{array}{c c c c} 1 & 2 & 3 & 4 \end{array} \\
\text{From:} \quad \begin{array}{c} 1 \\ 2 \\ 3 \\ 4 \end{array} & \left[\begin{array}{c c c c} 0 & 1 & 0 & 1 \\ 0 & 0 & 1 & 0 \\ 0 & 0 & 0 & 1 \\ 1 & 1 & 0 & 0 \end{array}\right]
\end{array}
$$

Now given such representation, the authors named above, as well as others, have used matrix multiplication to represent indirect connections from one person to another. For example, if the matrix is squared, then the ikth element of the new matrix (labelled $_2a_{ik}$) will be

$$_2a_{ik} = a_{ij}a_{jk}$$

The numerical value of $_2a_{ik}$ represents the number of connections from i to k at the first remove.

In the matrix above, the element $_2a_{12}$ of the squared matrix would be the first row multiplied by the second column:

$$_2a_{12} = 0 \times 1 + 1 \times 0 + 0 \times 0 + 1 \times 1 = 1$$

That is, there is a single connection from 1 to 2 in one remove. Examination of the sociogram shows that individual 4 provides the intermediate link: $1 \to 4 \to 2$.

By raising the matrix to higher powers, Luce and Perry have defined "n-chains," which are chains of n steps in length from i to j. If the matrix A is raised to the nth power, then the numerical value of each entry, $_na_{ij}$, will represent the number of n-chains from i to j. In the above sociogram and matrix, there would be one 3-chain from 1 to 3: $1 \to 4 \to 2 \to 3$. This can be found either by examining the sociogram or by cubing the matrix and looking at the entry $_3a_{13}$.

It is evident that some concept like these n-chains is necessary for characterizing the "connectedness" of the structure, as we would like to do here. But before developing these notions of connectedness, it is useful to note one other direction which this work has taken. Luce (1950) has gone on to develop a concept of n-cliques, which are "cliques" of persons all of whom stand in an n-chain or closer relation to one another. In empirical work where it is desired to break up a larger group into subgroups or cliques in terms of their sociometric connections, this method may be quite useful. Other methods of arriving at such "cliques" have been devised with computer techniques (Coleman and MacRae, 1960).

3.1 Development of measures of connectedness

If the general desire is to see how a structure would *function* given a process of contagion or influence which "flows" through it, some sort of notion of connectedness is required. Such a measure must be approached stepwise, first of all establishing a measure of connectedness for each pair of individuals, and then going on to characterize the structure as a whole. To obtain a pairwise measure of connectedness from *i* to *j*, it is necessary to first have at hand all the chains of any length from *i* to *j*, and then to obtain a summary measure by giving different weights to the chains of different lengths.

Surprisingly enough, it seems extremely difficult to find all the chains of different lengths from each person to each other. At first glance, it seems that the matrix multiplication method accomplishes this; but this method allows doubling back, so that the same connections are counted more than once. For example, in the sociogram above, matrix multiplication will show a 3-chain from 1 to 2, made up of the following links: $1 \rightarrow 4 \rightarrow 1 \rightarrow 2$. Ordinarily, such "doubling back" over the same paths would be undesirable.

However, I know of no practical method for eliminating the doubling back and yet still giving all the other *n*-chains from *i* to *j*. Of course, by laborious tracing out of paths in a sociogram the *n*-chains can be found; the problem lies in finding a practical method, which can be used with large groups as well as small ones.

An approximation has been found, however, and will be presented below. It differs from the complete solution in eliminating all paths from *i* to *j* which have one or more links in common with a shorter path from *i* to *j*. For example, in the 4-person sociogram above, the chain $1 \rightarrow 4 \rightarrow 2 \rightarrow 3$ would not be counted, because it uses the link $2 \rightarrow 3$ which is part of the chain $1 \rightarrow 2 \rightarrow 3$. This method thus errs in the opposite direction than that of the matrix multiplication; where that method counts too many chains, this one counts too few. However, the method will be presented below.

3.2 Method for determining the distinct *n*-chains from each element to each other

(a) Rather than using the matrix as a whole, separate each row vector out, so that each individual's chains are calculated separately. Call these row vectors a_i.

(b) To find the 2-chains from individual *i*, multiply the original matix *A* (modified slightly as indicated below, and labelled A_{i1}) on the left by the vector a_i. This will give a row vector (labelled a_{i2}) representing the 2-chains beginning with individual *i*. In vector notation:

$$a_i A_{i1} = a_{i2}$$

(c) To obtain the 3-chains from *i*, multiply the matrix A_{i1} (again slightly modified and labelled A_{i2}) on the left by the vector a_{i2}. This will give the row vector representing the 3-chains beginning with individual i. In vector notation,

$$a_{i2}A_{i2} = a_{i3}$$

(d) Modification of the matrix is as follows: each time the matrix is modified by replacing with zeroes the one's which have been "used up" to create the previous vector. This prevents re-use of these same relations.

The example given above will be used to show how this method operates:

$$a_1 = \begin{matrix} 0 & 1 & 0 & 1 \end{matrix}$$
$$a_{11} = \begin{pmatrix} 0 & 0 & 0 & 0 \\ 0 & 0 & 1 & 0 \\ 0 & 0 & 0 & 1 \\ 1 & 1 & 0 & 0 \end{pmatrix}$$

(The first row is replaced by zeroes, since the first row is used up by direct connections.)

$$a_1 A_{11} = a_{12} = \begin{matrix} 1 & 1 & 1 & 0 \end{matrix}$$
$$A_{12} = \begin{pmatrix} 0 & 0 & 0 & 0 \\ 0 & 0 & 0 & 0 \\ 0 & 0 & 0 & 1 \\ 0 & 0 & 0 & 0 \end{pmatrix}$$

(Only the a_{34} choice remains, for the others were used to make up 2-chains.)

$$a_{12}A_{12} = a_{13} = \begin{matrix} 0 & 0 & 0 & 1 \end{matrix}$$

No longer chains from 1 exist, since the remaining matrix, A_{13}, now consists entirely of zeroes. Matrices reconstructed from the vectors a_{in} are given below, showing the direct links, 2-chains, 3-chains, 4-chains, and 5-chains:

1-chains	2-chains	3-chains	4-chains	5-chains
$\begin{bmatrix} 0 & 1 & 0 & 1 \\ 0 & 0 & 1 & 0 \\ 0 & 0 & 0 & 1 \\ 1 & 1 & 0 & 0 \end{bmatrix}$	$\begin{bmatrix} 1 & 1 & 1 & 0 \\ 0 & 0 & 0 & 1 \\ 1 & 1 & 0 & 0 \\ 0 & 1 & 1 & 1 \end{bmatrix}$	$\begin{bmatrix} 0 & 0 & 0 & 1 \\ 1 & 1 & 0 & 0 \\ 0 & 1 & 1 & 1 \\ 0 & 0 & 0 & 1 \end{bmatrix}$	$\begin{bmatrix} 0 & 0 & 0 & 0 \\ 0 & 1 & 0 & 1 \\ 0 & 0 & 0 & 0 \\ 0 & 0 & 0 & 0 \end{bmatrix}$	$\begin{bmatrix} 0 & 0 & 0 & 0 \\ 0 & 0 & 0 & 0 \\ 0 & 0 & 0 & 0 \\ 0 & 0 & 0 & 0 \end{bmatrix}$

This approach, which has been programmed for a computer for use with large groups (see Appendix to this chapter), has the advantage of arriving at a "stopping point," which the original matrix multiplication does not do. It also provides a tabulation of the persons to which each member is ultimately connected. Having such a tabulation, it becomes possible to provide one kind of measure of the connectivity of a structure, based on the proportion of persons who are ultimately connected.

To determine for an actual structure who is connected to whom, it is merely necessary to examine each of these matrices of 1-chain, 2-chains, etc., until the final zero matrix is reached, indicating that there are no longer chains. If there is a 1 in the ijth cell of *any* of these matrices, then there is a connection from i to j. A summary matrix can be written, having entries of 1 unless the ijth entry in every matrix (of 1-chains, 2-chains, etc.) is zero. For the example above, the structure is fully connected, so that the summary matrix would be all 1's. Now for a larger group (and none of these algebraic procedures are useful for a small group like that in the example), such a summary matrix of ultimate connections can provide some quite fruitful measures. An example below will illustrate its usefulness.

Example

In the fall of 1957, and the spring of 1958, boys in a small high school in Illinois were asked, "What fellows here in school do you go around with most often?" (The data are from research reported in Coleman, 1961.) Table 14.5 shows the direct choices of each of the 73 boys, at the two times. (The students are ordered so that persons who choose one another are fairly close together. For a systematic method of carrying out such an ordering, see Beum and Brundage, 1950). From this matrix can of course be found the number of choices received by each individual (the sum of each column), and it can also be used to find the matrices of 2-chains, 3-chains, etc., and the summary matrix of total connectivity. This total connectivity matrix, presented in Table 14.6, shows a considerably different picture than does the matrix of direct choices. From this matrix, it is possible to derive three kinds of measures besides the entries themselves. First each row sum tells the number of persons to which each individual's choices connect him. For example, in the fall, No. 71 has indirect attachments to 63, 64, 66, 67, 69, and 70, altogether 6 of the 72 persons he could be attached to. At the other extreme, No. 4 has connections to a total of 32 people. The range in this group is from 6 up to a high of 32. Thus these rows can be used to provide measures which sharply differentiate different persons in terms of the number of persons their choices ultimately lead to. The possible use of such measures will be mentioned shortly.

The column totals are just as relevant as are the row totals, for they show the attachments made *to* the person in question. There are, for example, only 36 out of 72 persons whose choices do not lead, directly or indirectly, to No. 71. In contrast, No. 4 has only 15 persons connected through their choices to him, though his choices connect him to 32 persons.

One area of usefulness of these measures is related to processes of *flow*, considering these relations as paths for the flow. Suppose it is known (or desired to test) that a particular kind of communication or influence or imitation travels along these paths. Then these measures make it possible to state what the consequences should be of introducing an innovation at one point rather than another. If, for example, influence travels from the chosen to the chooser (and there is no loss through distance), then the introduction of an innovation by No. 71 would mean that the innovation ultimately reached all but 36 persons. Or an introduction by both No. 68 and No. 71 would reach everyone except 10, 25, 72, and 73. At the other extreme, there

Table 14.5

SOCIOMETRIC CHOICE MATRIX FOR BOYS IN A SMALL HIGH SCHOOL

(Row=chooser; column=chosen; column on right=total number of choices made)

```
 1  0000000000001100000100000000000000000000000000000011000000000000000000   6
 2  0000000000000000001110000000000000000000000000000000000000000000000000   3
 3  0000000001000001000000000000000000000000000000000000000000000000000000   3
 4  0000100000000000011000000000000000000000100000000000000000000000000000   5
 5  0000000000000000001000000000000000000010000000000000000000000000000000   3
 6  0000000000001000000101000000000000000000000000000000000000000000000000   4
 7  0000000000000001100000000000000000000000000000000000000000000000000000   2
 8  0000000000100100000000000000000000000000000000000000000000000000000000   3
 9  0000000000010000000111000000000000000000001000000000000000000000000000   6
10  0000000000000000000000000000000000000000000000000000000000000000000000   1
11  000000000000000C0010000000000000000000000000101100000000000000000000000   5
12  0000000000000000011100000000000000000000000000000000000000000000000000   4
13  0000000000000000100111000000000000000000000000000000000000000000000000   5
14  0000000000000000011000000000000000000000000000000000000000000000000000   3
15  000000000000000C000100000000000000000000000000000000000000000000000000   2
16  0000000000000000010000000000000000000101000000000000000000000000000000   4
17  0000011000000000000000000000000000000000000000000000000000000000000000   3
18  00000C0000100001001C000000000000000000000000000000000000000000000000000   4
19  0001000000100001010000000010000000000000000000000000000000000000000000   6
20  0000010000010000000110000000000010000000000000000000000000000000000000   6
21  0000000000000001000000000000000000000000000010011000000000000000000000   5
22  00000000000000000011000000000000010000000000010000000000000000000000000   5
23  0000000000000000000000C000000000001001000001011000000101001001001000000  10
24  00000C0000000000000000000000000000000000001000000000000000000000000000   2
25  00000C000000000000000000000000000000000000000000100000000000000000000000   1
26  000000000000000C00000000000001001100011100000000000000000000000000000000   7
27  000000000000000C0010000000000000100100000000000000000000000000000000000   4
28  0000000000000000000000000000000011000000000000000000000000000000000000   3
29  0000000000100000000000000000010000000000000000000000000000000000000000   3
30  00000C00000000000000000000000001000000000001000000000000000000000000000   3
31  0000000010000C0000000000C000000000010010000000000000000000000000000000   4
32  0000000000000000000001000001000000001000000000000001000000000000000000   5
33  00000C00000000000000C00000000000010001110000000000000000000000000000000   5
34  00000C000000000CC000U000000000000000010000010000000000000000000000000000   3
35  00000C000000000C000000000000100000000001000000000000000000000000000000   3
36  00000C0000000C00C00C000C0C000011000000011000000000000000000000000000000   5
37  00000C000000000C0000000000001000000U010000000000000000000000000000000000   3
38  00000C0000000CC00011000000000000000001001000000000000000000000000000000   5
39  00000C00000000CC0000000000011000100000000001000000000001000000000000000   6
40  00000C0000000CC00U000000000000101000000000000000000000000000000000000000   3
41  0000000000000010000000000000001100000000000000000000010000100000000000   5
42  0000000000000000000000000000010001010000000000000000000100000000100000   5
43  00000C000000CC0000000000000000U011000000000000000000000100000000100000   4
44  00000C0000000C0000U000000000000000010000000000000000000000000000000000   2
45  00000C0000000C0000C0000000000000000001000110100000000000010000000001000   6
46  00000C0000000CC00U000000000010001000000100000010001000000100000000000000   5
47  00000C000000000000000000000000000U1001001110000000000000000000000000000   5
48  00000C000000000C0000C0000001000000000101100000000000000000000000000000   5
49  00000C0000000C00C0000000000000000000011000000000001100000000000001100   5
50  00000C000000000C00000000000000000001000110000000000000000100000   5
51  00000C000000000000011000000000000000000000000000000000000000001000   4
52  00000C000000000C000000000000000011010010000000000000001000000   6
53  00000C000000000C00000000000000001010000000000000000000000000   3
54  00000C000000000C00000000000010001000010000001000001000010100   7
55  00000C000000000C00000000000010001000100001000000000000000000   4
56  00000C00000000C0000000000000000000000000000001000001100   4
57  00000C000000C0000000000000000010001000001000000000010001100   7
58  00000C00000C0C00C00000000000000000000000000000001000100000000   3
59  00000C000000000C00C0C00000001000000100001100000000000000000   4
60  00000C000000000C000000000C0000000000000000001001100100000000   5
61  00000C000000C00C00000000000000000000000000001000000100000000   3
62  00000C0000000C00000000000000000C00000000000000010000100000000   3
63  00000C0000000C00000000000000000000000000000000000000011011100   6
64  00000C00000000000000000000000000000000000000000U000011010100   5
65  00000C000000000CC00000000000000000000000000000010100000100000   4
66  00000C0000000C00000000000001000000000000000000000001001011100   6
67  00000C0000000C00C0000000000000000000000000000000011010010100   6
68  00000C0000C00000C0000000001000000000000000000011001000000000   5
69  00000C000000000C00000000000000000000000000000000011011000100   6
70  00000C000000000C00U0000000000000000000000000000010011010100   6
71  00000C0000000CC00000000C00000000000U00000U00000011011011000   7
72  00000C000000000C00C00000000000000000000000000000000000000000   1
73  00000C0000000C00000000000000000000000000000000000000000000000   1
```

(b) SPRING 1958

```
 1 00000000000000010000011000000000000000000000000000000000000000000000000000   4
 2 00000C001000000000000010000000000000C00000000000000000000000000000000000000   3
 3 000000C0000000000C0000000000000000000000000000000000000000000000000000000000   1
 4 00001C00001000C100100000000000000000000000001000000000000000000000000000000   6
 5 00010000000000000010000000000000000000000010000000000000000000000000000000   4
 6 00000C010000010001001000000001000000000000000000000000000000000000000000000   6
 7 00000C0000001000100010000000000000000000000000000000000000000000000000000000   4
 8 00000C000000011000000000000001000000000000000000000000000000000000000000000   4
 9 00000C0000000000011100000000000000000000000000000000000000000000000001000   5
10 00000C000000000C001100000000000000000000000000000000000000000000000000000   3
11 00010000000000010010000000000001000000001000000000000000000000000000000000   6
12 00000C000000000011100000000000000000000000000000000000000000000000000000000   4
13 0000110000000000100101000000000000000000000000000000000000000000000000000   6
14 00000C000000010000000010000000000000000000000000000000000000000000000000000   3
15 10000C00001000000011000000000000000000000000000000000000000000000000000000   5
16 00000C000000000000000000000000000000001000000000000000000100000100000000   4
17 10000C11000100000000100000000000000000000000000000000000000000000000000000   6
18 00000C00000000000001000000000000000000000000000000000000000000000000000000   2
19 00011C000101100C0000000000000000000000000000000000000000000001000000000   6
20 00000C001001001000101100000000000000000000000000000000000000000000000000   6
21 00000C00000000000000C1010000000000000100000000000010001000000000000000000   6
22 00000C000000000000011000000100000000001000000001000000000000000000000000   6
23 00000C0000000000C000000000000000000000000000000011000000000010000001100   6
24 00000C000000000000C00000000010000000000000000000000000000000000000000000   2
25 00000C000000000C0000000000000000000000000000000000000000000000000000000   1
26 00000C0000000000000000000000001010101001000000000000000000000000000000000   6
27 00001C000000000CC00000000000000001010010010000000000000000000000000000000   6
28 00000C00000000000C00C01000C00000000011000000000000000000000000000000000000   4
29 00000C00000000000C0C0000000000000001C01000001000000000C00000000000000000000   4
30 00000C0000000000C0C0000000000000000001010000000000000000000000000000000000   3
31 00000C000000000CC0000001000000000000010010000000001000000000000000000000   5
32 00000C000000000C0000000000001000100101100010000000000000000000000000000   7
33 00000C000000000C0C0C0000000000000010000111000000000000000000000000000000   5
34 00000C0000000000C000C0000000000000000000010000000000000000000000000000000   2
35 00000C0000000000C000000000000000000000000000000000000000000000000000000   1
36 00000C0000000000C000000000000010001000000111000000000000000000000000000000   6
37 00000C000000000000000000010010000000010000000000000000000000000000000000   4
38 00000C000000000000011000010000000C010000000000000000000000000C00000000000   5
39 00000C000C000C000000000000100000010000001000000000010000000001000   6
40 00000C00C0000C00C0000000001001000001000000000000000000000000000000000000   4
41 00000C000000000C01000000000001C0000001011000000000000000000000000100000   6
42 00000C00000000000C0000000001000000000101000000000000000000000000100000   4
43 00000C00000000CC0C000000000000001000000011000000000000000000000001000000   5
44 0000CCC0000000000000000000000000000000001001000000000000000000000C000   3
45 00000C000000000C0C000C00000000000000000C001010011C1C000C00000000000   6
46 00000C0000000CC0C00C00000000000000001000000010100110000000000000000   6
47 00000C0000000CC0C00C000000000000C0000000000000000000000000000000000   2
48 00000C000000000C0000C000C0C0000000000010010100110000000000000000   6
49 000C0C0C00000C000000C00000000000000000C0000001000111010C000000000000   6
50 00000C000000CC0C0000010000000C000C00000000001100000000000000000   4
51 00000C000C00C000001000C0000000000000C00C1001000011000000000000000   6
52 00000C00000000000000000000000000000C000000000000100010100000000000000   4
53 00000C000000000C00C000000000000000000000000000100100000000010000000   5
54 00000C00C0000C0C0C00000000000000000C00010001010010000100000000001000   6
55 00000C0C0C0C00C0C000C00000C00000000003001000100111000000000000000000   6
56 00000C00000000000000000000000000000000000000000000000000100001101100   6
57 00000C0C00000C0C0C000000000000000C0000000101000010C00000010001000   6
58 00000C0C000000CC00C00000000000000000000000000000000001000100000000   3
59 00000C00000000000000000000000C000010000001100000010000000000100100   6
60 00000C00C000000C00C00000000000000000C00C0C000100110000001100   6
61 00000CC0000C00C0C00000000000000000000C00000000001000001100000000   4
62 000000000000000C00C00000000000000000C0000000000000001000000U0001000   3
63 00000C000000000C00C0000000000000000000C000000000000000000000011011100   6
64 00000C000000000C00C0000000000000000000000000000000C0C00C00010001100   4
65 00000C0000000000C00C0000000000000000C000000000000000000000001101100   5
66 00000C00000000C00C0C0000000000000000000000000000C00C00011001001100   6
67 00000C000000000C0C000C0C0000000000000000000000C00000010010010001100   6
68 00000C0000000000C0000000000000C0000000000000C0C000000000100000100100   4
69 00000C00000000C0C00000000000000000000C00000000000000011011000100   6
70 00000C00000000C0CC00C0000000000000000C000000000000000001C011010100   6
71 000C0CC0000000CC0C0C00C000000000000000000000000C100000110001000   6
72 00000C000000000C00C0C00C000000000000000000000C00C000000C0C000000000   1
73 00000C000000000C00C00000000000000000000000000000000000000000000000   1
```

Table 14.6

Matrix of Ultimate Connectedness for Boys in a Small High School

(Row = chooser; column = chosen. First column on right = total number of persons to whom choices lead. Last row = total number of persons from whom choices lead. Last column = number of steps to reach ultimate connectedness)

(a) FALL 1957

#	Matrix	Lead	Steps
1	1000011110001111C1001110000000000000000100000010001010011010000011011011100	26	5
2	0100011100011CC1CC11100000000000000100000010001010100001011011011100	25	6
3	0010011110001111C1CC111000C0000000C00010000001000101001101C0C00C11011011100	27	6
4	00011C00011000C1C11C00000110011110111001111100111010110011100100100000	33	4
5	00C11C0001100001011C000001100111101111001111100111010110000101110010010000	33	4
6	00000111000111CC1001110000000000000000100000010001010011010000011011011100	24	4
7	000001110001111CC1001110C0000000000000100000010001011001101000000110110111100	24	6
8	0000011100011CC1001110000000000C000100000010001010011010000C11011011100	24	4
9	00C000111100111CC100111000000000000C00010000010001010011010000011011011100	25	5
10	00000C00010000CC000C0000000000000001000000000000000000000000000000000000	1	0
11	00011C00011000C1011000000011001111101111001111100110101100001011100100100000	33	6
12	000001110001111CC1C011100000000000000000100000010001010011010000011011011100	24	5
13	000001110001111CC100111000000000000000010000001000101001101000001101101110	24	3
14	000001110001111CC100111000000000000000000100000010001010011010000011011011100	24	5
15	00000111000111C10011100000000000000000100000010001010011010000011011011100	25	5
16	00011C00011000C1011000000011001111101111001111100110101100001011100100100000	33	4
17	000001110001111CC1C0111000000000000000100000010001010011010000011011011100	24	5
18	00011C00011000C1011000000011001111101111001111100110101100001011100100100000	33	5
19	00011C0001100001011C000001100111110111100111110011010110000101110010010000	33	5
20	00000111000111CC1C0111000000000000000010000001000101001101000000011011011100	24	4
21	000001110C0111CC100111000000000000000000100000010001010011010000011011011100	24	6
22	000001110001111CC10011100000000000000010000001000101001101000001101101110	24	5
23	00011C0001100001011000100110011110111001111100110101100001011100100100000	34	6
24	00000111000111CC100111010000000000000010000001000101001101000001101101110	25	7
25	00000C0000C0000C000C0000010000000000000000000000000000000000000000000000	1	0
26	00011C00011000C1011000000011001111101111001111100110101100001011100100100000	33	5
27	00011C0001100001011C00000011001111101111001111100110101100001011100100100000	33	6
28	00000111000111CC1C0100110000011000010000011010100110101000011011011100	30	5
29	00000111000111CC1C0110000000001000000010001001001101100000011011011100	25	4
30	00000C000100000C000C00000000011000101001000100110101100001011100100100000	19	5
31	00000C000100000C000C00000000011000101001000100110101100001011100100100000	19	6
32	00011C00011000C101100000001100111101111001111100110101100001011100100100000	33	6
33	00011C0001100001011000000011001111101111001111100110101100001011100100100000	33	6
34	0000011100011CC100111000000110000100011000011001010011010001011011011100	30	5
35	00000C000100000C000C0000000011000101001000100110101100001011100100100000	19	5
36	00011C0001100001011000000011001111101111001111100110101100001011100100100000	33	6
37	00000C00010000000000000000011000101001000100110101100001011100100100000	19	6
38	00000111000111CC100111000000000000001000010010011010000011011011100	24	6
39	000001110001111CC1001110000011000010001100000110010100111010100011011011100	30	4
40	00000C000100000C000C0000000011000101001000100110101100001011100100100000	19	5
41	00011C00011000C1011000000011001111101111001111100110101100001011100100100000	33	5
42	00011C0001100001011000000011001111101111001111100110101100001011100100100000	33	6
43	00011C00011000C1011000000011001111101111001111100110101100001011100100100000	33	6
44	00000C000100000C000C00000000011000101001000100110101100001011100100100000	19	5
45	00000C000100000C000C00000000000000010000001000100001101100001011011011100	12	2
46	00000111000111CC1C01110000011000010001100000110010100110101000011011011100	30	5
47	00000C000100000C000C00000000011000101001000100110101100001011100100100000	19	4
48	00000C000100000C000C00000000011000101001000100110101100001011100100100000	19	4
49	00000C000100000C000C0000000000000000010001000011011000001011011011100	12	2
50	00000C000100000C000C00000000011000101001000100110101100001011100100100000	19	3
51	000001110001111C010011100000000000000001000000100010100110100000011011011100	24	6
52	00000C000100000C000C00000000011000101001000100110101100001011100100100000	19	3
53	00000C000100000C000C00000000011000101001000100110101100001011100100100000	19	4
54	00000000000000000000000000000000000100010000011011011100	12	1
55	00000C000100000C000C0000000000000000000010001000011010000011011011100	12	2
56	00000000000000000000000000000000000000000001000000110110111100	8	1
57	00000C000100000CC000C00000000000000100010000110100000011011011100	12	1
58	00000C000100000C000C00000000011000101001000100110101100001011100100100000	19	8
59	00000111000111CC1C0100111000001100001000110000011001010011010100011011011100	30	5
60	00000C000100000C000C00000000011000101001000100110101100001011100100100000	19	8
61	00000C000100000C000C00000000011000101001000100110101100001011100100100000	19	8
62	00000C000100000C000C00000000011000101001000100110101100001011100100100000	19	8
63	00000000000000000000000000000000000000000000000000110110111100	7	1
64	00000000000000000000000000000000000000000000000000110110111100	7	1
65	00000C000100000CC000000000011000101001000100110101100001011100100100000	19	7
66	00000000000000000000000000000000000000000000000000110110111100	7	1
67	00000000000000000000000000000000000000000000000000110110111100	7	1
68	00000C000100000C000C00000000011000101001000100110101100001011100100100000	19	6
69	00000000000C0000C0000000000000000000000000000000000110110111100	7	1
70	00000000000000000000000000000000000000000000000000110110111100	7	1
71	00000000000000000000000000000000000000000000000000110110111100	7	0
72	00000000000000000000000000000000000000000000000000000000000010	1	0
73	00000C00000000000000000000000000000000000000000000000000000001	1	0

(b) SPRING 1958

```
 1 10011C00101100110C1111000001100010010110111011111101111111111111111111100    47   7
 2 01011C00101100C10C1111000001100010010110111011111101111111111111111111100    46   5
 3 00100C00000000C00C00000C000C0000000000000000000000000000000000000000000000     1   0
 4 00011C001C1100C1100111100000110001001010110111011111111111111111111111100    45   5
 5 00011C00101100C100111100000110001001011011011111101111111111111111111100    45   5
 6 10011111101111111101111000C01100010010110111011111011111111111111111111100    53   6
 7 10011111101111111101111000011000100101101110111111011111111111111111111100    53   7
 8 10011111101111111101111000011000100101101110111111011111111111111111111100    53   6
 9 00011C00101100C100111100001100010010110111011111101111111111111111111100    45   4
10 00011C00111100C101111100000110001001011011101111111111111111111111111100    47   6
11 00011C00101100C100111100000110001001011011101111101111111111111111111100    45   5
12 00011C00101100010011110000011000100101101110111111011111111111111111111100    45   6
13 10011111101111111101111000001100010010110111011011111111111111111111111100    53   6
14 10011111101111111101111000011000100101101110111111011111111111111111111100    53   7
15 10011C00101100100111100000110001001011011101111101111111111111111111100    47   6
16 00000C0000000000100000000000100010010000011100000000000010101111111111100    21   3
17 10011111101111111101111000001100010010110111011111101111111111111111111100    53   7
18 00011C00101100C101111000001100010010110111011111101111111111111111111100    46   6
19 00011C00101100C100111100000110001001011011011111011111111111111111111100    45   5
20 00011C00101100010011110000011000100101101110111111011111111111111111111100    45   5
21 00011C00101100C100111100000110001001011011101111011111111111111111111100    45   6
22 00011C00101100C100111100000110001001011011011111101111111111111111111100    45   6
23 00011C00101100C100111100001100010010110111011111011111111111111111111100    46   6
24 00011C00101100C100111101000110001001011011011111011111111111111111111100    46   6
25 00000C00000000C00000000000000000000000000000000000000000000000000000000     1   0
26 00011C00101100C100111100011111011111111011111101111111111111111111111100    54   5
27 00011C00101100C100111100001111001011111111011111101111111111111111111100    51   6
28 00011C00101100C100111100000110001001011011011111101111111111111111111100    45   5
29 00000C00000000C100000000001000100010000011100000000000101C1111111111100    21   6
30 00011C00101100C100111100001111001011111111011111101111111111111111111100    51   8
31 00011C00101100C100111100001111101111111111111111111111111111111111111100    54   7
32 00011C00101100C100111100001100110010110111011111011111111111111111111100    46   5
33 00000C00000000C0100000000000100010010000011100000000000101011111111111100    21   5
34 00011C00101100C100111100001100011010110111011111101111111111111111111100    46   6
35 00000C00000000C00000000000001000100000000000000000000000000000000000000     1   0
36 00000C00000000C100000000000100010010000011100000000000101011111111111100    21   5
37 00011C00101100C100111100001111001011111111011111101111111111111111111100    51   7
38 00011C00101100C100111100000110001001011011101111011111111111111111111100    45   5
39 00011C00101100C100111100000110001001011011011111011111111111111111111100    45   6
40 00011C00101100C100111100001111001011111111011111101111111111111111111100    51   7
41 00000C00000000C100000000000100010000011100000000000101011111111111100    21   4
42 00000C00000000C100000000000100010010000011100000000000101011111111111100    21   5
43 00000C00000000C100000000000100010010000011100000000000101011111111111100    21   4
44 00011C00101100C100111100001100010010110111111111111111111111111111111100    48   9
45 00011C00101100C100111100000110001001011011101111011111111111111111111100    45   6
46 00011C00101100C100111100000110001001011011101111011111111111111111111100    45   6
47 00011C00101100C100111100000110001001011011101111011111111111111111111100    45   8
48 00011C00101100C100111100000110001001011011101111011111111111111111111100    45   6
49 00011C00101100C100111100000110001001011011101111011111111111111111111100    45   6
50 00011C00101100C100111100000110001001011011101111111111111111111111111100    47   8
51 00011C00101100C100111100000110001001011011101111011111111111111111111100    45   5
52 00011C00101100C100111100000110001001011011101111011111111111111111111100    45   7
53 00011C00101100C100111100000110001001011011101111011111111111111111111100    45   8
54 00011C00101100C100111100000110001001011011101111011111111111111111111100    45   6
55 00011C00101100C100111100000110001001011011101111011111111111111111111100    45   7
56 00000000000000C000000000000000000000000000000000000101011111111111100    14   3
57 00011C00101100C100111100000110001001011011101111011111111111111111111100    46   6
58 00000000000000C0000000000000000000000000000000000000101011111111111100    14   2
59 00011C00101100C100111100000110001001011011101111011111111111111111111100    45   7
60 00000000000000C000000000000000000000000000000000000000101011111111111100    14   2
61 00000000000000C0000000000000000000000000000000000000000101011111111111100    14   2
62 00000000000000C000000000000000000000000000000000000000101011111111111100    14   3
63 00000000000000C000000000000000000000000000000000000000101011111111111100    14   3
64 00000000000000C000000000000000000000000000000000000000101011111111111100    14   4
65 00000000000000C000000000000000000000000000000000000000101011111111111100    14   2
66 00000000000000C000000000000000000000000000000000000000101011111111111100    14   3
67 00000000000000C000000000000000000000000000000000000000101011111111111100    14   2
68 00000000000000C000000000000000000000000000000000000000101011111111111100    14   3
69 00000000000000000000000000000000000000000000000000000101011111111111100    14   3
70 00000000000000000000000000000000000000000000000000000101011111111111100    14   3
71 00000000000000000000000000000000000000000000000000000101011111111111100    14   3
72 00000000000000000000000000000000000000000000000000000000000000000000010     1   0
73 00000000000000000000000000000000000000000000000000000000000000000000001     1   0
```

are some persons from whom there would be absolutely no flow at all; the innovation would die out immediately.

It might be, on the other hand, that influence travels in the other direction: from the chooser to his choice. In that case, there is much less differential in total amount of influence between different persons, as the row totals indicate. But there is still a great difference in *which* persons would be influenced, depending on where the innovation began.

Now this illustration of a process imposed upon a structure is only the very simplest possibility. What is more frequent is that two or more *different* attitudes or beliefs spring up at different points, and then spread until the conflicting beliefs meet. The points in the structure at which conflict would arise could be located by study of Table 14.6.

Such possibilities of different processes being imposed upon a structure are numerous; and each variation has its own particular consequences—consequences of the structure in combination with the given process. It is true, however, that such matrices are probably of more immediate use in empirical research for testing hypotheses about the relation between sociometric attachments and other attributes.

Finally, besides the internal measures for this structure, the group as a whole has a measure of connectivity. If all the rows or all the columns are summed, then this sum is the total number of pairwise connections for this group. Since there are $k(k - 1)$ connections possible (all the entries in the $k \times k$ matrix except the diagonal), then the proportion of connectivity in the fall structure is 1451/5256. This measure can be used to compare different groups in terms of their total connectivity (e.g., in the spring, connectivity is 2444/5256). Such connectivity is the reverse of cliquishness, for if the number of choices per person is constant, then any focussing of choices within a subgroup results in a lowered connectivity, for it creates a tightly knit subgroup which is cut off from the rest of the group.

In the Appendix to this chapter, a computer program which handles this approach to connectivity in slightly more general form is reproduced.

This problem of connectivity of the total group on the one hand, and intense relations within a subgroup on the other, is a classical problem in society, everywhere from politics to religion. Internal cohesion is simply the obverse of external cleavage; strong identification and association with others of the same religion means rejection of other religious groups and dissociation with their members.[8] Fractionation and cleavage within a political party means less cleavage between the parties, and vice versa. Or to take again this high school example, high association and choice within each clique would mean that there is very little association between cliques. More generally, the crucial question seems to be the *level* at which lines of

---

[8] Berelson, Lazarsfeld, and McPhee (1954) show the importance of such consensus-cleavage problems for democratic politics, as do Lipset, Trow, and Coleman (1956, p. 273).

dissociation occur, creating cohesive in-groups and separation between groups.

At present, little empirical research on comparative structures has been done, so that the utility and development of such notions of connectivity is mostly a matter for the future. However, once comparative data do become available, it seems likely that this notion of connectivity will prove extremely valuable in explaining differences between groups.

3.3 A Second Approach to the Question of Connectivity

Many problems about the flow of influence through a structure or lines of consensus and cleavage can be treated in a different way from that above. That is, one can start out with two or more segments of the total group, and ask how much choice there is bridging the line between these segments. For example, taking the structure of the high school in Tables 14.5 and 14.6, the students could be divided into their school classes, and then the question asked about how much connectivity there is between members of different classes. Then the structure could be divided in a multitude of other ways: according to attitude position, by religious groups, by academic standing, by family background, and so on. In a structure where choice was purely random, no categorization would correspond to lines of dissociation, for between any two segments, no matter how defined, there would be about as many choices as the sizes of the groups would lead one to expect. But no matter how non-random the structure, choices are always random with respect to *some* categorizations, producing just as many choices across categories as would be expected from chance.

This second approach to the connectivity of a structure, then, is one which first subdivides the group on the basis of some shared attribute, and then examines the connectivity between these particular subdivisions. By carrying out numerous such subdivisions, it becomes clear just what divisions correspond to actual structural separation. Then if some process such as a diffusion process is in operation, the boundaries which will confine the diffusion become clear. A good example of this, showing the diffusion of use of a new drug among physicians, and how it is confined within groups of doctors who have much contact with one another, but little contact with the other groups, is presented by Menzel and Katz (1955).

Another kind of process which might be studied together with this connectivity is controversy or conflict. Numerous community studies have shown that when controversies develop between groups which have many links of association between them, the controversy tends to dampen out and result in compromise. If, on the other hand, the controversy develops between segments of the community which are rather completely socially separated, then it has an explosive potential, and may quickly intensify.

4. MEASURES OF POLITICAL OR SOCIAL DIVERSITY: POLITICAL DIVERSITY IN ILLINOIS COUNTIES

The Blue Books issued by states in the U.S. list various statistics relevant to the state in general and to its politics in particular. The Illinois Blue Book for 1959–1960 contains some data with more than passing interest to a sociologist concerned with social and political processes. The data consist of a county-by-county listing of officers for all 102 counties in the state, together with their party identification. The question which immediately arises is one occasioned by a perennial problem in politics: just how much of a party split is there within these small groups of county officers, and how great is the party split between different counties? More concretely, out of eight officers in the county, the average number of Democrats is 2.75. Does this arise from about three Democratic officers in each county (in which case the split is wholly within each county), or from about $\frac{3}{8}$ of the counties having all Democratic officers and about $\frac{5}{8}$ having all Republican officers (in which case the split is wholly between counties), or, if neither of these, in what combination of the two? Is there a special tendency toward an even split within each county, or perhaps a tendency toward a single member of the opposition party in otherwise solid slates?

The standard set of officers in each county is eight; in all but five counties, there is a full complement of officers, with party identification for all eight. In fifteen other counties there are more than the standard set of eight officers, but these extra officers can be excluded for the problem at hand.

The data from the 97 counties with eight officers are listed in Table 14.7, showing the number of counties with 0, 1, 2, 3, 4, 5, 6, 7, and 8 Democratic officers. In Figure 14.3 this distribution is plotted, together with a binomial distribution which can serve as a null hypothesis: if in every county each Democratic candidate had the same chance of being elected (this probability being the total number of Democrats elected divided by the total number of officers, 267/776, or .344), the counties would have distributed themselves according to this binomial distribution.

It is evident that the distribution is far more dispersed than this null hypothesis would permit. Many more counties are heavily Republican or heavily Democratic in their officers than would be the case if each Democrat had the same chance of being elected, independent of which county he ran in. But how does one measure the amount of party split that remains within the county and the amount that resides between counties, in the state as a whole?

At this point, the technique discussed in Section 1 of this chapter becomes quite useful. This technique can be used to examine the actual variance among groups and to calculate what size group would have given rise to the same variance if the probability of election were independent of the group one is in. By comparing this to the actual size of the group, we arrive at the proportion

Table 14.7

PARTY AFFILIATION OF COUNTY OFFICERS IN
ILLINOIS, 1959–1960†

Number of Democratic officers	Number of counties
0	29
1	16
2	8
3	8
4	5
5	12
6	7
7	7
8	5

† *Illinois Blue Book*, 1959–1960, pp. 775–94.

of independence of choice that is within the county, and by subtraction from one, the proportion that is within the state, but between counties.

Applying the same general approach that leads to eq. (1.1) results in a calculation which compares the variance found to the variance of a binomial with n^* trials, where we solve for n^*.

$$\frac{\sum_{i=1}^{N} (m_i - \overline{m})^2}{N - 1} = \frac{\overline{m}(n - \overline{m})}{n^*} \qquad (4.1)$$

where m_i is the number of Democrats in group i

$\overline{m}$ is the average number of Democrats in a group (2.75 in this case)

N is the number of groups (97 in this case)

n is the size of the group (8 in this case)

and n^* is the hypothetical group size which would give a variance as large as the one found.

By solving the equation for n^* (giving 2.05 in this case), and then dividing by n, we obtain the amount of independence (relative to a total of 1.0) which resides within the group.

Carrying out this calculation shows that the groups have a variance equivalent to that which we would find if 2.05 candidates were elected to office rather than 8, and their election was independent of the county they were in. Dividing by 8 gives .256 as the proportion of each candidate's election chance that is independent of the county he is elected in. By subtraction, this gives .744 as the proportion of his election chance that does depend on his county. Thus the dependence of his election upon the county he is in is much higher than other factors (such as his personality, his ability, issues, etc.) that are independent of his county.

The question may be pursued further by use of a more explicit mathematical model, the contagious binomial of Chapter 11. This model gives us the
actual distribution of groups that would be found if the election of candidates
proceeded according to a binomial distribution, but one where the outcomes
were not independent, but highly interdependent—interdependent enough,
in fact, to produce a variance of the size found among these groups. Thus,
by fitting this model to the distribution found, we can see whether there is
any marked departure at particular points—whether, as mentioned earlier,
there may be a special tendency for an even split or for a single minority party
member in otherwise solid counties. In this model, in each county there is a

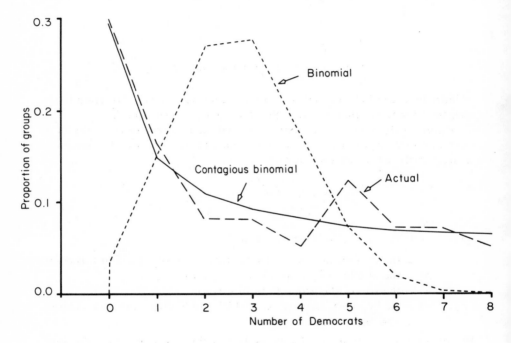

Figure 14.3

certain tendency α toward election of Democrats, a tendency β toward election
of Republicans, and a tendency γ that one man's election adds to the tendency
toward election of others of his party.

The equation necessary for relating the expected Democratic proportion
in each county to the mean and variance of the distribution is:

$$p_i = \frac{\binom{n}{i} \prod_{j=0}^{i-1} (a + jc) \prod_{j=0}^{n-i-1} (1 - a + jc)}{\prod_{j=0}^{n-1} (1 + jc)} \qquad (4.2)$$

where $a = \dfrac{\alpha}{\alpha + \beta}$ is The Democratic tendency [or transition rate] divided by the Democratic plus Republican tendencies

$c = \dfrac{\gamma}{\alpha + \beta}$ is the "contagion" tendency divided by the sum of the other two

p_i is the proportion of groups with i Democratic officials $(i = 0, 1, \ldots 8)$.

See eq. (6.5) in Chapter 11. The above equation is to be used with the convention that the term under the first product sign of the numerator is taken as one for p_0, and that under the second is taken as one for p_n. The equation is evaluated by estimating a and c from $\bar{m}$ and n^* found previously: $a = \bar{m}$, and

$$c = \frac{1 - n^*/n}{n^* - 1}.$$

Fitting this model to the data shows the relative sizes of α, β, and γ to be .34, .66, and .70 respectively. The values .34 and .66 derive simply from the proportion of Democrats and Republicans elected, respectively, while the value .70 for contagion derives from the amount of interdependence found previously. Using these values to calculate the expected number of groups of each composition gives the distribution shown in Figure 14.3 plotted together with the actual distribution. The actual distribution matches the theoretical one rather closely, particularly at the Republican end. From 5 to 8 Democrats, the two distributions deviate somewhat. The sharply higher actual number of 5-Democrat groups than given in the theoretical curve tempts one to speculate that perhaps a tendency exists to have a slightly unbalanced group, just to one side or the other of the 50-50 point. But there seems to be no such abundance of 3-Democrat groups, so that even this speculation is discouraged. In short, no tendencies toward special group compositions stand out; the tendency for within-county interdependence, or "contagion," seems equally spread through all compositions.

Thus the political diversity within Illinois in the election of county officers seems to lie principally between counties, rather than within them, in this data by a ratio of .256 : .744 . The composition of these groups seems to follow no particular pattern, but is instead spread throughout all group compositions. There seems to be little evidence for particular majority-minority, balanced or unbalanced compositions to occur.

5. SOURCE-ORIENTED MEASURES THROUGH PROCESS MODELS: GENERATIONAL MOBILITY

The most fundamental approach to the development of structural measures is through the use of processes imposed upon the structure. For as indicated earlier in the chapter, structural measures should be measures of aspects of sources of the structure or aspects of its consequences. The process imposed provides, if it is a process related to the inquiry for which the measure is to be used, an appropriate integrating device for compressing the complex structure into one or a few measures. In the case to be presented below, the lack of fit of the data indicates this by negation: it shows that mobility does not occur as if it were governed by the process proposed.

There are numerous problems in sociology that entail movement among various statuses: mobility among occupations, mobility among geographic locations, mobility among positions in an organization, and many others. When the number of statuses and flows between them is large, the resulting structure can be a complex one. Yet the techniques developed in Chapter 5 for estimating the transition rates in an arbitrarily large system of statuses makes possible the development of a continuous-time stochastic model for some of these structures.

The problem to be studied by this technique is that of inter-generational occupational mobility. Occupational mobility, both inter-generational and intra-generational, has been the object of several authors in the use of stochastic processes. Perhaps the furthest advanced of these is the work of Blumen, Kogan, and McCarthy (1955), who examined short-term mobility of workers among occupations. They found, by examination of changes over longer and shorter periods, that mobility did not occur according to a Markov process. Those who had made a move at one period were more likely to make another at a subsequent period than were those who had not. They resolved the problem by dividing the population into two groups: the "movers," characterized by high transition probabilities, and the "stayers," characterized by zero transition probabilities. They used a discrete-time model, but the continuous-time model would have hit the same non-Markovian obstacle. (See Coleman, 1964, for an analysis of such data with the model of Chapter 13.)

The data with which we will concern ourselves consist of only two observations (son's occupation and father's occupation), so that the Markovian properties of the system cannot be investigated. It is very unlikely that the inter-generational process is Markovian: that is, if the father is in the same occupation as was the grandfather, the son is more likely to stay in his father's occupation than if the father himself had shifted.

However, in order to bring this massive structure of occupational mobility into some kind of order, the occupations can be classified into a smaller number of categories. One such classification is according to prestige groups. The general prestige that an occupation commands in the society imposes a linear order among groups of occupations, such that the prestige of an occupation is approximately the same as that of all others within the category, higher than all those in lower categories, and lower than all those in higher categories.

When categories of occupations in a society are ordered according to prestige, and the mobility rates between categories are standardized according to the number of persons in the category of origin and the number of jobs in the category of destination, the table of mobility rates shows a sloping away from the main diagonal, as if mobility follows the prestige ordering. White (1963b) shows this, using data from England published by Glass (1954), and data from Denmark published by Svalagosta (1959). These data indicate that all other things equal (that is, the number of jobs in a given category equal), a man is more likely to move to an occupation close to his father's in prestige than one farther away.[9]

This character of the data suggests that mobility between occupational categories may be mirrored by a kind of stochastic process in which mobility proceeds only along the line of prestige. This kind of process can be described heuristically as follows. Let the states in which the individual may find himself be 1, 2, . . ., n, where n is the number of prestige categories of occupations, and the states are numbered from high (1) to low (n). If his father's occupation is in category i, he begins life in state i. From that state, he can move to another, but only to an adjacent state, to $i + 1$ or $i - 1$. At every stage of life, even before he enters an occupation, he is in a given state. In early years, during training, the state may be thought of as representing the occupational category he would enter if his further training followed his present pattern. Thus, at his birth, his background would project him into the same status as his father. As he develops, his abilities or special circumstances may alter his current life chances, putting him into the next higher or lower state; then in that state, depending on abilities and circumstances, his life chances may be further altered, again moving him up or down one state.[10] That is, throughout his life, but particularly in the formative stages, he is visualized as in a given state determined by his occupation or his expected occupation; and he may move to an adjacent state, but never to a non-adjacent one.[11]

This assumption that transitions are only to an adjacent state is certainly not precisely true. Everyone knows of cases in which the banker, by a turn of fate, becomes ditch digger, or the lowly clerk becomes store manager by

[9] Goodman (1963b), however, shows in a reanalysis of these data that if the prestige categories are grouped, the tendency to move to a "closer" occupation does not exist, given that one moves at all.

[10] The process through which this occurs among British working class children is graphically illustrated by a study of 88 men and women who, starting in the working class, passed the 11-plus examination, and then graduated from grammar school with academic credits. Their movement from their fathers' status to their present one was of exactly the sort described here: revised expectations on their part as they moved first one jump out of their family's status, then another, and in some cases still others. Description of downward mobility among middle-class children followed the same lines. See Jackson and Marsden (1962).

[11] The fact that the process of change between states is far more rapid before entering the labor force than after indicates that the Markovian assumption is an idealized version of what actually occurs. However, in the absence of more detailed data on the intervening stages, such an assumption must be retained here.

marrying the owner's daughter. But the intent of the model is not to mirror reality in all its facets. It is, instead, to see just *how much* of reality can be mirrored by a highly-constrained process. That is, our question will be: How well does this rather restrictive assumption allow us to account for the data on inter-generational mobility?

The Model of the Above Process

The mathematical model for the above may be described by a set of differential equations.

Let p_i $(i = 1,2,\ldots,n)$ be the probability at time t (leaving the argument t implicit) that the individual is in state i.

Then the general process without the linear constraint is described by n equations as follows:

$$\frac{dp_i}{dt} = q_{1i}p_1 + q_{2i}p_2 + \ldots + q_{ii}p_i + \ldots + q_{ni}p_n \quad 1 \leqslant i \leqslant n \quad (5.1)$$

where q_{ji} are the transition rates from state ij to state i and q_{ii} is defined as

$$-\sum_{\substack{j=1 \\ j \neq i}}^{n} q_{ij}.$$

With the constraint of movement along a linear order, the equations are:

$$\frac{dp_1}{dt} = -q_{12}p_1 + q_{21}p_2 \tag{5.2}$$

$$\frac{dp_i}{dt} = q_{i-1,i}\,p_{i-1} + q_{i+1,i}\,p_{i+1} - (q_{i,i-1} + q_{i,i+1})\,p_i \quad (1 < i < n) \tag{5.3}$$

$$\frac{dp_n}{dt} = q_{n-1,n}\,p_{n-1} - q_{n,n-1}\,p_n \tag{5.4}$$

For the n categories, there are $n - 1$ boundaries between categories in the linear order, and with two transition rates across each boundary, this gives $2(n - 1)$ free parameters to the model. There are n^2 frequencies in the $n \times n$ table, with n constraints (the number of sons originating in each of n categories), and consequently $n^2 - n$, or $n(n - 1)$ degrees of freedom. Thus the model uses $2(n - 1)$ degrees of freedom, and leaves $(n - 2)(n - 1)$ degrees.

The procedure to be used here will be to estimate the transition rates on the basis of the mobility into status categories adjacent to a given occupation, then to regenerate a table of expected frequencies given these transition rates, then to examine the deviation between actual and expected frequencies. If the deviations are small, we can say that the process outlined above can largely account for the mobility that occurs, and we can use the transition rates as measures of mobility. If the deviations are large, we must look elsewhere. If they are systematic, then this may tell us something about the kind of deviations from this process that occurs in inter-generational mobility.

Since the process above describes the behavior of a given individual, there are N independent identical processes for the N individuals in the sample. In such a case of a sum of independent identical processes, the proportion of persons in a given cell approaches as an expected value the probabilities above. Consequently, proportions will be taken as estimates of the probabilities, and

Table 14.8

INTER-GENERATIONAL MOBILITY BETWEEN OCCUPATIONAL STATUS CATEGORIES IN
ENGLAND AND DENMARK

ENGLAND

SON'S OCCUPATION

			1	2	3	4	5	6	7	
	(High)	1	50	19	26	8	18	6	2	129
		2	16	40	34	18	31	8	3	150
FATHER'S		3	12	35	65	66	123	23	21	345
OCCUPATION		4	11	20	58	110	223	64	32	518
		5	14	36	114	185	714	258	189	1510
		6	0	6	19	40	179	143	71	458
	(Low)	7	0	3	14	32	141	91	106	387
			103	159	330	459	1429	593	424	3497

DENMARK

SON'S OCCUPATION

			1	2	3	4	5	
	(High)	1	18	17	16	4	2	57
		2	24	105	109	59	21	318
FATHER'S		3	23	84	289	217	95	708
OCCUPATION		4	8	49	175	348	198	778
	(Low)	5	6	8	69	201	246	530
			79	263	658	829	562	2391

the transition rates will be estimated from these, according to the procedure described in Chapter 5, Section 8, and using the computer program reproduced in the Appendix to that chapter. The process is constrained by arbitrarily fixing at zero the transition rates into non-adjacent categories, as indicated by eqs. (5.2), (5.3), and (5.4). The data for the process, from England and Denmark (taken from White, 1963b), are given in Table 14.8. These data give rise to sets of transition rates as shown in Table 14.9, and the transition rates in turn generate mobility as given in Table 14.10.

It is evident that the process as posed does not fit the data. The regenerated data in Table 14.10 show that the q_{ij}'s were constructed by use of the frequencies in adjacent status categories, since these frequencies match the actual data; but this does not spread enough people beyond, into the non-adjacent statuses. Far too many persons are left in their original location. There is an extreme difference between England and Denmark, and one is tempted to say that the process fits better for Denmark than for England. However, the numbers of status categories, which are somewhat arbitrary, differ in the two cases, and this

Table 14.9

ESTIMATES FOF q_{ij}'S BY USE OF FREQUENCIES IN CELLS ADJACENT TO i

ENGLAND

SON'S OCCUPATION

		1	2	3	4	5	6	7
(High)	1	−.210	.210	0	0	0	0	0
	2	.152	−.542	.390	0	0	0	0
FATHER'S	3	0	.174	−.609	.435	0	0	0
OCCUPATION	4	0	0	.254	−1.214	.960	0	0
	5	0	0	0	.273	−.645	.371	0
	6	0	0	0	0	.849	−1.172	.323
(Low)	7	0	0	0	0	0	.491	−.491

DENMARK

SON'S OCCUPATION

		1	2	3	4	5
(High)	1	−.637	.637	0	0	0
	2	.161	−1.003	.842	0	0
FATHER'S	3	0	.292	−1.052	.760	0
OCCUPATION	4	0	0	.558	−1.173	.615
(Low)	5	0	0	0	.915	−.915

influences the results. The fact that it does indicates a severe defect in the model as conceptualized, for the number of categories should not affect the ability of the model to fit the data. For example, if a category adjacent to i, category $i + 1$, is of very small size, this means that $n_{i,i+1}$ will be very small, as will $q_{i,i+1}$, which will restrict artificially the passage of those in i to other categories, $i + 2$, $i + 3$, etc.

It is clear that either the conceptualization of the process, or the method of estimation which uses frequencies in statuses adjacent to i, is defective, and some modification is necessary. What then is the value of this unsuccessful attempt to construct structural measures explicitly derived from a process? The value lies principally in the lack of success itself: it shows that the behavior does not correspond to the process described earlier, shifting in a linear fashion from the status of origin to the status of destination. Its devia-

Table 14.10

CALCULATED MOBILITY BY USE OF q_{ij}'S FROM TABLE 14.9

ENGLAND

SON'S OCCUPATION

		1	2	3	4	5	6	7	
(High)	1	106.1	19	3.4	.4	0.1	0	0	129
	2	16	91.8	34	6.1	2	.2	0	150
FATHER'S	3	3	35	203.1	65.9	34	3.8	.3	345
OCCUPATION	4	.3	5.5	57.9	190.8	222.7	36.5	4.4	518
	5	.1	1.5	24.8	184.7	996.1	257.7	45	1510
	6	0	.1	1.9	21	178.8	185.3	70.9	458
(Low)	7	0	0	.2	3.2	40	90.9	252.6	387
		125.4	152.8	325.3	472.1	1473.8	574.3	373.3	3497

DENMARK

SON'S OCCUPATION

		1	2	3	4	5	
(High)	1	31.5	17	6.7	1.6	.2	57
	2	24	138.5	108.8	38.8	8	318
FATHER'S	3	7.2	83.8	335.9	216.6	64.4	708
OCCUPATION	4	1.4	24.1	174.7	380.1	197.7	778
(Low)	5	.2	5	52.6	200.7	271.5	530
		64.4	268.5	678.7	837.7	541.7	2391

tions from the data indicate the kinds of modification of the process that might produce a fit, and thus would generate q_{ij}'s which could be used as measures of the structure.

APPENDIX

```
C       SOCIOMETRIC CONNECTEDNESS
C       PROGRAM TO FIND ULTIMATE CONNECTEDNESS OF SOCIOMATRIX
        DIMENSION NMAT(1000), NMAL(1000), NCYCL(1000)
        DIMENSION CT(1000), SST(1000)
        DIMENSION NFR(1000,10), NCT(1000), ST(1000), NEW(1000), NTOT(1000
       1, NEW2(1000), NOUT(1000)
        READ INPUT TAPE 5,105,NPROB
        DO 70 IV=1,NPROB
C       READ IN NUMBER OF INDIVIDUALS, MAX NUMBER OF CHOICES, AND
C           ATTENUATION CONSTANT
        READ INPUT TAPE 5,100,N,NC,AS
        NP=N+1
        DO 10 I=1,N
        NMAL(I)=0
        CT(I)=0.
        ST(I)=0.
        SST(I)=0.
        NCYCL(I)=0
C       READ CHOICE DATA INTO NFR(I,J). NFR(I,J) IS ID NO. OF THE JTH
C           CHOICE OF I. THIS ID NO. IS ALSO INDEX NUMBER
C       ID NUMBER OF ITH CARD MUST BE I
        READ INPUT TAPE 5,101, (NFR(I,J),J=1,NC)
        WRITE OUTPUT TAPE 6,101, (NFR(I,J),J=1,NC)
     10 CONTINUE
        NMAL(NP)=0
C       FIND NUMBER OF CHOICES OF I AND STORE IN NCT(I)
        DO 21 I=1,N
        DO 22 J=1,NC
        IF (NFR(I,J)) 23,23,55
     55 CONTINUE
        IF (NFR(I,J)-N) 25,25,23
     23 NCT(I)=J-1
        GO TO 21
     25 CONTINUE
C       INCREMENT FORWARD AND BACKWARD CONNNECTEDNESS MEASURES
        L=NFR(I,J)
        CT(I)=CT(I)+AS
        ST(L)=ST(L)+AS
     22 CONTINUE
        NCT(I)=NC
     21 CONTINUE
C       WRITE INPUT DATA AS MATRIX
        DO 97 I=1,N
        NTT=NCT(I)+1
        DO 99 L=1,NP
        NMAT(L)=0
        NMAL(L)=0
     99 CONTINUE
        DO 98 M=1,NTT
        L=NFR(I,M)
        NMAT(L)=1
        NMAL(L)=NMAL(L)+1
     98 CONTINUE
        NMAT(NP)=NTT
        NMAL(NP)=NMAL(NP)+NTT
        WRITE OUTPUT TAPE 6,106,I,(NMAT(L),L=1,NP)
     97 CONTINUE
        WRITE OUTPUT TAPE 6,107, (NMAL(I),I=1,NP)
C       CONSTRUCT EACH INDIVIDUALS CHAIN
        DO 11 I=1,N
        WRITE OUTPUT TAPE 6,103
```

```
      DO 19 J=1,N
      NEW(J)=0
      NTOT(J)=0
   19 CONTINUE
      NTT=NCT(I)+1
      NT= NCT(I)
      NTOT(NTT)=I
      IF (NCT(I)) 56,56,57
   56 CONTINUE
      WRITE OUTPUT TAPE 6,103
      WRITE OUTPUT TAPE 6,102,I
      WRITE OUTPUT TAPE 6,103
      GO TO 37
   57 CONTINUE
      DO 18 J=1,NT
      NEW(J)= NFR(I,J)
      NTOT(J)= NFR(I,J)
   18 CONTINUE
      A=AS
      DO 17 NCY= 1,N
C     FORM ATTENUATION CONSTANT FOR THIS CYCLE
      A= A*AS
      IJ=0
      IK=0
C     FOR EACH NEW CYCLE, FIND NEW PERSONS CHOSEN BY PREVIOUS NEW
C         PERSONS AND ADD TO TOTAL CHAIN
      DO 12 J=1,NT
      K=NEW(J)
      NTK=NCT(K)
C     PICK UP EACH CHOICE OF NEW CHOICES, AND ADD THEM
      DO 13 KJ=1,NTK
      L=NFR(K,KJ)
      DO 14 JJ=1,NTT
      IF (NTOT(JJ)-L) 14,15,14
   14 CONTINUE
      IJ=IJ+1
      NTT=NTT+1
C     ADD TO TOTAL CHOICE CHAIN
      NTOT(NTT)=L
      NEW2(IJ)=L
   15 IK=IK+1
C     ADD TO NTH CYCLE OUTPUT
      NOUT(IK)=L
C     INCREMENT CONNECTEDNESS MEASURES
      CT(I)=CT(I)+A
      ST(L)=ST(L)+A
   13 CONTINUE
   12 CONTINUE
C     WRITE OUT CURRENT STATUS OF TOTAL CHOICE CHAIN
      WRITE OUTPUT TAPE 6,102,NCY, I,(NTOT(M),M=1,NTT)
C     WRITE OUT NTH CYCLE CHOICES
      WRITE OUTPUT TAPE 6,102,NCY, I,(NOUT(M),M=1,IK)
      IF (IJ) 40,40,41
   40 CONTINUE
      WRITE OUTPUT TAPE 6,102,I
      GO TO 30
   41 CONTINUE
C     WRITE OUT NEW ADDITIONS TO CHAIN
      WRITE OUTPUT TAPE 6,102,NCY, I,(NEW2(M),M=1,IJ)
   31 CONTINUE
      DO 32 IP=1,IJ
      NEW(IP)=NEW2(IP)
```

```
      32 CONTINUE
         NCYCL(I)=NCYCL(I)+1
         NT=IJ
      17 CONTINUE
      30 CONTINUE
      37 CONTINUE
C        WRITE OUT ITH ROW OF CONNECTEDNESS MATRIC
         WRITE OUTPUT TAPE 6,104,N, (ST(IQ),IQ=1,N)
         DO 35 IQ=1,N
C        INCREMENT TOTAL STATUS MEASURES
         SST(IQ)=SST(IQ)+ST(IQ)
         ST(IQ)=0.
      35 CONTINUE
C        STORE TOTAL CHOICE CHAIN ON TAPE
         WRITE TAPE 10,NTT
         WRITE TAPE 10,I,(NTOT(M),M=1,NTT)
         WRITE OUTPUT TAPE 6,103
      11 CONTINUE
         REWIND 10
         DO 34 I=1,N
         READ TAPE 10,NTT
         READ TAPE 10,I,(NTOT(M),M=1,NTT)
C        WRITE OUT TOTAL CHOICE MATRIX, WITH NUMBER OF CYCLES AT END
         DO 72 L=1,N
         NMAT(L)=0
      72 CONTINUE
         DO 71 M=1,NTT
         L=NTOT(M)
         NMAT(L)=1
         NMAL(L)=NMAL(L)+1
      71 CONTINUE
         NMAT(NP)=NTT
         NMAL(NP)=NMAL(NP)+NTT
         WRITE OUTPUT TAPE 6,106,I,(NMAT(L),L=1,NP),NCYCL(I)
      34 CONTINUE
         REWIND 10
C        WRITE OUT TOTAL PERSONS CHOOSING INTO I
         WRITE OUTPUT TAPE 6,107, (NMAL(I),I=1,NP )
C        WRITE OUT FORWARD AND BACKWARD CONNECTEDNESS
         WRITE OUTPUT TAPE 6,104,N, (CT(IQ),IQ=1,N)
         WRITE OUTPUT TAPE 6,104,N,(SST(IQ),IQ=1,N)
      70 CONTINUE
         CALL EXIT
     100 FORMAT (1XI4,1XI4,F10.5)
     101 FORMAT (8X21I3)
     102 FORMAT (23(1XI4),/(10X21(1XI4)))
     103 FORMAT (/)
     104 FORMAT (1XI4,15F8.2,/(5X15F8.2))
     105 FORMAT (I3)
     106 FORMAT (1XI3,1X73I1,1XI3,1XI3)
     107 FORMAT (//(5X15I8))
C        SAMPLE DATA
         END
  *      DATA
      1     NPROB
         4      3      .5
            1   2   4
            2   3
            3   4
            4   2   1
```

CHAPTER 15

THE METHOD
OF RESIDUES

The example of natural science has led social scientists to treat postulate systems in a very narrow and restricted way. Because in mechanics a law holds or does not hold, a theory is confirmed or denied, many of us have set about finding and explaining the "true" regularities and uniformities of behavior, holding this aim to be the one proper object of our science. Perhaps this may be, in the long run, the one primary goal to which we should aspire—or perhaps not. But for the present, to limit our goals to those of proposing and confirming explanatory postulate systems may lead us to overlook valuable aids to research and theory.

One such aid is of this sort: in considering a given complex social phenomenon, certain aspects of it are explainable by "sociologically trivial" assumptions, or by matters irrelevant to the substantive matters under investigation. If we examine what part of the behavior can be explained by these "trivial" factors, then the remainder stands out to be explained by less trivial factors. Ordinarily such separating out of the sociologically trivial elements must be done qualitatively and nonrigorously. But in certain structural phenomena, where the data are in the form of numbers of people, this separating out may be done quantitatively and rigorously. The example below will illustrate the general strategy.

1. THE "DISTANCE-INTERACTION HYPOTHESIS"

Much nonsense, and some sense along with it, has been written about rates of interaction between persons in different geographical locations, such as cities. A great deal of effort has been devoted to the task of uncovering a definite law which accounts for the amount of communication or travel between any two cities in terms of their populations and the distance which separates them. (See for example, Stouffer, 1940, Zipf, 1946, Stewart, 1942, Ikle, 1954.) Now it is certainly true that there is some relationship between amount of population and amount of travel; there is more travel between New York City and Washington, D.C., than between White Plains, New York and Arlington, Virginia, even though the two pairs of cities are roughly the same distances apart. Similarly, there should be some relation between amount of travel and distance between two cities; the number of people travelling from Bowling Green, Kentucky, to Russelville, Kentucky, thirty miles away, is certainly greater than that from Bowling Green to Elko, Nevada, a town of about the same size as Russelville, but fifteen hundred miles away.

These obvious facts, together with the pervasiveness of the law of gravity in physics, have beguiled some investigators into proposing a "law of social gravity," analogous to that of physics. This "law" goes something as follows: "The number of trips between two cities is proportional to the product of the population and inversely proportional to the distance between them." Yet it is obvious, upon examining the data which have been gathered, that they simply don't fit such a law very well; and that no matter how the analogy to physical gravity be twisted into a different form, the data still do not conform. There is simply too much variation between cities.

Does one then give up and search elsewhere for a social regularity? To the contrary; the approach suggested here is to make some simple and reasonable null assumptions, and then to use the *deviations* from the predictions consequent upon these assumptions as a measure of various matters, as, for example, the "social distance" between two groups. The null assumptions which might be made in the present case are these:

(1) All pairs of persons a given distance apart have the same likelihood of interacting in a given interval of time.

(2) Given equal population densities, a person is just as likely to take a trip d miles as to take a trip d' miles.

These two assumptions are very simple ones; their implications for amount of travel, however, are not so simple. It is precisely for this reason that it is useful to "factor out" their effects.

The effect of the first assumption on amount of travel between two cities is evident as follows: if in city j there are n_j persons, then an individual in city i has n_j potential pair relations with persons in city j. But there are n_i persons in city i, so that the total number of pairs is $n_i n_j$. Thus each pair of cities can be characterized by the product of their populations; and according to assumption (1), this means that the number of trips or communications between the pair of cities (disregarding distance) should be proportional to this product, $n_i n_j$.

The effect of the second assumption is not quite so evident. If a person is just as likely to travel d miles as d' miles for all values of d and d', then this does *not* mean that he is just as likely to visit someone in town x, 500 miles away, as he is to visit someone in town y, 50 miles away. The circle on which a town 50 miles away lies is $50 \times 2\pi$ miles in circumference. The circle on which a town 500 miles away lies is $500 \times 2\pi$ in circumference. Thus on the larger circle there are $500 \times 2\pi$ miles along which a town might lie; on the smaller circle, there are only $50 \times 2\pi$ miles. Therefore, there are, on the average, ten times as many persons and towns on the larger circle; any particular person will be visited only one-tenth as often as will a given person on the smaller circle.

More generally, the implications of this assumption are that the number of trips one makes to a given individual or a given town will be inversely proportional to its distance, d.

The joint consequence of these two hypotheses is that, under these null or "ideal" conditions, the rates of interaction between two areas which contain n_1 and n_2 persons and which are d_{12} distance apart will be proportional to $n_1 n_2 / d_{12}$. That is, to determine equivalent or equal interaction between groups which are distributed over some geographic area, it is necessary to standardize for size and distance by using this factor. The factor might be considered an expected rate of interaction which might occur if no sociological effects were operative.

This factor, $n_1 n_2 / d_{12}$, is the same one which has been posed as the "law of social gravity," and to which various investigators have tried to fit actual interaction data. Note that as long as such an approach is used, there is nothing to do but to accept or reject this hypothesis, or perhaps to attempt a modification which fits the data better.[1] In contrast, what is proposed here is that this factor be used simply as a base line, or standardization, which can cancel out differences in interaction due to these sociologically trivial factors, and illuminate the differences due to more interesting matters. What is suggested, in essence, is the use of this factor as a base line for the *measurement* of interaction between spatially distinct groups, such as cities, or blocks within a city, or states, or other geographically separated units. Without such a base line, or standardizing factor, differences which are due simply to the

---

[1] This latter approach has been tried by several authors, who have raised the question of whether an equation in which distance was raised to some higher power than one would not fit the data better (see, for instance, Ikle, 1954).

Table 15.1

VALUES OF z_{ij}

	1 N.Y.	2 Chi.	3 L.A.	4 Phila.	5 Detroit	6 Boston	7 S.F.	8 Pitts.	9 St.L.	10 Cleve.	11 Wash.	12 Balt.	13 Minn.	14 Buff.	15 Cin.	16 Mil.	17 K.C.	18 Hous.	19 Prov.	20 Seattle	z_i
1 New York	x																				1.087
2 Chicago	1.268	x																			1.267
3 Los Angeles	2.030	2.035	x																		1.491
4 Philadelphia	.014	.396	.323	x																	.307
5 Detroit	.723	.683	.733	.415	x																.790
6 Boston	1.159	.809	.602	.376	.569	x															.811
7 San Francisco	2.422	2.076	3.458	.575	1.009	1.044	x														2.440
8 Pittsburgh	.653	.598	.414	.584	.462	.351	.652	x													.531
9 St. Louis	.797	.782	.848	.289	.391	.584	.928	.416	x												.762
10 Cleveland	.797	1.107	.822	.355	.674	.981	.876	.398	.658	x											.786
11 Washington	1.528	2.263	2.615	.206	1.452	1.651	5.330	1.455	1.836	1.556	x										2.155
12 Baltimore	.107	.211	.152	.004	.137	.298	.232	.290	.139	.158	.066	x									.172
13 Minneapolis	1.438	1.997	1.335	.247	1.223	.474	1.261	.515	.592	1.092	3.445	.104	x								1.394
14 Buffalo	.681	.411	.317	.354	.381	.683	.490	.547	.243	.255	.914	.206	.501	x							.402
15 Cincinnati	.747	.840	.392	.262	.496	.702	.508	.554	.719	1.088	.889	.165	.292	.241	x						.556
16 Milwaukee	.951	.101	.592	.225	1.384	.377	.674	.585	.265	1.286	2.545	.086	2.054	.217	.247	x					.728
17 Kansas City	1.196	2.127	3.564	.413	1.002	.439	1.911	.660	3.482	.961	3.648	.363	2.893	.256	1.281	.252	x				1.359
18 Houston	1.665	1.507	1.594	.305	.432	.656	1.425	.459	.970	.772	3.647	.231	.614	.482	.598	.180	2.727	x			1.005
19 Providence	.465	.274	.267	.112	.129	.020	.233	.106	.198	.282	.606	.110	.304	.149	.241	.093	.235	.120	x		.218
20 Seattle	2.022	2.684	6.228	.372	2.724	.576	12.277	.397	.331	.824	4.698	.203	6.103	.302	.293	1.713	1.686	.707	.200	x	2.422

size of the unit or to the distance between units will be confounded with differences due to less trivial matters, and analysis of the source of the latter differences will be impossible.

An analysis of a set of data will show the avenues opened up by such an approach. The data concern airline trips between principal cities in the United States during the month of March, 1950. They are listed in the form of a matrix, with cell entries constructed as follows:

$x_{ij} (= x_{ji})$ = the number of trips between cities i and j in March, 1950, which originated in i and ended in j or vice versa;

n_i = the total population of the standard metropolitan area of which city i is the central city; and

d_{ij} = the air distance in miles between cities i and j.

Then

y_{ij} = the travel rate between cities i and j per pair of potentially interacting persons, i.e., the travel rate standardized for population size, where

$$y_{ij} = \frac{x_{ij}}{n_i n_j} \tag{1.1}$$

This "population-standardized" rate is then standardized for distance by multiplying by d_i. This gives

w_{ij} = the travel rate between cities i and j standardized both for population and distance, where

$$w_{ij} = y_{ij} d_{ij} \tag{1.2}$$

Finally, the w_{ij}'s are divided by the average w_{ij}, taken over the whole matrix. The resulting quantity is

z_{ij} = the "population-and-distance-standardized" travel rate between cities i and j, divided by the average rate for all pairs of cities in the matrix.

$$z_{ij} = \frac{w_{ij}}{\dfrac{\Sigma\Sigma w_{ij}}{N(N-1)}} \tag{1.3}$$

where there are N cities in the matrix. The matrix shown in Table 15.1 is a matrix of z_{ij}'s. Those values greater than 1.0 are greater than the average; those values less than 1.0 are less than the average.

Particular entries in the table show a number of interesting facts about relations between cities: some of the highest values (from 3.46 to 12.27) are those between the three West Coast cities, while some of the lowest values (as low as .004) are those between various East Coast cities. This does not,

Table 15.2

VALUES OF v_{ij}

	1 N.Y.	2 Chi.	3 L.A.	4 Phila.	5 Detroit	6 Boston	7 S.F.	8 Pitts.	9 St.L.	10 Cleve.	11 Wash.	12 Balt.	13 Minn.	14 Buff.	15 Cin.	16 Mil.	17 K.C.	18 Hous.	19 Prov.	20 Seattle
1 New York	x																			
2 Chicago	.920	x																		
3 Los Angeles	1.252	1.078	x																	
4 Philadelphia	.041	1.020	.708	x																
5 Detroit	.841	.682	.622	1.712	x															
6 Boston	1.314	.788	.498	1.511	.888	x														
7 San Francisco	.913	.671	.951	.768	.523	.527	x													
8 Pittsburgh	1.130	.888	.522	.358	1.100	.815	.503	x												
9 St. Louis	.962	.810	.748	1.238	.650	.946	.499	1.029	x											
10 Cleveland	.933	1.111	.701	1.472	1.085	1.539	.456	.952	1.100	x										
11 Washington	.652	.829	.814	.312	.852	.945	1.014	1.271	1.119	.918	x									
12 Baltimore	.575	.972	.593	.077	1.011	2.138	.553	3.180	1.067	1.170	.179	x								
13 Minneapolis	.949	1.131	.643	.577	1.110	.419	.371	.695	.557	.996	1.147	.433	x							
14 Buffalo	1.559	.807	.529	2.874	1.201	2.097	.500	2.566	.796	.806	1.057	2.995	.895	x						
15 Cincinnati	1.237	1.194	.474	1.537	1.129	1.559	.375	1.879	1.699	2.490	.742	1.726	.377	1.082	x					
16 Milwaukee	1.201	1.096	.546	1.010	2.406	.639	.380	1.513	.478	2.246	1.623	.687	2.025	.741	.612	x				
17 Kansas City	.810	1.236	1.760	.990	.933	.399	.577	.914	3.366	.900	1.246	1.556	1.528	.470	1.697	.255	x			
18 Houston	1.524	1.184	1.064	.989	.544	.805	.581	.860	1.268	.977	1.684	1.341	.439	1.194	1.071	.246	1.998	x		
19 Providence	1.959	.991	.821	1.675	.749	.114	.439	.914	1.191	1.643	1.290	2.935	.999	1.703	1.989	.588	.793	.548	x	
20 Seattle	.768	.875	1.725	.501	1.423	.293	2.077	.300	.179	.433	.900	.488	1.808	.310	.218	.972	.512	2.906	.379	x

of course, mean that the *total* standardized travel between the East Coast cities is less; it probably expresses the fact that trains and autos are used more on the East Coast than on the West Coast for travel between large cities.

Beyond the examination of individual rates, it becomes possible to do several other things. First, by summing the z_{ij}'s over each city, and dividing by $N - 1$, each city can be given a measure, indicating its average level of travel to these other cities. If this measure is greater than 1.0, its average airline travel is greater than the over-all average; if less than 1.0, its average travel is less.

These values are placed in the column marginals for each city in the matrix. They show a number of interesting results: San Francisco has the highest standardized rate, Seattle second, Washington, D.C., third, and Baltimore the lowest. San Francisco's and Seattle's rates probably indicate again the high use of airplanes relative to autos and trains in the West; Washington's, however, is something else again. It is undoubtedly due to travel on government business. It indicates a breakdown of the general conception of airline travel representing interactions between persons, thus able to be standardized by the potential pairs of persons $n_i n_j$. In this case, the amount of business carried on between Washington and other cities is far more than simply proportional to its population. Since this business accounts for a good part of the airline travel, the travel rate is high.

The low rate at Baltimore is undoubtedly in part due to the influence of Washington, which is so close by, and whose airport in 1950 offered better service by virtue of its high rate of travel. The generally low rate of eastern seaboard cities again suggests the use of trains rather than airplanes between these cities.

There are a number of other ways in which more information may be extracted from such a matrix as this, taking out successively one factor after another and examining the residuals. The simplest is to "factor out" for each city its average standardized travel rates. That is, each entry z_{ij} in the matrix can be divided by the two average rates z_i and z_j, to obtain a residual, v_{ij}, for that pair of cities over and above the general rates for each city. The matrix of v_{ij}'s in Table 15.2 is such a matrix. These residuals show much less variation than their predecessors, for all the variation due to the cities' general travel rates is removed, and what is left is specific to the pair.

A second factor whose effect may be removed is distance, insofar as it has an effect over and above the simple dispersal effect proposed in postulate (2) above. It seems unlikely that people make exactly as many trips of 100 miles as of 200; exactly as many of 200 as of 300; and so on. This makes it useful to examine the variation in z_{ij} with d_{ij}. A least squares analysis will show the variation of travel with distance between cities when population effects, dispersal effects, and each city's general rate are factored out (as they are in obtaining the second matrix, in Table 15.2). The coefficients of the regression equation become an empirical result, which may or may not be of interest in a given investigation, just as the average standardized rates calculated for the first matrix were empirical measures which may or may not be of interest. But once this result is found, then the added effect of distance

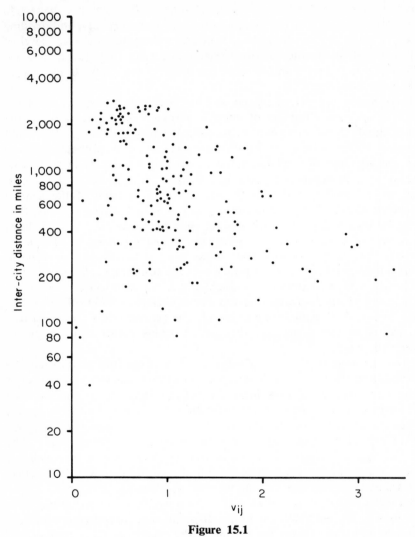

Figure 15.1

can be "factored out," just as were the earlier effects, to give a new set of residuals.

In this example, it appears that distance has little or no effect beyond the dispersal effect already incorporated in postulate (2). This is seen by plotting the residuals v_{ij} from Table 15.2 versus d_{ij}, as is done in Figure 15.1. It is apparent that there is little relationship, so this factor will be neglected. However, if distance were important then the new residual s_{ij} is

$$s_{ij} = v_{ij} - bd_{ij} \tag{1.4}$$

where b is the regression coefficient for distance.

The remaining residuals shown in Table 15.2 stand to be explained by some factors as yet unexamined, political, economic, or social-psychological.[2] For example, it may be that travel occurs only between persons of the same race. If this is so, then a factor

$$r_{ij} = \frac{n_{ia}n_{ja} + n_{ib}n_{jb}}{n_i n_j} \tag{1.5}$$

should be introduced into the analysis. This factor is the ratio of the number of same-race pairs between the cities to the number of total pairs (where n_{ia} = number of whites in city i, and n_{ib} = number of Negroes in city i). By multiplying each residual in Table 15.1 by the appropriate r_{ij}, the factor of racial separation is taken into account. What this would mean is that we would expect much less travel between two cities which were racially divided than between two which were not, even if Negroes and whites each travelled equal amounts. For each white in city i, the effective size of city j is only the number of whites it contains; for each Negro, the effective size is only the number of Negroes it contains. [More generally, there would be nonzero coefficients of travel between dissimilar pairs as well as between similar pairs, so that the numerator in eq. (1.5) would have two more terms, $n_{ia}n_{jb}$ and $n_{ib}n_{ja}$, with each term preceded by a coefficient.] However, in the case of airline travel, which includes so much business travel such separation between races or other groups would be minimal, so that this factor will not be introduced into the analysis of this example.

It is evident that the entries in successive residual matrices will become more and more uniform, as one after another cause of the differences in travel is eliminated. The analysis could go on in this fashion, proceeding to examine and then eliminate one by one the various factors which are presumed to affect airplane travel. We begin with the most trivial, least sociologically interesting differences, and proceed to take up one by one factors which are more and more important. The differences which finally remain can be termed the "unexplained" social distances between cities.

Now, how does such an analysis differ from factor analysis or similar statistical techniques for locating the "factors" which account for the variance in some phenomenon? The difference seems to lie in two places: first, this phenomenon is out in the open, so that the factors, and how they operate to affect the interaction rates, are not a matter of inference, but of explicit

---

[2] It must be kept in mind that for most modes of travel natural geographic barriers, such as rivers and mountains, may also be an important factor.

knowledge. Second, the factors themselves are legitimately quantitative, for they are derived from counting numbers of people or physical distances, as the above analysis indicates. There is no illegitimate introduction of quantification simply because quantitative data are needed to carry out the analysis. Taken together, these two differences are of considerable importance, for the primary objections to inferences about underlying factors when factor analysis is used are these two: the arbitrary linear form of the relation between the unknown factor and the consequent behavior, and the arbitrary metricization resulting from the use of scores which are not legitimate real numbers. In other words, when phenomena are *sociological*, that is, out in the open and based on numbers of people, rather than inside the individual and based on measurement of some concept, the legitimate use of mathematics to analyze the phenomena is greatly facilitated.

In summary, then, this strategy is as follows:

(a) When faced with complex sociological phenomena, in which the data exist in terms of numbers of people, there are certain sociologically trivial factors which make impossible any inference about sociologically interesting causes. By setting down postulates encompassing these trivial factors and no others, one can obtain an "expected" value for the phenomenon which would derive from these assumptions and no others.

(b) Then it is possible to use these expected values to standardize the original data to give numbers which can be compared for substantive causes—not, as has been attempted by numerous authors in the distance-interaction example used above, to establish a universally valid "social law."

(c) From this point, there may be other factors which are not sociologically trivial, but which can be extracted from the standardized data, and thus considered as measures of a given effect. This then leaves a residual phenomenon to be accounted for by still other factors.

(d) The process can be carried on so long as it is possible to account for some part of the variation by the introduction of another factor for which numerical data exist.

(e) The final results of this effort are of two kinds:

(1) Measures have been constructed for the effect of numerous kinds of factors on the phenomenon; and

(2) In the process of obtaining these measures, a provisional model has been constructed to account for the nonresidual part of the phenomenon at hand.

A class of phenomena which are particularly amenable to this general approach are social-structural data, of the form of group membership data and sociometric-type data. Chapters 14 and 16 are devoted to the development of such measures and the analysis of such kinds of data.

CHAPTER 16

THE STUDY
OF LOGICAL
IMPLICATIONS

An important strategy in the use of mathematics in sociology is the study of logical implications of very simple assumptions. The example to be developed in this chapter concerns the relative sizes of groups in a larger community of interacting persons and the consequence of these size differences for the maintenance of norms or beliefs peculiar to each group.

Georg Simmel was perhaps the first and remains one of the few sociologists to consider the importance of *numbers* of people in a group. He examined the effects of the absolute size of a group (e.g., the difference between a dyad and a triad, or the increase from a small group to a mass), as well as the effects of relative sizes of parts of the group (e.g., the number of leaders relative to the number of followers, the size of the majority relative to the size of the minority). Simmel not only had an unerring sense of what kinds of knowledge sociology could fruitfully concern itself with; he was also fascinated with the way in which mere armchair reflection that traced out the logical implications of apparently trivial facts could add to our knowledge of the way social systems operate.

Yet Simmel was not a systematic theorist, nor did he use any mathematics. Consequently, he did little more than point out, in terms of "more" and "less," some of the implications of size variations. He failed to take advantage of the quantification which is available when we deal with numbers of people in a group or subgroup. In the present example, I want to extend in quantitative directions the kind of strategy for social theory which Simmel recognized and called to our attention.

1. RELATIVE SIZES OF GROUPS AND RELATIVE STRENGTH OF GROUP NORMS IN A COMMUNITY

Suppose there are two groups of fixed membership in a community, say two religious groups such as Methodists and Baptists, or two ethnic groups such as German-Americans and Swedish-Americans. Or suppose in a college the students are all members of one of two fraternities. Such groups are characterized by beliefs, values, and norms which are peculiar to them and not shared by members of the other group or groups in the community. For example, Baptists believe in baptism by immersion, while Methodists believe in baptism by sprinkling, a difference which has caused controversy in many communities. Or one fraternity believes it has the best intramural basketball team, while the other believes its team is best.

Is there anything which can be said about the strength of such beliefs and norms and their likelihood of survival in the community merely as a consequence of the relative sizes of the groups (neglecting, of course, the effects of other differences between the groups, such as economic or prestige differences)? For example, does the larger group tend to have the stronger norms, or does the smaller group? In order to examine the possible consequences, let us put down a simple and intuitively reasonable postulate, and see the effects consequent upon it.

Postulate 1. The strength of an individual's belief on an issue varies in direct proportion to the number of times he hears in conversation this same belief "reflected back" to him. Thus if p_{ii} is the proportion of his conversations which are with persons of the same belief as he, then the strength of his belief will vary in proportion to p_{ii}.

The postulate may or may not be true, but assume for present purposes that it is. Many qualitative results in social research conform to its general implications. For example, in voting studies it has been found that the proportion of workers voting in favor of the "left" party varies directly with the degree to which the workers are isolated from other groups which vote differently. At one extreme is coal miners, who constitute almost a hundred per cent of the communities in which they live, and vote very strongly for the left party in every country. At the other extreme are domestic servants, who have almost no fellow-associates, and tend to vote as do their employers.

Immediately one question must be raised, however, about the meaning of "strength of belief." If the postulate above is to be more than a mere definition of "strength of belief," and is to be emprically true or false, then this concept of strength of belief must have some independent behavioral significance. In the example above, the behavioral significance is voting for the left party. For the present it is enough to recognize that such a definition is necessary, and to assume that it is given.

Now suppose the conditions of association in the community are such that association between people is effectively *random* with respect to this grouping. That is, a Baptist is no more likely to associate with other Baptists than is a Methodist. Under these conditions of association, what will be the frequency with which a member of each group hears his own beliefs expressed by his associates? Let there be n_1 members of group 1 (e.g., the Methodists) and n_2 members of group 2 (e.g., the Baptists). Then each person in group 1 associates with $n_1 - 1$ others of his same group and n_2 members of the other group. Therefore, the proportion of his associations which reflect his own opinion is $(n_1 - 1)/(n_1 + n_2 - 1)$, that is, the number of other members in group 1 divided by the total of other persons in the community. For simplicity in what follows, the $- 1$ will be neglected, so that the proportion of like-minded associates is (approximately)

$$p_{11} = \frac{n_1}{n_1 + n_2} \tag{1.1}$$

$$p_{11} = p_1 \tag{1.1'}$$

(where $p_1 =$ the proportion of community members in group 1). Therefore, using postulate 1, the strength of group 1's beliefs will be proportional to p_1 and the strength of group 2's beliefs will be proportional to p_2. The relative strengths of beliefs will be p_1/p_2.

Thus if the community is made up of 100 Baptists and 900 Methodists, this means that the Baptists constitute only .1 of the total, and the strength of their beliefs relative to that of the Methodists is

$$\frac{p_1}{p_2} \times \frac{.1}{.9} = .111$$

Therefore, under these conditions of random association, a group which constitutes only .1 of the total has a strength of beliefs equal to only about 11% of that of the group which is nine times its size. This deduction expresses in quantitative terms the age-old qualitative generalization that a deviant subgroup finds it difficult to maintain its beliefs in the face of a large majority with which its members are in association.

This, then, is the first, and very simple deduction from postulate 1: under conditions of random association among members of the community, the strengths of beliefs on issues which divide the groups are in the ratio p_1/p_2, where p_1 and p_2 are the proportions of the community in each group. This deduction generalizes readily to situations of more than two groups; still

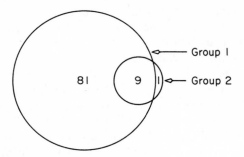

Figure 16.1

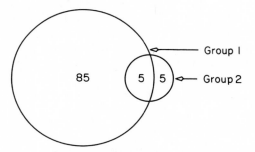

Figure 16.2

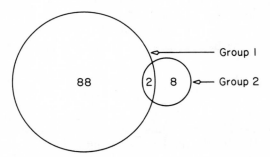

Figure 16.3

the ratio of strengths of belief for any two groups i and j is p_i/p_j. It extends as well to a comparison between two communities. Suppose community A is split equally between five churches, so that $p_{1a} = p_{2a} = p_{3a} = p_{4a} = p_{5a} =$

.20. And suppose community B is split equally between two churches, so that $p_{1b} = p_{2b} = .5$. Then if there were random association in both communities, the religious matters were equally relevant in both communities, the strength of religious beliefs in each group in community A would be only two-fifths of that in community B. In community A, the "resonating" responses each individual receives are diluted to 20% by opposing responses; in community B, they are diluted to only 50%.

2. WITHDRAWAL TO MAINTAIN GROUP NORMS

But we know that small groups often do develop strong norms. How can a small group come to have a strength of belief approaching that of the larger group? Obviously, its members can change their patterns of association, so as to associate more with group members and less with the out-group. In a community split 9 : 1, random association can be represented by Figure 16.1, which shows the overlapping association between the two groups. Here 81 out of 90 of a group 1 member's associations are with other members of group 1, while only 1 out of 10 of a group 2 member's associations are with other members of his own group. It is the ratio $1/10$ to $81/90$ which gives (with postulate 1) the ratio of strengths of belief. But now suppose the small-group members would be able to decrease their association with the larger group so that the association looked as in Figure 16.2. Now the strength of group 1's beliefs is proportional to $85/90$, which is an increase of p_{11} from .90 to .94. But the strength of group 2's beliefs has increased much more, with p_{22} increasing from .10 to .50. If the association were further decreased between the two groups, then the smaller group's strength of belief would continue to move up toward that of group 1. For example, when the overlap is as shown in Figure 16.3, then $p_{11} = 88/90 = .98$, while p_{22} has increased to $8/10 = .8$. At the extreme, where there is no association between the two groups, $p_{22} = p_{11} = 1.0$, so that group 2 finally has a strength of belief equal to that of group 1. Both have increased their strengths of belief by drawing further and further apart, but the smaller group has increased much more than the large.

Thus one alternative which the members of the smaller group have for increasing the strength of their group norms is to reduce their association with the outside and increase their internal association. This is not at all detrimental to the larger group members' beliefs; to the contrary, this dissociation increases their strength of belief as well. Thus there is a motivation on the part of both the small-group members and the large-group members to increase association within their own group and to decrease it with members of the other group. That is, insofar as the group members desire to increase the strength of their group norms and beliefs, such motivation exists. Under certain conditions, of course, there would not be the desire for dissociation with the out-group, but rather a desire to associate with nonbelievers in order to convince them.

At first glance, it seems that if group members are motivated to increase the strength of their own beliefs, they would continue to decrease their association with out-group members indefinitely, except under conditions in which one or both groups are trying to impose their values on the other. That is, for strengthening internally the group's norms, it is (by virtue of postulate 1) to both groups' interests to reduce association with the others to zero. Why doesn't this frequently occur? One reason is simple: each individual is not only a member of *one* group; he has multiple attachments with many different groups and individuals. He is a member of a religious group, an occupational group; he belongs to a union, to fraternal organizations, to community groups of one sort or another. Since these different group boundaries seldom coincide, to reduce out-group associations along one criterion (e.g., religion) means to increase out-group associations along other criteria (e.g., social class). Also, of course, there are numerous other constraints upon association patterns, so that association is far from determined by group values alone.

Such elaborations can be put aside for the moment. The general deduction from the postulate is clear: group members may increase the strength of their norms by increasing their association with fellow-members, decreasing it with nonmembers; and if n_{11} is the frequency of association of members of group 1 with other 1's, n_{12} is the frequency of 1's with 2's, then the relative strengths of the norms is given by

$$p_{11} = \frac{n_{11}}{n_{11} + n_{12}} \tag{1.2}$$

$$p_{22} = \frac{n_{22}}{n_{22} + n_{12}} \tag{1.3}$$

But one question remains: Given a certain tendency to reject out-group members, then how effective will this tendency be in increasing p_{11} for different-sized groups? In other words, if a small group has a certain tendency to reject out-group members, will this have the same effectiveness as an equal tendency on the part of a large group?

3. EASE OF WITHDRAWAL AS A FUNCTION OF GROUP SIZE

The relation between such a tendency to reject outsiders and p_{ii} for a given group size can be found as follows: Let β_i = probability of rejecting association with an out-group member when one meets him and going on to the next person one meets. Then the proportion of one's associates which are from the in-group, p_{ii}, is given by summing the following terms:

(a) With probability p_i, one meets an in-group member at first.

(b) With probability $1 - p_i$, one meets an out-group member; with probability β_i this out-group man is rejected, given that he is met; and with probability p_i one next meets an in-group member. Therefore, the probability of meeting an in-group member at the second meeting (i.e., after rejecting one out-group member) is $(1 - p_i)\beta_i p_i$.

(c) With probability $(1 - p_i)\beta_i(1 - p_i)$ one meets an out-group member at the second meeting (after rejecting the first); with probability β_i, this man is rejected, and with probability p_i one next meets an in-group member. Thus the probability of meeting an in-group member at the third meeting is $(1 - p_i)\beta_i(1 - p_i)\beta_i p_i$, or $(1 - p_i)^2\beta_i^2 p_i$.

(d) Similarly, the probability of meeting an in-group member at the fourth meeting is $(1 - p_i)\beta_i(1 - p_i)\beta_i(1 - p_i)\beta_i p_i$, or $(1 - p_i)^3\beta_i^3 p_i$

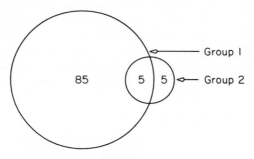

Figure 16.4

The sum of all terms is

$$p_{ii} = p_i + (1 - p_i)\beta_i p_i + (1 - p_i)^2\beta_i^2 p_i + \ldots (1 - p_i)^n\beta_i^n p_i - \ldots \qquad (1.4)$$

This is a geometric series which sums to

$$p_{ii} = \frac{p_i}{1 - (1 - p_i)\beta_i} \qquad (1.5)$$

$$p_{ii} = \frac{p_i}{1 - \beta_i + \beta_i p_i} \qquad (1.6)$$

or with p_{ii} as a function of β_i,

$$\beta_i = \frac{p_{ii} - p_i}{p_{ii}(1 - p_i)} \qquad (1.7)$$

These equations give the relation between β_i, the *tendency* to reject outsiders, and p_{ii} the resulting amount of association with fellow-group members. In order to see how p_{ii} varies with β_i, let us take the example used earlier, in which association was like that in Figure 16.4. Thus $p_{11} = .94$ and $p_{22} = .5$. Suppose first that this shift from random association was due to rejection of members of the large group on the part of the small-group members. Then what would β_2 have to be to produce this?

$$\beta_2 = \frac{.5 - .1}{.5(1 - .1)} = \frac{.4}{.45} = .89$$

That is, each small-group member must reject .89 of all out-group members he meets, assuming that meetings are random.

But now suppose that the configuration of Figure 16.4 results from rejection on the part of members of the *large* group. How much rejection will it require?

$$\beta_1 = \frac{.94 - .9}{.94(1 - .9)} = \frac{.04}{.094} = .43$$

Each large-group member must reject .43 of the out-group members he meets. His tendency to reject is less than *half* as great as that of the small-group member to produce the same separation of the two groups. Thus he needs less than half as much motivation to dissociate as does the small-group member. Again the small group is at a disadvantage in maintaining its beliefs. Though it gains disproportionately by dissociation from the out-group, the same amount of dissociation is much harder for its members to bring about.

Figure 16.5 plots β_i vs. n_{ij}/n for various group sizes, and shows this relation more generally. The y-axis, n_{ij}/n, or $p_{ij}p_i$, corresponds to the 5/100 intergroup associations of Figure 16.4. In the above example, $p_{ij}p_i$ is .05, and the β_i necessary to produce this configuration can be read off the line for $p = .9$ and the line for $p = .1$. The β_i's are .43 and .89.

Figure 16.5 shows what is intuitively evident: that as the groups become more equal in size, the β_i's necessary to produce a given dissociation are more alike. It also shows that to produce random association (which is .09 for a 9:1 split, .16 for an 8:2 split, .21 for a 7:3 split, and so on), then β_i is zero for both p_i and $1 - p_i$; and to produce complete dissociation, $\beta_i = 1.0$ for both p_i and $1 - p_i$. It is for the intermediate degrees of dissociation, somewhere between random mixing and complete separation, that the small-group member needs a rejection tendency so much greater than does the large-group member to produce a given dissociation.

At the same time, it is true that a given degree of dissociation produces a bigger percentage increase in the small group's strength of belief than in the large group's strength of belief. In the preceding example, p_{22} changed from .10 to .50 while p_{11} changed only from .90 to .94. Thus for equal tendencies to reject, the small group's strength of norms might be increased as much or more by the dissociation its rejection would produce than the large group's would be increased by the dissociation it would produce. Figure 16.6 gives p_{ii} as a function of β_i, showing that for equal β_i's, a group with $p_i = .1$ will show a considerably greater increase than will a group with

$p_i = .9$. Thus if group 2 in the previous example had a β of only .43, this would produce a p_{11} of .17 (as compared to a random p_{11} of .10), while the same tendency to reject on the part of group 1 members would produce a p_{22} of .94, only .04 increase over the random of .90.

In summary, then, these quantitative deductions, together with their qualitative implications for large and small groups, stem from postulate 1:

(1) Given random association, strength of norms is proportional to p_i.
(2) The tendency to reject out-group members necessary to produce a given degree of dissociation between groups is given by Figure 16.5.
(3) The in-group association, p_{ii}, as a function of a group's tendency to reject others is given by Figure 16.6.

4. PSYCHOLOGICAL REJECTION OF THE OUT-GROUP

Apart from this tendency to reject out-group members upon meeting, are there any other ways in which members of a group can circumvent the consequences of postulate 1? That is, how can they increase their strength of belief if their association patterns are fixed? The alternative of dissociation discussed above would never allow a small group in association with a larger one to have stronger norms than the larger. Yet this is surely possible. One way in which it could occur is through a *psychological* rejection of the out-group member's statements. For example, in the 9:1 split, the small-group members may be able to erect a psychological defense against any statement by the out-group, and thus reduce the effectiveness of the intergroup association for them to a low value. While the large-group members were still affected by the association, the small-group members would not be.

It is probably empirically true that such psychological rejection is common between members of different ethnic groups, different cultural and religious groups, different political parties, different social classes, and other well-defined social groups. At the same time, such tendencies are probably far from absolute, so that there is seldom the ability to reject completely the views of the out-group.[1]

The consequences of such psychological rejection are somewhat different than those of the social rejection discussed above. Psychological rejection is *asymmetric* in its consequences, allowing the rejecting group to reduce the other's effect upon it without reduction of its effect on the other group. Thus

---

[1] In extreme situations, this tendency may be quite pronounced. Bettelheim has noted that East European Jews in German concentration camps were much better able to survive than non-Jews or their West European counterparts. He attributes this difference to the fact that East European Jews were raised in ghettos and with a rejection of Gentiles from childhood, and no expectation of humanitarian treatment from them, so that the administration of the concentration camp could inflict little psychological damage upon them.

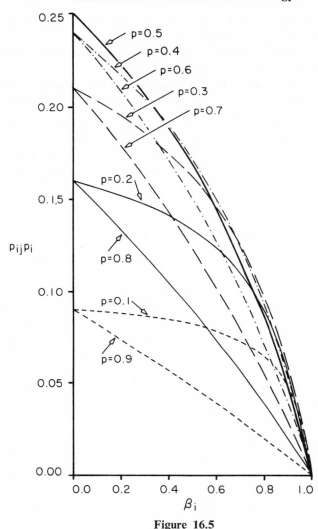

Figure 16.5

by this means, a small group can maintain its norms at a strength equal to, or higher than, that of a larger group in association with it.

The psychological rejection is proposed to occur in much the same way that the social rejection occurs, through a "tendency to reject," which is the probability of rejecting an out-group members' statement. To find the consequences of such a tendency, the following two terms can be defined:

β_i^* = the probability of rejecting an out-group member's statement; and
p_{ii}^* = the proportion of accepted statements which are made by one's fellow-group members.

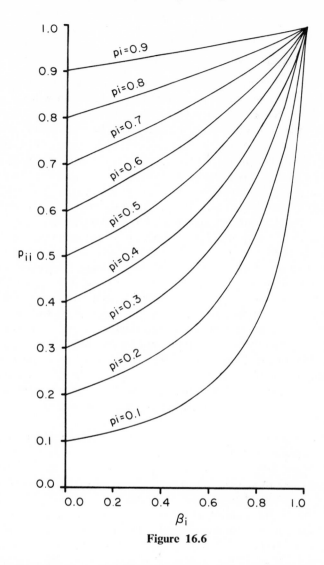

Figure 16.6

Then if p_{ii} is the probability of meeting a member of the in-group and $1 - p_{ii}$ the probability of meeting an out-group member, β_i^* may be found just as was β_i:

$$p_{ii}^* = p_{ii} + (1 - p_{ii})\beta_i^* p_{ii} + (1 - p_{ii})^2 \beta_i^{*2} p_{ii} - \dots \qquad (1.8)$$

or

$$p_{ii}^* = \frac{p_{ii}}{1 - \beta_i^*(1 - p_{ii})} \qquad (1.9)$$

or

$$\beta_i^* = \frac{p_{ii}^* - p_{ii}}{p_{ii}^*(1 - p_{ii})} \tag{1.10}$$

If there is random association, then p_{ii} becomes p_i, the proportion of group i in the total. But more generally, the psychological rejection will be coupled with some social rejection as well, which means that p_{ii} is greater than p_i.

The effects of such psychological rejection can be read off the charts of Figures 16.5 and 16.6 as before, with p_{ii} in eqs. (1.9) and (1.10) taking the place of p_i in the charts, p_{ii}^* taking the place of p_{ii}, and β_i^* taking the place of β_i. Using the charts, it is possible to investigate in particular the relation of small and large groups under two conditions: (a) conditions in which the *sources* of psychological rejection are equal, and (b) conditions in which the *consequences* of psychological rejection are equal. Assume first that there is random association, so that all the rejection is psychological and thus asymmetric in its consequences.

The consequences of equal sources of psychological rejection may be found from Figure 16.6 by reading off the p_{ii}'s corresponding to a particular β_i for different-sized groups, p_i. For example, if in a community split 8 : 2 there is random association but psychological rejection to the extent that $\beta_i^* = .4$, then the small group (represented by the line for $p_i = .2$) would have a p_{ii}^* of only .29, while the large (represented by the line for $p_i = .8$) would have a $p_{ii}^* = .87$. On the other hand, if there were equal consequences, that is, equal strengths of belief, say at $p_{ii}^* = .85$, then the β_i^*'s necessary to produce this p_{ii}^* would be very different. The large group, with $p_i = .8$, would require a β_i^* of only .3, while the small group, with $p_i = .2$, would require a β_i^* of .96.

Again, comparison may be made between two communities, one split between many groups and one split between few. If community A is split into five groups of .20 each, while B is split into two groups of .50 each, then (assuming random association in each community), equal tendencies to reject, at $\beta_i^* = .50$, would produce p_{ii}^*'s in the ratio .33 : .67, or 1 : 2 (see Figure 16.6). That is, the strength of beliefs in the 5-group community would only be *half* those in the 2-group community. On the other hand, if the consequence, that is, the strength of group beliefs, were equal in the two communities, say at $p_{ii}^* = .6$, then the necessary rejection tendencies to produce this equality would be $\beta_i^* = .83$ for everyone in the 5-group community, and only $\beta_i^* = .33$ for everyone in the 2-group community.

If there is some dissociation between groups, so that random association no longer prevails, then the disparity between different-sized groups is reduced. For example, suppose there is dissociation in the 8 : 2 split such that the configuration shifts from 64-16-4 (random) to 72-8-12, as diagrammed opposite. Then the relevant lines to use for relating β_i^* and p_{ii}^* are .6 = (12/20) for the .2 group and .9 (= 72/80) for the .8 group. Inspection of these lines in

Figure 16.6 will show that the disparity between p_i^*'s for a given β_{ii}^* is less than for the .2 and .8 lines, and the disparity between β_i^*'s for a given p_{ii}^* is less than for the .2 and .8 lines.

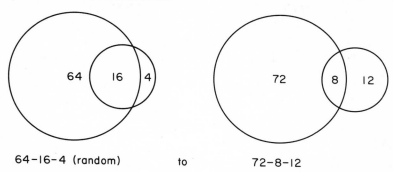

64–16–4 (random)   to   72–8–12

5. MAINTENANCE OF CULTURAL EQUILIBRIUM

It is interesting to examine one other logical implication of these processes. The condition of equal consequences of psychological rejection means that each group has the same "resonance" of its beliefs, that is, the same ability to maintain its norms. It is reasonable to consider such a situation as one of *cultural equilibrium*, because in any other situation, the differing strengths of beliefs would lead to a loss of cultural identity by the weaker group, and absorption by the group with greater strength of beliefs.

For such a situation of cultural equilibrium to exist, p_{ii}^* must be equal for all groups. Figure 16.2 shows the β_i^* necessary to maintain such a cultural equilbrium in a system composed of various-sized groups. By reading across a given horizontal line representing a given p_{ii}, the values of β_i^* necessary to maintain cultural equilibrium for different-sized groups are located. If, for example, a social system is split into three social groups, A, B, C, in proportion 60: 30: 10, and if the majority group ($p_i = .6$) has a β_i^* of zero, then group B must have a β_i^* of .72, and group C must have a β_i^* of .93 to maintain cultural equilibrium. That is, groups B and C must reject the statements of .72 and .93 of all outsiders in order to maintain cultural equilibrium.

CHAPTER 17

DIFFUSION
IN INCOMPLETE
SOCIAL STRUCTURES

1. INTRODUCTION

One of the most pervasive processes in the study of social behavior has been the process of diffusion: diffusion of ideas, of technology, of cultural traits, of rumors, of opinion, of fads and fashions, and of population itself. Some social theorists have, in fact, made diffusion their central mechanism of social change (e.g., Tarde, 1903, Pemberton, 1936, and many early social anthropologists), and many others have examined empirical cases of diffusion (e.g., McVoy, 1940, Kniffen, 1951, Ryan and Gross, 1943, Coleman, Katz, and Menzel, 1957, Hagerstrand, 1952, and Lionberger, 1954). The empirical investigations have covered a remarkably wide range of topics, from hybrid corn (Ryan and Gross) to automobiles (Hagerstrand) to the practice of boiling drinking water (Wellin, 1955).

This body of research has resulted in a considerable cumulation of general knowledge about the way diffusion in human populations proceeds. For example, diffusion processes appear to differ sharply as the unit of adoption varies, say from an individual to a community. In fluoridation of water systems, for example, the unit of adoption is circumscribed by the district served by a common water supply—ordinarily a city or town. In the diffusion of automobile purchase, the unit of adoption is the individual purchaser. In the former case, processes of community decision-making and social conflict come into play which are absent in the latter. Or, as another example, it is evident from several studies that different media of transmission perform different functions in leading to adoption of an innovation: interpersonal communication plays more nearly a role of influence, or legitimation of the new attribute, while mass media often plays more nearly an informative role.

Despite these complexities, social diffusion has attracted the attention of some mathematically inclined persons. Quantitative variables are provided quite naturally by the process, in the form of *time* and *number of persons* who have adopted, and in some cases, geographic area. Steward Dodd (1955), Anatol Rapoport (1953), Hagerstrand (1960), De Fleur and Larsen (1958), and others have had some success in developing mathematical models to describe the gross aspects of cases of diffusion.

By far the most sophisticated mathematical work and the most serious empirical studies have been in medical epidemics. Basically two types of models have been developed, for describing two different situations (see Bailey, 1957). One describes diffusion (i.e., contagion) of a disease throughout a population, and assumes complete intermixing of the population, with the rate of propagation (or in stochastic models, the probability of infection in a given short period of time) proportional to the product of the number of infectives and the number of susceptibles. The other describes contagion within households, and utilizes a chain of binomial distributions to describe the probability of 2, 3, 4, and more infections in the household, stemming from an initial infective in the household. Both these types of models have had considerable success in describing the progress and distribution of a communicable disease in the two contexts in which they are applicable.

One of the assumptions made by nearly all the models of social diffusion is that of a completely intermixed population. In person-to-person diffusion (as contrasted to constant-source diffusion), the models assume that the number of contacts between the haves and have-nots is proportional to the product of the numbers of each. In a population where each person has equal numbers of contacts with each other person, such an assumption correctly describes the situation, for the product of n_1 and n_2 (the numbers of haves and have-nots, respectively) is equal to the number of *relations* that exist between the two groups. But when this assumption is not true (as it never is in human populations), then a serious bias may be introduced by it. For if diffusion begins with one person, then the person he diffuses to will not be a random person—he will usually be in contact with many of the same people as was the first person. A result of this is that as diffusion proceeds, the group of haves may be people who have a great many contacts with each other, but few with the have-nots. At that point, the number of relations across the have–have-not boundary may be far fewer than would be implied by the model, and in fact the diffusion might die out. More generally, the departure of social structures from complete intermixing always slows the diffusion, and in general, slows it differentially at different stages of the process.

This is not the place to review the small body of investigation into diffusion in incomplete structures, but two authors' work should be mentioned: Rapoport attempted to incorporate a "distance bias" in otherwise random communication nets (1953), but this work has been followed up very little. Hagerstrand (1960) has simulated on a digital computer the geographic spread of a farm innovation with striking success, using data on geographic mobility as the communication structure.

2. STOCHASTIC AND DETERMINISTIC MODELS WITH COMPLETE INTERMIXING

The principal work in social diffusion to date has started out with the deterministic or stochastic version of a classical growth model. In deterministic form it may be expressed as

$$\frac{dn_1}{dt} = kn_1n_2 \tag{2.1}$$

where n_1 is the number of haves, n_2 is the number of have-nots, and k is the coefficient of conversion. The assumption behind this model is that the potential for diffusion is proportional to the number of pair relations between the haves and have-nots, which is simply the product, n_1n_2. Implicitly, this assumes that the item spreads through its users, and that each user is in contact with all nonusers. This equation gives rise to the familiar logistic curve of adoption over time.[1]

In the stochastic version of the same process, it is the rate of change of the probability p_i that there are i haves which is considered. Thus for each state i, there is a differential equation expressing the probability as a function of the probability of being in states i and $i - 1$, and of the product of the number of haves and have-nots (i and $n - i$ when the group is in state i). The general equation (except for p_0 and p_n) is

$$\frac{dp_i}{dt} = -(n - i)ikp_i + (n - i + 1)(i - 1)kp_{i-1} \tag{2.2}$$

---

[1] This equation, and the stochastic one as well, can be usefully modified by adding another term to account for diffusion from some constant source (e.g., advertising). In the deterministic equation this would be $+k_2n_2$, where k_2 is the coefficient of conversion from the constant source.

Even such an apparently simple process is not simple for analytic solution, since it is not close to being Markovian, as the products in eq. (2.2) make clear. (See Bailey, 1957, p. 39, for solution of a slight variant of this model, and Chapter 10, p. 310, above for discussion of the identical model.) But despite its complexity, it provides no more aid for social structures that are not completely intermixed than does the deterministic version. In order to treat such structures, it is necessary somehow to modify the assumption that the driving force for the process is proportional to the product of the number of haves and have-nots. It is to this task that we now turn.

3. INCOMPLETE SOCIAL STRUCTURES: I. SMALL SEPARATE GROUPS

The major aspect of empirical structures that causes diffusion to go astray is not a randomly spread incompleteness, but the fact that these structures turn back on themselves. The friends of my friends are likely also to be my friends—far more likely than their frequency in the total population would predict. As a consequence, the diffusion may spread only to a tight little in-group. Thus what is required is a model that approximates such in-groupness so that the structural characteristics of a given system can be taken into account. (Obviously, to mirror the full complexity of such structures would require detailed measurement followed by a simulation with the structure mapped onto the memory of a computer.)

Two approaches appear to show considerable promise. The first approach approximates the actual structure by assuming a number of discrete groups, *within* which communication is complete, but *between* which it is absent or nearly so. The first and simplest form of the model has the following assumptions, treated here in the form of two-person groups:

(1) The population of n persons is assumed to be composed of $n/2$ pairs of persons in full communication with one another, but without communication to others.

(2) If one member of the pair is a "have," the second has a transition rate of βdt of becoming a have in a small increment of time dt.

(3) In addition, independently of the other member of the pair, each person has a transition rate αdt of becoming a have in the increment of time dt, due to outside communication from some constant source.

(4) All individuals and all pairs are alike.

We may then use these assumptions to write a stochastic process characterizing the 2-person group. The group may be in one of three states:

State 0: both members have-nots,
State 1: one member have, one have-not, and

State 2: both members haves.

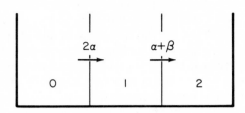

The process may be described by three differential equations, for the probability of being in state 0, state 1, and state 2:
or

$$\frac{dp_0}{dt} = -2\alpha p_0 \tag{3.1}$$

$$\frac{dp_1}{dt} = 2\alpha p_0 - (\alpha + \beta)p_1 \tag{3.2}$$

$$\frac{dp_2}{dt} = (\alpha + \beta)p_1 \tag{3.3}$$

The group has a transition rate 2α for moving out of state 0, that is, simply the sum of the transition rates for the two members. When it is in state 1, then its transition rate out is simply the transition rate of the member who is still a have-not, that is, $\alpha + \beta$. Since the groups are continually seeded from the start by the constant source (i.e., through α), we would ordinarily be interested in the case with initial conditions $p_0 = 1$, $p_1 = 0$, $p_2 = 0$.

These equations may be solved by first solving the equation for p_0, using its solution in the equation for p_1, and so on. The solution, for the probability at any time t that a pair is in state i, is[2]

$$p_0 = e^{-2\alpha t} \tag{3.4}$$

$$p_1 = \frac{2\alpha(e^{-2\alpha t} - e^{-(\alpha+\beta)t})}{\beta - \alpha} \tag{3.5}$$

$$p_2 = \frac{\alpha + \beta}{\beta - \alpha}(1 - e^{-2\alpha t}) - \frac{2\alpha}{\beta - \alpha}(1 - e^{-(\alpha+\beta)t}) \tag{3.6}$$

These equations show the probability of a pair being in any state at a given time, so that by multiplying by the total number of pairs, $n/2$, we find the expected number of pairs in each state. The progress of diffusion through the population of individuals is given by

[2] For the special case when $\beta = \alpha$, substitute α for β in the original equations (3.1–3.3), which are then easily solved.

$$E(n_1) = E(\text{groups in state 1}) + 2E(\text{groups in state 2})$$

$$= \frac{n}{2}\, p_1 + 2\frac{n}{2}\, p_2 \tag{3.7}$$

$$E(n_1) = n\left[1 - \frac{\beta}{\beta - \alpha} e^{-2\alpha t} + \frac{\alpha}{\beta - \alpha} e^{-(\alpha + \beta)t}\right] \tag{3.8}$$

where $E(n_1)$ is the expected number of persons in state 1; or, alternatively, the probability of an individual being a have at time t is given by the expression in brackets in eq. (3.8).

It is interesting to note how the process of diffusion is affected by this pairwise structure, by examining this equation at the extremes. If the interpersonal diffusion parameter, β, approaches zero, so that diffusion within the pair is nonexistent, then the last term of (3.8) becomes $e^{-\alpha t}$ and the next to last term drops out, so that the expected number of haves is

$$E(n_1) = n(1 - e^{-\alpha t}) \tag{3.9}$$

This is the equation for constant-source diffusion in the *absence* of any interpersonal contact whatsoever. If, at the other extreme, β approaches infinity, so that diffusion from one member to the other is almost immediate, then the last term drops out, and (3.8) becomes

$$E(n_1) = n(1 - e^{-2\alpha t}) \tag{3.10}$$

This again is identical to a constant-source diffusion, but with an individual transition rate of 2α rather than α—so that the pair is acting just as a single person, but with "two sets of eyes in his head." Figure 17.1 shows the cumulative expected proportion of haves for various values of α and β.

An interesting example of this kind of structure in operation occurred in a recent study of physicians introducing new drugs, carried out by the author and others (1957). Some of the doctors shared offices with a partner, while others practiced alone. In examining the date of first use of the drug by these two sets of doctors, the curves of first use shown in Figure 17.2 were found. The upper curve represents the cumulative proportion of adopters for the doctors with partners, while the lower curve represents the cumulative proportion of adopters for those who practiced alone. Initially, we were puzzled at the shape of the office-partner curve: although it shows a higher rate of diffusion than that of the doctors who practiced alone, its *shape* is no different—there is no suggestion of the inflection point showed by the logistic curve of interpersonal diffusion, and exhibited by doctors in the same study who were integrated into the larger social network of physicians. But equations (3.8), (3.9), and (3.10) show why: the social structure of isolated pairs does not transform a constant-source diffusion process into one showing the characteristic logistic form, but maintains nearly the same form, with merely

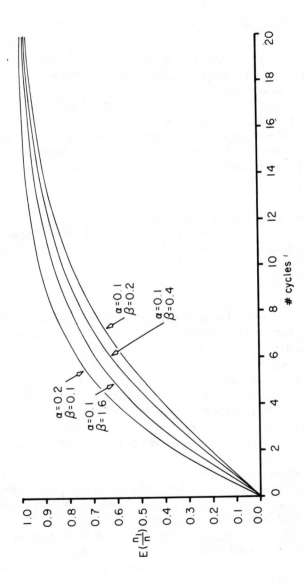

Figure 17.1

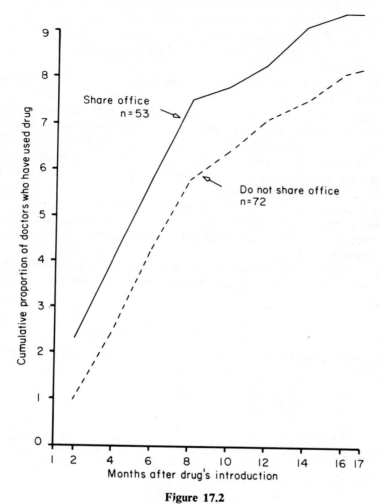

Figure 17.2

**First Use of New Drug by Doctors Who Share Office and Those Who
Practice Alone**

a higher diffusion rate.[3] These data should not be taken as good for purposes
of fitting this model, but merely as illustrative of an effect of social structure
on diffusion that was inexplicable until the process above was understood.

Models for a combination of interpersonal and constant-source diffusion

---

[3] If these data were from a larger sample size, and were uncontaminated by doctors
with more than one office partner, it would be worth while estimating α and β. However,
to do so, it would be necessary to use the proportion of *groups* with no haves, as well as
the proportion of haves shown in Figure 17.2.

in other complete structures of this sort (e.g., size 3, 4, . . .) are possible as well, proceeding along the lines of the pairwise structure. The models become increasingly more difficult to integrate, though use of the Laplace transform reduces the work.

However, rather than following out this model for structures with larger groups, it is useful to introduce a slight modification of a more interesting sort. This modification reintroduces a little more of the complexity of an empirical structure, by allowing some communication between persons in different groups. In the model above, each person had a transition rate from the constant source, and depending on the state of his partner, one from him as well. It is possible to add a third transition rate, proportional to the *total* number of persons who are haves.

Each person has a transition rate toward adoption γn_1, where n_1 is the number of persons who have already adopted in the *total* system. Thus his total transition rate is $\alpha + \gamma n_1$ if his partner is a have-not, and $\alpha + \beta + \gamma n_1$ if his partner is a have.

It is not possible to treat this exactly, since n_1 is a random variable whose state we do not know at any time. However, we know that the expected value of n_1 is

$$E(n_1) = \frac{n}{2}(p_1 + 2p_2) \qquad (3.11)$$

Consequently, we use $E(n_1)$ in place of n_1, and the equations for the group's states are

$$\frac{dp_0}{dt} = -2\left[\alpha + \frac{\gamma n}{2}(p_1 + 2p_2)\right]p_0 \qquad (3.12)$$

$$\frac{dp_1}{dt} = 2\left[\alpha + \frac{\gamma n}{2}(p_1 + 2p_2)\right]p_0 - \left[\alpha + \beta + \frac{\gamma n}{2}(p_1 + 2p_2)\right]p_1 \quad (3.13)$$

$$\frac{dp_2}{dt} = \left[\alpha + \beta + \frac{\gamma n}{2}(p_1 + 2p_2)\right]p_1 \qquad (3.14)$$

One equation may be quickly eliminated, since $p_0 + p_1 + p_2 = 1$. However, there remain a pair of nonlinear differential equations, which cannot be solved in closed form, but must be subject to parametric analysis. Parameter studies have been carried out with a digital computer, and examples of results are shown in Figures 17.3, 17.4, 17.5, and 17.6. Figure 17.3 shows, for a structure with groups of size 3, the effect of increasing $\gamma n/3$ (that is, either increasing the contacts between groups, γ, or increasing the total number of groups, $n/3$, while keeping constant the frequency of contacts between groups). The curves of cumulative number of haves approach a logistic curve as this between-group effect increases, but also, the over-all rate increases sharply. Figure 17.4 shows, for groups of size 3, and 300 total persons (100 three-person groups), the effect on adoption when the total number of contacts

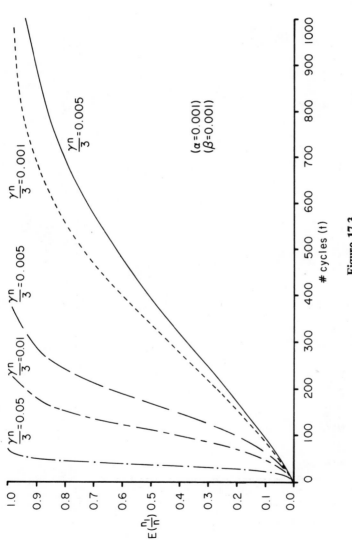

Figure 17.3

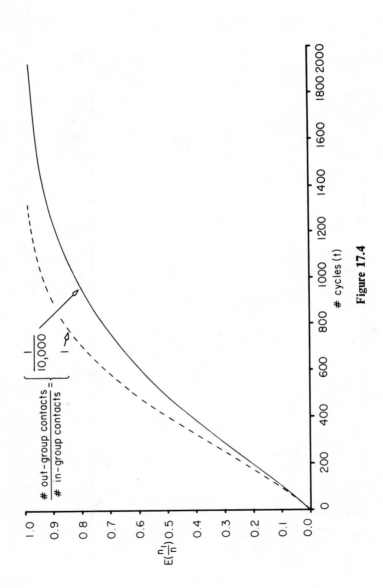

Figure 17.4

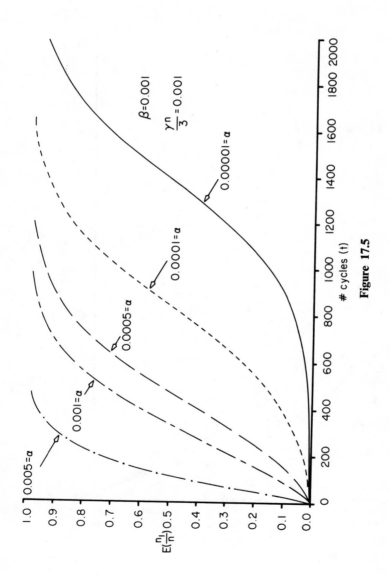

Figure 17.5

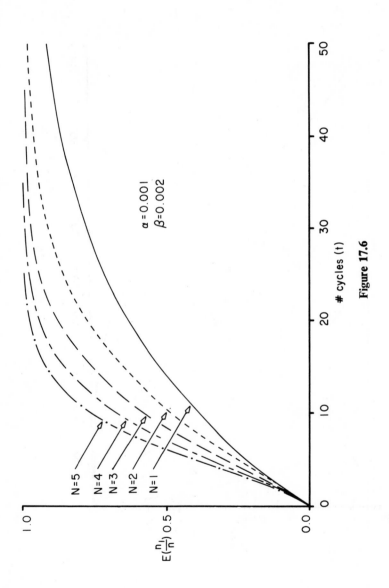

cycles (t)

Figure 17.6

with an out-group member to an in-group member increases from 1/10,000 to 1. Figure 17.5 shows, for a single ratio of in-group to out-group contacts, the effect of an increasing amount of stimulus from the constant source. Figure 17.6 shows the effect of increasing the group size from 1 to 5, while holding constant the constant-source stimulus and the contact between group members (with no between-group contact).

4. INCOMPLETE SOCIAL STRUCTURES: II. PARTIALLY INTER-PENETRATING GROUPS

A totally different approach to the problem is provided by the existence of large groups in society that have limited contact with one another. For example, studies of association patterns show that persons associate primarily with others of the same religion, or of the same economic class. Sociometric

Table 17.1

	To: Freshman	Sophomore	Junior	Senior	
Fresh.	216	15	4	1	236
Soph.	11	230	16	5	262
Junior	2	16	134	33	185
Senior	1	4	15	126	146
	230	265	169	165	829

From: (at left of Soph./Junior rows)

data and observational data often yield patterns like that shown in Table 17.1 (in this case, among boys in a high school). As the table indicates, most boys name as associates others in their own grade.

Thus in such a system, if an item (e.g., a clothing fad) began to diffuse in one grade, it might spread very quickly through that grade, but not "catch on" in other grades for some time. This is, in fact, what often happens in schools; and it is this kind of phenomenon that may be examined by the approach described below.

For simplicity, consider two groups, A and B, which are partially interpenetrating, but which associate more within than between. The data which would give the amount of this interpenetration is shown in Table 17.2, where n_a is the number of people in group A, and n_b the number in group B.

If this were a table showing actual pairwise associations at a slice in time, then it would necessarily be symmetric in the off-diagonal cells. That is, n_{ba} would equal n_{ab}—the number of A's associating with B's would equal the number of B's associating with A's. Often, the data are not entirely symmetric, being based on interviews with each person. However, symmetry will be assumed here, for the very concept of association implies it.

Now if group A's unconverted members were in contact only with A's,

Table 17.2

ASSOCIATION WITHIN AND BETWEEN GROUPS A AND B

		A	B	
		A	B	
A		n_{aa}	n_{ab}	$n_{a.}$
B		n_{ba}	n_{bb}	$n_{b.}$
		$n_{.a}$	$n_{.b}$	n

the deterministic diffusion equation for group A would follow the basic eq. (2.1):

$$\frac{dx_a}{dt} = k_1 x_a (1 - x_a) \tag{4.1}$$

where x_a is the proportion of A's converted, and k_1 is a coefficient of conversion, proportional to the frequency of contact. Similarly for the B's,

$$\frac{dx_b}{dt} = k_2 x_b (1 - x_b) \tag{4.2}$$

where the quantities are defined analogously to those in (4.1). But now if the fraction $(1 - x_a)$ of unconverted A's are in contact with converted B's as well as A's, this adds to the rate of change of x_a, as follows:

$$\frac{dx_b}{dt} = k_{11} x_a (1 - x_a) + k_{12} x_b (1 - x_a) \tag{4.3}$$

where, because the interpenetration is only partial, $k_{12} < k_{11}$. Similarly for the rate of new converts in group B:

$$\frac{dx_b}{dt} = k_{21} x_b (1 - x_b) + k_{22} x_b (1 - x_b) \tag{4.4}$$

It is important to recognize the implicit assumptions about contacts in these equations. It is assumed that each person in group A is alike in his probability of contacting a B and that of contacting an A; each has identical probabilities of contacting an A (proportional to k_{11}), and each has identical (and smaller) probabilities of contacting a B (proportional to k_{12}). There is no subset of A's who associate with the B's and are isolated from the other A's. If there were, then eq. (4.3) could not describe the process. For example, the converted B's whose effect appears in the last term of (4.3) would not work on all the unconverted A's $(1 - x_a)$, but only upon that fraction of A's who associate with them and are unconverted.

Now to return to Table 17.2, the probabilities upon which k_{11}, k_{12}, k_{21}, and k_{22} are based can be estimated from such data. We must, of course, make the above assumption that there is no difference in association patterns between the A's who happened at this time to be associating with B's, and all the other A's.

The estimates of the relative frequencies of contact, p_{ij}, assuming the data were in the form of Table 17.2, are

Proportion of an A's contact with B's:

$$p_{ab} = \frac{n_{ab}}{n_{a.}} \qquad (4.5)$$

and similarly for all other cases:

$$p_{aa} = 1 - p_{ab} \qquad (4.6)$$

$$p_{ba} = \frac{n_{ba}}{n_{b.}} \qquad (4.7)$$

$$p_{bb} = 1 - p_{ba} \qquad (4.8)$$

Under the necessary condition of symmetry, $n_{ba} = n_{ab}$, so that

$$p_{ba} = \frac{n_{ba}}{n_{b.}} = \frac{n_{ab}}{n_{b.}} = \frac{n_{a.}}{n_{b.}} \frac{n_{ab}}{n_{a.}} = \frac{n_a}{n_b} p_{ab} \qquad (4.9)$$

and

$$p_{bb} = 1 - \frac{n_a}{n_b} p_{ab} \qquad (4.10)$$

These data, then, provide estimates of the relative sizes of the k_{ij}'s (up to transformation by a scale constant, k):

$$k_{11} = k(1 - p_{ab})$$

$$k_{12} = k p_{ab}$$

$$k_{21} = k \frac{n_a}{n_b} p_{ab}$$

$$k_{22} = k \left(1 - \frac{n_a}{n_b} p_{ab} \right)$$

With these substitutions, eqs. (4.3) and (4.4) become

$$\frac{dx_a}{dt} = k[(1 - p_{ab})x_a + p_{ab}x_b](1 - x_a) \qquad (4.11)$$

$$\frac{dx_b}{dt} = k\left[\frac{n_a}{n_b} p_{ab}x_a + \left(1 - \frac{n_a}{n_b} p_{ab}x_b\right)\right](1 - x_b) \qquad (4.12)$$

These equations describe deterministically the process of diffusion when there is partial interpenetration between two subgroups. The degree of interpenetration is determined by the parameter p_{ab}, derived from such association data as shown in Table 17.1 and represented in Table 17.2.

The equations (4.11) and (4.12) are a pair of nonlinear differential equations that cannot be integrated to find explicit values of $x_a(t)$ and $x_b(t)$. However, they are amenable to parameter studies on a computer to investigate effects of different values of p_{ab} and of the relative group sizes, n_a/n_b. First, however, a classical investigation of the points of singularity in the (x_a, x_b) plane, and the behavior of the system in the region of these points, will allow some qualitative deductions.

This investigation shows four singular points, of which only two are in the quadrant where x_a and x_b are positive. These singular points are at $(0,0)$ and $(1,1)$. At $(0,0)$, the system is unstable and at $(1,1)$, it is stable (as intuitive considerations would already have told us). The general behavior of a point (x_a, x_b) describing the path of the system through time is roughly shown by the trajectories in Figure 17.7. (These trajectories do not show the time necessary to reach $(1,1)$, but only the relative positions of each group with change in time.)

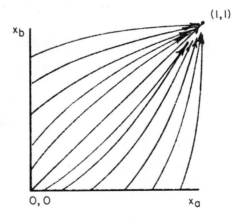

Figure 17.7

Both groups move toward the stable equilibrium where the item has diffused to all members. If the system starts out with many in A having the item and none in B [for example, at .5, 0], then group A, in which it started initially, gains faster, only later slowing down as it nears its upper limit of 1.0.

There are at least two variations of interest in the qualitative examination of this system: variations in degree of interpenetration (p_{ab}), and variations in relative group size (n_a/n_b). What happens as the groups are more and more isolated from one another (e.g., as $p_{ab} \rightarrow 0$)? The diagram of the trajectories becomes like that of Figure 17.8. The trajectories become much more concave relative to the 45° line. That is, if something starts in group A, it will grow there very rapidly until it is nearly universal, before it catches on in group B. Such a case is shown by the trajectory labelled (1). This means also that a stochastic disturbance near the origin would have a much greater effect when p_{ab} is very low than in the preceding case, when p_{ab} is relatively high. A stochastic disturbance might easily throw the system off the 45° line onto a trajectory such as (1), where it would diffuse through A before much affecting B.

The effect of changes in the relative group size occurs only in the presence of some separation of the group (that is, when p_{ab} is less than chance).[4]

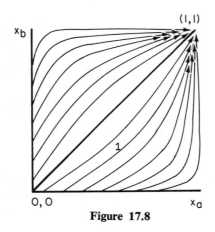

Figure 17.8

When there is some separation of the groups, then the effects of a large discrepancy in size of groups A and B is shown in Figure 17.9. There is asymmetry in the speed with which groups catch the item from one another. If it begins in the small group ("minority" in Figure 17.9), or a stochastic disturbance starts it off there, then it will diffuse through this group before it goes far in the larger one. But if it begins in the larger group, it will catch on very quickly in the smaller group, so that the groups rapidly become more nearly equal in the proportion of haves.

It is useful to add a word about a different case—when there is greater diffusion-laden contact between the two groups than within the same group. This might occur between the sexes, for example, where there was more contact between sexes than there was within each sex. In such a situation,

---

[4] Or when p_{ab} is greater than chance, although that situation of association with unlikes is not considered here. It will be mentioned below.

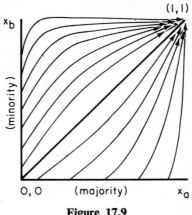

Figure 17.9

where there is much greater association among unlikes than expected from chance, the trajectories would look like Figure 17.10(a) (for equal-size groups). In this situation, any initial imbalance between the two groups is quickly righted, and they become nearly equal in their proportions of haves. If the groups are of unequal size, the trajectories show an asymmetry as in Figure 17.10(b). Here, if the item begins in the smaller group, almost all the initial diffusion is into the larger group, thus equalizing the groups. If it begins in the large group, there is less equalization, as Figure 17.10(b) indicates.

Another situation of this same sort may be mentioned. So far the assumption has been that the *total* frequency of association was the same in both groups. But in some cases, especially where association is principally with unlikes, there may be much greater total frequency of contact in one group

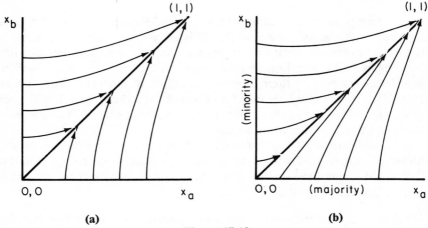

(a)   (b)

Figure 17.10

than in the other. A good example is sexual contact among adolescents, and the diffusion of venereal disease. The number of boys who have sexual relations in adolescence is much greater than the number of girls, and consequently the average frequency of intercourse for these girls is much higher. Considering only those who are promiscuous (i.e., free intermixing among the pool of potential partners), a table of frequency of contact might look like this:

	A	B	
A	0	50	300 total A's (e.g., boys)
B	50	0	100 total B's (e.g., girls)

In such a case, what would the trajectory of diffusion be, if the item entered in one or the other group? Such a case is shown in Figure 17.11. It exhibits

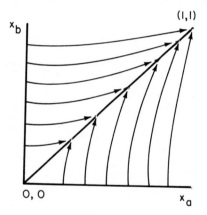

Figure 17.11

symmetry, as if the groups were of equal size, and would quickly move near the 45° line, where the proportion of haves was nearly the same in both groups. This means that the *number* of haves in the larger group would be larger, in proportion to the relative group sizes.

A further step in this same direction involves expanding the number of groups beyond two. Analogous to eqs. (4.11) and (4.12) can be written the general equation for diffusion in group i in a system of m partially interpenetrating groups:

$$\frac{dx_i}{dt} = k \sum_{j=1}^{m} p_{ij} x_j (1 - x_i) \qquad (4.13)$$

where $p_{ij} = n_{ij}/n_i$, and $n_{ij}\ (= n_{ji})$ is the number of associations between groups i and j in any slice of time.

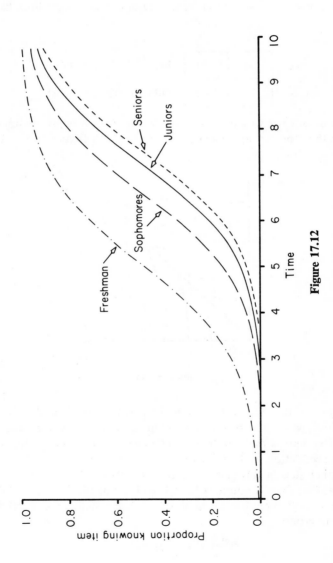

Figure 17.12

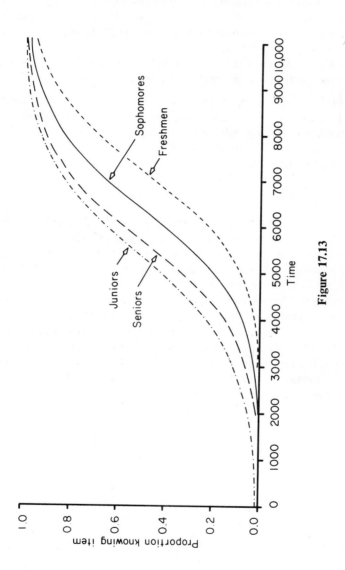

Figure 17.13

Once the problem is opened up in this way, numerous additional questions of interest arise. For example, what is the lag in diffusion grom group 1 to group 3, where there is little or no association between 1 and 3, but association of each group with an intermediary, 2? This is the situation among the high school boys whose association patterns are shown in Table 17.1. Freshmen have almost no associations with seniors, and there is not much between freshmen and juniors or between sophomores and seniors. Between adjacent grades there is more association.

Using eq. (4.13) and taking the average of n_{ij} and n_{ji} as the frequency of association between each pair of grades (and letting $p_{ii} = 1 - \sum\limits_{j \neq i} p_{ij}$), the data of Table 17.1 were used to calculate the relative rates of diffusion in each grade when the item being diffused began among the freshmen (starting with 3 freshmen having adopted the item). The results are shown in Figure 17.12. Figure 17.13 shows the relative rates of diffusion when the item began with three juniors.

5. CONCLUSION

The problem of diffusion in incomplete social structures presents considerable difficulty for the development of formal diffusion models. The two approaches presented here approximate some of the structural irregularities exhibited by actual social systems, and allow an examination of their consequences for diffusion. The models have, of course, only made a start on the general problem. There are other approaches that offer considerable interest. One is to approximate the varying "social distance" of persons by models of diffusion on a line, in a plane, and in higher-dimensional spaces. Models of this type would assume persons distributed uniformly over the given space, and examine the rate of spread over the space. Some work has been carried out in this direction for medical epidemics (see Bailey, 1957, p. 32), but no great progress has been made.

CHAPTER 18

TACTICS
AND STRATEGIES IN
THE USE OF MATHEMATICS

It is clear from the preceding chapters that there are many paths for the use of mathematics in social science. Taking as given that some uses of mathematics will be fruitful for social science, it becomes apparent that a wide range of uses exists from which we can pick and choose. Though sociology may not be ready for its Newton to provide a solid mathematical basis for sociological theory, there remain numerous other uses of mathematics which may prove of considerable immediate value. These uses constitute diverse tactics and strategies which, little by little, help bring social phenomena within our ken.

But the very diversity of uses to which mathematics has been put makes it mandatory to know what to pick—to have a general orientation which suggests that certain strategies and tactics will be more fruitful than others. Composed partly of hunches that certain lines will be productive, partly of prejudices, partly of unverbalized assumptions, such an orientation is one's major guide to the use of mathematics.

The intention of this chapter will be to lay out general strategies which I feel will be productive, to suggest why others may not be, and to mention a number of tactics or "tricks" which may help in one way or another to chip away at the ever-resistant problems of social behavior.

Some of these strategies and tactics are pursued further in the chapters of this book; others are merely stated here without further development. Taken as a whole, the chapter is a personal article of faith, faith that certain directions of work will help most in learning about social behavior. It is intentionally biased, representing not at all commonly agreed-upon directions of work, but a set of private hunches about fruitful directions of work.

1. THE SOMETIMES-TRUE THEORIES OF SOCIAL PROCESS

There is a widespread misconception that theories are either "true" or "false." A number of examples in physical science stand in direct contradiction to this. In chemical kinetics, for example, there exist a whole set of mathematical theories or models to account for reaction rates. There is an equation for first-order reactions (in which the reaction rate is dependent on the concentration of a single reacting substance), another for second-order reactions (rate dependent on concentration of two reactants), and so on. Each of these theories or models is tautologically true, *when* their postulates are fulfilled. The equation for the first-order process is simply the mathematical means of deducing what the reaction rate will be when the rate depends only on the concentration of a single reactant. It is not developed on the premise that reaction rates *will* always be of this sort. If it were, it would be sometimes true, but more often false.

What is the nature of the theoretical and empirical work in the case of these theories? The first part of the work is simply developing the equations and showing that they adequately account for reaction rates in some specific cases; the other part, which is still continuing in chemical reaction rates, is the determination of which of these sometimes-true theories adequately describes specific reactions. Models which attempt to describe social processes provide several comparable examples. One such process is that of diffusion of an innovation throughout a population. In the example of Chapter 1, the socially integrated doctors seemed to innovate through a "chain reaction" or "snowballing" process in their adoption of the new drug, while the isolated ones adopted via direct diffusion from the constant stimuli provided by original agents of dissemination: advertisements, drug salesmen, articles in medical journals, and so on. Two different equations describe the two processes, and there are numerous other modifications as well, each describing a particular form of the process.

The "sometimes-true" nature of such processes lies simply in this: in some cases diffusion may be through a chain reaction process; in other cases, it may be diffusion from a central-source, or in stages from a central source to staging points, and then directly to the people; or perhaps a combination of the chain-reaction and central source processes; in still other cases, diffusion may be by chain reaction, but as in the case of popular songs, an individual continues influencing others for only a limited time; in some cases (again as with popular songs) there may be competition between two or more different products or behaviors; and so on, with innumerable variations. Thus none of these processes is absolutely or unilaterally true; *any* one of them can be true in a specific instance. The problem in any given application is to know *which* of the many processes is followed in this case.

But social diffusion is just one example of such sometimes-true theories of social processes. Probability models in general are of this sort. Bernoulli trials, giving rise to the binomial distribution, and the Poisson process, giving rise to the Poisson distribution, are theories which are sometimes true and sometimes not. It is trivial to state it, but each of these theories is true when its postulates are fulfilled, untrue when they are not. Numerous probability models are slight modifications of these basic models, modifications which hold under certain circumstances, not under others. They are not theories to be confirmed or disconfirmed in general, but only confirmed or disconfirmed in specific applications. As a result, they are not theories which explain "how people behave"; they are theories or models which describe how people behaved in this or that circumstance. Probability models are often described in terms of particular ways of drawing balls from an urn. The model, then, is the mathematical theory describing the implications of this particular method of drawing balls from the urn. It goes without saying that the model becomes a theory of a social process whenever the social process parallels the method of drawing balls from the urn which generated the model. Models of medical or social contagion are often generated by such urn schemes, and like the diffusion processes described above, are sometimes true, sometimes not.

Telephone traffic problems have given rise to a number of these sometimes-true theories, models which are designed to apply to a specific problem of waiting times, switching, holding times, and the like. Other work of this sort, which has great potential relevance for social processes, has been begun by Vito Volterra (1931) and extended by Davis (1960). Volterra treated a situation in which two or more species compete for the same food (translate: two or more innovations compete for the same audience), and the situation in which one species feeds off another.

Such cases bring to mind numerous similar social phenomena. There are many instances in which one activity sets off another, but the second eats into the time originally given to the first. One would expect something like this with respect to television viewing of baseball games and attendance at games: game attendance gathers a large audience for baseball on television, but some become satisfied with the television, thus reducing the game attendance. Or somewhat differently: one popular song in a new style sets off a craze for songs in that style; but the time and money spent on the new songs cuts off the resources available for the first. The song is "killed off" by the new songs it spawns. Yet this is just a conjecture; little is in fact known about the life-cycle of popular songs, and the influence of various factors in their rise and decline. And also it should be emphasized that this and other rough analogies must be treated carefully; once verbal models or theories of growth and demise are set down, they must be carefully translated into the appropriate equations, rather than analogizing from a roughly similar situation in the area of species competition.

What then is the tactic being proposed? It is this: that one fruitful line of development, particularly in the area of social processes of the sort discussed above, will be not to ask what is *the* theory of a certain kind of behavior, or what are *the* postulates which correctly describe a general area of behavior. The tactic proposed here is to set about developing and applying a number of sometimes-true theories which relate consequences to postulates, and which may adequately describe behavior in a given situation. This tactic seems particularly appropriate for social processes (in contrast to psychological processes) because social systems are much more variable and flexible than psychological systems; people relate to each other in innumerable social configurations, and each configuration is described by its own particular theory or model. This term "model," incidentally, seems to have come into use precisely to characterize these sometimes-true theories. The term "theory" has the connotations of being ultimately true or false, while it is precisely characteristic of these sometimes-true theories or models that they are *neither* true nor false.

In the empirical work which accompanies such theory-development, two general approaches seem reasonable: the aggregate data can be used to infer which of the possible processes were actually operative in a given case; such a procedure was used in the example of Chapter 1. This is the *explanatory* use of a theory, to employ the dichotomy proposed in Chapter 1. Or, at the other extreme, on the basis of what one knows about what goes on in a given situation, a model can be constructed embodying such knowledge; from this, the aggregate consequences of the process can be deduced. This procedure is the *synthetic* use of theory, in terms of the dichotomy in Chapter 1. Perhaps in many applications there will be some combination of these two extremes: something is known about the process to enable selection of a class of possible models; and then the aggregate data allow selection from among these models.

Note, however, that there is nowhere the proposal simply to engage in curve-fitting, without an underlying model which expresses a social process. If the data happen to fit a simple curve, this may provide an economical statement of the data, in terms of the one or two parameters of the distribution curve. But if there is no underlying model with a reasonable substantive interpretation, little has been gained by such curve-fitting.

The strategy of developing sometimes-true theories of social process is exemplified throughout this book, but especially in Chapters 10 and 11. There several models of contagion, competition, and related processes are derived by modifying the Poisson process in different ways.

2. BREAKING DOWN A SINGLE COMPLEXITY INTO MULTIPLE SIMPLICITIES

A second strategy for quantitative sociology is a method for quantitatively measuring complex social phenomena. Briefly, it is this: when it is desired to use a complex array of sociological data to characterize a single unit (e.g., the "social structure"), then the strategy is to set up *several* models for different sorts of tendencies which may be exhibited by the data. More simply, the strategy is to reduce the complex data to a number of single-dimensional measures which can characterize the group.

Perhaps the best example of the use of such a strategy is in structural sociology, in which one is given, say, sociometric data, and the desire is to characterize the structure of the group, so that it may be compared to that of other groups or to that of the same group at a different point in time. Now obviously the wealth of information which constitutes the data in such a situation cannot be compressed into a single scalar measure. For example, a matrix of sociometric choices contains all the information about one aspect of the group's structure, and it cannot be compressed into one or two measures. An obvious strategy, then, is to formulate models which express what one attribute of the structure would be like under "ideal" circumstances. For example, to determine the "hierarchization" of a sociometric structure, one would set up a model for the expected distribution of choices received among the members of the group, under the assumption of random choice or no hierarchization. Such a model then gives an ideal which can serve as a base line or standardization from which deviation can be measured. The deviation of the actual distribution from this base line constitutes a measure of hierarchization. Similar models, expressing other characteristics of the structure under random assumptions (such as the number of mutual choices, the number of cycles of various lengths, the probability of any two persons being directly or indirectly connected, and so on) can then be constructed to measure other characteristics of the structure.

Why is it that such a strategy seems peculiarly appropriate for social structural data? Probably because such data have these characteristics: (a) they are given in terms of numbers of people, so that quantitative models based on counting rather than measurement of some "concept" can be set up; and (b) they contain a great deal of information, which must either be sacrificed by construction of a single scalar measure, broken up into several such measures, or fully encompassed by an elaborate model. The proposal here being made is to choose the middle path: that we can do more than construct a simple scalar measure, but are not ready for an encompassing model.

In a sense, we are privileged to examine the "insides" of a sociological unit—a group, community, or society—with the task of giving measures for the unit as a whole. The task is just the opposite to that in physics and in psychology, where one is given the external manifestations of the unit as a whole and faced with the problem of inferring what kind of "insides" could have given such manifestations. Of course, it is true that such a perspective applies best to certain combinations of problems and data in sociology: problems concerning the group or community as a unit, and data on relations between the members of that unit.

It may be, however, that this general strategy is far more widely applicable than the area of "structural sociology" discussed above. Consider the area of personality assessment and intellectual assessment, where the tool of factor analysis has been widely used. Factor analysis is just such a tool as we have described, for it takes a complex set of relations—this time between items, or test scores, or other quantitative scores—and attempts to reduce this complexity of relations to a few simple "dimensions." As mentioned in Chapter 1, the advantage provided by simple counting in social-structural problems is absent in techniques like factor analysis. But this should not obscure the point: that in areas other than structural sociology a strategy of simplifying complex structures can be useful.

3. THE OVERLAY OF STRUCTURAL VARIATIONS ON SIMPLE PROCESSES

A third strategy is intimately related to these last two, the development of "sometimes-true" models of social processes, and the breakdown of complex structures into simple measures. One of the major barriers to the use of the diffusion and other models discussed earlier is that they ordinarily assume complete intermixing within a given social structure. In contrast, actual structures differ markedly from this, in systematic directions. In view of this, it appears that only under the most peculiar circumstances would the process models which assume complete intermixing be applicable. In order to make them applicable, two possibilities seem available: (a) throw away the simple model which assumes complete mixing, and construct more complicated models which mirror existing nonrandom structures; or (b) keep the simple process models with their assumption of randomness, but super-impose upon them correction factors derived from an analysis of the structure in which the process is operating. The former approach is the most rigorous, and thus the "safest"; extreme care must be used in compounding structural variations with the basic process model. Yet despite this disadvantage, the second approach seems to be a promising one, for it means that one basic model can serve for numerous structures, and a new model need not be constructed for each application. Also, this approach can be used with our present mathematical equipment, while the more rigorous method seems so difficult mathematically that it might be some time away in the future, except in the most simple cases, such as those of Chapter 17.

Thus one promising strategy in the use of mathematics is this super-position of structural variations on models of simple process. Population genetics provides an excellent example of this: genetic models for changes in gene frequency and for gene-frequency equilibrium ordinarily employ the assumption of panmixia, that is, random mating throughout the population. But few populations—plant, animal, or human—conform to such assumptions of random mating. This presents a dilemma, for it is hardly worth while to develop separate theories or models for each structural variation which might arise in a population. As a provisional way out, the notion of a "population isolate" has been developed. The population isolate is the group of such size in a given population that mating within this group is approximately random. A Swedish mathematical geneticist, Gunnar Dahlberg (1947), has developed a method for calculating the size of these hypothetical entities in human populations, and thus allowing the use of the process theories which assume panmixia. This is not at all an ultimate solution, but one which is serviceable until the ultimate solution comes. An example of a juxtaposition of structural variation and social processes is provided by Chapter 17.

4. THE METHOD OF RESIDUES

In celestial mechanics, Newton used with great profit a strategy which, suitably modified, might prove useful in social sciences. Certain laws were available which described the motion of heavenly bodies. But the bodies did not precisely conform to these simple laws. Newton used these simple laws to extract that part of the motion which they could account for. The "residue" was left as a problem to work on, as a matter to be explained. The method of residues, then, consisted of constructing an explicit law or model based on simple assumptions, using this model to account for as much of the behavior as possible, and taking the remainder as a problem to be solved.

The strategy proposed here is the construction of mathematical models in social science explicitly for this purpose. The implicit use of this strategy is evident in numerous areas of social science. A large part of statistics consists of the construction of models which will provide an "expectation" with which to compare actual data. We can then, in a sense, "factor out" that part of the behavior which is explained by the statistical model and go on to search out the causes of deviation from expectation.

In many cases, it is only the deviation, the residue, which is of interest. Often in measures of characteristics of networks, for example, we need a model to show just what the network would look like if all connections were *random*. It is the departure from randomness, the residue remaining after application of the model, which is of interest.

The suggestion here is that the method of residues is useful for many other models than purely statistical ones. The model is used to factor out the sociologically trivial, leaving as residue the sociologically interesting. If desired, the model can then be elaborated to include one after another factors of more interest, each of them reducing the residue left to be explained.

In Chapter 15 this approach is used to study amounts of travel between spatially dispersed points. This specific application is used to show the contrast to an approach which attempts to build a simple "law of social gravity" or a "distance-interaction law" as a universal law which describes rates of travel between disperse points.

5. QUALITATIVE GENERALIZATIONS AND THEIR USES

Many of the results of sociological research stand in the form of qualitative propositions or generalizations. "The larger the group, the greater the tendency for differentiation of role," for example. Whether at the social-psychological level or at a more macroscopic level, the form is often the same: "The greater X, the greater will be Y." Sometimes these generalizations are arrived at by analysis of quantitative data; sometimes they are the result of qualitative studies; and sometimes they derive from general experience and speculation.

How are such results to be used in mathematical models or theories, if at all? One approach is to take a set of such generalizations as the *postulates* of a theory; a diametrically opposed approach is to develop a theory of which these generalizations are the *consequences*. I want to propose here that one of these approaches will be of considerable value, the other of much less value.

Excellent examples of the first approach are contained in papers by Simon and Simon and Guetzkow (see Simon, 1957). In the first of these papers, Simon takes as his starting point three generalizations relating strength of positive sentiments, amount of interaction, and the number of common activities of individuals. These generalizations had been set down by Homans in *The Human Group*, extrapolating from the results of several researches on small, face-to-face groups. The paper by Simon and Guetzkow takes a similar but more complex set of related generalizations from work by Festinger and others on communication, cohesion, and opinion change in groups.

The mathematical models developed in these papers consist of a set of simultaneous differential equations, each equation showing the change in one of the variables as a function of the others. Because the generalizations are only in terms of "more" or "less," and because the concepts or variables are not defined so as to allow quantitative measurement, the equations can be set down only in the most general form, and the consequences deduced from them are only qualitative. (For a comprehensive exposition and examination of these models, see Coleman, 1960.) Nevertheless, some deductions can be made, and even without the deductions the set of equations puts down in precise form the essence of the generalizations, which is often lost in the verbal maze which surrounds our theories and propositions in social science.

Consider now the other approach: suppose these same propositions which serve as Simon's postulates are taken as qualitative *consequences* of an underlying quantitative theory. An example of this is a recent proposal by Thibaut and Kelley (1959) and others that a theory of exchange be developed to account for the propositions relating group cohesion and opinion change which have been set down by a number of investigators. Their proposal is that a kind of economic model, in which opinions are traded for affiliation with the group (not, of course, in a cold and calculating way, but in the sense that something is given up in order to gain something that is wanted more), could account for the existing propositions in this area. Note the difference between this and the other approach: here the propositions are taken as consequences, and effort is directed toward finding an underlying theory which will explain them. In the first approach, the propositions are taken as postulates from which a theory is synthesized, going on toward further deductions.

The second approach appears to me to hold far more potentialities than the first. Consider the use that was made of qualitative generalizations in the early stages of physical science. It was observed, for example, that the harder one pushed a movable object, the faster it accelerated; the smoother the surface, the faster the object accelerated; and the more inclined a plane, the faster the object accelerated. Now these separate propositions of the form "the more X, the more Y," were not taken as postulates of a theory, but as qualitative observations to be explained by an underlying theory. Or consider the experiment by Robert Boyle, in which he created a vacuum in a jar which had a watch ticking in it. (See James B. Conant, 1950, for a discussion of this experiment.) He found that the stronger the vacuum he created, the fainter became the tick of the watch. This crucial experiment, and the generalization resulting from it, did not provide a postulate to be linked with other postulates in a theory. Instead it provided insight into the underlying state of affairs: it confirmed the notion that the surrounding atmosphere consisted of an actual substance, air, which served to propagate sound among other things. This generalization helped provide the basis for the conception of air as a compressible fluid.

In other words, the usefulness of qualitative propositions or generalizations in physical science has not been as direct building blocks for theory. They have served instead as signposts along the road toward theory, and as results against which the deductions of a theory could be tested. Matters may be different in social science, but I doubt it.

6. NORMATIVE MODELS vs. DESCRIPTIVE MODELS

In economic theory, there is a continuing debate which finds little parallel in other social sciences. This is a debate between the advocates of a descriptive economic theory, which mirrors as well as possible the actual functioning of economic systems, and normative theory, which tells how the economy should function in order to meet some ethical goal. Welfare economics, which attempts to provide a theory by which economic decisions can maximize some over-all "social welfare," is perhaps the outstanding example of a normative theory.

In any such controversy, most of the rest of social science would side with the descriptive theorists, refusing to incorporate specific values about what "ought to be" into the heart of their science. But there is also a broader definition of normative theory, and the theories included under this broader roof are of a good deal more interest. They are best described by illustration. In economics, linear programming is a model designed to answer specific questions of the following sort: What is the optimum way for the output of a set of producers who are spatially disperse to be allocated to a set of consumers who are also spatially disperse? Essentially it is a problem of distribution in such a way as to minimize the over-all costs of transportation. Such a theory is hardly descriptive, for it is not describing how such allocations are in fact made; but it is different from the strictly normative theories in that it is not tied to a vague or mythical social utility or social welfare. It is tied instead to an explicit goal which can easily be measured.

Game theory is another such normative theory, normative in the sense that it tells how games *should* be played rather than how they are actually played; but normative only in the sense that it tells the way to maximize gain or minimize losses, not the way games should be played in some ethical or moral sense.

There are few comparable theories in other areas of social science. The reason is simple: the calculations in linear programming, game theory, and other such models are not predicated upon laws or human behavior. People are not involved in these theories; thus the theories can by-pass behavioral laws which present a formidable obstacle to normative or goal-directed theories in other social sciences. For example, in organization theory, the maximization of a given organizational goal requires intricate knowledge of the way people behave under various circumstances.

But in this general class of seminormative theories are some directions which might prove fruitful for social sciences other than economics. An example is a recent theory of the political system by Anthony Downs (1957). Although Downs proposes this theory as a descriptive theory of democratic politics, it is hardly that. Its major value is that it shows the functioning of a political system whom men are assumed to have no other motives than those of pure self-interest. By so doing, it performs at least one major practical function, as follows. The problem of setting up the conditions (the legal constitution, as well as the social conditions) under which a democracy can survive involves a set of protective mechanisms. Most of these are protections against the possible use of pure self-interest on the part of the occupants of leadership positions or subgroups of the population. Such a theory as Downs's helps indicate the kind of mechanisms that are necessary; the kinds of conditions which will make it possible for a democracy to function *even* when its leaders and citizenry are motivated by nothing but self-interest. Thus whether or not the theory is adequately descriptive, it can act as a normative theory in saying: this is what is necessary to maintain a functioning democracy, *if* people come to be motivated by pure self-interest.

Possibly also in the area of the theory of organizations there is usefulness for such a nondescriptive theory. Whenever some structure is to be designed to guard against the destructive character of self-interest (which is precisely what bureaucratic organizations attempt), then such a nondescriptive or seminormative theory may be useful. It can be developed without the foundation of an adequate descriptive theory of behavior, for it by-passes that problem by postulating that people act purely rationally to maximize a selfish goal. Whether they always do in fact is irrelevant, since the theory would be used to locate the protective mechanisms necessary to guard against such behavior.

It may be that under certain conditions, such theories can serve a second use as well. They may serve a descriptive use in much the same way that the laws of mechanics describe the path of a stick thrown in the air. By knowing only the initial velocity (including the direction), the predicted path of the stick may be calculated. The equations would take into account both the initial velocity and the change in velocity due to gravitational acceleration. However, this actual path would differ from the predicted one because of air resistance in conjunction with the shape of the stick and motion of the air. Under conditions of high wind, or a light stick, or an irregular shape like that of a boomerang, the actual path would deviate very much from the predicted one. In such a case, the theory or model would have to be greatly complicated to take into account the air resistance. Nevertheless, the basic equations for the ideal case (i.e., stick thrown in a vacuum) would be important in the more complicated model. Now by analogy, these seminormative theories based on rational self-interest may provide, in many areas of social science, basic theories which can be modified by taking into account factors which produce deviations from rationality.

I have oversimplified the problem (just as economists often do in their discussions of "utility") in implying that there are no complications in deciding what are the goals that individuals want to maximize. Even so, the possibilities of this tactic seem worth further investigation.

7. PROBABILISTIC MATHEMATICS vs. DETERMINISTIC MATHEMATICS

There is a continuing controversy in mathematical social science over deterministic models vs. probabilistic or stochastic ones. The controversy can be found in almost any area, except where the advocates of stochastic processes have completely won the battle, or except where the model can be formulated only in one of the two ways. Stochastic processes tend to be the vogue these days, and advocates of simpler deterministic models have usually been won over or have retreated into silence when the stochastic-process advocates have invaded their territory. The telling argument, which appears at first to be a conclusive one, is that social or psychological processes are in fact probabilistic, so that a deterministic process is only a poor substitute for the stochastic model, which is exact in mirroring what goes on.

It is unfortunate that such arguments tend to win the battle, for there are disadvantages to the probabilistic versions along with advantages. In the paragraphs below, a few of the advantages of each approach will be presented.

In addition it is possible to see the advantages and disadvantages of each approach by a perusal of a book such as that of Bailey (1957), which presents both deterministic and probabilistic versions of particular processes. Bailey suggests a strategy "which tends to regard deterministic treatments as approximately valid in certain circumstances, and at any rate worth examining in any given situation. We then pass on to more precise (and usually mathematically more difficult) stochastic formulations, paying special attention to any striking features suggested by the deterministic model" (p. 11).

One process which illustrates well some of the advantages and disadvantages of each approach is a birth-death process, which might be applied to population growth, to social and physical contagion, as well as other phenomena. The deterministic model, with birth rate coefficient α and death rate coefficient β (constant over time), is a differential equation:

$$\frac{dn}{dt} = \alpha n - \beta n \qquad (7.1)$$

where n is the existing population size. The corresponding stochastic model is characterized by a set of differential equations, one for the probability of being in each state:

$$
\left\{
\begin{array}{l}
\text{change in} \\
\text{probability of} \\
\text{being in state } i
\end{array}
\right\}
= -
\left\{
\begin{array}{l}
\text{probability of} \\
\text{being in state} \\
i \text{ at time } t, \\
\text{times prob-} \\
\text{ability of shift-} \\
\text{ing if in state } i
\end{array}
\right\}
+
\left\{
\begin{array}{l}
\text{probability of} \\
\text{being in state} \\
i - 1 \text{ at time} \\
t, \text{ times prob-} \\
\text{ability of shift-} \\
\text{ing to state } i \\
\text{if in state} \\
i - 1
\end{array}
\right\}
+
\left\{
\begin{array}{l}
\text{probability of} \\
\text{being in state} \\
i + 1 \text{ at time} \\
t, \text{ times prob-} \\
\text{ability of shift-} \\
\text{ing to state } i \\
\text{if in state} \\
i + 1
\end{array}
\right\}
$$

The three conditional probabilities on the right-hand side are $(\alpha + \beta)i$, $\alpha(i-1)$, and $\beta(i+1)$, respectively, since the probability of birth or death is proportional to the existing size (which is i, $i-1$, and $i+1$, respectively, for the three states). This gives equations of the following form:

$$\frac{dp_i}{dt} = -(\alpha + \beta)ip_i + \alpha(i-1)p_{i-1} + \beta(i+1)p_{i+1} \qquad (7.2)$$

The stochastic equations (7.2) are precisely accurate, assuming that the system is governed by coefficients α and β, while the deterministic equation (7.1) is only an "approximation." Yet (7.2) itself is an approximation, neglecting many factors that may be more important than stochastic disturbances. And if (7.1) can be used in certain circumstances, then something is gained by virtue of its greater simplicity.

The formal connection between (7.1) and (7.2) is that (7.1) is the expected value or mean value for the probability distribution. Thus in all cases where the deterministic equation gives the expected value, and where we would need only the expected value of the distribution, the simpler deterministic model is much to be preferred.[1] The stochastic process appears to do two things that the deterministic one does not in this example. It can give the probability that a population will die out, due to chance fluctuation. This probability is greater than zero, even though the birth rate coefficient α be greater than the death rate coefficient β. In some social applications of models like this, it may be important to estimate this probability. For example, a variation upon this model might be used to characterize the growth in population of a popular song. It would be important to know the probability that a song with given coefficients α and β would die out after a given level of "seeding," that is, plugging by a disc jockey or other advertising.

Secondly, the stochastic process includes, as an intrinsic part of the model, a way of testing the fit of the model to the data. That is, since the total probability distribution is known, then it is possible to test whether the fluctuations of the data are simply chance fluctuation within the limits predicted by the model, or deviate beyond this.

However, these seem the *only* added advantages of the stochastic process. The deterministic model can (as in this example) reflect the same basic process as does the stochastic one, and do so much more simply. Thus it might be possible to treat processes of a far greater degree of complexity than the cumbersome stochastic equations would allow. To be sure, the advantage of having a test of the fit as an intrinsic part of the model is attractive; yet it must be weighed against the advantage of simpler mathematics provided by the deterministic model. (And if the deterministic model is simply an equation for the mean value of the probabilistic one, then the total distribution can be

---

[1] See Coleman (1962b) for a discussion of the conditions under which the deterministic equation gives the expected value.

appended whenever it is necessary to test the fit of the model.) This simpler mathematics may allow investigation of problems which remain completely closed so long as the extra burden of the total distribution is carried along, for the basic model may be made more complex without reaching unmanageable mathematics. And the argument that the stochastic process is more "fundamental" is not a valid argument at all.

This example, in fact, has shown the probabilistic model to its best advantage, for often it gives no added information analogous to the "probability of dying out" in this example. One of the tendencies in the use of probabilistic models is to develop a kind of "know-nothing" approach toward the behavior that the model is intended to reflect. That is, some probabilistic models do little more than formalize our ignorance. They make little or no definite statements about cause and effect or relations between variables. Ordinary Markov chains, used as models of voting preferences or attitudes, have this tendency, for example. (See Anderson, 1954.) They say nothing about variables which might *affect* voting preferences, nothing about the variables which bring about change in attitudes or vote preferences. They allow statements of only the following sort: "With a certain probability, p, Democrats at time t will still be Democrats at time $t + 1$." Such statements are only a kind of formal language for expressing our ignorance about the causes of vote changes or attitudinal changes. This is not to say that stochastic models cannot be set up to express relations between variables; this is just what Chapters 3 to 9 are about. It is to say only that there is an ever-present danger with probabilistic models that we will use them to say little or nothing —but to say it elegantly—about the behavior at hand.

In this book, both kinds of treatments are used. Throughout Chapters 3 to 9, the processes under study are various continuous-time stochastic processes. Yet in most of the chapters, attention is focussed on the deterministic form, that is, the mean of the probability distribution. This is done because we are interested in developing models with enough complexity to be of some use, and do not want to be stopped sooner than necessary by complicated mathematics. In general, our approach has been to use the whole probability distribution only in cases where the data are likely to be in the form of a distribution rather than a single value. Such cases are treated in Chapters 10 and 11.

8. THE USE OF ELECTRONIC COMPUTERS AS A SUBSTITUTE FOR MATHEMATICS

Recently a peculiar development has occurred in the construction of formal models. This is the use of electronic computers to substitute for mathematical derivations. The postulates of a model can be programmed onto the computer (thus making the computer program the theory itself), and then the computer will calculate the behavior which the program (i.e., theory) dictates.

The computer serves, then, as a substitute for the mathematical *deductions*. The postulates of the model play the same role they always did—except that this time they are used by the computer in carrying out numerical analysis, while ordinarily they are used by the mathematician in carrying out general deductions. The primary disadvantage of this procedure (which is called the Monte Carlo technique when the model is a probabilistic one) is that it never provides a *general* abstract solution; it provides only particular numerical solutions depending on the prior setting of the model's parameters. Furthermore, when the model is probabilistic, any single run on the computer provides only one case, whereas a great many cases are needed to get a picture of the mean value or the over-all probability distribution. The computer cannot solve problems in algebra; it can only carry out computations when actual numbers are fed into it.

This "particularism" of the computer's calculations is a serious disadvantage, but is often outweighed by the added complexity that the computer allows in a model. Models which are far beyond our ability to solve in general can be programmed onto a computer, and numerical solutions can be obtained for a wide range of parameter values. In fact, the possibilities opened up by computers in this direction seem extremely great. A major stumbling block in the use of mathematics in social science may have been finally overcome: the fact that mathematics can handle only quite simple situations, while problems in social science are extremely complex. For example, if even a very simple process—say, one of interpersonal influence— is operating in an ordinary community, composed of intricate networks of relations (far from the complete intermixing often assumed by models), then it is hopeless to attempt any general deductions about the resulting distribution of attitudes. But if this structure, whatever its complexity, is mapped out on the storage cells of a computer, and the influence process is programmed upon the computer, then the computer can very easily calculate, for particular situations, what was impossible to solve in general.

It is too early in the use of computers for such purposes to say more than this. However, a few years should see some real results in very new directions, all due to the fact that the computer can encompass, for particular cases, a complexity which ordinary mathematics cannot even approximate in its general deductions.

REFERENCES

Anderson, T. W.: "Probability Models for Analyzing Time Changes in Attitudes," in *Mathematical Thinking in the Social Sciences*, P. F. Lazarsfeld (ed.) (New York: The Free Press of Glencoe, 1954), Ch. 1.

―――― and L. A. Goodman: "Statistical Inference about Markov Chains," *Ann. Math. Stat.*, *28*, 1957, 89–110.

Asch, S. E.: "Effect of Group Pressure upon the Modification and Distortion of Judgments," in *Groups, Leadership, and Men*, Harold Guetzkow (ed.) (Pittsburgh: Carnegie Press, 1951).

Ashby, W. Ross: *Design for a Brain* (New York: John Wiley & Sons, Inc., 1952).

Bailey, Norman T. J.: *The Mathematical Theory of Epidemics* (London: Charles Griffin, 1957).

Bales, R. F., Fred L. Strodbeck, Theodore M. Mills, and Mary E. Roseborough: "Channels of Communication in Small Groups," *Amer. Sociol. Rev.*, *16*, 1951, 461.

Bartlett, M. S.: *An Introduction to Stochastic Processes* (New York: Cambridge University Press, 1955).

Bavelas, A.: "A Mathematical Model for Group Structures," *Appl. Anthropol.*, *7*, 1948, 16.

Berelson, Bernard, P. Lazarsfeld, and W. McPhee: *Voting* (Chicago: University of Chicago Press, 1954).

―――― and Gary Steiner: *Human Behavior: An Inventory of Findings* (New York: Harcourt, Brace, and World, 1964).

Berge, Claude: *The Theory of Graphs and Its Applications*. Translated by Alison Doig (New York: John Wiley & Sons, Inc., 1962. First published, Paris: Dunod, 1958).

Bergmann, Gustav, and Kenneth W. Spence: "Psychophysical Measurement," in *Psychological Theory*, Melvin H. Marx (ed.) (New York: The Macmillan Company, 1951).

Bertalanffy, L. von: "An Outline of General System Theory," *Brit. Jour. Phil. Sci.*, *1*, 1950, 134.

Beum, Corlin, and Everett C. Brundage: "A Method for Analyzing the Sociomatrix," *Sociometry*, *13*, 1950, 141–145.

Bharucha-Reid, A. T.: *Elements of the Theory of Markov Processes and Their Applications* (New York: McGraw-Hill Book Co., Inc., 1960).

Blau, Peter M.: "Structural Effects," *Amer. Sociol. Rev.*, *25*, 1960, 178–193.

Block, Jack: "The Difference Between Q and R," *Psychol. Rev.*, *62*, 1955, 356.

Blumen, I., M. Kogan, and P. J. McCarthy: *The Industrial Mobility of Labor as a Probability Process* (Ithaca: Cornell University Press, 1955).

Bridgman, P. W.: *Dimensional Analysis* (New Haven: Yale University Press, 1922).

Bush, R. R., and W. K. Estes (eds.): *Studies in Mathematical Learning Theory* (Stanford: Stanford University Press, 1959).

―――― and F. Mosteller: *Stochastic Models for Learning* (New York: John Wiley & Sons, Inc., 1955).

Butler, D. E.: "An Examination of the Results," *The British General Election of 1950* (London: Macmillan, 1951), 306–333.

―――― *The British General Election of 1951* (London: Macmillan, 1952).

Cadart, Jacques: "Les Elections Générales du 26 mai 1955 en Grande-Bretagne," *Revue Française de Science Politique*, *5*, 1955, 799–812.

Campbell, N. R.: *Measurement and Calculation* (London: Longmans, Green & Co., 1928).

Cartwright, D., and F. Harary: "Structural Balance: A Generalization of Heider's Theory," *Psychol. Rev.*, *63*, 1956, 277–293.

―――― and A. Zander: *Group Dynamics* (New York: Harper & Row, 1953).

Cattell, Raymond: *Factor Analysis: An Introduction and Manual for the Psychologist and Social Scientist* (New York: Harper & Row, 1952).

Chandraskhar, S.: "Stochastic Problems in Physics and Chemistry," in *Selected Papers on Noise and Stochastic Processes*, Murray Wax (ed.) (New York: Dover Publications, Inc., 1954).

Cohen, Bernard: *Conflict and Conformity* (Cambridge: The M.I.T. Press, 1963).

Coleman, James S.: "Independence of Acts in a Social Unit," Tech. Report No. 2, Bur. Appl. Social Res., 1953. Unpublished.

―――― "An Expository Analysis of Some of Rashevsky's Social Behavior Models," in *Mathematical Thinking in the Social Sciences*, P. F. Lazarsfeld (ed.) (New York: The Free Press of Glencoe, 1954).

―――― "Political Cleavage Within the International Typographical Union." Unpublished Ph.D. dissertation, Columbia University, 1955.

―――― *Community Conflict* (New York: The Free Press of Glencoe, 1957a).

―――― "Multidimensional Scale Analysis," *Amer. Jour. Sociol.*, *63*, 1957b, 253–263.

―――― "Relational Analysis: The Study of Social Organization with Survey Methods," *Human Organization*, *17*, 1958.

—— "The Mathematical Study of Small Groups," in *Mathematical Thinking in the Measurement of Behavior*, Herbert Solomon (ed.), Part I (New York: The Free Press of Glencoe, 1960), pp. 7–149.

—— *The Adolescent Society* (New York: The Free Press of Glencoe, 1961).

—— "Reward Structures and the Allocation of Effort," in *Mathematical Methods in Small Group Processes*, Joan H. Criswell, Herbert Solomon, and Patrick Suppes (eds.), *8*, 119–132 (Stanford: Stanford University Press, 1962a).

—— Comment on Harrison White, "Chance Models of Systems of Casual Groups," *Sociometry*, *25*, 1962b, 172–176.

—— "Comment on 'On the Concept of Influence,' " *Public Opinion Quarterly*, *27*, 1963, 63–82.

—— *Models of Change and Response Uncertainty* (Englewood Cliffs: Prentice-Hall, 1964).

—— and John James: "The Equilibrium Size Distribution of Freely-Forming Groups," *Sociometry*, *24*, 1, March, 1961.

—— Elihu Katz, and Herbert Menzel: "The Diffusion of an Innovation among Physicians," *Sociometry*, *20*, 1957, 253–270.

—— and D. MacRae, Jr.: "Electronic Processing of Sociometric Data for Groups up to 1,000 in Size," *Amer. Sociol. Rev.*, *25*, 1960, 722–727.

Comrey, A. L.: "An Operational Approach to Some Problems in Psychological Measurement," *Psychol. Rev.*, *57*, 1950, 217–228.

Conant, James B.: "Robert Boyle's Experiments in Pneumatics," *Harvard Case Histories in Experimental Science*, No. 1 (Cambridge: Harvard University Press, 1950).

Cooley, W. W., and P. R. Lohnes: *Multivariate Procedures for the Behavioral Sciences* (New York: John Wiley & Sons, Inc., 1962).

Coombs, Clyde H.: "Psychological Scaling Without a Unit of Measurement," *Psychol. Rev.*, *57*, 1950, 145.

—— *Theory of Data* (New York: John Wiley & Sons, Inc., in press).

Dahlberg, Gunnar: *Mathematical Methods for Population Genetics* (Basle: S. Karger, 1947).

Davidson, Donald, and Patrick Suppes: "Finitistic Rational Choice Structures," Report No. 3, Stanford Value Theory Project, March, 1955.

—— J. C. C. McKinsey, and Patrick Suppes: "Outlines of a Formal Theory of Value, I," *Phil. Soc.*, *22*, 1955, 140.

—— Sidney Siegel, and Patrick Suppes: "Some Experiments and Related Theory on the Measurement of Utility and Subjective Probability," Report No. 4, Stanford Value Theory Project, Aug , 1955.

Davis, Harold T.: *Introduction to Nonlinear Differential and Integral Equations* (Washington D.C.: Atomic Energy Commission, Government Printing Office, 1960).

Davis, James A., J. L. Spaeth, and Carolyn Huson: "A Technique for Analyzing the Effects of Group Composition," *Amer. Sociol. Rev.*, *26*, 1961, 215–225.

Davis, Kingsley: "A Case of Extreme Isolation in a Child," *Amer. Jour. Sociol.*, *52*, 1947, 432–437.

—— and W. Moore: "Rejoinder to Tumin's 'Some Principles of Stratification: A Critical Analysis,' " *Amer. Sociol. Rev.*, *18*, 1953, 387–397.

De Fleur, Melvin H., and Otto N. Larsen: *The Flow of Information* (New York: Harper & Row, 1958).

Deming, W. E.: *Statistical Adjustment of Data* (New York: John Wiley & Sons, Inc., 1948).

Dingle, Herbert: "A Theory of Measurement," *Brit. Jour. Phil. Sci.*, *1*, 1950, 5.

Dodd, Stewart C.: "Diffusion Is Predictable: Testing Probability Models for Laws of Interaction," *Amer. Sociol. Rev.*, *20*, Dec., 1955, 392.

Doob, J. L.: *Stochastic Processes* (New York: John Wiley & Sons, Inc., 1953).

Downs, Anthony: *An Economic Theory of Democracy* (New York: Harper and Row, 1957).

Duncan, Otis D., and Beverly Duncan: "A Methodological Analysis of Segregation Indexes," *Amer. Social Rev.* *20*, 1955, 210.

Duncan, W. J.: *Physical Similarity and Dimensional Analysis* (London: Edward Arnold, 1953).

Durkheim, Emile: *Suicide*. Translated by John A. Spaulding and George Simpson (New York: The Free Press of Glencoe, 1951).

Economist: "Electoral Facts," *158*, Jan. 7, 1950, 5–7.

Estes, W. K., and C. J. Burke: "Application of a Statistical Model to Simple Discrimination Learning in Human Subjects," *Jour. Exp. Psychol.*, *50*, 1955, 81–88.

Faris, R. E. L., and W. Dunham: *Mental Disorders in Urban Areas* (Chicago: University of Chicago Press, 1939).

Farrell, M. J.: "The Demand for Motor-Cars in the United States," *Journal of the Royal Statistical Society*, Part II, *117*, 1954, 171–200.

Feller, William: "On a General Class of 'Contagious' Distributions," *Annals Math. Statist.*, *14*, 1943, 389–400.

———— *An Introduction to Probability Theory and Its Applications*, 2nd ed. (New York: John Wiley & Sons, Inc., 1957).

Festinger, L.: "The Analysis of Sociograms Using Matrix Algebra," *Human Relations*, 2, 1949, 153–158.

———— *A Theory of Cognitive Dissonance* (Stanford: Stanford University Press, 1957).

Finney, D. J.: *Probit Analysis*, 2nd ed. (Cambridge: Cambridge University Press, 1952).

Flament, Claude: "Analyse Pluridimensionnelle des Structures Hierarchiques Intransitives," *Bulletin du Centre de Etudes et de Recherches Psychotechniques*, 7, 1958, 171–179.

———— *Applications of Graph Theory to Group Structure* (Englewood Cliffs: Prentice-Hall, 1963).

Foskett, John M.: "Social Structure and Social Participation," *Amer. Sociol. Rev.*, *20*, 1955, 431.

Foster, C. C., A. Rapoport, and C. J. Orwant: "A Study of a Large Sociogram II; Elimination of Free Parameters," *Behavioral Science*, *8*, 1963, 56–65.

Frank, Ronald: "Brand Choice as a Probability Process," *Jour. Business*, *35*, Jan., 1962.

Fry, Thornton: *Probability and its Engineering Uses* (New York: D. Van Nostrand Co., Inc., 1928).

Galilei, Galileo: *Two New Sciences* (New York: Dover Publications, Inc., n.d.), first published in Italian in 1638.

Glass, D. V. (ed.): *Social Mobility in Britain* (New York: The Free Press of Glencoe, 1960).

Goodman, Leo A.: "Some Alternatives to Ecological Correlation," *Amer. Jour. Sociol.*, *64*, 1959, 610–625.

—— "Modifications of the Dorn-Stouffer-Tibbitts Method for 'Testing the Significance of Comparisons in Sociological Data,' " *Amer. Jour. Sociol.*, *66*, 1961, 355.

—— "Statistical Methods for Analyzing Processes of Change," *Amer. Jour. Sociol.*, *68*, 1962, 57–78.

—— "On Mathematical Methods for the Study of Systems of Groups." Mimeographed (University of Chicago, 1963a).

—— "Statistical Methods for the Analysis of Mobility Tables." Mimeographed (University of Chicago, 1963b).

Gross, Neal, and William E. Martin: "On Group Cohesiveness," *Amer. Jour. Sociol.*, *57*, 1952, 546. With "Comment" by Stanley Schachter, 554.

Guetzkow, Harold (ed.): *Simulation in Social Science* (Englewood Cliffs: Prentice-Hall, Inc., 1962).

Gullicksen, Harold: "Paired Comparisons and the Logic of Measurement," *Psychol. Rev.*, *53*, 1946, 199.

Hagerstrand, Torsten: "On Monte Carlo Simulation of Diffusion." Mimeographed (Lund, Sweden: University of Lund, 1960).

Hagerstrand, Torsten: "The Propagation of Innovation Waves," *Lund Studies in Geography*, Series B, Human Geography, No. 4, 1952.

Hald, A.: *Statistical Theory and Its Engineering Applications* (New York: John Wiley & Sons, Inc., 1952).

Hammer, Carl: "Rank Correlation of Cities and Refinement," Mimeographed, Bureau of Applied Social Research, Columbia University, 1951.

Harary, F.: "On Local Balance and n-Balance in Signed Graphs," *Mich. Math. J.*, *3*, 1955, 37–41.

—— "On the Measurement of Structural Balance," *Behavior. Sc.*, *4*, 1959, 316–323.

—— and B. Lipstein: "The Dynamics of Brand Loyalty: A Markovian Approach," *Operations Research*, *10*, 1962, 19–39.

—— and R. Z. Norman: *Graph Theory as a Mathematical Model in Social Science.* (Ann Arbor, Institute for Social Research, 1953.)

—— and Ian Ross: "A Procedure for Clique Detection Using the Group Matrix," *Sociometry*, *20*, 1957, 205–215.

Harper, Dean: "Some New Applications of Dichotomous Algebra to Survey Analysis and Latent Structure Analysis." Unpublished Ph.D. dissertation, Columbia University, 1961.

Haskey, H. W.: "A General Expression for the Mean in a Simple Stochastic Epidemic," *Biometrika*, *41*, 1954, 272–275.

536   References

Havighurst, Robert J., and Allison Davis: "A Comparison of the Chicago and Harvard Studies of Social Class Differences in Child Rearing," *Amer. Sociol. Rev.*, *20*, 1955, 438.

Hayek, F. A.: *The Counter-Revolution of Science: Studies on the Abuse of Reason* (New York: The Free Press of Glencoe, 1952).

Hays, David G., and Robert R. Bush: "A Study of Group Action," *Amer. Sociol. Rev.*, *19*, 1954, p. 693.

Hempel, Carl G.: "Fundamentals of Concept Formation in Empirical Science," in *International Encyclopedia of Unified Science* (Chicago: University of Chicago Press, 1952).

Hill, J. M. M., and E. L. Trist: "A Consideration of Industrial Accidents as a Means of Withdrawal from the Work Situation," *Human Relations*, *6*, 1953, 357–380.

Homans, G. C.: *The Human Group* (New York: Harper & Row, 1950).

——— *Social Behavior: Its Elementary Forms* (New York: Harcourt, Brace and World, Inc., 1961).

Horvath, W. J., and C. C. Foster: "Stochastic Models of War Alliances," *Jour. Conflict Resolution*, *1*, 1963, 110–116.

Hovland, Carl I., Arthur A. Lumsdaine, and Fred D. Sheffield: *Experiments on Mass Communication*, Vol. III (Princeton: Princeton University Press, 1949).

Hull, Clark L.: *Principles of Behavior* (New York: Appleton-Century-Crofts, 1943).

——— C. I. Hovland, R. T. Ross, M. Hall, D. T. Perkins, and F. B. Fitch: *Mathematical-Deductive Theory of Rote Learning* (New Haven: Yale University Press, 1940).

Hyman, Herbert A.: "Toward a Theory of Public Opinion," *Public Opinion Quart.*, *21*, 1957, 54–60.

Ikle, Fred Charles: "Sociological Relationship of Traffic to Population and Distance," *Traffic Quart.*, *8*, 1954, 123–136.

Illinois Blue Book, 1959–1960 (Springfield: State of Illinois, 1960).

Inkeles, A., and P. Rossi: "National Comparisons of Occupational Prestige," *Amer. Jour. Sociol.*, *61*, 1956, 329–339.

Jackson, Brian, and Dennis Marsden: *Education and the Working Class* (New York: Monthly Review Press, 1962).

James, John: "The Distribution of Free-Forming Small Group Size," *Amer. Sociol. Rev.*, *18*, 1953, 569.

Johnson, H. M.: "Are Psychophysical Problems Genuine or Spurious," *Amer. Jour. Psychol.*, *58*, 1945, 189–211.

Katz, Leo: "A New Status Index Derived from Sociometric Analysis," *Psychometrika*, *18*, 1953, 39–43.

Keller, Joseph: "Comment on 'Channels of Communication in Small Groups,'" *Amer. Sociol. Rev.*, *16*, 1951, 842.

Kemeny, John G., and J. Laurie Snell: *Mathematical Models in the Social Sciences* (Boston: Ginn & Company, 1962).

——— L. Snell, and G. L. Thompson: *Finite Mathematics* (Englewood Cliffs: Prentice-Hall, Inc., 1956).

Kendall, M. G.: "Regression, Structure, and Functional Relationship, Parts I and II," *Biometrika*, *38*, 1951, 11–25 and *39*, 1952, 96–108.

—— and A. Stuart: "The Law of Cubic Proportions in Election Results," *Brit. Jour. Sociol.*, *1*, 1950, 183–197.

—— and —— "La Loi du Cube dans les Elections Britanniques," *Revue Française de Science Politique*, 2, 1952, 270–276.

Key, V. O., Jr.: *Southern Politics in State and Nation* (New York: Alfred A. Knopf, Inc., 1949).

Kniffen, F.: "The American Covered Bridge," *Geograph. Rev.*, 1951, 114.

Koch, Sigmund: "The Logical Character of the Motivation Concept, I," *Psychol. Rev.*, *48*, 1951, 15.

Koopmans, T. C., and Olav Reiersøl: Three Papers on Identification Problems, Cowles Commission Papers, New Series No. 39 (originally published in *Psychometrika*, *15*, 1950, *Annals of Math. Statist.*, *21*, 1950, and *Econometrika*, *18*, 1950).

Kornhauser, Ruth R.: "The Warner Approach to Social Stratification," in *Class, Status, and Power*, R. Bendix and S. M. Lipset (eds.) (New York: The Free Press of Glencoe, 1953), pp. 225–255.

Kuehn, Alfred A.: "An Analysis of the Dynamics of Consumer Behavior and Its Implications for Marketing Management." Unpublished Ph.D. dissertation, Carnegie Institute of Technology, 1958.

Landau, H. G.: "On Dominance Relations and the Structure of Animal Societies. I. Effect of Inherent Characteristics; II. Some Effects of Possible Social Factors; III. The Condition for a Score Structure," *Bull. Math. Biophysics*, *13*, 1951, 1–19, 245–262, and *15*, 1953, 143–148.

——"On Some Problems of Random Nets," *Bull. Math. Biophysics*, *14*, 1952, 203–212.

Lansing, J. B., and L. R. Klein: "Decisions to Purchase Consumer Durable Goods," *Jour. of Marketing*, *20*, 1955, 109–132.

Lawrence, Douglas H., and Leon Festinger: *Deterrents and Reinforcement* (Stanford: Stanford University Press, 1962).

Lazarsfeld, Paul F.: "A Conceptual Introduction to Latent Structure Analysis," in *Mathematical Thinking in the Social Sciences*, P. F. Lazarsfeld (ed.) (New York: The Free Press of Glencoe, 1954), Ch. 7, pp. 347–387.

—— "Latent Structure Analysis," in *Psychology: A Study of a Science, Conceptual and Systematic*, Vol. 3, Sigmund Koch (ed.) (New York: McGraw-Hill Book Co., Inc., 1959), 476–543.

—— "The Algebra of Dichotomous Systems," *Studies in Item Analysis and Prediction*, Herbert Solomon (ed.) (Stanford: Stanford University Press, 1961).

—— and Allen H. Barton: "Qualitative Measurement in the Social Sciences," in *The Policy Sciences*, Daniel Lerner and Harold D. Lasswell (eds.) (Stanford: Stanford University Press, 1951), p. 155.

Leeman, Cavin P.: "Patterns of Sociometric Choice in Small Groups: A Mathematical Model and Related Experimentation," *Sociometry*, *15*, 1952, 220.

Lewin, Kurt: *Principles of Topological Psychology*. Trans. by F. and G. M. Heider (New York: McGraw-Hill Book Company, Inc., 1936).

—— "The Nature of Field Theory," in *Psychological Theory*, Melvin H. Marx (ed.) (New York: The Macmillan Company, 1951).

538 References

Li, C. C.: *Population Genetics* (Chicago: University of Chicago Press, 1955).

Lionberger, Herbert F.: "The Relation of Informal Groups to the Diffusion of Farm Innovation in a Northeast Missouri Farm Community," *Rural Sociol.*, *19*, 1954, 233–243.

——— *Adoption of New Ideas and Practices* (Ames, Iowa: Iowa State University Press, 1960).

Lippitt, R., and R. K. White: "Patterns of Aggressive Behavior in Experimentally Created Social Climates," *Jour. Soc. Psychol.*, *10*, 1939, 271–299.

Lipset, S. M., and R. Bendix: "Social Status and Social Structure: A Re-examination of Data and Interpretations: *I* and *II*," *Brit. Jour. of Sociol.*, *2*, 1951, *I*, 153; *II*, 241.

——— and Juan Linz: "The Social Bases of Diversity in Western Democracy." Mimeographed, Center for Advanced Study in the Behavioral Sciences, 1956.

——— and Natalie Rogoff: "Class and Opportunity in Europe and America," *Commentary*, Dec., 1954.

——— Martin Trow, and James Coleman: *Union Democracy* (New York: The Free Press of Glencoe, 1956).

Lotka, A. J.: *Elements of Physical Biology* (Baltimore: Williams & Wilkins Co., 1925).

Lowenthal, Daniel: "Trends in the Licensing of Popular Song Hits." Mimeographed, Bureau of Applied Social Research, Columbia University, 1953.

Luce, R. Duncan: "Connectivity and Generalized Cliques in Sociometric Group Structure," *Psychometrika*, *15*, 1950, 169–190.

——— *Individual Choice Behavior* (New York: John Wiley & Sons, Inc., 1959).

——— and Albert D. Perry: "A Method of Matrix Analysis of Group Structure," *Psychometrika*, *14*, 1949, 94–116.

Lundberg, O.: *On Random Processes and Their Application to Sickness and Accident Statistics* (Uppsala, Sweden: Almqvist and Wicksells, 1940).

Mach, E.: *Die Mechanik in ihrer Entioickelung historisth-kritisch Dargestellt.* 3rd ed. (Leipzig: 1897), p. 73. Translation in *Pareto's General Sociology*, L. J. Henderson (Cambridge: Harvard University Press, 1935), p. 30.

March, James G.: "An Introduction to the Theory and Measurement of Influence," *Amer. Polit. Sci. Rev.*, *49*, 1955, 431.

——— "Party Legislative Representation as a Function of Election Results," *Public Opinion Quart.*, *21*, 1957–58, 521–542.

Marschak, Jacob: "Toward a Preference Scale for Decision-Making," in *Readings in Game Theory and Political Behavior*, Martin Shubik (ed.) (Garden City, New York: Doubleday & Company, Inc., 1954).

Marshall, Andrew W., and Herbert Goldhamer: "An Application of Markov Processes to the Study of Epidemiology of Mental Disease," *Jour. Amer. Statist. Assoc.*, *50*, 1955, 99.

Maxwell, A. E.: *Analyzing Qualitative Data* (New York: John Wiley & Sons, Inc., 1961).

Maxwell, James Clerk: *Matter and Motion* (New York: Dover Publications, Inc., n.d. First published, 1877).

McPhee, W. N.: *Formal Theories of Mass Behavior* (New York: Free Press of Glencoe, 1963).

McVoy, Edgar C.: "Patterns of Diffusion in the United States," *Amer. Sociol. Rev.*, 5, 1940, 219–227.

Menzel, Herbert: "A New Coefficient for Scalogram Analysis," *Public Opinion Quart.*, 17, 1953, 268.

—— and E. Katz: "Social Relations and Innovation in the Medical Profession: The Epidemiology of a New Drug," *Public Opinion Quart.* 19, 1955, 337.

—— and E. Suchman: "The Interplay of Demographic and Psychological Variables in the Analysis of Voting Surveys," in *The Language of Social Research*, Paul F. Lazarsfeld and Morris Rosenberg (eds.) (New York: The Free Press of Glencoe, 1955).

Merton, Robert K.: *Social Theory and Social Structure* (New York: The Free Press of Glencoe, 1949).

Mood, Alexander M.: *Introduction to the Theory of Statistics* (New York: McGraw-Hill Book Co., Inc., 1950).

Moreno, J. L., and H. H. Jennings: "Sociometric Measurements of Social Configurations," *Sociometry Monographs*, 3, 1945.

Morgan, James N., M. H. David, W. J. Cohen, and H. E. Brazer: *Income and Welfare in the United States* (New York: McGraw-Hill Book Co., Inc., 1962).

Mosteller, Frederick, and Philip Nogee: "An Experimental Measurement of Utility," *Jour. Polit. Economy*, 59, 1951, 371.

Mount, George R.: "An Analytic Account of the Principles of Measurement," *Psychol. Reports*, Monograph Supp. 2, 1956.

Nagel, Ernest "Principles of the Theory of Probability," in *International Encyclopedia of Unified Science*, 1, No. 6 (Chicago: University of Chicago Press, 1939).

National Opinion Research Center: "Jobs and Occupations: A Popular Evaluation," in *Class, Status, and Power*. R. Bendix and S. M. Lipset (eds.) (New York: The Free Press of Glencoe, 1953), pp. 411–426.

Parsons, Talcott: "On the Concept of Influence," *Public Opinion Quart.*, 1963.

—— *The Social System* (New York: The Free Press of Glencoe, 1951).

—— and E. A. Shils: *Toward a General Theory of Action* (Cambridge: Harvard University Press, 1951).

Pearl, Raymond: *The Biology of Population Growth* (New York: Alfred A. Knopf, Inc., 1925).

Pemberton, H. E.: "The Curve of Culture Diffusion Rate," *Amer. Sociol. Rev.*, 1, 1936, 547–566.

Publisher's Weekly, 1949.

Ramsey, F. P.: *The Foundations of Mathematics and Other Logical Essays* (New York: Harcourt, Brace & World, Inc., 1931).

Rapoport, Anatol: "Outline of a Probabilistic Approach to Animal Sociology: I, II," *Bull. Math Biophysics*, 11, 1949, 183–196, 273–281

—— "Nets with Distance Bias," *Bull. Math. Biophysics*, 13, 1951, 85–91.

—— "Spread of Information Through a Population with Sociostructural Bias: I. Assumption of Transitivity; II. Various Models with Partial Transitivity; III. Suggested Experimental Procedures," *Bull. Math. Biophysics*, 15, 1953, 523–533, 535–546, and 16, 1954, 75–81.

—— and W. J. Horvath: "A Study of a Large Sociogram," *Behavioral Science*, 6, 1961, 279–291.

Rashevsky, Nicholas: *Mathematical Biology of Social Behavior* (Chicago: University of Chicago Press, 1951).

Reese, T. H.: "Application of Physical Measurement to Psychological Magnitudes," *Psychol. Monographs*, No. 50, 1943.

Richardson, L. F.: "Generalized Foreign Politics," *Brit. Jour. Psychol.*, *Monograph Supp.*, *23*, 1939, 939.

Robinson, E. S., and C. W. Darrow: "Effect of Length of Lists upon Memory for Numbers," *Amer. Jour. Psychol.*, *35*, 1924, 235–243.

Rogoff, Natalie: *Recent Trends in Occupational Mobility* (New York: The Free Press of Glencoe, 1953).

Ryan, Bryce, and Neal Gross: "The Diffusion of Hybrid Corn in Two Iowa Communities," *Rural Sociol. 8*, 1943, 15–24.

Savage, L. J.: *The Foundations of Statistics* (New York: John Wiley & Sons, Inc., 1954).

Schreier, Fred T.: *Human Motivation; Probability and Meaning* (New York: The Free Press of Glencoe, 1957).

Shannon, C. E.: *The Mathematical Theory of Communication* (Urbana: University of Illinois Press, 1949).

Shepard, Roger N.: "The Analysis of Proximities: Multidimensional Scaling with an Unknown Distance Function," *Psychometrika*, *27*, 1962, I, 125–139, II, 219–246.

Shimbel, Alphonso: "An Analysis of Theoretical Systems of Differentiating Tissue," *Bull. Math. Biophysics*, *10*, 1948, 131–143.

—— "Applications of Matrix Algebra to Communication Nets," *Bull. Math. Biophysics*, *13*, 1951, 165–178.

Shock, Nathan: "Growth Curves," in *Handbook of Experimental Psychology*, S. S. Stevens (ed.) (New York: John Wiley & Sons, Inc., 1951), 330–346.

Simon, Herbert: *Models of Man* (John Wiley & Sons, Inc., 1957).

Solomon, Herbert (ed.): *Studies in Item Analysis and Prediction* (Stanford: Stanford University Press, 1961).

Solomonoff, Ray, and Anatol Rapoport: "Connectivity of Random Nets," *Bull. Math. Biophysics*, *13*, 1951, 153–157.

—— "An Exact Method for the Computation of Connectivity of Random Nets," *Bull. Math. Biophysics*, *14*, 1952, 153–157.

Somers, R. H.: "The Rank Analogue of Product-Moment Partial Correlation and Regression," *Biometrika*, *46*, June, 1959, 241–246.

Statistical Abstract of the Fifteenth Census of the United States (*1930*) (Washington, D.C.: Government Printing Office, 1933), Table 140, p. 277.

Stephan, Frederick F., and Elliot G. Mischler: "The Distribution of Participation in Small Groups: An Exponential Approximation," *Amer. Soc. Rev.*, *17*, 1952, 598.

Stephenson, William: *The Study of Behavior: Q-Technique and Its Methodology* (Chicago: University of Chicago Press, 1953).

Stevens, S. S. (ed.): "Mathematics, Measurement, and Psychophysics," in *Handbook of Experimental Psychology* (New York: John Wiley & Sons, Inc., 1951), pp. 1–49.

———— "Science of Science," in *Psychological Theory*, M. H. Marx (ed.) (New York: The Macmillan Company, 1951), pp. 21–54.

———— "The Measurement of Loudness," *J. Acoust. Soc. Amer.*, 27, 1955, 815–829.

———— and E. H. Galanter: "Ratio Scales and Category Scales for a Dozen Perceptual Continua," *Jour. Exp. Psychol.*, 54, 1957, 377–411.

Stewart, John Q.: "A Measure of the Influence of a Population at a Distance," *Sociometry*, 5, 1942, 63–71.

Stokes, Donald E., and Gudmund R. Iversen: "On the Existence of Forces Restoring Party Competition," *Public Opinion Quart.*, 26, 1962, 159–171.

Stouffer, Samuel A.: "Intervening Opportunities: A Theory Relating Mobility to Distance," *Amer. Sociol. Rev.*, 5, 1940.

———— *Measurement and Prediction* (Princeton: Princeton University Press, 1950).

———— "Measurement in Sociology," *Amer. Sociol. Rev.*, 18, 1953, 591–597.

———— et al.: *The American Soldier: Adjustment During Army Life* (Princeton: Princeton University Press, 1949). I, II.

Suppes, Patrick, and Richard C. Atkinson: *Markov Learning Models for Multiperson Interactions* (Stanford: Stanford University Press, 1960).

———— and Murial Winet: "An Axiomatization of Utility Based on the Notion of Utility Differences," *Management Sci.*, 1, 1955, 259.

Svalastoga, K.: *Prestige, Class, and Mobility* (London: Heinemann & Co., 1959).

Tainiter, M.: "An Application of a Markovian Model to the Prediction of the Reliability of Electronic Circuits." Mimeographed, IBM Research Center, Yorktown Heights, N.Y., Sept. 29, 1962.

Takacs, L.: *Stochastic Processes* (New York: John Wiley & Sons, Inc., 1960).

Tarde, Gabriel: *The Laws of Imitation* (New York: Holt, Rinehart & Winston, Inc., 1903).

Telser, Lester G.: "Least Squares Estimates of Transition Probabilities," in *Measurement in Economics*, Carl F. Christ *et al.* (Stanford: Stanford University Press, 1963), pp. 270–292.

Thibaut, J., and H. Kelley: *The Social Psychology of Groups* (New York: John Wiley & Sons, Inc., 1959).

Thorndike, E. L.: *Animal Intelligence* (New York: The Macmillan Company, 1911).

Thorndike, F.: "Applications of Poisson's Probability Summation," *Bell System Tech. Jour.*, 5, 1926, 604–624.

Thurstone, L. L.: "The Relation Between Learning Time and Length of Task," *Psychological Review*, 37, 1930, 44–53.

———— *Multiple-Factor Analysis* (Chicago: University of Chicago Press, 1947).

Torgerson, Warren S.: *Theory and Methods of Scaling* (New York: John Wiley & Sons, Inc., 1958).

Tumin, Melvin M.: "Some Principles of Stratification: A Critical Analysis," *Amer. Sociol. Rev.*, 18, 1953, 387–397.

Volterra, Vito: *Leçons Sur la Théorie Mathématique de la Lutte Pour la Vie* (Paris: Gauthier-Villars, 1931).

Von Neumann, J., and O. Morgenstern: *Theory of Games and Economic Behavior* (Princeton: Princeton University Press, 1947).

Weiss, Robert J.: *Processes of Organization* (Ann Arbor: University of Michigan Press, 1956).

Wellin, Edward M.: "Water Boiling in a Peruvian Town," in *Health, Culture, and Community*, Benjamin Paul (ed.) (New York: Russell Sage Foundation, 1955).

White, Harrison: "Chance Models of Systems of Casual Groups," *Sociometry, 25,* 1962, 153–171.

———— *An Anatomy of Kinship* (Englewood Cliffs: Prentice-Hall, Inc., 1963a).

———— "Cause and Effect in Social Mobility Tables," *Behavioral Science, 8,* 1963b, 14–27.

Wheeler, Stanton: Personal Communication, 1963.

Wietzenhofer, Andre M.: "Mathematical Structures and Psychological Measurements," *Psychometrika, 16,* 1941, 385.

Wiggins, Lee M.: "Mathematical Models for the Interpretation of Attitude and Behavior Change: The Analysis of Multi-Wave Panels." Unpublished Ph.D. dissertation, Columbia University, 1955.

Wightman, William P. D.: *The Growth of Scientific Ideas* (New Haven: Yale University Press, 1953).

Wilson, Alan: "7090 Program for Analysis of Variance." Mimeographed, Survey Research Center, University of California at Berkeley, 1963.

Wood, Mary Margaret: *Paths of Loneliness* (New York: Columbia University Press, 1953).

Zipf, George Kingsley: "The P_1P_2/D Hypothesis: On the Intercity Movement of Persons," *Amer. Sociol. Rev., 11,* 1946, 677–686.

———— *Human Behavior and the Principle of Least Effort* (Cambridge: Addison-Wesley Press, 1949).

INDEX

INDEX

A

accidents, industrial, 304
acquisition-to-loss ratio, 373
action, Parsons-Shils theory of, 39
activity, consensus as function of, 248-251; as function of consensus, 242-248
age, illiteracy and, 261-262
aggregate equilibrium, 161, 250
aggregate psychology, 88-89
aggregation problem, 84
algebra, on computer, 529; matrix, 14-15; transformation of input data and, 56
ambiguity, 48; in index formation, 77
American Sociological Society, 50
Anderson, T. W., $53n.$, $342n.$, 528
"approximate" method for calculating q_{ij}, 134
Army rank calculations, 207-209
Asch, S. E., 32, 353, 355, 377
attention-state, 176
attitude measurement, 9
attitudes, correlation of, 400
attitudinal states, 149-151
attributes, dichotomous, 116-117, 190, 254-255; dichotomous independent, 199; diffusion of, 42; independent and dependent, 139-140, 199; individual and situational, 229-235; interdependent, 405, 420-429; multicategory items and, 420-429; multiple items and, 402-403; among related persons, 405; relations between, 132-138; scaling of, 18-19; social and psychological organization of, 381-405; two-attribute systems and, 123-131
automobiles, income and, 258; purchase of, 257

B

Bailey, Norman T. J., 46, $310n.$, 311, $362n.$, 493, 495, 514, 526
balance, theory of, 15
Bales, Robert, 29, 40
Bartlett, M. S., 107
Barton, A., 76
Bavelas, A., 16
Bendix, Reinhard, 430
Berelson, Bernard P., 135, 339, $454n.$
Berge, Claude, 8, 15
Bergmann, Gustav, $56n.$
Bernoulli model, 35
Bernoulli trials, 72, 74
Bertalanffy, Ludwig von, $42n.$
Bettelheim, B., $489n.$
Beum, O. Corlin, 449
Bharucha-Reid, A. T., 107, 380, 413
binomial distribution, 72, 330-332, 341-342; contagious, 342, 411-415; Poisson distribution and, 294, 298-299; response and, 385; voting and, 337
biology, probit analysis and, 263-264
birth-death process, 526
birth rates, 254
Block, Jack, $21n.$
Blumen, I., 14, 460
Boltzmann, Ludwig, $442n.$
Bortkewitsch, 291
Boyle, Robert, 76, 523
Bridgman, P., 83
Brownian motion, 114
Brundage, Everett C., 449
bureaucracy, theory of, 39
Burke, C. J., $382n.$
Bush, R. R., 38, 46, 51

333-336; equilibrium models and, 315-378; with exhaustion, 293-299, 305; exhaustible-contagious, 308-311; mathematical problems of, 377-380; social phenomena and, 291; transition rates and, 379; truncated, 366, 367n.; two-way contagious, 326-332; unsolved problems and future directions for, 375-380
political activity, average, 241
political diversity, measures of, 456-459
Polya, G., 301
Polya distribution, 301, 330, 345n., 376
population density measures, 12
population growth, theories of, 43-45
postulate systems, qualitative, 47-50
predictive models, 10, 52-53
prestige, measurement of, 27, 90-92
probabilistic mathematics, vs. deterministic, 526-528
probability, change in, 526; latent structure analysis and, 18; stochastic process and, 42
probability distribution, 294, 527; computers and, 529
probability theory, 291n.; and contagious Poisson distribution, 312-314; Poisson distribution and, 293-294, 312-314
probit analysis, 263-268
process models, 459-468
professional orientation, effect of on drug adoption, 156-162
programming, of computers, 524, 528
propinquity, group size and, 277-283
propositions, emergent, 241-252; group-level, 242-245, 248-251; individual-level, 242
psychological consistency, 402
psychological organization, vs. social, 400
psychological processes, equilibrium states and, 269-287
psychological unidimensionality, 398-402
psychologists, mathematical theories of behavior and, 38
public opinion, stimuli and, 387
punisher, vs. performer, 354
punishments, effects of, 360-361; mutual, 355-360

Q

Q technique, 21

qualitative attributes, 103-131
qualitative generalizations, 26n., 522-524
qualitative postulate systems, 47-50
quantification, 8; problems of, 55-92
quantitative generalizations, 8-9, 25-34
quantitative measurement, of behavior, 12; problems of, 55-92
quantitative theories, paucity of, 55

R

Ramsey, F. P., 58n., 67, 69
random distribution, 443
random nets, 444
random samples, 26
random shocks, 107, 121-126, 135, 140-144, 161, 176, 194, 197-198, 214-215, 227, 232, 236, 243, 249
random variable, normally distributed, 25
rank-frequency relations, 28-30
Rapoport, Anatol, 46, 330n., 444-445, 493-494
Rashevsky, Nicholas, 51
ratio scales, 63
reaction rate, in first-order reactions, 516
Reese, T. H., 56n.
regression analysis, 25, 98-102, 202
Reiersøl, O., 99
Reiss, Albert J., 240n.
rejection, group size and, 486-488; psychological, 488-491
relationship, intensified, 224, 229; model, 105-106
residues, method of, 199, 469-478, 521-522
resonance, activity and, 242-244
respectification, 7
response, change and, 406-429; to different items at one time, 395-398; free, 404; to multiple items, 402-403; successive, to one item, 383-389; trend and, 390-395; unreliability of, 156
rewards, effects of, 360-361; vs. punishments, 357-359; structure of, 353-361
Richardson, Lewis, 49
risk, utility under, 65-66
Robinson, E. S., 297
Rogoff, Natalie, 14, 83
role behavior, 5
Ross, Ian, 15
Rossi, P., 27
Ryan, Bryce, 492